Introduction to Vector Functions

This book is in the
ADDISON-WESLEY SERIES IN MATHEMATICS

LYNN H. LOOMIS, *Consulting Editor*

JAMES A. HUMMEL *University of Maryland*

INTRODUCTION TO VECTOR FUNCTIONS

ADDISON-WESLEY PUBLISHING COMPANY
READING, MASSACHUSETTS · PALO ALTO · LONDON · DON MILLS, ONTARIO

 LIBRARY OF CONGRESS CATALOG CARD NO. 67-17259.

Preface

Until quite recently, most students of engineering completed their mathematics education with a single course in differential equations following the traditional calculus course. The same was true of many science majors. Some physical science and engineering students might take a course titled something like "Advanced Mathematics for Engineers." This course would usually concentrate on the application of certain mathematical techniques and would avoid (or at least play down) the theory behind these techniques.

It is now recognized that scientists and engineers require much more advanced mathematical tools in their work and that as time goes on, this need will increase. Most of these more advanced techniques cannot be applied blindly. A real understanding of them is required. In order to learn and understand these things, the student should learn some of the fundamental mathematical facts upon which they are based.

A number of studies have been made of this problem. The most common recommendation is that students who are interested in the applications of mathematics to the physical sciences and engineering should learn the fundamentals of linear algebra and the calculus of functions of several variables immediately after completing the standard calculus course. An understanding of this material is needed for an efficient study of more advanced mathematical methods (including differential equations).

In the past, such courses were limited to mathematics majors with only a few rare exceptions. Hence, most textbooks were designed for mathematics majors. The emphasis was on those aspects of the subject which would lead to higher level courses. The few textbooks written for students interested in the application of these topics were usually too deficient in theory to suit modern needs.

In this book, linear algebra and the calculus of functions of several variables are discussed in a more theoretical way than is customary in texts designed for engineers. This is not a book for mathematics majors however. A mathematics major would be better advised to choose courses which are more oriented toward the modern mathematical point of view. That is not to say that there is anything here that would be wrong for a mathematics major. It is just that he could probably make faster progress in a somewhat more modern approach.

This book presents the theory which is needed for application, but, unlike most texts written with the engineer and scientist in mind, no applications are actually discussed. A few simple examples are given to show that some of the topics do have application, but any nontrivial applications are left for courses in other fields. As it happens, many students will already be familiar with one of the major uses of these topics—the material which is known as "vector analysis"—from their physics course.

This book is written in a somewhat formal style. Definitions, theorems, and proofs follow in the rigorous mathematical fashion. Here and there some relaxation is allowed. A few definitions which are used only in a single section or which are only of minor importance are given only in passing. The proofs of the theorems are rigorous (with, I believe, only one exception) but some are given in a more discursive style than might be used in a text meant for mathematics majors alone. Some proofs are incomplete. The student is advised to complete such proofs himself.

I realize that engineers dislike formal definitions, but students of science and engineering need to learn about the mathematical style of reasoning. At this level, the plausibility and analogy arguments that are commonly used outside mathematics can lead to incorrect results. However, the student should remember that it is the concepts and results which are important, not the proofs themselves. Memorizing proofs is not recommended. Learning to understand the idea of the proof is much more valuable.

It is up to the instructor to decide how much emphasis he wishes to place on the proofs. There are a few theorems whose proofs are quite difficult and could well be skipped. However, some discussion of the proofs of the major theorems should always be included. Probably the most important result of the book is the implicit function theorem (Theorems 6–7, 6–8, and 6–11). Theorem 6–7 should be discussed carefully and its proof examined as fully as possible. Both proofs given for Theorem 6–8 are rather difficult, but it would be instructive to at least outline them even if they cannot be discussed in detail. The important thing is that the theorem itself be understood.

There is enough material in the text for a full year course (six to eight semester hours, depending on the ability and previous training of the students). It is important that the material not be hurried too much. If the instructor feels it necessary to spend extra time on some sections, there are opportunities for adjustment by deleting other material, particularly in the first four chapters.

For example, the instructor might find it useful to delete some or all of Sections 2–7 through 2–10. However the part of Section 2–8 beginning with Definition 2–10 should be included. Also, the definition of the transpose in Section 2–9 should always be included. Similarly, all of Chapter 3 could be skipped, or merely summarized if the students already know something about determinants.

In Chapter 4, the material starting with Section 4–6 can be dropped quite easily. In any case, it will probably be necessary to leave out Sections 4–8, 4–9, and 4–10. The brief introduction to group theory given in Sections 4–8 and 4–9 has very little to do with the rest of the course. It is included as an "added attraction" which can be covered if there is some extra time available. Section 4–10 introduces some of the more common matrix groups. There is a great deal of interest in these groups these days, and it was felt that at least their definitions should be included. The sections on group theory cover only the bare minimum of the theory, just enough to allow the discussion of the matrix groups in Section 4–10.

The chapters on the calculus of functions of several variables concentrate on the ideas of vector spaces. Instead of a function of several variables, we try to think of a function of a single variable which is in an n-dimensional space. We then break this variable up into its components again for the calculations, but it is hoped that the reader will gain a feeling for the vector space point of view.

Throughout these chapters, it is assumed that the reader has already learned some of the mechanics of partial differentiation and multiple integration in the basic calculus course. Thus, the emphasis is on the theory in order to provide an explanation of the mathematical reasoning behind some of these techniques. For example, the student is assumed to have seen the heuristic argument that gives the approximate area for the element of area in polar coordinates as $r\,\Delta r\,\Delta\theta$ and that hence an integral in polar coordinates must be of the form $\int f(r, \theta) r\,dr\,d\theta$. In this book we prove that this result is correct. However, we do not attempt to make the "approximate area" argument rigorous (although this could be done) but instead we stick to rectangular decomposition for the integral and then obtain the desired results from the "change of variable" point of view.

The mathematician may wonder why the formal calculus of exterior differential forms has been so slighted in this book. My feeling was that too much time would have had to be spent in motivating and developing a mathematically satisfactory version of this theory for the type of student under consideration. Instead, I avoided the theory for the most part and then only added a few remarks (in Section 7–9) which may serve to show the value of a properly developed calculus of exterior differential forms. For this brief set of comments, I did not even bother to introduce the correct "wedge product" notation. I hope that this short introduction will be enough to motivate the student to a more careful study of this topic in some further course if the opportunity should arise.

Most of the material in this book has been tested in class. A few changes were made on the basis of this testing, and a few new sections were added. As might be expected, some students complained that the material was too theoretical, but even so, they learned a great deal about linear algebra and the calculus of n-dimensional space. Some students were surprised to discover that many of the techniques they had learned in other courses had a rigorous mathematical basis. The students who took this course had a much better understanding of the theoretical foundations of these subjects and could make use of these concepts in more advanced courses in their own fields of interest. These students developed a remarkably high level of mathematical sophistication, which I think will be of more value to them in the future than any mere collection of formulas and techniques.

I wish to thank the many people who have assisted me in the preparation of this book with their advice and suggestions. Without their help the book would contain many more errors. In particular, I would like to thank Professor Stanley Jackson for his many comments and valuable suggestions. I would also like to express my appreciation to the Addison-Wesley Publishing Company for the assistance they have given in the preparation of this book.

College Park, Maryland J.A.H.
January 1967

Contents

CHAPTER 1

Vector Spaces

1–1. THE VECTOR SPACE R^n

You are undoubtedly familiar with ordinary three-dimensional vectors as used in physics and engineering. These vectors are often described as being "quantities having both direction and magnitude" despite the fact that this phrase by itself has no exact meaning. Vectors are also sometimes described as "being" directed line segments. The word "being" is placed in quotation marks here because it quickly becomes clear when studying vectors that vectors are *not* directed line segments. Rather, they are a property of directed line segments which does not change under parallel translation.

Vectors are often represented in the form

$$\mathbf{A} = a_1\mathbf{i} + a_2\mathbf{j} + a_3\mathbf{k},$$

where **i**, **j**, and **k** are special unit coordinate vectors. In more modern usage, the vectors **i**, **j**, and **k** are replaced by the symbols $\mathbf{e}_1$, $\mathbf{e}_2$, and $\mathbf{e}_3$. In either way, a vector is specified by a given triple of numbers, $[a_1, a_2, a_3]$. The three numbers a_1, a_2, and a_3 define the vector completely. In ordinary three-dimensional cartesian space, the correspondence between a vector and a directed line segment is given by making the above vector correspond to the directed line segment whose initial point is at the origin and whose terminal point is at the point whose coordinates are (a_1, a_2, a_3). An arbitrary directed line segment BC whose initial point has coordinates (b_1, b_2, b_3) and whose terminal point has coordinates (c_1, c_2, c_3) is associated with the vector

$$\mathbf{D} = (c_1 - b_1)\mathbf{i} + (c_2 - b_2)\mathbf{j} + (c_3 - b_3)\mathbf{k}.$$

The coordinates of the vector are obtained by subtracting the corresponding coordinate of the initial point from the corresponding coordinate of the terminal point.

Since the three components define the vector, we could just as well merely list these three numbers and call that triple of numbers the vector. That is, we could write

$$\mathbf{A} = [a_1, a_2, a_3].$$

There are two basic operations used in working with vectors in three-dimensional space. The first is called *scalar multiplication.* The real numbers are called scalars to distinguish them from vectors. Scalar multiplication involves the multiplication of a vector by a scalar. This changes the "magnitude" of the vector without changing its "direction." In terms of the components of the vectors, scalar multiplication can be defined in the form

$$t\mathbf{A} = t[a_1, a_2, a_3] = [ta_1, ta_2, ta_3].$$

The second vector operation is *vector addition*. This can be defined in terms of the *parallelogram law*, or algebraically in the form

$$\mathbf{A} + \mathbf{B} = [a_1, a_2, a_3] + [b_1, b_2, b_3] = [a_1 + b_1, a_2 + b_2, a_3 + b_3].$$

These ideas form the background on which we wish to make a mathematical development of vectors of an arbitrary number of dimensions. This development will lead us into a number of interesting ideas. We will learn what is meant by n-dimensional space and discover a connection with the solutions of systems of linear equations. We will also find it possible to give a rigorous treatment of the theory of determinants of arbitrary orders.

Let us start, therefore, by generalizing and making more precise the idea of a triple of numbers. We begin with ordered pairs and the concept of the cartesian product of two sets.

Definition 1–1. Let A and B be two sets. Then the *cartesian product* of A and B is the set of all ordered pairs whose first element is in A and whose second element is in B; that is,

$$A \times B = \{\langle a, b\rangle \mid a \in A, b \in B\}.$$

The name, cartesian product, comes from the fact that the cartesian plane can be thought of as being the cartesian product of the set of all real numbers with itself. We will use the letter R to denote the set of all real numbers. The cartesian plane can then be identified with the set $R \times R$.

Note that the concept of order is important in the ordered pair. If the sets A and B are different, then there is no difficulty in distinguishing between the elements in an ordered pair. However, when the two sets are the same, then it becomes important to be able to distinguish between the first and second elements in an ordered pair. The points $\langle 2, 3\rangle$ and $\langle 3, 2\rangle$ are completely different in the cartesian plane.

There is no need to stop with the cartesian product of just two sets. We can do the same thing with any number of sets.

Definition 1–2. Let $A_1, A_2, \ldots, A_n$ be n sets. By the *cartesian product* of these n sets, denoted by $A_1 \times A_2 \times \cdots \times A_n$, we mean the set of all ordered n-tuples of elements with the kth element coming from A_k. That is, the set $A_1 \times A_2 \times \cdots \times A_n$ is defined to be

$$\{\langle a_1, a_2, \ldots, a_n\rangle \mid a_1 \in A_1, a_2 \in A_2, \ldots, a_n \in A_n\}.$$

If all of the sets are the same, $A_1 = A_2 = \cdots = A_n = A$, then the cartesian product of these n sets is denoted by A^n.

For example, R^2 is the set of all ordered pairs of real numbers. This set can be identified with the cartesian plane. Similarly, R^3 is the set of all ordered triples of real numbers. The set R^3 can be identified with the set of all points in the three-dimensional space or, as we mentioned above, with the set of all three-dimensional vectors. However, when we try to discuss vectors, we must have more than just the set of triples of numbers. We must also have the algebraic operations of vector addition and scalar multiplication. Only when these are added will R^3 become the set of three-dimensional vectors.

In the above two definitions we have used the "pointed" brackets, $\langle\ \rangle$, to denote an ordered n-tuple. This is a commonly used notation. In the following definition we will use "square" brackets, [ ], to represent the same ordered n-tuple when we wish to think of this n-tuple as a vector.

Definition 1–3. The real numbers (the elements of R) are called *scalars.* The elements of R^n are called *vectors* and are denoted by boldface letters or by placing the n-tuple in square brackets. The operations of scalar multiplication and vector addition in R^n are defined by

$$t\mathbf{A} = t[a_1, a_2, \ldots, a_n] = [ta_1, ta_2, \ldots, ta_n] \tag{1–1}$$

and

$$\begin{aligned}\mathbf{A} + \mathbf{B} &= [a_1, a_2, \ldots, a_n] + [b_1, b_2, \ldots, b_n] \\ &= [a_1 + b_1, a_2 + b_2, \ldots, a_n + b_n].\end{aligned} \tag{1–2}$$

The numbers $a_1, a_2, \ldots, a_n$ in the n-tuple $\mathbf{A}$ are called the *components* of $\mathbf{A}$. The *zero vector* is the vector

$$\mathbf{0} = [0, 0, \ldots, 0].$$

The *negative* of a vector $\mathbf{A}$ is the vector $-\mathbf{A} = (-1)\mathbf{A}$.

In general, when we use some boldface capital letter to denote a vector, we will try to follow the convention of using the corresponding small letter to denote its components. We may not be able to follow this convention in every case, but we will use it as much as possible.

In the development we are going to follow, it will often be useful to think of a vector in R^n as being written in a vertical column with the first component at the top. To save space in the text, it is usually more convenient to write the components in horizontal form. Just remember that the *standard form* of the vector is the "column form," or vertical arrangement of the components.

This is the main reason for using square brackets to represent vectors. These brackets are supposed to remind us that the vector should be arranged as a column of components.

Formula (1–2) written in column form would be

$$\mathbf{A} + \mathbf{B} = \begin{bmatrix} a_1 \\ a_2 \\ \vdots \\ a_n \end{bmatrix} + \begin{bmatrix} b_1 \\ b_2 \\ \vdots \\ b_n \end{bmatrix} = \begin{bmatrix} a_1 + b_1 \\ a_2 + b_2 \\ \vdots \\ a_n + b_n \end{bmatrix}.$$

The operations defined on the vector space R^n are exactly the same as the operations defined on three-dimensional vectors when $n = 3$. Hence R^3, as defined here, is algebraically the same as the ordinary three-dimensional vectors which you are already familiar with. Therefore the vector space R^n is a direct generalization of the space of three-dimensional vectors.

A triple of numbers can be thought of as representing either a three-dimensional vector or a point in three-dimensional space. Later, we may find it convenient to use both of these views at the same time. We will, however, use the same notation to represent both concepts. This will not cause any difficulty.

Just as R^3 is a three-dimensional space, we can think of the elements of R^n as being "n-dimensional" vectors, or points in an "n-dimensional space." In a later section we will define "dimension" so as to make this statement true. There is nothing mysterious or unusual about this. The idea of dimension means nothing more or less than what we choose to let it mean.

It is useful to visualize the algebraic operations in R^n in terms of their equivalents in R^3. There are times when this visualization does not carry over to the higher-dimensional space, but these occasions are exceptions rather than the rule. Since they do occur, however, when we reach a conclusion based on our understanding of the three-dimensional space, we must always be sure to verify it in R^n by using the proofs which apply to the latter space.

When we think of the n-tuples in R^n as defining the coordinates of points in n-dimensional space, we do not bother to change the notation. If $\mathbf{A}$ and $\mathbf{B}$ are two distinct points of R^n, then we can think of the directed line segment AB from $\mathbf{A}$ to $\mathbf{B}$ and the vector associated with this directed line segment (just as we do in R^3). This vector would be $\mathbf{B} - \mathbf{A} = \mathbf{B} + (-\mathbf{A})$. With this picture we could then visualize vector addition in R^n in terms of the same parallelogram law that is used in R^3.

Note that when two three-dimensional vectors are added, the two vectors determine a plane which contains the parallelogram that gives the result of the addition. Similarly, two vectors in R^n will determine a plane. The addition of two n-dimensional vectors will therefore take place in a two-dimensional part of the whole space. This is the reason that we are able to use our knowledge of three-dimensional vectors with such effect in R^n. We will consider this point of view further in the next and later sections.

In three dimensions it is useful to make use of the coordinate vectors $\mathbf{i}$, $\mathbf{j}$, and $\mathbf{k}$. These are the vectors of "unit length" which can be thought of as "pointing along" the coordinate axes. We find it just as useful to introduce similar vectors in R^n. Here, however, we are forced into using a notation which can be adapted to any number of dimensions.

Definition 1–4. The *coordinate vectors* in R^n are the vectors

$$\begin{aligned}
\mathbf{e}_1 &= [1, 0, 0, \ldots, 0],\\
\mathbf{e}_2 &= [0, 1, 0, \ldots, 0],\\
\mathbf{e}_3 &= [0, 0, 1, \ldots, 0],\\
&\vdots\\
\mathbf{e}_n &= [0, 0, 0, \ldots, 0, 1].
\end{aligned}$$

This notation makes it impossible to distinguish between the coordinate vectors in different R^n. The vector $\mathbf{e}_1$ in R^3 and the vector $\mathbf{e}_1$ in R^2 are *not* the same. We could, of course, complicate our notation so as to indicate the dimension, but we will not find it necessary to do so. The dimension of the space will always be obvious from the context. Thus a vector $\mathbf{e}_k$ will be a vector whose kth component is a 1, and whose remaining components are zero. The number of components will be whatever is necessary for the vector to be in the space we are working with at the time.

As a consequence of this definition, we are able to write any vector as the sum of scalar multiples of these coordinate vectors. That is,

$$\begin{aligned} \mathbf{A} &= [a_1, a_2, \ldots, a_n] \\ &= a_1\mathbf{e}_1 + a_2\mathbf{e}_2 + \cdots + a_n\mathbf{e}_n \\ &= \sum_{i=1}^{n} a_i\mathbf{e}_i. \end{aligned} \tag{1–3}$$

This last representation makes implicit use of certain "obvious" properties of vector addition and scalar multiplication. Rather than leave these properties to our intuition alone, we will now list the basic algebraic properties of vector addition and scalar multiplication. The particular properties we choose to single out are those which are motivated by the fundamental properties of the real number system. These properties—the commutative laws, the associative laws, the existence of identities and inverses, and the distributive law—have their analogs in the system of vectors.*

▶ **Theorem 1–1.** Vector addition and scalar multiplication in R^n satisfy the following eight properties. For any vectors **A**, **B**, and **C** in R^n and any scalars s and t:

P1. $\mathbf{A} + \mathbf{B} = \mathbf{B} + \mathbf{A}$.

P2. $\mathbf{A} + (\mathbf{B} + \mathbf{C}) = (\mathbf{A} + \mathbf{B}) + \mathbf{C}$.

P3. There exists a vector **0** such that for any vector **A**,

$$\mathbf{A} + \mathbf{0} = \mathbf{0} + \mathbf{A} = \mathbf{A}.$$

P4. For any vector **A**, there exists a corresponding vector $-\mathbf{A}$ such that

$$\mathbf{A} + (-\mathbf{A}) = \mathbf{0}.$$

P5. $(st)\mathbf{A} = s(t\mathbf{A})$.

P6. $(s + t)\mathbf{A} = s\mathbf{A} + t\mathbf{A}$.

P7. $t(\mathbf{A} + \mathbf{B}) = t\mathbf{A} + t\mathbf{B}$.

P8. $(1)\mathbf{A} = \mathbf{A}$.

These properties all follow obviously from Definition 1–3. The reader can verify them easily. The vector whose existence is asserted in P3 is exactly the vector **0** of

---

* The symbol ▶ used in front of the statement of this theorem is used throughout the text to denote theorems which are particularly important.

Definition 1–3. The vector $-\mathbf{A}$ of P4 is the vector $(-1)\mathbf{A} = -\mathbf{A}$, also of Definition 1–3. The last property of the theorem may seem rather trivial, but it turns out to be necessary to have a complete set of properties. We will see why this is so below.

These properties could be extended in a completely obvious way to allow the sum of any finite number of vectors to be written in any order and without using any parentheses. (See Problem 4 at the end of this section.) Such extensions would then allow an equation such as (1–3) to be written. We will not give formal proofs of these extensions. Complete proofs would require use of mathematical induction. No particularly deep difficulties arise in the proofs, and it is unlikely that the reader will make any errors in the use of these properties.

We usually write

$$\mathbf{A} + (-\mathbf{B}) = \mathbf{A} - \mathbf{B} \tag{1–4}$$

and call the right-hand side of this expression the *difference* of the two vectors. The distributive laws, P6 and P7, will hold just as well for the difference as for the sum. This can be proved using only the eight properties of the theorem (see Problems 1 and 2 at the end of this section).

From the eight properties of this theorem, we could prove all of the "obvious" computational facts. However, in order to be able to do so, we *must* have P8. This can be seen quite easily by noticing that the space of all pairs of real numbers with addition defined by $\langle x_1, x_2\rangle + \langle y_1, y_2\rangle = \langle x_1 + y_1, x_2 + y_2\rangle$ and scalar multiplication defined by $t\langle x_1, x_2\rangle = \langle tx_1, 0\rangle$ satisfies the first seven properties but not the eighth.

To give the reader an idea of how the "obvious" computational facts follow from these properties, we will outline the proofs of the following theorems. For the proof of the first theorem, we do not need to assume P8. All we need is that $(1)\mathbf{A}$ exists and has a negative.

Theorem 1–2. It follows from the first seven properties of Theorem 1–1 that for any vector $\mathbf{A}$, $0\mathbf{A} = \mathbf{0}$.

Proof

$$\begin{aligned}(1)\mathbf{A} &= (0 + 1)\mathbf{A}\\ &= 0\mathbf{A} + (1)\mathbf{A}.\\ (1)\mathbf{A} - (+1)\mathbf{A} &= [0\mathbf{A} + (1)\mathbf{A}] - (1)\mathbf{A},\\ \mathbf{0} &= 0\mathbf{A} + [(1)\mathbf{A} - (1)\mathbf{A}]\\ &= 0\mathbf{A}. \blacksquare^*\end{aligned}$$

The next theorem shows that the eight properties of Theorem 1–1 imply that $(-1)\mathbf{A}$ is the negative of $\mathbf{A}$, $-\mathbf{A}$.

---

* The symbol ▌ is used to denote the end of the formal proof of a theorem. It is not the same as Q.E.D., since it does not imply that proof is complete. It merely means that we will not give any more of the proof, whether it is complete or not.

Theorem 1–3. It follows from the eight properties of Theorem 1–2 that

$$-\mathbf{A} = (-1)\mathbf{A}.$$

Proof

$$\begin{aligned}
\mathbf{0} &= 0\mathbf{A} \\
&= (-1 + 1)\mathbf{A} \\
&= (-1)\mathbf{A} + (1)\mathbf{A} \\
&= (-1)\mathbf{A} + \mathbf{A}. \\
\mathbf{0} - \mathbf{A} &= [(-1)\mathbf{A} + \mathbf{A}] - \mathbf{A}. \\
-\mathbf{A} &= (-1)\mathbf{A} + [\mathbf{A} - \mathbf{A}] \\
&= (-1)\mathbf{A} + \mathbf{0} \\
&= (-1)\mathbf{A}. \ \blacksquare
\end{aligned}$$

In the problems at the end of this section the reader is asked to supply reasons for each step in the proofs of these two theorems. We note that these proofs are somewhat artificial, and it is unlikely that the reader would be able to produce such a proof without a great deal of trial and error until he has had some experience in such matters. Some simpler proofs are asked for in the problems.

The introduction of n-dimensional vectors is not a purely mathematical fiction. While the vectors usually considered in physics (force, momentum, velocity, angular velocity, and so on) are all three dimensional, there are many places where vectors of higher dimension can be used to represent physical quantities. The "four vectors" considered in relativity theory are one obvious example, but there are many others.

Indeed, almost any time that a physical situation can be described by a system of n numbers, it is likely that vector notation can be introduced with advantage. The reason for this is that the notions of linearity are very important in most physical situations, and it is exactly the idea of linearity that is basic to the definition of vectors given above.

Fig. 1–1

For example, suppose that n masses are arranged in a straight line between two fixed supports and are connected by $n + 1$ ideal (massless) springs as shown in Fig. 1–1. The position of the entire system can be given by an n-tuple, $\mathbf{X} = [x_1, x_2, \ldots, x_n]$, where x_i is the displacement of the ith mass from its equilibrium position.

Where is the linearity in this representation? It is in what is usually called the principle of superposition. If the system is displaced and released, the position vector will be a function of time. According to the principle of superposition, this function will depend linearly on the initial displacement vector. That is, if we multiply the initial displacement by the scalar c, then the displacement at any given future time will be multiplied by the same scalar. Also, if the initial displacement is the sum of two other displacements, then the position at time t will be the sum of the two positions which would have occurred at time t as a result of the individual displacements.

PROBLEMS

1. Using only the properties of Theorem 1–1 and the definition given by Eq. (1–4), prove that for any scalar s and any vectors **A** and **B**,

$$s(\mathbf{A} - \mathbf{B}) = s\mathbf{A} - s\mathbf{B}.$$

2. Following the same instructions as in Problem 1, prove that

$$(s - t)\mathbf{A} = s\mathbf{A} - t\mathbf{A}.$$

3. Prove that it follows from the first seven properties of Theorem 1–1 that $(-1)\mathbf{A}$ is the inverse of $(1)\mathbf{A}$.
4. Using only the properties of Theorem 1–1, prove that

$$\mathbf{A} + (\mathbf{B} + (\mathbf{C} + \mathbf{D})) = ((\mathbf{A} + \mathbf{B}) + \mathbf{C}) + \mathbf{D}.$$

5. Using only the properties of Theorem 1–1, prove that

$$\mathbf{A} + (\mathbf{B} + \mathbf{C}) = (\mathbf{B} + \mathbf{A}) + \mathbf{C}.$$

6. Suppose that

$$\sum_{i=1}^{n} a_i\mathbf{e}_i = \sum_{i=1}^{n} b_i\mathbf{e}_i.$$

What can you conclude about the relationship between the a_i and the b_i?
7. Supply a reason for each line of the proof of Theorem 1–2. Every reason must be one of the properties of Theorem 1–1 or a property of the real numbers.
8. Supply a reason for each line of the proof of Theorem 1–3. Where did you have to make use of P8?
9. If the sets $A_1, A_2, \ldots, A_k$ have $n_1, n_2, \ldots, n_k$ elements, respectively, how many elements are there in $A_1 \times A_2 \times \cdots \times A_k$?
10. How do the sets $A \times (B \times C)$, $(A \times B) \times C$, and $A \times B \times C$ differ?
11. Let Z be the set of all integers (positive negative and zero). Show that Z^n does not satisfy the properties of Theorem 1–1. Would it satisfy them if the scalars used in scalar multiplication were restricted to be in Z?
12. Assume that the first seven properties of Theorem 1–1 are true. Prove that P8 is equivalent to the statement that if $t\mathbf{A} = \mathbf{0}$, then either $t = 0$ or $A = \mathbf{0}$.

1–2. VECTOR SPACES

In the last section, we called R^n a *vector space* several times without ever defining what we meant by this term. The purpose of this section is to give a precise definition of this extremely useful concept and to begin our study of some of the properties of vector spaces. First, however, we must make some preliminary comments.

We assume that the reader is already familiar with the concept of a function, but we will repeat the definition here so that we can be sure that we are all using the same notation and terminology. Given two sets A and B, a function f from A to B is a collection of ordered pairs $\langle a, b\rangle$ from $A \times B$ such that every element $a \in A$

appears in one and only one pair in the collection. If the pair $\langle a, b\rangle$ is in the function, then we call b the *value* of the function at a and we write $b = f(a)$. The set A is called the *domain* (or sometimes the *domain of definition*) of the function. The set B is called the *range* (more correctly, *a range*) of the function. The set $f(A) = \{f(a) \mid a \in A\}$ is called the *image* of A under f, or more simply, the *image* of f. All of this is symbolized by writing

$$f: A \to B. \tag{1–5}$$

More correctly, a function f consists of three sets: the domain A, the range B, and the subset F of $A \times B$. This distinction is usually ignored since the set A and the image of f can always be recovered from the set F. In elementary considerations we never find it necessary to distinguish between two functions $f: A \to B_1$ and $f: A \to B_2$ which are identical except for their ranges (both of which contain the image of f).

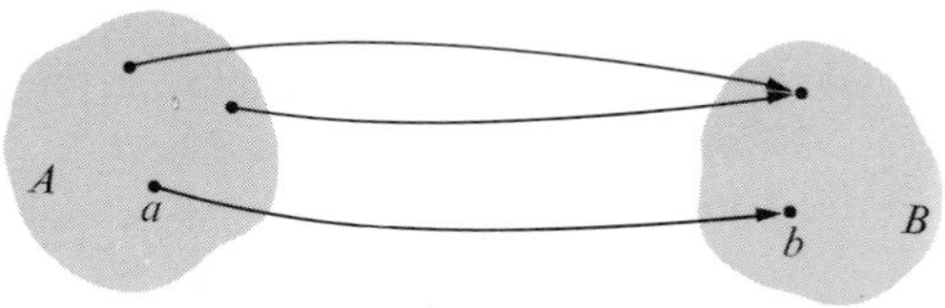

Fig. 1–2

Although the proper definition of the function f is as a subset of $A \times B$, it is usually more useful in practice to think of the function as an operator, or mapping, which takes each element of A and associates with it some element of the set B. One way to think of this is illustrated in Fig. 1–2. The function is represented as a collection of arrows leading from the set A to the set B. For any element a in A, the value of the function at a is the element $f(a)$ which can be found at the opposite end of the arrow leading from a. The requirement of the definition can be thought of as saying that there is one and only one arrow leading from each element of A. Note, however, that there is no violation of the definition if several different arrows lead to the same point of B.

Now we can give the general definition of a vector space.

Definition 1–5. Let R be the set of real numbers and let V be a set of elements denoted by $\mathbf{A}, \mathbf{B}, \mathbf{C}, \ldots$ Then V is called a *vector space over the reals* if and only if

1. There is a function $\alpha: V \times V \to V$, called *vector addition*, which we write in the form $\alpha(\mathbf{A}, \mathbf{B}) = \mathbf{A} + \mathbf{B}$.
2. There is a function $\mu: R \times V \to V$, called *scalar multiplication*, which we write in the form $\mu(t, \mathbf{A}) = t\mathbf{A}$.
3. The operations of vector addition and scalar multiplication satisfy the eight properties given in Theorem 1–1.

Note that when we write $\mathbf{A} + \mathbf{B}$ or $t\mathbf{A}$, what we mean is the single element which is the value of the function α or μ at the pair of elements $\mathbf{A}$ and $\mathbf{B}$ or t and $\mathbf{A}$, respectively.

Since we have used the properties of Theorem 1–1 in this definition, it follows automatically that R^n must be a vector space in the sense of this definition. This immediately raises a question. Are there any other vector spaces than the R^n? The answer, of course, is yes. Otherwise there would be very little reason to consider such a definition.

An obvious extension of R^n would be the space S of all infinite sequences $\{a_n\}$* of real numbers. Vector addition and scalar multiplication are defined just as in R^n, and it is easily seen that S is also a vector space.

Another example of a vector space that is of considerable interest and importance is the space of all functions that are defined and continuous in a given interval.

Let a and b be two real numbers with $a < b$. Let $I = \{x \mid a \leq x \leq b\}$. Let $C(I)$ be the set of all real-valued functions which are defined and continuous for all $x \in I$. Then $C(I)$ is a vector space. To see this, we must first *define* vector addition and scalar multiplication on the set $C(I)$. The *vectors* of this vector space are the functions themselves. Let f and g be two functions in $C(I)$. We must define the function $f + g$. We do this by giving the value of the function $f + g$ at every $x \in I$. This will then define the function. Let the value of the function $f + g$ at x be denoted by $(f + g)(x)$. We define

$$(f + g)(x) = f(x) + g(x).$$

Why is the resulting function, $f + g$, in the set $C(I)$?

To define scalar multiplication on $C(I)$, we give the values of the function tf in terms of the values of the function f and the scalar t. The value at each $x \in I$ is given by

$$(tf)(x) = t[f(x)].$$

It is then simple to verify that $C(I)$ satisfies the requirements of Definition 1–5. For example, let us verify the property P1. Let x be any number in I. Then

$$\begin{aligned}(f + g)(x) &= f(x) + g(x) && \text{(by definition)}\\ &= g(x) + f(x) && \text{(commutative law for addition of real numbers)}\\ &= (g + f)(x) && \text{(by definition).}\end{aligned}$$

Since this is true for every x, we have $f + g = g + f$. In the problems at the end of this section, the reader is asked to complete the proof of the fact that $C(I)$ is actually a vector space. Some additional examples of other vector spaces are also given in this problem set.

---

* This notation for a sequence is in common use despite the fact that it is ambiguous. Braces are used to denote sets, but a sequence is not a set; it is a function defined on the natural numbers. Since a function is a set of ordered pairs, the sequence should be written as $\{\langle n, a_n\rangle \mid n = 1, 2, \ldots\}$. When we write "the sequence $\{a_n\}$" we will mean this. The symbol $\{a_n\}$ is then just a short way of writing the more complete expression. Observe also that a sequence is sometimes denoted by listing the elements of the sequence in order, e.g., "the sequence $a_1, a_2, \ldots$"

It is possible to define vector spaces over the complex numbers (or other fields). In this book, we are interested only in vector spaces over the reals. Thus, we will drop the qualifying phrase. When we speak of a *vector space*, we will mean a vector space over the reals in the sense of the definition given above unless otherwise specified.

Definition 1–6. Let V be a vector space and let W be a subset of V. Then W is called a *subspace* of V if and only if W is itself a vector space with the same scalar multiplication and vector addition as in V.

Let us see what is needed to ensure that a subset W of a vector space V is a subspace of V. First, P1 must be true. Let $\mathbf{A}$ and $\mathbf{B}$ be two vectors in W. Then $\mathbf{A}$ and $\mathbf{B}$ are automatically in V, and so is $\mathbf{A} + \mathbf{B}$. The question is, is $\mathbf{A} + \mathbf{B}$ in W? If not, then vector addition is not a function defined from $W \times W$ to W, and hence W could not possibly be a vector space with the same vector addition as in V. Therefore we must assume that W is *closed* under vector addition (the vector addition of V) before we can even begin to discuss the truth of the properties of Theorem 1–1.

If W is closed under vector addition, then $\mathbf{A} + \mathbf{B}$ is in W, and P1 will be true automatically. Since $\mathbf{A} + \mathbf{B} = \mathbf{B} + \mathbf{A}$ in V, it is true in W as well. In a similar way, once we assume that W is closed under vector addition, P2 must hold in W since it holds in V.

Let us skip to P5. Again, we see that this property will be satisfied automatically, provided that *W is closed under scalar multiplication.* Properties P6, P7, and P8 follow just as easily.

However, if we assume that W is closed under scalar multiplication, then we can prove that the last two properties, P3 and P4, are also satisfied. We saw in the last section that $0\mathbf{A} = \mathbf{0}$; hence if W is anything but the empty set and is closed under scalar multiplication, the vector $\mathbf{0}$ must be in W. Finally, if $\mathbf{A}$ is any vector in W, then the vector $-\mathbf{A}$ must also be in W, since $-\mathbf{A} = (-1)\mathbf{A}$ from Theorem 1–3. We have therefore proved:

Theorem 1–4. If W is a nonempty subset of a vector space V, and if W is closed under vector addition and scalar multiplication, then W is a subspace of V.

Much of our work on vector spaces is concerned with subspaces. We will now describe the basic method which can be used to obtain an important class of subspaces of a given vector space.

Definition 1–7. Let $\mathbf{A}_1, \mathbf{A}_2, \ldots, \mathbf{A}_k$ be any k vectors in a vector space V. Then by a *linear combination* of these vectors we mean a vector sum

$$\mathbf{C} = s_1\mathbf{A}_1 + s_2\mathbf{A}_2 + \cdots + s_k\mathbf{A}_k = \sum_{i=1}^{k} s_i\mathbf{A}_i,$$

where the s_i are any scalars.

Definition 1–8. Let $\mathbf{A}_1, \mathbf{A}_2, \ldots, \mathbf{A}_k$ be any k vectors in a vector space V. Then by $L\{\mathbf{A}_1, \mathbf{A}_2, \ldots, \mathbf{A}_k\}$ we mean the set of all vectors in V which are linear combinations of the $\mathbf{A}_i$. This set is called *the subspace generated by the* $\mathbf{A}_i$.

To make this last definition consistent, we must prove the next theorem.

▶ **Theorem 1–5.** For any set of vectors $\mathbf{A}_1, \mathbf{A}_2, \ldots, \mathbf{A}_k$ in V, $L\{\mathbf{A}_1, \mathbf{A}_2, \ldots, \mathbf{A}_k\}$ is a subspace of V.

Proof. Because of Theorem 1–4, we only have to show that the sum of two linear combinations of the $\mathbf{A}_i$ is a linear combination of the $\mathbf{A}_i$ and that a scalar multiple of a linear combination of these vectors is also a linear combination. However, these facts are easy to verify:

$$\sum_{i=1}^{k} s_i\mathbf{A}_i + \sum_{i=1}^{k} t_i\mathbf{A}_i = \sum_{i=1}^{k} (s_i + t_i)\mathbf{A}_i,$$

and

$$t\sum_{i=1}^{k} s_i\mathbf{A}_i = \sum_{i=1}^{k} (ts_i)\mathbf{A}_i. \blacksquare$$

In this proof we made use of the generalizations of the commutative, associative, and distributive properties of the vector operations. As explained before, we will not bother to give the actual proofs of these generalizations, but we will not hesitate to make whatever use of them we need to.

These algebraic properties are part of the linearity of the vector space. While they are quite "obvious," they are true only because of our assumptions about the space, not because they "have" to be. We must often be careful that we do not assume these "obvious" properties in situations where we have no right to do so. For example, the response to a drug does not in general double when the dose is doubled.

The subspace generated by a single nonzero vector, $L\{\mathbf{A}\}$, consists of all scalar multiples of that vector. In three-dimensional space, we can visualize a vector (triple of numbers) as being a point in the space. Then the subspace generated by $\mathbf{A} \neq \mathbf{0}$ will be represented as being the set of all points on a line through the origin, namely the line through the point whose coordinates are given by the components of $\mathbf{A}$.

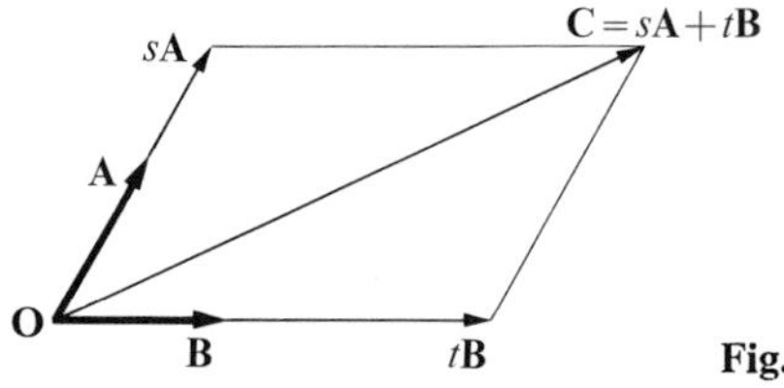

Fig. 1–3

If we have two nonzero vectors, $\mathbf{A}$ and $\mathbf{B}$, which are not scalar multiples of each other, then $L\{\mathbf{A}, \mathbf{B}\}$ can be visualized as a plane through the origin. This will be the plane through the points represented by $\mathbf{A}$, $\mathbf{B}$, and $\mathbf{O}$ (the origin). Fig. 1–3 illustrates how any point of this plane can be visualized as being a linear combination of the two given vectors.

Definition 1–9. Let V be a vector space. If $L\{\mathbf{A}_1, \mathbf{A}_2, \ldots, \mathbf{A}_k\} = V$, then we say that the vectors $\mathbf{A}_i$ form a set of *generators* for V.

It is clear that a subspace defined as in Definition 1–8 will have a set of generators. What can we assert about some arbitrary subspace? Will it have a set of generators? This is one of the questions that we will attempt to answer in future sections. For the moment, note that if we are willing to allow an infinite number of vectors in the set, then every vector space has a set of generators, since the set of all vectors in the space forms a set of generators for the space. Obviously we could cut this number down a great deal. Again, this point will be discussed further in the next few sections.

The terminology used here needs some justification, however. We say that the vectors form a *set* of generators, but we write them in the form $\mathbf{A}_1, \mathbf{A}_2, \ldots, \mathbf{A}_k$, that is, as a sequence of vectors, not all of which need to be different. A *set* differs from a sequence in not depending on the order of the elements and in not containing any repetition of elements

Theorem 1–6. The subspace $L\{\mathbf{A}_1, \mathbf{A}_2, \ldots, \mathbf{A}_k\}$ is not altered by a change in the order of the vectors $\mathbf{A}_1, \mathbf{A}_2, \ldots, \mathbf{A}_k$. If two of the vectors in this sequence are the same, then one of these can be eliminated without changing the subspace generated.

Proof. The commutative property of vector addition shows that the change in the order of the $\mathbf{A}_i$ will not change the subspace generated. Changing the order of the terms in a linear combination will not change the vector being represented.

To prove the second half of the theorem, let us suppose that two of the vectors in the sequence are equal. Since a change in the order of the vectors does not change the subspace generated, we can assume that the two equal vectors are $\mathbf{A}_1$ and $\mathbf{A}_2$. Let $L_1 = L\{\mathbf{A}_1, \mathbf{A}_2, \mathbf{A}_3, \ldots, \mathbf{A}_k\}$ and $L_2 = L\{\mathbf{A}_1, \mathbf{A}_3, \ldots, \mathbf{A}_k\}$. Suppose that a vector $\mathbf{B}$ is in L_1. Then there exist scalars $s_1, s_2, \ldots, s_k$ such that

$$\begin{aligned}\mathbf{B} &= s_1\mathbf{A}_1 + s_2\mathbf{A}_2 + s_3\mathbf{A}_3 + \cdots + s_k\mathbf{A}_k \\ &= s_1\mathbf{A}_1 + s_2\mathbf{A}_1 + s_3\mathbf{A}_3 + \cdots + s_k\mathbf{A}_k \\ &= (s_1 + s_2)\mathbf{A}_1 \quad + s_3\mathbf{A}_3 + \cdots + s_k\mathbf{A}_k,\end{aligned}$$

and hence $\mathbf{B}$ is a linear combination of the vectors $\mathbf{A}_1, \mathbf{A}_3, \ldots, \mathbf{A}_k$ and is therefore in L_2.

On the other hand, if a vector is in L_2, then it is a linear combination of the $\mathbf{A}_i$ not including $\mathbf{A}_2$. But the same linear combination can be thought of as being a linear combination of *all* the $\mathbf{A}_i$ (with the coefficient of $\mathbf{A}_2$ being 0). Hence any vector in L_2 is also in L_1. These two facts together tell us that $L_1 = L_2$, and the proof of the theorem is complete. ▌

Note that when we are to prove that two sets are equal, we must show that they consist of exactly the same elements. This is done, just as in the above proof, by showing that every element in the first set is contained in the second and, conversely, that every element which is contained in the second is also contained in the first.

The above theorem shows that we are allowed to speak of the subspace generated by a *set* of vectors. The braces may help us remember this fact.

PROBLEMS

1. Finish the proof of the fact that $C(I)$ is a vector space.
2. Let P_n be the set of all polynomials of degree n or less having real coefficients, that is, polynomials of the form $a_nx^n + a_{n-1}x^{n-1} + \cdots + a_1x + a_0$. Prove that P_n is a vector space when vector addition is defined as the sum of the two polynomials and scalar multiplication is the multiplication of the polynomial by a scalar.
3. Let $f_1, f_2, \ldots, f_n$ be n real-valued functions defined and continuous on the interval I. Prove that the set of all linear combinations of these functions is a vector space.
4. Let V be a vector space. Is $L\{\mathbf{0}\}$ a subspace of V? Describe this set.
5. In each of the following, $\mathbf{X} = [x_1, x_2, \ldots, x_n]$ is to be a vector in R^n. Is the given subset of R^n a subspace of R^n? Prove your answer. Note that in order to prove that something is not true, it suffices to give a single example showing its failure.

   a) $V_a = \{\mathbf{X} \mid x_1 = 0\}$
   b) $V_b = \{\mathbf{X} \mid x_1 = x_2 = 0\}$
   c) $V_c = \{\mathbf{X} \mid x_1 = x_2\}$
   d) $V_d = \{\mathbf{X} \mid x_1 = 1\}$
   e) $V_e = \{\mathbf{X} \mid x_1 = x_2 = 1\}$
   f) $V_f = \{\mathbf{X} \mid 2x_1 + 3x_2 = 0\}$
   g) $V_g = \{\mathbf{X} \mid 2x_1 + 3x_2 = 1\}$
   h) $V_h = \{\mathbf{X} \mid x_1^2 + x_2^2 = 0\}$
   i) $V_i = \{\mathbf{X} \mid x_1^2 + x_2^2 = 1\}$
   j) $V_j = \{\mathbf{X} \mid x_1 \le x_2\}$
   k) $V_k = \{\mathbf{X} \mid x_1x_2 = 0\}$
6. Prove that $L\{\mathbf{A}_1, \mathbf{A}_2, \ldots, \mathbf{A}_k, \mathbf{0}\} = L\{\mathbf{A}_1, \mathbf{A}_2, \ldots, \mathbf{A}_k\}$.
7. Let $\mathbf{B} \in L\{\mathbf{A}_1, \mathbf{A}_2, \ldots, \mathbf{A}_k\}$. Prove that $L\{\mathbf{B}, \mathbf{A}_1, \mathbf{A}_2, \ldots, \mathbf{A}_k\} = L\{\mathbf{A}_1, \ldots, \mathbf{A}_k\}$.
8. Prove that $R^n = L\{\mathbf{e}_1, \mathbf{e}_2, \ldots, \mathbf{e}_n\}$.
9. Let S be some set of vectors and let T be a subset of S. Prove that $L\{S\} \supset L\{T\}$.
10. Let S be the space of all infinite sequences of real numbers. Prove that the following are subspaces of S:

    a) S_1: all sequences $\{a_n\}$ of S such that $\sum |a_n| < \infty$.
    b) S_∞: all sequences $\{a_n\}$ of S such that $\sup \{|a_n| \mid n = 1, 2, \ldots\}^* < \infty$.
    c) S_2: all sequences $\{a_n\}$ of S such that $\sum a_n^2 < \infty$.

1-3. LINEAR INDEPENDENCE

In the last section we saw that a subspace $L\{\mathbf{A}_1, \mathbf{A}_2, \ldots, \mathbf{A}_k\}$ is unchanged by reordering the vectors or by eliminating any duplication of the vectors in the sequence $\mathbf{A}_1, \mathbf{A}_2, \ldots, \mathbf{A}_k$. In Problem 6 of the last section we also saw that a zero vector could be eliminated from the set of vectors without changing the space generated. We open

---

* If A is some set of real numbers, then $\sup A$ is the *supremum* or *least upper bound* of A. This is the real number α for which (1) $\alpha \ge x$ for every x in A and (2) if $b < \alpha$ then there exists at least one y in A such that $y > b$. If the set A has no upper bound, we write formally $\sup A = +\infty$. There is a corresponding definition for the *infimum*, or *greatest lower bound* for a set, which is denoted by $\inf A$. If the supremum of a set A belongs to the set, it is called the *maximum* of the set, and we denote it by $\max A$. Similarly, the *minimum* of a set is denoted by $\min A$, provided that it exists.

this section by considering some other situations in which two sets of vectors generate the same subspace.

Theorem 1–7. Let S be a set of vectors and let T be the same set of vectors except that one vector in the set S has been multiplied by a nonzero scalar c. Then $L\{S\} = L\{T\}$. That is, if $c \neq 0$, then

$$L\{\mathbf{A}_1, \mathbf{A}_2, \ldots, \mathbf{A}_k\} = L\{c\mathbf{A}_1, \mathbf{A}_2, \ldots, \mathbf{A}_k\}.$$

Proof. Note that the fact that the order of the vectors in a sequence can be changed without changing the subspace generated means that it suffices to prove the special case given in the last line of the theorem. We have $\mathbf{B} \in L\{S\}$ if and only if $\mathbf{B} = s_1\mathbf{A}_1 + \cdots + s_k\mathbf{A}_k$ for some set of scalars $s_1, s_2, \ldots, s_k$. Similarly, $\mathbf{B} \in L\{T\}$ if and only if $\mathbf{B} = t_1c\mathbf{A}_1 + t_2\mathbf{A}_2 + \cdots + t_k\mathbf{A}_k$ for some set of scalars $t_1, t_2, \ldots, t_k$.

Now suppose that $\mathbf{B} \in L\{S\}$, then

$$\mathbf{B} = s_1\mathbf{A}_1 + \cdots + s_k\mathbf{A}_k = (s_1/c)c\mathbf{A}_1 + \cdots + s_k\mathbf{A}_k,$$

and hence $\mathbf{B} \in L\{T\}$.

Conversely, if $\mathbf{B} \in L\{T\}$, then

$$\begin{aligned}\mathbf{B} &= t_1c\mathbf{A}_1 + t_2\mathbf{A}_2 + \cdots + t_k\mathbf{A}_k \\ &= (t_1c)\mathbf{A}_1 + t_2\mathbf{A}_2 + \cdots + t_k\mathbf{A}_k,\end{aligned}$$

and hence $\mathbf{B}$ is in $L\{S\}$. ▌

Where in this proof did we have to make use of the hypothesis that $c \neq 0$?

By applying this theorem more than once, we see that any number of the vectors in the sequence could be multiplied by any nonzero constants without changing the subspace generated. Now we prove:

Theorem 1–8. $L\{\mathbf{A}_1, \mathbf{A}_2, \ldots, \mathbf{A}_k\} = L\{\mathbf{A}_1 + \mathbf{A}_2, \mathbf{A}_2, \ldots, \mathbf{A}_k\}$. That is, the space generated by a set of vectors is not changed if some vector of the set is replaced by the sum of itself and another vector of the set.

Proof. Let $L_1 = L\{\mathbf{A}_1, \mathbf{A}_2, \ldots, \mathbf{A}_k\}$ and $L_2 = L\{\mathbf{A}_1 + \mathbf{A}_2, \mathbf{A}_2, \ldots, \mathbf{A}_k\}$. First, we show that $L_1 \subset L_2$. Suppose that $\mathbf{B} \in L_1$. Then

$$\begin{aligned}\mathbf{B} &= s_1\mathbf{A}_1 + s_2\mathbf{A}_2 + \cdots + s_k\mathbf{A}_k \\ &= s_1(\mathbf{A}_1 + \mathbf{A}_2) + (s_2 - s_1)\mathbf{A}_2 + s_3\mathbf{A}_3 + \cdots + s_k\mathbf{A}_k.\end{aligned}$$

Hence $\mathbf{B} \in L_2$.

In the other direction, suppose that $\mathbf{B} \in L_2$. Then

$$\begin{aligned}\mathbf{B} &= t_1(\mathbf{A}_1 + \mathbf{A}_2) + t_2\mathbf{A}_2 + \cdots + t_k\mathbf{A}_k \\ &= t_1\mathbf{A}_1 + (t_1 + t_2)\mathbf{A}_2 + \cdots + t_k\mathbf{A}_k,\end{aligned}$$

and therefore we can conclude that $\mathbf{B} \in L_1$. Putting these two parts together proves the theorem. ▌

Theorems 1–7 and 1–8 together show that we can replace any vector, say $\mathbf{A}_2$, in a sequence by the vector $\mathbf{A}_2 + c\mathbf{A}_i$, where c is any scalar and $\mathbf{A}_i$ is any other vector in the sequence. This replacement will not change the subspace generated by the sequence. If $c = 0$, then there is nothing to prove here. If $c \neq 0$, then we can go through the following steps (letting $\mathbf{A}_i = \mathbf{A}_1$ as an example):

$$\begin{aligned} L\{\mathbf{A}_1, \mathbf{A}_2, \ldots, \mathbf{A}_k\} &= L\{c\mathbf{A}_1, \mathbf{A}_2, \ldots, \mathbf{A}_k\} && \text{(by Theorem 1–7)} \\ &= L\{c\mathbf{A}_1, \mathbf{A}_2 + c\mathbf{A}_1, \ldots, \mathbf{A}_k\} && \text{(by Theorem 1–8)} \\ &= L\{\mathbf{A}_1, \mathbf{A}_2 + c\mathbf{A}_1, \ldots, \mathbf{A}_k\} && \text{(by Theorem 1–7).} \end{aligned}$$

Theorem 1–9. If $\mathbf{A}_k$ is a linear combination of $\mathbf{A}_1, \mathbf{A}_2, \ldots, \mathbf{A}_{k-1}$, then

$$L\{\mathbf{A}_1, \mathbf{A}_2, \ldots, \mathbf{A}_k\} = L\{\mathbf{A}_1, \mathbf{A}_2, \ldots, \mathbf{A}_{k-1}\}.$$

Proof. We have

$$L\{\mathbf{A}_1, \ldots, \mathbf{A}_{k-1}\} \subset L\{\mathbf{A}_1, \ldots, \mathbf{A}_{k-1}, \mathbf{A}_k\}$$

automatically. To go in the other direction, suppose that $\mathbf{B} \in L\{\mathbf{A}_1, \ldots, \mathbf{A}_k\}$. Then there exists a sequence of scalars, s_i, such that $\mathbf{B} = s_1\mathbf{A}_1 + \cdots + s_k\mathbf{A}_k$. However, we are given by hypothesis that $\mathbf{A}_k = t_1\mathbf{A}_1 + \cdots + t_{k-1}\mathbf{A}_{k-1}$ for some set of scalars t_i. Hence

$$\begin{aligned} \mathbf{B} &= s_1\mathbf{A}_1 + \cdots + s_{k-1}\mathbf{A}_{k-1} + s_k\mathbf{A}_k \\ &= \sum_{i=1}^{k-1} s_i\mathbf{A}_i + s_k \sum_{i=1}^{k-1} t_i\mathbf{A}_i = \sum_{i=1}^{k-1} (s_i + s_k t_i)\mathbf{A}_i. \end{aligned}$$

This shows that $\mathbf{B} \in L\{\mathbf{A}_1, \ldots, \mathbf{A}_{k-1}\}$, which proves the theorem. ∎

These theorems can be used in a practical manner to simplify the description of a subspace. The method can be demonstrated with the help of an example.

Suppose that we wish to find the subspace generated by the following set of four vectors from R^5:

$$[0, 2, 4, -1, 5],\ [3, 6, -3, 0, 3],\ [0, -5, -10, 6, -16],\ [5, 11, -3, -1, 8].$$

Let V be the subspace of R^5 generated by these vectors.

Although we said that we would prefer to think of the vectors as having their components arranged vertically, it is computationally easier to arrange the components in rows. Our first step is to write these rows one above another. This gives us a rectangular array of numbers. We understand that the rows of this array are the vectors, and hence it is not necessary to put commas between the components or to use separate brackets for each row. The array for the four given vectors would thus be:

$$\begin{bmatrix} 0 & 2 & 4 & -1 & 5 \\ 3 & 6 & -3 & 0 & 3 \\ 0 & -5 & -10 & 6 & -16 \\ 5 & 11 & -3 & -1 & 8 \end{bmatrix}.$$

We may now proceed to use the above theorems to obtain a simpler set of vectors. At each stage we will describe the operation performed:

$\begin{bmatrix} 3 & 6 & -3 & 0 & 3 \\ 5 & 11 & -3 & -1 & 8 \\ 0 & 2 & 4 & -1 & 5 \\ 0 & -5 & -10 & 6 & -16 \end{bmatrix}$	The rows have been interchanged to bring the zeros in the first column to the bottom. (Theorem 1–6.)
$\begin{bmatrix} 1 & 2 & -1 & 0 & 1 \\ 5 & 11 & -3 & -1 & 8 \\ 0 & 2 & 4 & -1 & 5 \\ 0 & -5 & -10 & 6 & -16 \end{bmatrix}$	The first row was multiplied by $\frac{1}{3}$ to make the first entry a 1. (Theorem 1–7).
$\begin{bmatrix} 1 & 2 & -1 & 0 & 1 \\ 0 & 1 & 2 & -1 & 3 \\ 0 & 2 & 4 & -1 & 5 \\ 0 & -5 & -10 & 6 & -16 \end{bmatrix}$	The first row was multiplied by -5 and added to the second row to get a zero in the first column. (Theorem 1–8.) The second row already has a 1 as its first nonzero entry.
$\begin{bmatrix} 1 & 0 & -5 & 2 & -5 \\ 0 & 1 & 2 & -1 & 3 \\ 0 & 0 & 0 & 1 & -1 \\ 0 & 0 & 0 & 1 & -1 \end{bmatrix}$	Row 2 was multiplied by -2 and added to row 1; by -2 and added to row 3; and by 5 and added to row 4, thus putting zeros in the second column. (Theorem 1–8.) Since rows 3 and 4 are identical, one can be deleted. (Theorem 1–6.)
$\begin{bmatrix} 1 & 0 & -5 & 0 & -3 \\ 0 & 1 & 2 & 0 & 2 \\ 0 & 0 & 0 & 1 & -1 \end{bmatrix}$	Row 3 was multiplied by -2 and added to row 1; row 3 was multiplied by 1 and added to row 2. (Theorem 1–8.)

We have therefore arrived at a set of three vectors, $[1, 0, -5, 0, -3]$, $[0, 1, 2, 0, 2]$, and $[0, 0, 0, 1, -1]$, which will also generate the same space V. These three vectors are in a particularly useful form. It is quite easy to see whether or not a given vector is in the subspace, and if it is, to find the coefficients of the linear combination needed to give it.

For example, is the vector $\mathbf{C} = [3, 2, -11, -2, -3]$ in the subspace V? Let us call the three vectors found above, $\mathbf{B}_1, \mathbf{B}_2$, and $\mathbf{B}_3$, respectively. Of these three, only $\mathbf{B}_1$ has a nonzero first component, $\mathbf{B}_2$ is the only one with a nonzero second component, and only $\mathbf{B}_3$ is nonzero in the fourth component. Therefore

$$s_1\mathbf{B}_1 + s_2\mathbf{B}_2 + s_3\mathbf{B}_3 = [s_1, s_2, u, s_3, v],$$

where u and v are numbers which depend on s_1, s_2, and s_3. Therefore the only possible linear combination of $\mathbf{B}_1$, $\mathbf{B}_2$, and $\mathbf{B}_3$ which could give us $\mathbf{C}$ is

$$\mathbf{C} = 3\mathbf{B}_1 + 2\mathbf{B}_2 - 2\mathbf{B}_3.$$

If we calculate the right-hand side of this expression, we find that equality does hold and therefore that **C** is in the subspace V.

The above result allows us to characterize the space V in a fairly simple form. If **X** represents the vector $[x_1, x_2, x_3, x_4, x_5]$, then we can write

$$\begin{aligned} V &= L\{\mathbf{B}_1, \mathbf{B}_2, \mathbf{B}_3\} \\ &= \{\mathbf{X} \mid x_3 = -5x_1 + 2x_2, x_5 = -3x_1 + 2x_2 - x_4\}. \end{aligned}$$

The first, second, and fourth components of any vector in V serve to determine the coefficients of $\mathbf{B}_1$, $\mathbf{B}_2$, and $\mathbf{B}_3$ completely. As a result, any vector in V can be expressed in only one way as a linear combination of the $\mathbf{B}_i$.

Note what it is that makes this calculation so easy. Each row of the final array has a "1" as its first nonzero entry. Each row has more zeros at the start than the previous row, and the first nonzero entry in any row is the only nonzero entry in that column. An array of numbers which satisfies these properties is said to be in *reduced row echelon form.*

Definition 1–10. A rectangular array of numbers is said to be in *row echelon form* if the number of zeros before the first nonzero entry in each row is properly greater than in the row above. If some row consists entirely of zeros, all subsequent rows must do so also. In such an array, the first nonzero entry of each row is called the *principal entry* of that row, and the column containing that entry is called a *principal column* of the array. An array is said to be in *reduced row echelon form* if it is in row echelon form, every principal entry is equal to one, and each principal entry is the only nonzero entry in its column.

In the above example, we found that every vector in the subspace generated could be given in a unique way as the linear combination of vectors whose components were the rows of the array in reduced row echelon form. When will such a result be true in general? That is, when can we be sure that every vector in $L\{\mathbf{A}_1, \mathbf{A}_2, \ldots, \mathbf{A}_k\}$ can be expressed in a *unique* way as a linear combination of the vectors $\mathbf{A}_i$? We will investigate this question by assuming this statement to be false, and seeing what happens.

Suppose then that there is some vector in this subspace which can be expressed in two different ways as a linear combination of the $\mathbf{A}_i$. That is,

$$\mathbf{X} = \sum_{i=1}^{k} s_i\mathbf{A}_i = \sum_{i=1}^{k} t_i\mathbf{A}_i,$$

where not all of the s_i are equal to the corresponding t_i. Subtracting these two expressions for the vector **X** from each other gives

$$\sum_{i=1}^{k} (s_i - t_i)\mathbf{A}_i = \sum_{i=1}^{k} \lambda_i\mathbf{A}_i = \mathbf{0},$$

where each $\lambda_i = s_i - t_i$. Here, since not all of the s_i and t_i are equal, not all of the λ_i will be zero.

Conversely, suppose there exists a set of λ_i, not all zero, such that $\sum_{i=1}^{k}\lambda_i\mathbf{A}_i = \mathbf{0}$. Then there is a vector in $L\{\mathbf{A}_1, \mathbf{A}_2, \ldots, \mathbf{A}_k\}$ which has two different representations as a linear combination of the $\mathbf{A}_i$. In particular, the vector $\mathbf{0}$ has the expression given above and also the different expression $\sum_{i=1}^{k} 0\mathbf{A}_i = \mathbf{0}$. We have therefore shown that a vector in the space $L\{\mathbf{A}_1, \mathbf{A}_2, \ldots, \mathbf{A}_k\}$ has a *unique* expression as a linear combination of the $\mathbf{A}_i$ if and only if the only linear combination of the $\mathbf{A}_i$ which has the value zero is the one all of whose coefficients are zero.

The concept which has just been introduced is important enough to deserve a special name.

Definition 1–11. A sequence of vectors $\mathbf{A}_1, \mathbf{A}_2, \ldots, \mathbf{A}_k$ is called *linearly dependent* if and only if there is a sequence of scalars λ_i, not all zero, such that $\sum_{i=1}^{k} \lambda_i\mathbf{A}_i = \mathbf{0}$. If a sequence of vectors is not linearly dependent, then it is called *linearly independent.*

With this definition, we see that we have actually proved above:

▶ **Theorem 1–10.** The vectors in the subspace $L\{\mathbf{A}_1, \mathbf{A}_2, \ldots, \mathbf{A}_k\}$ have unique expressions as linear combinations of the $\mathbf{A}_i$ if and only if the sequence of the $\mathbf{A}_i$ is linearly independent.

Let us now prove some of the properties of linear dependence.

Theorem 1–11. A sequence of vectors is linearly dependent if either of the following conditions hold:

1. The zero vector is a member of the sequence.
2. Two vectors in the sequence are identical.

Proof. To prove 1, let us suppose that $\mathbf{A}_1 = \mathbf{0}$, for example. Then

$$\sum_{i=1}^{k} \lambda_i\mathbf{A}_i = \mathbf{0}$$

if we set $\lambda_1 = 1$ and all of the other $\lambda_i = 0$. Here, not all of the λ_i are zero, and hence the sequence $\mathbf{A}_i$ will be linearly dependent.

In case 2, suppose, for example, that $\mathbf{A}_1 = \mathbf{A}_2$. Then we will again have

$$\sum_{i=1}^{k} \lambda_i\mathbf{A}_i = \mathbf{0}$$

if we set $\lambda_1 = 1$, $\lambda_2 = -1$, and all the other $\lambda_i = 0$. Again, not all of these λ_i are equal to zero, and we can conclude that the sequence is linearly dependent. ▌

The last theorem shows that we can speak of a *set* of linearly independent vectors. If a sequence of vectors is linearly independent, then there can be no duplication in the sequence. On the other hand, the linear dependence or independence of a sequence of vectors is independent of the order in which the vectors are given. (Why?) Therefore linear independence is a property of a set of vectors.

Theorem 1–12. If a sequence of vectors is linearly dependent, then at least one of them is a linear combination of the others.

Proof. If the sequence $\mathbf{A}_1, \mathbf{A}_2, \ldots, \mathbf{A}_k$ is linearly dependent, then there is a sequence of scalars λ_i, not all zero, such that

$$\lambda_1\mathbf{A}_1 + \lambda_2\mathbf{A}_2 + \cdots + \lambda_k\mathbf{A}_k = \mathbf{0}.$$

Suppose that $\lambda_j \neq 0$. Then we can divide this equation through by λ_j. For each i, set $\lambda_i/\lambda_j = s_i$. Then $s_j = 1$, and we can rewrite the above equation in the form

$$\mathbf{A}_j = -s_1\mathbf{A}_1 - \cdots - s_{j-1}\mathbf{A}_{j-1} - s_{j+1}\mathbf{A}_{j+1} - \cdots - s_k\mathbf{A}_k,$$

which proves the theorem. ▌

This theorem also has a converse which we will find useful.

Theorem 1–13. If $\mathbf{B}$ is a linear combination of the vectors $\mathbf{A}_1, \mathbf{A}_2, \ldots, \mathbf{A}_k$, then the sequence $\mathbf{B}, \mathbf{A}_1, \mathbf{A}_2, \ldots, \mathbf{A}_k$ is linearly dependent.

The proof of this theorem is left as an exercise.

Theorem 1–14. If a sequence of vectors is linearly dependent, then the addition of one or more vectors to the sequence will produce a new sequence which is also linearly dependent.

Proof. Since the original sequence is assumed to be linearly dependent, there is some linear combination of these vectors, with coefficients not all zero, which gives the zero vector. We can add the new vectors to the linear combination without changing the result if we merely supply each with a zero coefficient. A coefficient which was not zero before cannot be made zero by merely adding a new coefficient to the sequence. ▌

Theorem 1–14 is logically equivalent to

Theorem 1–15. If a set of vectors is linearly independent, then so is any subset of this set.

PROBLEMS

For each of the following sets of vectors, use the reduction process described at the beginning of this section to obtain a simpler set of vectors which generate the same subspace.

1. [2, 1, 6, −3], [−1, 5, −14, 5], [3, −3, 18, 2]
2. [3, −2, −1, 5], [1, −1, −1, 2], [2, 1, 4, 1]
3. [5, 5, −1, 7], [−1, −1, 3, 4], [2, 2, −11, 4]
4. [0, 4, 4, 13], [0, −7, −7, 4], [0, 3, 3, −1]
5. [0, 5, 3, −2], [0, 6, −1, 8], [0, 1, 4, −2]

6. Show that the operations of Theorems 1–7 and 1–8 are reversible; that is, show that they can be undone by operations of the same types.
7. Prove that the operations given in Theorems 1–7 and 1–8 when applied to a linearly independent set of vectors will result in a linearly independent set of vectors.
8. Prove that the set of vectors $\mathbf{e}_1, \mathbf{e}_2, \ldots, \mathbf{e}_n$ in R^n are linearly independent.
9. Prove Theorem 1–13.
10. The nonzero vectors $\mathbf{A}_1, \mathbf{A}_2, \ldots, \mathbf{A}_k$ are such that their components are the rows of a rectangular array which is in reduced row echelon form. Prove that the vectors are linearly independent.
11. Would the result of Problem 10 still be true if the array were merely in row echelon form? Justify your answer.

1–4. BASES

The last four theorems of Section 1–2 tell us a great deal about linearly independent sets of vectors. With only a little effort we can use this information to obtain a most important result. First, let us prove a slightly stronger version of Theorem 1–12.

Theorem 1–16. Let $\mathbf{A}_1, \mathbf{A}_2, \ldots, \mathbf{A}_k$ be a sequence of nonzero vectors which is linearly dependent. Then there is some first vector $\mathbf{A}_j$ in the sequence, with $1 \leq j < k$, such that

1. the sequence $\mathbf{A}_1, \mathbf{A}_2, \ldots, \mathbf{A}_j$ is linearly independent, and
2. the vector $\mathbf{A}_{j+1}$ is a linear combination of the vectors $\mathbf{A}_1, \ldots, \mathbf{A}_j$.

Proof. Consider the following successive sequences of vectors:

$$
\begin{array}{l}
\mathbf{A}_1 \\
\mathbf{A}_1, \mathbf{A}_2 \\
\mathbf{A}_1, \mathbf{A}_2, \mathbf{A}_3 \\
\vdots \\
\mathbf{A}_1, \mathbf{A}_2, \ldots, \mathbf{A}_k.
\end{array}
$$

By Theorems 1–14 and 1–15, if any one of these sequences is linearly independent, then so is each previous. Likewise, if one of them is linearly dependent, then each subsequent sequence is also. By hypothesis, the last of these sequences is linearly dependent. The first of them, consisting of the vector $\mathbf{A}_1$ alone, is linearly independent. Therefore there must be some last sequence in the series which is linearly independent. Let this be the sequence $\mathbf{A}_1, \ldots, \mathbf{A}_j$. Then the next sequence in the series will have to be linearly dependent. We will then have

$$\sum_{i=1}^{j+1} \lambda_i \mathbf{A}_i = \mathbf{0}$$

with not all of the λ_i equal to zero. In particular, $\lambda_{j+1} \neq 0$, since otherwise we would have $\sum_{i=1}^{j} \lambda_i \mathbf{A}_i = \mathbf{0}$ with not all of the $\lambda_i = 0$, and this would be a contradiction to the statement that $\mathbf{A}_1, \ldots, \mathbf{A}_j$ is linearly independent. We can therefore divide the above equation through by λ_{j+1} and solve for $\mathbf{A}_{j+1}$ in terms of the $\mathbf{A}_i$ with $i \leq j$. This proves the theorem. ▌

Now we turn to the main theorem of this section.

▶ **Theorem 1–17.** Suppose that the vectors $\mathbf{B}_1, \mathbf{B}_2, \ldots, \mathbf{B}_n$ are a set of generators for a space V and that the set of vectors $\mathbf{A}_1, \mathbf{A}_2, \ldots, \mathbf{A}_k$ is a linearly independent set of vectors which is contained in the same space. Then we must have $n \geq k$.

Proof. We start by first proving that if $\mathbf{C}_1, \mathbf{C}_2, \ldots, \mathbf{C}_k$ are k vectors in R^n, and if $k > n$, then the $\mathbf{C}_i$ must be linearly dependent. For each i, let

$$\mathbf{C}_i = [c_{i1}, c_{i2}, \ldots, c_{in}]$$

and consider the following rectangular array whose rows are these vectors:

$$\begin{bmatrix} c_{11} & c_{12} & \cdots & c_{1n} \\ c_{21} & c_{22} & \cdots & c_{2n} \\ \vdots & & & \vdots \\ c_{k1} & c_{k2} & \cdots & c_{kn} \end{bmatrix}.$$

Using the row reduction technique on this array, we obtain an array which will be in row echelon form. The second row of the reduced array must have at least one initial zero entry. The third row will have at least two, and so on. Since $k > n$, the last row must consist entirely of zeros. At each step of the row reduction process, a row is replaced by itself plus a linear combination of rows above it. It then follows that the rth row of the reduced array must be a linear combination of $\mathbf{C}_1, \mathbf{C}_2, \mathbf{C}_3, \ldots, \mathbf{C}_r$ in which the coefficient of $\mathbf{C}_r$ is one. In particular, since the kth row is identically zero, we must have

$$\lambda_1\mathbf{C}_1 + \lambda_2\mathbf{C}_2 + \cdots + \lambda_k\mathbf{C}_k = \mathbf{0},$$

where $\lambda_k = 1$. This therefore shows that the $\mathbf{C}_i$ are linearly dependent.

Now we turn to the proof of the theorem as stated. We are given the n $\mathbf{B}_j$, which generate the space V, and the k $\mathbf{A}_i$, which are linearly independent and are contained in the space V. We wish to show that $k \leq n$.

Suppose, on the contrary, that $k > n$. Since the $\mathbf{B}_j$ generate V, each $\mathbf{A}_i$ is a linear combination of the $\mathbf{B}_j$. That is, for each i there must exist $c_{i1}, c_{i2}, \ldots, c_{in}$ such that

$$\mathbf{A}_i = c_{i1}\mathbf{B}_1 + c_{i2}\mathbf{B}_2 + \cdots + c_{in}\mathbf{B}_n.$$

For each i, let

$$\mathbf{C}_i = [c_{i1}, c_{i2}, \ldots, c_{in}].$$

The $\mathbf{C}_i$ are then a set of k vectors in R^n. By what we just showed, they must be linearly dependent, and hence there must exist $\lambda_1, \lambda_2, \ldots, \lambda_k$, not all zero, such that

$$\sum_{i=1}^{k} \lambda_i\mathbf{C}_i = \mathbf{0}.$$

Looking at the individual components of this equation, we see that

$$\sum_{i=1}^{k} \lambda_i c_{ij} = 0$$

must hold for every $j = 1, 2, \ldots, n$. But then

$$\sum_{i=1}^{k} \lambda_i \mathbf{A}_i = \left(\sum_{i=1}^{k} \lambda_i c_{i1}\right)\mathbf{B}_1 + \left(\sum_{i=1}^{k} \lambda_i c_{i2}\right)\mathbf{B}_2 + \cdots + \left(\sum_{i=1}^{k} \lambda_i c_{in}\right)\mathbf{B}_n$$

$$= \mathbf{0},$$

which contradicts the assumption that the $\mathbf{A}_i$ were linearly independent. We therefore conclude that our assumption must have been false and thus we have $k \leq n$. ▮

Some time spent on understanding the proof of this theorem would be well worth the reader's effort. In the next section we will see that this result is the principal key to the simplification of our study of vector spaces.

This theorem puts an upper limit on the number of vectors in a set of linearly independent vectors. The result is in the form of an inequality. Can equality occur? The answer, of course, is yes. In fact, we can always arrange matters so that a finite set of generators for some subspace are themselves linearly independent.

A consequence of the results obtained in Section 1–3 is that if a sequence of vectors is linearly dependent, then there is a linearly independent subsequence which generates the same subspace. It is obvious that we can remove any repeated vectors from a sequence without changing the space generated. Hence we need to consider only *sets* of vectors in stating and proving this result. (Why do we not need to worry about the order of the vectors in the sequence?)

▶ **Theorem 1–18.** Let S be a finite set of vectors containing at least one nonzero vector. Then there is a subset S_1 of S which is linearly independent and which is such that $L\{S_1\} = L\{S\}$.

Proof. To prove this, we merely need to use Theorems 1–16 and 1–9 alternately. If S is not already a linearly independent set, then by Theorem 1–16 one of the vectors of S is a linear combination of the others. By Theorem 1–9, this vector can be removed from the set without changing the space generated. If the resulting set is still not linearly independent, we repeat the process. Eventually, we must arrive at a linearly independent set. ▮

A set of vectors which generates a vector space and which is already linearly independent cannot be reduced further in this fashion. Such a set of vectors is given a special name.

Definition 1–12. A set of vectors in a vector space V is called a *basis* for V if and only if the set is linearly independent and generates V.

Note that the vectors $\mathbf{e}_i$ form bases for the vector spaces R^n. They are called the *standard bases* of the R^n.

If a finite set of vectors generates a space, then some subset of that set will be a basis for the space. This follows from Theorem 1–18. There is no unique basis for a given space. Many different bases can be found for a space. Problem 5 at the end of this section illustrates this. It should also be observed that the row reduction process described in the last section produces a basis for the space generated by the original set of vectors. This basis is not usually a subset of the original set however.

We are now in a position to define what we mean by a finite-dimensional vector space.

Definition 1–13. A vector space V is called *finite dimensional* if and only if there exists a basis for V consisting of a finite number of vectors.

Now we prove the surprising consequence of Theorem 1–17.

Theorem 1–19. Every basis of a finite-dimensional vector space contains the same number of vectors.

Proof. Suppose that $\mathbf{B}_1, \mathbf{B}_2, \ldots, \mathbf{B}_n$ and $\mathbf{A}_1, \mathbf{A}_2, \ldots, \mathbf{A}_m$ are two different bases for the same vector space V. Then the $\mathbf{B}_i$ generate V and the $\mathbf{A}_i$ form a linearly independent set. From Theorem 1–17 we conclude that

$$n \geq m.$$

On the other hand, the $\mathbf{B}_i$ are a linearly independent set and the $\mathbf{A}_i$ form a set of generators for V. Therefore, again from Theorem 1–17 we can conclude that

$$n \leq m.$$

These two results together tell us that $n = m$. Hence any two bases contain the same number of vectors. ∎

Definition 1–14. If V is a finite-dimensional vector space, then the *dimension* of V (written dim V) is the number of vectors in a basis for V.

Note that until we had proved Theorem 1–19, this definition would not make sense. According to this definition, the space R^n is of dimension n, since the standard basis, $\mathbf{e}_1, \mathbf{e}_2, \ldots, \mathbf{e}_n$, contains n vectors. In particular, the vector space R^3, which we have called the set of three-dimensional vectors, is of dimension three in the sense of this definition, thus justifying our terminology.

Throughout the remainder of this book we will be concerned with finite-dimensional vector spaces only.

We can now see how the dimension of a subspace generated by a given set of vectors can be determined. All we need to do is go through the row reduction process as described in Section 1–3. The rows which remain when the array is in reduced row echelon form (or merely in row echelon form) represent vectors which are linearly independent and which generate the same subspace. They thus form a basis for this space. Looking at it in another way, the dimension of the space generated is the number of nonvanishing rows in the reduced array.

How can we tell whether a given set of vectors is linearly independent or not? From the definition of a basis, we see that a set of vectors is linearly independent if and only if it is a basis for the subspace it generates. With the help of Theorem 1–19 and Definition 1–14, this is equivalent to the statement that *a set of k vectors is linearly independent if and only if the subspace it generates is of dimension k.*

To determine whether a given set of vectors is linearly independent, we therefore need only go through the row reduction process. If any of the rows becomes identically zero, the original set of vectors was linearly dependent. If none of the rows vanish, then the space is of the same dimension as the number of original vectors, and the latter must have been linearly independent.

It might seem that the standard basis for R^n would be the only one we would normally be interested in. However, there are often situations in which another basis might be more useful. For example, if the system of springs and masses described on page 7 consists of two equal masses and three equal springs, if the initial displacement of the masses is $[a, a]$ (i.e., both masses are displaced an equal distance in the same direction), and if they are released with no initial velocity, then the position of the masses at time t will be given by $[a \cos \omega_1 t, a \cos \omega_1 t]$, where ω_1 is some constant. (We assume the ideal situation with no damping.)

Similarly, if the initial displacement is $[a, -a]$, then the position at time t will be given by $[a \cos \omega_2 t, -a \cos \omega_2 t]$. Thus, if the initial displacement is $\mathbf{X} = y_1\mathbf{B}_1 + y_2\mathbf{B}_2$, where $\mathbf{B}_1 = [1, 1]$ and $\mathbf{B}_2 = [1, -1]$, then the position at time t is

$$y_1 \cos \omega_1 t\mathbf{B}_1 + y_2 \cos \omega_2 t\mathbf{B}_2.$$

In this particular example, the basis $\mathbf{B}_1, \mathbf{B}_2$ is the appropriate one to use to describe the physical situation most easily. (The vectors $\mathbf{B}_1$ and $\mathbf{B}_2$ are usually called the *modes* of this particular vibrating system.)

PROBLEMS

1. Prove that the vectors $\mathbf{e}_1, \mathbf{e}_2, \ldots, \mathbf{e}_n$ in R^n are linearly independent.
2. What is the largest number of linearly independent vectors that can be found in R^n? Give a reason for your answer.
3. Suppose that $\mathbf{A}_1, \mathbf{A}_2, \ldots, \mathbf{A}_k$ are linearly independent and that $\mathbf{B}_1 = \mathbf{A}_1, \mathbf{B}_2 = \mathbf{A}_1 + \mathbf{A}_2, \mathbf{B}_3 = \mathbf{A}_1 + \mathbf{A}_2 + \mathbf{A}_3, \ldots, \mathbf{B}_k = \mathbf{A}_1 + \mathbf{A}_2 + \cdots + \mathbf{A}_k$. Prove that $\mathbf{B}_1, \mathbf{B}_2, \ldots, \mathbf{B}_k$ are linearly independent.
4. Let $\mathbf{B}_1, \mathbf{B}_2, \ldots, \mathbf{B}_n$ be a basis for the space V. Suppose that $\mathbf{A}_1, \mathbf{A}_2, \ldots, \mathbf{A}_k$ are linearly independent vectors in $V\,(k < n)$. Prove that there are $n - k$ of the $\mathbf{B}_i$ such that $\mathbf{A}_1, \mathbf{A}_2, \ldots, \mathbf{A}_k, \mathbf{B}_{i_1}, \mathbf{B}_{i_2}, \ldots, \mathbf{B}_{i_{n-k}}$ is also a basis for V (i.e., any linearly independent set can be completed to a basis).

5. Determine which of the following sets of vectors are linearly independent. If a given set is not linearly independent, what is the dimension of the space it generates?
   a) [1, 2, 0, 3], [4, −1, 2, 0], [2, −5, 2, −6]
   b) [1, 1, −1, 2], [2, 3, −4, 3], [2, −2, 7, 8]
   c) [1, 2, 0, 2], [2, 1, 0, 1], [1, −1, 1, −1]
   d) [1, 0, 0, 1], [1, 1, 0, 0], [1, 0, 1, 0], [0, 2, −3, 1]
   e) [1, 3, 7, 2], [4, 7, 6, 1], [5, 11, 13, 4], [3, 4, 1, 1], [6, −8, 12, −2]
   f) [52, 39, −91, 117], [28, 21, −49, 63], [−20, −15, 35, −45], [60, 45, −105, 135]

1-5. THE DIRECT SUM

Any basis in a finite-dimensional vector space V behaves very much like this standard basis in R^n. This similarity is explained more fully by the following theorems.

Theorem 1-20. Let $\mathbf{B}_1, \mathbf{B}_2, \ldots, \mathbf{B}_n$ be a basis for the vector space V. Then any vector $\mathbf{X}$ in V has a unique expression in the form

$$\mathbf{X} = x_1\mathbf{B}_1 + x_2\mathbf{B}_2 + \cdots + x_n\mathbf{B}_n. \tag{1-6}$$

Proof. Since the $\mathbf{B}_i$ form a basis, they generate the space V. Hence any vector $\mathbf{X} \in V$ will have at least one representation in the form (1-6). However, the $\mathbf{B}_i$ are linearly independent. Hence, from Theorem 1-10, a representation in the form (1-6) must be unique. ▌

We have defined a basis as being a set of vectors. However, whenever the vectors in a basis are listed, this listing defines an order. We shall find it helpful to make use of this order and to think of a basis as being an ordered n-tuple of vectors.

Definition 1-15. Let $\mathcal{B} = \langle \mathbf{B}_1, \mathbf{B}_2, \ldots, \mathbf{B}_n \rangle$ be a basis for the vector space V ($\mathcal{B}$ is an ordered n-tuple of vectors). Let a vector $\mathbf{X}$ in V have a representation in the form (1-6). Then the numbers $x_1, x_2, \ldots, x_n$ are called the *components of* $\mathbf{X}$ *with respect to the basis* $\mathcal{B}$. We write

$$\mathbf{X} = [x_1, x_2, \ldots, x_n]_{\mathcal{B}}.$$

Using this definition, we can prove

Theorem 1-21. Let $\mathcal{B}$ be a basis for the vector space V. Let $\mathbf{A} = [a_1, a_2, \ldots, a_n]_{\mathcal{B}}$ and $\mathbf{B} = [b_1, b_2, \ldots, b_n]_{\mathcal{B}}$ be vectors in V and let t be some scalar. Then

$$\mathbf{A} + \mathbf{B} = [a_1 + b_1, a_2 + b_2, \ldots, a_n + b_n]_{\mathcal{B}},$$

and

$$t\mathbf{A} = [ta_1, ta_2, \ldots, ta_n]_{\mathcal{B}}.$$

The proof of this theorem is left as an exercise. The results of this theorem show that vectors in an arbitrary n-dimensional vector space behave exactly like the vectors in R^n so far as vector addition and scalar multiplication go. However, these are the only properties that appear in the definition of a vector space. Therefore, once we pick a basis for a vector space, we can represent it as in Definition 1–15 and operate with the vectors just as if they were vectors in R^n.

In the proof of Theorem 1–18 we talked about the removal of linearly dependent vectors from a sequence of vectors. The method used, depending as it did on Theorem 1–16, will leave a linearly independent subset at the start of the sequence unchanged.

Theorem 1–22. Let V be a vector space of dimension n and let $\mathbf{A}_1, \mathbf{A}_2, \ldots, \mathbf{A}_k$ be a linearly independent set of vectors in V with $k < n$. Then there exist vectors $\mathbf{B}_1, \mathbf{B}_2, \ldots, \mathbf{B}_{n-k}$ in V such that $\mathbf{A}_1, \ldots, \mathbf{A}_k, \mathbf{B}_1, \ldots, \mathbf{B}_{n-k}$ is a basis for V.

Proof. Roughly speaking, this theorem states that any linearly independent set of vectors in a finite-dimensional vector space can be completed to be a basis for that space. To prove this theorem, we need only observe that V has some basis, say $\mathbf{C}_1, \mathbf{C}_2, \ldots, \mathbf{C}_n$, and therefore the sequence of vectors $\mathbf{A}_1, \ldots, \mathbf{A}_k, \mathbf{C}_1, \ldots, \mathbf{C}_n$ will generate the space V. Using Theorem 1–16, we can remove linearly dependent vectors from this sequence. We always remove the first linearly dependent vector in the sequence. This must be one of the $\mathbf{C}_i$ since the set of $\mathbf{A}_i$ are given as linearly independent. When we are finished, we will have a basis which contains all of the $\mathbf{A}_i$, as is required in the theorem. ∎

This theorem, besides being of some interest in its own right, has a number of applications. In some cases, these applications are easiest to understand if we eliminate all mention of bases from the statement. An example of this is the following theorem

Theorem 1–23. Let L be a subspace of the finite-dimensional vector space V. Then there exists a subspace M of V such that

1. L and M have only the vector $\mathbf{0}$ in common, and
2. every vector $\mathbf{X}$ in V has a unique representation in the form
$$\mathbf{X} = \mathbf{A} + \mathbf{B},$$
where $\mathbf{A} \in L$ and $\mathbf{B} \in M$.

Proof. If L consists of the zero vector alone, then $M = V$, and the conclusions of the theorem follow. If $L = V$, then setting $M = \{\mathbf{0}\}$ again satisfies the requirements of the theorem.

Suppose then that L is a proper subspace of V which contains more than the zero vector alone. There exists a basis for L. Suppose that $\mathbf{A}_1, \mathbf{A}_2, \ldots, \mathbf{A}_k$ is such a basis. Using Theorem 1–22, we can complete this to be a basis for the whole space V. Let $\mathbf{B}_1$, $\mathbf{B}_2, \ldots, \mathbf{B}_{n-k}$ be the remaining vectors in this basis. Set $M = L\{\mathbf{B}_1, \mathbf{B}_2, \ldots, \mathbf{B}_{n-k}\}$. Now we can verify the two conclusions of the theorem.

Since $\mathbf{A}_1, \ldots, \mathbf{A}_k, \mathbf{B}_1, \ldots, \mathbf{B}_{n-k}$ is a basis for V, every vector in V can be written in the form
$$\mathbf{X} = a_1\mathbf{A}_1 + \cdots + a_k\mathbf{A}_k + b_1\mathbf{B}_1 + \cdots + b_{n-k}\mathbf{B}_{n-k} \tag{1–7}$$
in a unique way. Such a vector is in the subspace L if and only if all the b_i are zero. On the other hand, a vector is in M if and only if all the a_i are zero. When can a

vector then be common to both L and M? Only when all the a_i and b_i are zero. Therefore the only vector common to L and M is the vector $\mathbf{0}$. This proves statement (1) of the theorem.

The first half of the second conclusion of the theorem is immediate. Every vector $\mathbf{X}$ has an expression in terms of this basis as given by (1–7). We can set

$$\mathbf{A} = a_1\mathbf{A}_1 + \cdots + a_k\mathbf{A}_k$$

and

$$\mathbf{B} = b_1\mathbf{B}_1 + \cdots + b_{n-k}\mathbf{A}_{n-k}.$$

Then $\mathbf{A} \in L$, $\mathbf{B} \in M$ and $\mathbf{A} + \mathbf{B} = \mathbf{X}$. Theorem 1–10 shows that this representation is unique, but it might be instructive to give a direct proof of this fact.

Suppose that for some vector $\mathbf{X}$, we have $\mathbf{X} = \mathbf{A} + \mathbf{B} = \mathbf{A}' + \mathbf{B}'$, where both $\mathbf{A}$ and $\mathbf{A}'$ are in L, both $\mathbf{B}$ and $\mathbf{B}'$ are in M, and we do not have both $\mathbf{A} = \mathbf{A}'$ and $\mathbf{B} = \mathbf{B}'$. Then we must have

$$\begin{aligned}\mathbf{X} &= a_1\mathbf{A}_1 + \cdots + a_k\mathbf{A}_k + b_1\mathbf{B}_1 + \cdots + b_{n-k}\mathbf{B}_{n-k}\\ &= a_1'\mathbf{A}_1 + \cdots + a_k'\mathbf{A}_k + b_1'\mathbf{B}_1 + \cdots + b_{n-k}'\mathbf{B}_{n-k}\end{aligned}$$

with not all the $a_i = a_i'$ or $b_i = b_i'$. Subtracting these two representations of the vector $\mathbf{X}$, we find that

$$(a_1 - a_1')\mathbf{A}_1 + \cdots + (b_{n-k} - b_{n-k}')\mathbf{B}_{n-k} = \mathbf{0}.$$

The condition that either $\mathbf{A} \neq \mathbf{A}'$ or $\mathbf{B} \neq \mathbf{B}'$ becomes, in this case, the condition that not all of the coefficients in the last expression are zero. This condition contradicts the fact that the $\mathbf{A}_i$ and $\mathbf{B}_i$ together form a basis and hence are linearly independent. Therefore we must have $\mathbf{A} = \mathbf{A}'$ and $\mathbf{B} = \mathbf{B}'$. The decomposition is thus unique. ▌

Definition 1–16. When a pair of subspaces L and M of a vector space V satisfy conditions (1) and (2) of Theorem 1–23, we say that V is the *direct sum* of L and M and we write

$$V = L \oplus M. \tag{1–8}$$

When we write an expression of the form (1–8) we are therefore implying the two statements in Theorem 1–23. Observe that when $V = L \oplus M$, a basis for L and a basis for M together will make a basis for V. Therefore

$$\dim(L \oplus M) = \dim L + \dim M. \tag{1–9}$$

An example showing how we can actually find such a pair of spaces may be of interest here. Suppose that $L = L\{[0, 1, -1, 3, 2], [0, 3, 2, 4, 6]\}$. First, it is convenient to obtain a simpler pair of vectors which generate the same space L. This is done by means of the method described in Section 1–3. That is,

$$\begin{bmatrix}0 & 1 & -1 & 3 & 2\\ 0 & 3 & 2 & 4 & 6\end{bmatrix} \to \begin{bmatrix}0 & 1 & -1 & 3 & 2\\ 0 & 0 & 5 & -5 & 0\end{bmatrix}$$
$$\to \begin{bmatrix}0 & 1 & -1 & 3 & 2\\ 0 & 0 & 1 & -1 & 0\end{bmatrix} \to \begin{bmatrix}0 & 1 & 0 & 2 & 2\\ 0 & 0 & 1 & -1 & 0\end{bmatrix}.$$

We therefore have the simpler expression $L = L\{[0, 1, 0, 2, 2], [0, 0, 1, -1, 0]\}$. Now we wish to find a subspace M of R^5 such that $R^5 = L \oplus M$. We add the five vectors of the standard basis to the two vectors we have already. Again, we write the vectors horizontally, one above the other, to form a rectangular array. This gives

$$\begin{bmatrix} 0 & 1 & 0 & 2 & 2 \\ 0 & 0 & 1 & -1 & 0 \\ 1 & 0 & 0 & 0 & 0 \\ 0 & 1 & 0 & 0 & 0 \\ 0 & 0 & 1 & 0 & 0 \\ 0 & 0 & 0 & 1 & 0 \\ 0 & 0 & 0 & 0 & 1 \end{bmatrix}.$$

Now let us find which rows can be removed, using the ideas of Theorem 1–16. (The method we use here is not the best one to use in practical cases. Later in this section we will show how the subspace M can be found by inspection.) We see that the top three lines are clearly linearly independent, since any linear combination of them with nonzero coefficients will have a nonzero component in either the second, third, or first places. If we add the next line, does the set become linearly dependent? No, because if it did, line four could be written as a linear combination of the first three lines. To do this, however, the coefficient of the first line would have to be 1, and the coefficients of the second and third lines would have to be zero (why?). This is impossible, so that the first four lines are linearly independent.

Exactly the same sort of reasoning shows that the fifth line cannot be a linear combination of the first four lines and therefore that the first five lines are linearly independent.

Since the largest set of linearly independent vectors in R^5 is five vectors, the remaining two rows will have to be linear combinations of the first five. We have therefore obtained

$$R^5 = L \oplus M,$$

where

$$M = L\{\mathbf{e}_1, \mathbf{e}_2, \mathbf{e}_3\} \quad (\text{in } R^5). \tag{1-10}$$

Once we have obtained the direct-sum decomposition of a space, then the decomposition of any vector in terms of these subspaces is unique. However, given a subspace L, the space M such that $V = L \oplus M$ is not uniquely determined. In fact there may be many such spaces. To determine M, all we need is a basis for V such that the first k vectors are a basis for L. The remaining vectors will automatically form a basis for the space M. Any process which will produce such a set of vectors will give us a subspace.

For example, using the same example that we considered above, we can separate the top two rows (which already form a basis for L) from the remaining rows. We can then go through the same reduction process which lead to the reduced row echelon form, except that we will leave the top two rows unchanged. They are used merely to clear out all of the other entries in the second and third columns. This process proceeds as follows:

$$\begin{bmatrix} 0 & 1 & 0 & 2 & 2 \\ 0 & 0 & 1 & -1 & 0 \\ 1 & 0 & 0 & 0 & 0 \\ 0 & 1 & 0 & 0 & 0 \\ 0 & 0 & 1 & 0 & 0 \\ 0 & 0 & 0 & 1 & 0 \\ 0 & 0 & 0 & 0 & 1 \end{bmatrix} \to \begin{bmatrix} 0 & 1 & 0 & 2 & 2 \\ 0 & 0 & 1 & -1 & 0 \\ 1 & 0 & 0 & 0 & 0 \\ 0 & 0 & 0 & -2 & -2 \\ 0 & 0 & 1 & 0 & 0 \\ 0 & 0 & 0 & 1 & 0 \\ 0 & 0 & 0 & 0 & 1 \end{bmatrix}$$

$$\to \begin{bmatrix} 0 & 1 & 0 & 2 & 2 \\ 0 & 0 & 1 & -1 & 0 \\ 1 & 0 & 0 & 0 & 0 \\ 0 & 0 & 0 & 1 & 1 \\ 0 & 0 & 0 & 1 & 0 \\ 0 & 0 & 0 & 1 & 0 \\ 0 & 0 & 0 & 0 & 1 \end{bmatrix} \to \begin{bmatrix} 0 & 1 & 0 & 2 & 2 \\ 0 & 0 & 1 & -1 & 0 \\ 1 & 0 & 0 & 0 & 0 \\ 0 & 0 & 0 & 1 & 1 \\ 0 & 0 & 0 & 0 & -1 \\ 0 & 0 & 0 & 0 & -1 \\ 0 & 0 & 0 & 0 & 1 \end{bmatrix}$$

$$\to \begin{bmatrix} 0 & 1 & 0 & 2 & 2 \\ 0 & 0 & 1 & -1 & 0 \\ 1 & 0 & 0 & 0 & 0 \\ 0 & 0 & 0 & 1 & 1 \\ 0 & 0 & 0 & 0 & 1 \\ 0 & 0 & 0 & 0 & 0 \\ 0 & 0 & 0 & 0 & 0 \end{bmatrix} \to \begin{bmatrix} 0 & 1 & 0 & 2 & 2 \\ 0 & 0 & 1 & -1 & 0 \\ 1 & 0 & 0 & 0 & 0 \\ 0 & 0 & 0 & 1 & 0 \\ 0 & 0 & 0 & 0 & 1 \\ 0 & 0 & 0 & 0 & 0 \\ 0 & 0 & 0 & 0 & 0 \end{bmatrix}.$$

We have therefore obtained the result that $R^5 = L \oplus M'$, where

$$M' = L\{\mathbf{e}_1, \mathbf{e}_4, \mathbf{e}_5\}.$$

Both this and the previous result are correct, showing that there may be more than one direct-sum decomposition, even when one of the subspaces is specified.

The reader will observe that the method used here is easier to apply than the one used earlier. However, we do not even have to go through this much work. Once we have gone through the row reduction process with the generators of L, we can write down the generators of an M by inspection.

For example, suppose that the space L is generated by the rows of

$$\begin{bmatrix} 0 & 0 & 1 & 0 & 1 & 3 & 0 & -1 \\ 0 & 0 & 0 & 1 & -2 & 4 & 0 & 0 \\ 0 & 0 & 0 & 0 & 0 & 0 & 1 & 2 \end{bmatrix}.$$

We have three vectors in R^8. Five vectors will be required to generate a subspace M such that $R^8 = L \oplus M$. The only real requirement on these five vectors is that the eight vectors together must form a basis for R^8.

In this example, the required space would be $M = L\{\mathbf{e}_1, \mathbf{e}_2, \mathbf{e}_5, \mathbf{e}_6, \mathbf{e}_8\}$. We merely have to use all of the $\mathbf{e}_i$ corresponding to the nonprincipal columns of the array. That is, these $\mathbf{e}_i$ have a nonzero component in those columns of the array which do not contain one of the initial nonzero coefficients. It is clear that the resulting set of eight vectors is linearly independent since the only way a linear combination of these could be zero would be to have all three coefficients of the first three vanish. These are the only contributors to the 3rd, 4th, and 7th components. But then, the coefficients of the five remaining vectors must similarly be zero. Therefore we have obtained the desired decomposition.

PROBLEMS

1. Prove Theorem 1–21.
2. Suppose that $V = L\{\mathbf{A}_1, \mathbf{A}_2, \ldots, \mathbf{A}_n\}$ and that dim $V = n$. Prove that $\mathbf{A}_1, \mathbf{A}_2, \ldots, \mathbf{A}_n$ form a basis for V.
3. Prove formula (1–9).
4. Explain why M in (1–10) is *not* R^3 even though $R^3 = L\{\mathbf{e}_1, \mathbf{e}_2, \mathbf{e}_3\}$.

For each of the following sets of vectors:

a) Find the dimension of the subspace L of R^5 generated by this set.
b) Give a basis for this subspace L.
c) Find a subspace M such that $R^5 = L \oplus M$.

5. [6, 18, −12, 30, 42], [7, 21, −14, 35, 49]
6. [1, −1, 1, 2, −7], [2, 3, 7, −1, 6], [3, −4, 2, −2, 11]
7. [2, 1, 3, −1, −5], [1, 2, −1, 2, −4], [1, −1, 4, −3, −1], [0, 3, −5, 5, −3]
8. [1, 1, 1, 0, 0], [0, 1, 1, 1, 0], [0, 0, 1, 1, 1], [0, 0, 0, 1, 1], [0, 0, 0, 0, 1]
9. [1, 0, 2, 0, −1], [0, 1, 0, 1, 0], [1, 1, 1, 1, −1]
10. [5, 5, −1, −1, −1], [1, 1, 0, 0, 0], [0, 0, 2, 2, 2]
11. Prove that a vector space is finite dimensional if and only if it is generated by a finite set of vectors.
12. For each of Problems 5 through 10, write the vector [1, 2, 3, 4, 5] as the sum of two vectors, one in L and the other in the subspace M determined for that particular problem.

CHAPTER 2

Linear Transformations

2–1. LINEAR TRANSFORMATIONS

In this section we will discuss a subclass of the set of all functions whose domain is one vector space and whose range is another vector space. This subclass is the set of linear transformations. Much of the importance of the study of vector spaces is in the properties of these linear transformations.

Definition 2–1. A function $T: V \to W$ whose domain and range are vector spaces is called a *linear transformation* if and only if

1. for every pair of vectors $\mathbf{A}$ and $\mathbf{B}$ in V,

$$T(\mathbf{A} + \mathbf{B}) = T(\mathbf{A}) + T(\mathbf{B}); \tag{2–1}$$

2. for every vector $\mathbf{A} \in V$ and every scalar t,

$$T(t\mathbf{A}) = tT(\mathbf{A}). \tag{2–2}$$

It is customary when working with linear transformations to leave the parentheses off the vector being operated on, except when absolutely needed. Thus, the value of the transformation T at $\mathbf{A}$ will be written $T\mathbf{A}$ instead of $T(\mathbf{A})$. Note that we must still write $T(\mathbf{A} + \mathbf{B})$, however; the parentheses cannot be left off in this case.

Many authors prefer to write the symbol for the linear transformation *after* the vector being operated on instead of before it, as we are doing. Each method has its advantages and disadvantages. The method we are using is slightly better suited to the work we will do with the calculus later in the text. The reader is warned, however, that he may find the opposite method used in other books.

A linear transformation is, in general, a vector-valued function of a vector. The domain and range spaces can be any vector spaces at all. However, there are two special cases which occur often enough to deserve special mention. One case is when the domain and range spaces V and W are the same. The other is when the range space, W, is of dimension one. A vector space of dimension one can be identified with R, the set of real numbers. There is only one element in the basis, and there is a one-to-one correspondence between the set of all real numbers and the set of all vectors in the space. Hence we can think of such a linear transformation as a "real-valued" function of a vector. A linear transformation whose range is R is often called a *linear functional.*

A nontrivial example might be of interest. Let $f(x)$ be a function in the vector space $C(I)$ defined on page 10 (f is a real-valued function, continuous for $a \leq x \leq b$).

Then the transformation $T\colon C(I) \to R$ defined by

$$T(f) = \int_a^b f(x)\,dx$$

is a linear transformation. The reader should verify this.

As an example of a linear transformation whose range is a vector space, we can return to the motion of a pair of masses connected by springs, as described on page 7. We saw there that the position of the masses at time t would be $\mathbf{X}(t) = y_1 \cos \omega_1 t\mathbf{B}_1 + y_2 \cos \omega_2 t\mathbf{B}_2$, where the initial position was $\mathbf{X}(0) = y_1\mathbf{B}_1 + y_2\mathbf{B}_2$ and $\mathbf{B}_1 = [1, 1]$, $\mathbf{B}_2 = [1, -1]$. The reader can easily verify that for a fixed t, $\mathbf{X}(t)$ is a linear transform of $\mathbf{X}(0)$.

Another, perhaps more interesting, example of a linear transformation is the Fourier transform. The Fourier transform of a function $f(t)$ is the function

$$F(\omega) = \frac{1}{\sqrt{2\pi}} \int_{-\infty}^{\infty} e^{-i\omega t} f(t)\,dt.$$

This integral happens to define a complex-valued function, but this is a nonessential point. There is also some variation in the constant used outside of the integral sign.

The Fourier transform exists for a suitable class of functions defined for all t, $-\infty < t < \infty$. This class of functions can be considered to be a vector space, the functions being the vectors, in a manner similar to $C(I)$. Then the Fourier transform is a linear transformation of this space onto itself. A remarkable feature of this transformation is that if $F(\omega)$ is the transform of $f(t)$, then the transform of $F(\omega)$ is $f(-t)$.

The surprising thing about the Fourier transform is its physical significance. At first glance it appears to be merely a mathematical device. One could accept the fact that it might be useful in solving certain problems, but as defined here, it seems to have nothing to do with "real life." However, if one considers $f(t)$ to represent a signal, such as a radio signal [t being the time, $f(t)$ being the field strength], then the Fourier transform $F(\omega)$ measures the power that is in the signal at the frequency ω. The behavior of many devices is best understood in terms of how they operate on the frequency components of the signal, that is, on how they act on $F(\omega)$. A bandpass filter for example makes $F(\omega) = 0$ outside of some interval. Its action on the signal is much more complex but can be determined with the help of the Fourier transform.

These examples are merely mentioned here so that the reader can see that the machinery we are developing is of some practical importance. It might be noted that the last example, like that of $C(I)$, concerns an infinite-dimensional space. The spaces we study here will all be finite-dimensional. Although many of the results we will obtain will remain true in the infinite-dimensional case, there are a great many difficulties in the study of infinite-dimensional spaces that do not occur in the finite-dimensional case. It also happens that most infinite-dimensional spaces which appear in practice can be approximated by finite-dimensional spaces in some sense, and so our results will not be as special as they might seem.

The set of all linear transformations from a given domain into a given range can itself be turned into a vector space.

Definition 2–2. Let V and W be two given vector spaces. Then by $L[V; W]$ we mean the set of all linear transformations $T : V \to W$. Let S and T be two linear transformations in $L[V; W]$ and let t be any scalar. Then by the *sum* of S and T we mean the transformation $S + T$ defined by

$$(S + T)\mathbf{X} = S\mathbf{X} + T\mathbf{X}. \tag{2–3}$$

By the *scalar multiple* of T by t, we mean the transformation tT defined by

$$(tT)\mathbf{X} = t(T\mathbf{X}). \tag{2–4}$$

It should be observed that in order to define a function, it suffices to define its value at every point, just as has been done in this definition. In order to verify our assertion that $L[V; W]$ is a vector space, we should show that the functions $S + T$ and tT defined by (2–3) and (2–4) are themselves linear transformations and hence elements of $L[V; W]$. Then we must show that the vector sum and scalar multiplication so defined satisfy the eight postulates of a vector space. We start with the theorem:

Theorem 2–1. The functions $S + T$ and tT defined by (2–3) and (2–4) are linear transformations in $L[V; W]$.

Proof. It is clear that the domains of these new functions is still V and that the range is still W. All that is required is to show that these new functions are linear, that is, they satisfy (2–1) and (2–2). Let us prove that the function $S + T$, defined by (2–3), satisfies (2–1). The remaining parts of the proof can then be left as an exercise.

Let $\mathbf{A}$ and $\mathbf{B}$ be any two vectors in V. Then

$$\begin{aligned}(S + T)(\mathbf{A} + \mathbf{B}) &= S(\mathbf{A} + \mathbf{B}) + T(\mathbf{A} + \mathbf{B}) && \text{by (2–3)}\\ &= (S\mathbf{A} + S\mathbf{B}) + (T\mathbf{A} + T\mathbf{B}) && \text{by (2–1)}\\ &= (S\mathbf{A} + T\mathbf{A}) + (S\mathbf{B} + T\mathbf{B}) && \text{why?}\\ &= (S + T)\mathbf{A} + (S + T)\mathbf{B} && \text{by (2–3).} \ \blacksquare\end{aligned}$$

The fact that these operations satisfy the eight postulates given in Theorem 1–1 is also left as an exercise. The reader is advised to go through this exercise carefully. In particular, he should certainly prove P3 and P4.

The most convenient way to describe and work with a linear transformation is in terms of its matrix.

Definition 2–3. A *matrix* is a rectangular array of numbers of the form

$$A = [a_{ij}] = \begin{bmatrix} a_{11} & a_{12} & \cdots & a_{1n}\\ a_{21} & a_{22} & \cdots & a_{2n}\\ \vdots & & & \vdots\\ a_{m1} & a_{m2} & \cdots & a_{mn}\end{bmatrix}. \tag{2–5}$$

Such a matrix is called an $m \times n$ matrix, where m is the number of rows and n is the number of columns. The vector $[a_{i1}, a_{i2}, \ldots, a_{in}]$ is called the ith *row vector* of the matrix, and the vector $[a_{1j}, a_{2j}, \ldots, a_{mj}]$ is called the jth *column vector* of the matrix. Two matrices are equal if and only if they have the same number of rows and columns and every entry of one is equal to the corresponding entry of the other.

The notation $[a_{ij}]$ is purely symbolic and is used only to denote the general form of the elements which appear in the matrix. The first subscript always refers to the row and the second subscript to the column. Note that the same order is also followed in naming the size of the matrix. An $m \times n$ matrix has m rows and n columns.

Definition 2–4. Let T be a linear transformation between the finite-dimensional vector spaces V and W, $T: V \to W$. Let $\mathcal{B} = \langle \mathbf{B}_1, \mathbf{B}_2, \ldots, \mathbf{B}_n \rangle$ be a basis for V and let $\mathcal{B}^* = \langle \mathbf{B}_1^*, \mathbf{B}_2^*, \ldots, \mathbf{B}_m^* \rangle$ be a basis for W. For each $j = 1, 2, \ldots, n$, let

$$T\mathbf{B}_j = \mathbf{C}_j = \sum_{i=1}^{m} a_{ij}\mathbf{B}_i^*. \tag{2–6}$$

Then the *matrix of the linear transformation T with respect to the bases $\mathcal{B}$ and $\mathcal{B}^*$* is the matrix $A = [a_{ij}]$ whose entries are defined by (2–6).

Note that the column vectors of the matrix A defined here are the vectors whose components are the components of $\mathbf{C}_j = T\mathbf{B}_j$ with respect to $\mathcal{B}^*$. That is, recalling Definition 1–15, we have

$$T\mathbf{B}_j = \begin{bmatrix} a_{1j} \\ a_{2j} \\ \vdots \\ a_{mj} \end{bmatrix}_{\mathcal{B}^*}.$$

As mentioned before, we will usually write the vectors in horizontal form so as to save space, but the formula given above is the one that should be thought of.

Given an arbitrary vector $\mathbf{X}$ in the space V, how can we use this matrix to find the image of $\mathbf{X}$ under the transformation T? Here the important thing is the linearity. Every vector $\mathbf{X} \in V$ can be expressed as a linear combination of the $\mathbf{B}_j$, since these form a basis for the space V. We can then use the linearity to compute

$$\begin{aligned} T\mathbf{X} &= T\left(\sum_{j=1}^{n} x_j\mathbf{B}_j\right) = \sum_{j=1}^{n} T(x_j\mathbf{B}_j) = \sum_{j=1}^{n} x_jT\mathbf{B}_j \\ &= \sum_{j=1}^{n} x_j \sum_{i=1}^{m} a_{ij}\mathbf{B}_i^* = \sum_{j=1}^{n}\sum_{i=1}^{m} x_ja_{ij}\mathbf{B}_i^* \\ &= \sum_{i=1}^{m}\sum_{j=1}^{n} a_{ij}x_j\mathbf{B}_i^*. \end{aligned}$$

We have therefore proved

▶ **Theorem 2–2.** Let $\mathbf{X} = [x_1, x_2, \ldots, x_n]_{\mathcal{B}}$ and let $T\mathbf{X} = \mathbf{Y} = [y_1, y_2, \ldots, y_m]_{\mathcal{B}^*}$. Let T have the matrix $A = [a_{ij}]$ with respect to the bases $\mathcal{B}$ and $\mathcal{B}^*$. Then for each i

$$y_i = \sum_{j=1}^{n} a_{ij}x_j. \tag{2–7}$$

This theorem says that the ith component of $\mathbf{Y} = T\mathbf{X}$ with respect to the basis $\mathcal{B}^*$ is found by taking the sum of the products of the components of $\mathbf{X}$ with respect to the basis $\mathcal{B}$ and the entries in the ith row of the matrix. We will discuss this in more detail in a later section; for the moment it suffices to observe how this component can be written. It is here that we begin to find it most useful to think of our representations of vectors as being written in vertical columns. Then we can write

$$\begin{bmatrix} y_1 \\ \vdots \\ y_i \\ \vdots \\ y_m \end{bmatrix}_{\mathcal{B}^*} = \begin{bmatrix} a_{11} & a_{12} & \cdots & a_{1n} \\ \vdots & & & \vdots \\ a_{i1} & a_{i2} & \cdots & a_{in} \\ \vdots & & & \vdots \\ a_{m1} & a_{m2} & \cdots & a_{mn} \end{bmatrix} \begin{bmatrix} x_1 \\ \vdots \\ x_i \\ \vdots \\ x_n \end{bmatrix}_{\mathcal{B}^*} = \begin{bmatrix} a_{11}x_1 + a_{12}x_2 + \cdots + a_{1n}x_n \\ \vdots \qquad\qquad \vdots \\ a_{i1}x_1 + a_{i2}x_2 + \cdots + a_{in}x_n \\ \vdots \qquad\qquad \vdots \\ a_{m1}x_1 + a_{m2}x_2 + \cdots + a_{mn}x_n \end{bmatrix}_{\mathcal{B}^*}.$$

The entries in the column on the right are obtained by moving across the corresponding row of the matrix A and simultaneously down the column of the x_j, multiplying the first element in the row of A by the first element in the column of $\mathbf{X}$, the second element in the row of A by the second element in the column of $\mathbf{X}$, and so on. Adding all of these products gives the proper entry for the vector $\mathbf{Y}$.

When R^n and R^m are the spaces being considered, we can use the standard bases in the above result. In this case, the x_i and y_i are already the components of the vectors in terms of the standard bases. When this occurs, we leave off any indication of bases. When no indication is given, we understand that it is the standard bases which are used.

Let us give an example showing a typical computation. Suppose that we have a transformation $T\colon R^3 \to R^2$ which has the matrix (in terms of the standard bases)

$$\begin{bmatrix} 1 & 0 & 2 \\ -1 & 1 & -1 \end{bmatrix}.$$

Note that this means that $T\mathbf{e}_1 = [1, -1]$, $T\mathbf{e}_2 = [0, 1]$, and $T\mathbf{e}_3 = [2, -1]$. If we are asked for the image of $[3, -1, 4]$, we can compute it in the following way:

$$\begin{bmatrix} 1 & 0 & 2 \\ -1 & 1 & -1 \end{bmatrix} \begin{bmatrix} 3 \\ -1 \\ 4 \end{bmatrix} = \begin{bmatrix} 3 + 0 + 8 \\ -3 - 1 - 4 \end{bmatrix} = \begin{bmatrix} 11 \\ -8 \end{bmatrix}.$$

We have therefore found that $T[3, -1, 4] = [11, -8]$.

PROBLEMS

1. Complete the proof of Theorem 2–1.
2. Show that the operations defined by (2–3) and (2–4) satisfy the eight properties of Theorem 1–1, thus completing the proof of the fact that $L[V; W]$ is a vector space.
3. In terms of a fixed pair of bases for V and W, let $A = [a_{ij}]$ and $B = [b_{ij}]$ be the matrices of $S:V \to W$ and $T:V \to W$, respectively. What is the matrix of tT for some scalar t? What is the matrix of $S + T$?
4. Let $\mathbf{X} = [x_1, x_2, x_3]$ and $\mathbf{Y} = [y_1, y_2, y_3]$ be vectors in R^3. In each of the following parts, a function $F:R^3 \to R^3$ is defined by giving $\mathbf{Y} = F(\mathbf{X})$. State and prove whether or not the function so defined is a linear transformation. If it is, give its matrix in terms of the standard bases.

   a) $y_1 = 3x_1 - x_3$
   $y_2 = x_1 + 2x_2 - x_3$
   $y_3 = x_1 + x_2 - 5x_3$

   b) $y_1 = x_1$
   $y_2 = -x_1$
   $y_3 = x_3$

   c) $y_1 = x_1$
   $y_2 = x_1x_2$
   $y_3 = x_1x_2x_3$

   d) $y_1 = 0$
   $y_2 = x_2$
   $y_3 = x_1 - x_2 + x_3$

   e) $y_1 = x_2$
   $y_2 = x_3$
   $y_3 = x_1$

   f) $y_1 = -x_1$
   $y_2 = -x_2$
   $y_3 = -x_3$.

5. Let
$$A = \begin{bmatrix} 1 & -3 & 4 \\ 0 & 2 & -1 \\ 3 & 0 & 2 \end{bmatrix}, \qquad B = \begin{bmatrix} 5 & -8 & 2 \\ 2 & 0 & 1 \end{bmatrix}$$
   be the matrices of the linear transformations $S:R^3 \to R^3$ and $T:R^3 \to R^2$, respectively. For each of the following vectors, compute $T\mathbf{X}$ and $S\mathbf{X}$.

   a) $\mathbf{X} = [1, -3, 5]$ b) $\mathbf{X} = [-2, 7, -1]$ c) $\mathbf{X} = [1, 0, -1]$
   d) $\mathbf{X} = [-1, 0, 0]$ e) $\mathbf{X} = [x_1, x_2, x_3]$

6. If $T:R^3 \to R^3$ has the matrix A as given in the last problem, does there exist a vector $\mathbf{X}$ such that $T\mathbf{X} = [1, 0, 0]$? If so, what is it?
7. Let P_n be the vector space defined in Problem 2 on page 14. Is the operation of differentiation a linear transformation on this space? What is the range of this operation?
8. Prove that for any linear transformation T, we must have $T\mathbf{0} = \mathbf{0}$.
9. Prove that the linear transformation which carries $\mathbf{X}(0) = [x_1, x_2] = y_1\mathbf{B}_1 + y_2\mathbf{B}_2$ into $\mathbf{X}(t) = [w_1, w_2] = y_1 \cos \omega_1 t\mathbf{B}_1 + y_2 \cos \omega_2 t\mathbf{B}_2$, where $\mathbf{B}_1 = [1, 1]$ and $\mathbf{B}_2 = [1, -1]$, has the matrix
$$\begin{bmatrix} a & b \\ b & a \end{bmatrix},$$
   where $a = \frac{1}{2}\cos \omega_1 t + \frac{1}{2}\cos \omega_2 t$ and $b = \frac{1}{2}\cos \omega_1 t - \frac{1}{2}\cos \omega_2 t$.

2–2. THE IMAGE SPACE OF A LINEAR TRANSFORMATION

In Section 1–2 we defined the image of a function. We pointed out that the image need not be exactly the same as the range of the function. Also in that section we pointed out that when a function was given, each element in the domain corresponded to exactly one element in the range, but that it was possible for an element in the range to be the image of more than one element in the domain. We will now discuss these facts in greater depth. First, however, we make some definitions. We include a formal definition of the image here, for the sake of completeness.

Definition 2–5. Let $F: V \to W$ be a function whose domain is the set V and whose range is the set W. (These need not be vector spaces.)

1. The *image* of V under F, called for short the *image* of F, is

$$\operatorname{im} F = F(V) = \{F(X) \mid X \in V\}.$$

2. The function F is called *onto* if and only if $\operatorname{im} F = W$.
3. The function F is called *one-to-one* if and only if no two different elements in V have the same image in W.

We should note that the term *surjective* is coming into use to replace the term *onto*, and that the term *injective* is replacing one-to-one. In the case of linear transformations, the terms *epimorphism* and *monomorphism* are also being used for *onto* and *one-to-one*, respectively. The older terms are still in common use, however, and since they have strong descriptive qualities, we will use them here.

Observe that a function is *onto* if and only if every element of the range is the image of *at least one* of the elements of the domain. A function is *one-to-one* if and only if every element of the range is the image of *at most one* element of the domain. We should also notice that F is one-to-one if and only if $F(X_1) = F(X_2)$ implies $X_1 = X_2$. The last condition is the one that will usually be used to actually prove that a given function is one-to-one.

If a funtion $F: V \to W$ is not *onto*, we can make it so by restricting the range of the function to be the image of V under F. The function $F: V \to \operatorname{im} V$ is always onto. Strictly speaking, this latter function is different from the original one, since the domain and range are part of the entire set of things that we call the function, but it does no harm to consider the two to be essentially the same function. Note that the collection of ordered pairs is the same.

If the function is not one-to-one, there is usually very little that we can do about it. In some cases, it is possible to restrict the domain and obtain a new one-to-one function, but it is an unusual case when we are willing to allow this. For example, the function $f: R \to R$ given by $f(x) = x^2$ is neither one-to-one nor onto. If we set $R^+ = \{x \mid x \geq 0\}$ then the function $f: R \to R^+$ will be onto, but it is still not one-to-one. Here, if we were willing to restrict the domain, we would find that $f: R^+ \to R^+$ is now both one-to-one and onto.

We will now restrict ourselves to the consideration of these concepts for the case of linear transformations. We will discover some interesting consequences.

▶ **Theorem 2–3.** Let $T: V \to W$ be a linear transformation between the vector spaces V and W. Then $\text{im}\, T$ is a subspace of W.

Proof. Recall that in order to show that a subset of a vector space is a subspace, it suffices to show that the set is closed under vector addition and scalar multiplication.

First, let us prove that $\text{im}\, T$ is closed under vector addition. Suppose that $\mathbf{X}$ and $\mathbf{Y}$ are two vectors in $\text{im}\, T$. Then there must exist vectors $\mathbf{A}$ and $\mathbf{B} \in V$ such that $\mathbf{X} = T\mathbf{A}$ and $\mathbf{Y} = T\mathbf{B}$. But then

$$\begin{aligned} \mathbf{X} + \mathbf{Y} &= T\mathbf{A} + T\mathbf{B} \\ &= T(\mathbf{A} + \mathbf{B}) \end{aligned}$$

by the linearity of T. This shows that $(\mathbf{X} + \mathbf{Y})$ is the image of $(\mathbf{A} + \mathbf{B})$ under T and hence is in $\text{im}\, T$. We have therefore proved that $\text{im}\, T$ is closed under vector addition.

The remaining part of the proof, showing that $\text{im}\, T$ is closed under scalar multiplication, is even easier and can safely be left as an exercise. ▌

The computational problem of actually finding the image of V under T is quite easy to solve when we are given the matrix of the transformation. Every vector in V is a linear combination of the basis vectors $\mathbf{B}_j$, and hence every vector in $\text{im}\, T$ is a linear combination of the vectors $\mathbf{C}_j = T\mathbf{B}_j$. That is, if $\mathbf{Y}$ is any vector in $\text{im}\, T$, then there must be some $\mathbf{X} \in V$ such that $\mathbf{Y} = T\mathbf{X}$. However, there must exist scalars $x_1, x_2, \ldots, x_n$ such that

$$\mathbf{X} = x_1\mathbf{B}_1 + x_2B_2 + \cdots + x_n\mathbf{B}_n,$$

and then

$$\mathbf{Y} = x_1T\mathbf{B}_1 + x_2T\mathbf{B}_2 + \cdots + x_nT\mathbf{B}_n.$$

Conversely, any linear combination of the vectors $T\mathbf{B}_i$ must be the image of the corresponding linear combination of the $\mathbf{B}_i$. These statements thus prove the following theorem.

Theorem 2–4. Let $T: V \to W$ be a linear transformation between the vector spaces V and W and let $\langle \mathbf{B}_1, \mathbf{B}_2, \ldots, \mathbf{B}_n \rangle$ be a basis for V. Then

$$\text{im}\, T = L\{T\mathbf{B}_1, T\mathbf{B}_2, \ldots, T\mathbf{B}_n\}.$$

We saw in Definition 2–4 that the column vectors of the matrix of a transformation T represent the vectors $T\mathbf{B}_i$ in terms of the basis $\mathcal{B}^*$ of the range space W. These vectors generate $\text{im}\, T$ according to the comments made above. Of course, a simpler set of vectors which generate the same space can be obtained by going through the usual reduction process. However, the resulting reduced set of vectors are still in terms of the basis $\mathcal{B}^*$. Reduction to the standard vectors in R^m would require another step, unless the standard basis were already being used in the matrix representation.

For example, suppose that the transformation T between R^2 and R^3 has the matrix

$$\begin{bmatrix} 1 & 3 \\ 2 & -1 \\ 0 & 14 \end{bmatrix}$$

in terms of the bases

$$\begin{aligned} \mathcal{B} &= \langle [1, 2], [-1, 0] \rangle, \\ \mathcal{B}^* &= \langle [1, 2, 0], [0, 1, 3], [-1, -1, 1] \rangle. \end{aligned}$$

Then we have

$$\operatorname{im} T = L\{[1, 2, 0]_{\mathcal{B}^*}, [3, -1, 14]_{\mathcal{B}^*}\} = L\{[1, 0, 4]_{\mathcal{B}^*}, [0, 1, -2]_{\mathcal{B}^*}\},$$

where the last pair of vectors have been computed by the reduction process.

If we wished to convert these results back to the standard basis in R^3, we merely need to observe that

$$\begin{aligned} [1, 0, 4]_{\mathcal{B}^*} &= [1, 2, 0] + 4[-1, -1, 1] = [-3, -2, 4], \\ [0, 1, -2]_{\mathcal{B}^*} &= [0, 1, 3] - 2[-1, -1, 1] = [2, 3, 1]. \end{aligned}$$

Hence

$$\operatorname{im} T = L\{[-3, -2, 4], [2, 3, 1]\}.$$

A further application of the reduction method could be used to simplify this result again. However, it would have been better to make the conversion at the start. Thus, if we were asked to produce a basis (in standard vectors) for $\operatorname{im} T$ for this problem, our best course would have been to compute first $[1, 2, 0]_{\mathcal{B}^*} = [1, 4, 6]$ and $[0, 1, -2]_{\mathcal{B}^*} = [-11, -9, 11]$. Then we easily find

$$\begin{aligned} \operatorname{im} T &= L\{[1, 2, 0]_{\mathcal{B}^*}, [3, -1, 14]_{\mathcal{B}^*}\} \\ &= L\{[1, 4, 6], [-11, -9, 11]\} \\ &= L\{[1, 0, -\tfrac{14}{5}], [0, 1, \tfrac{11}{5}]\}. \end{aligned}$$

Now we turn to the problem of the dimension of the space $\operatorname{im} T$. We find that in case the transformation is one-to-one, the situation is particularly simple.

Theorem 2–5. If $T: V \to W$ is one-to-one, and $\{\mathbf{A}_1, \mathbf{A}_2, \ldots, \mathbf{A}_k\}$ is a linearly independent set of vectors in V, then the set of vectors $\{T\mathbf{A}_1, T\mathbf{A}_2, \ldots, T\mathbf{A}_k\}$ is linearly independent in W.

Proof. Suppose that

$$\lambda_1 T\mathbf{A}_1 + \lambda_2 T\mathbf{A}_2 + \cdots + \lambda_k T\mathbf{A}_k = \mathbf{0}.$$

To prove the theorem, we must show that all of the $\lambda_i = 0$. However, the linearity of T tells us that

$$T(\lambda_1 \mathbf{A}_1 + \lambda_2 \mathbf{A}_2 + \cdots + \lambda_k \mathbf{A}_k) = \mathbf{0}.$$

We know that $T\mathbf{0} = \mathbf{0}$. The fact that T is given as one-to-one means that no other vector is mapped to $\mathbf{0}$. Hence

$$\lambda_1\mathbf{A}_1 + \lambda_2\mathbf{A}_2 + \cdots + \lambda_k\mathbf{A}_k = \mathbf{0},$$

and the fact that the $\mathbf{A}_i$ were given to be linearly independent lets us conclude that all of the $\lambda_i = 0$. ▮

This theorem has two immediate consequences whose proofs will be left to the reader.

Theorem 2–6. If $T:V \to W$ is one-to-one and $\langle \mathbf{B}_1, \mathbf{B}_2, \ldots, \mathbf{B}_n \rangle$ is a basis for V, then $\langle T\mathbf{B}_1, T\mathbf{B}_2, \ldots, T\mathbf{B}_n \rangle$ is a basis for im T.

▶ **Theorem 2–7.** If $T:V \to W$ is one-to-one, then

$$\dim V = \dim (\text{im } T).$$

PROBLEMS

1. Complete the proof of Theorem 2–3 by showing that im T is closed under scalar multiplication.
2. Prove Theorem 2–6.
3. Prove Theorem 2–7.
4. Find a basis for the image of the transformations given by (a), (b), and (d) of Problem 4 of Section 2–1.
5. Find a basis for the image space of each of the transformations given in Problem 5 of Section 2–1.
6. The following are matrices of linear transformations from R^3 in the standard basis to R^4 with the basis $\mathcal{B}^* = \langle [1, 1, 1, 1], [1, 1, -1, -1], [1, -1, 1, -1], [1, -1, -1, 1] \rangle$. Find a basis for the image space in each case (in terms of the standard vectors in R^4).

   a) $\begin{bmatrix} 1 & 0 & 2 \\ 2 & -1 & 0 \\ 0 & 1 & 1 \\ 3 & 2 & -1 \end{bmatrix}$ b) $\begin{bmatrix} 0 & 0 & 1 \\ 1 & 0 & 0 \\ 0 & 1 & 0 \\ 1 & 0 & 1 \end{bmatrix}$ c) $\begin{bmatrix} 1 & 3 & 1 \\ 0 & 1 & 2 \\ 1 & 4 & 3 \\ 2 & 7 & 4 \end{bmatrix}$ d) $\begin{bmatrix} 1 & 2 & 3 \\ 2 & 3 & 4 \\ 3 & 4 & 5 \\ 4 & 5 & 6 \end{bmatrix}$.
7. Let $T:R^n \to R^m$ be a linear transformation. Prove:

   a) If $n < m$, then T cannot be onto. b) If $n > m$, then T cannot be one-to-one.

2–3. THE KERNEL OF A LINEAR TRANSFORMATION

If a linear transformation T is one-to-one, then there is at most one vector $\mathbf{X}$ such that $T\mathbf{X} = \mathbf{0}$. Of course, there is one, the vector $\mathbf{0}$. On the other hand, if a linear transformation T is that $T\mathbf{X} = \mathbf{0}$ has only the one solution $\mathbf{X} = \mathbf{0}$, then $T\mathbf{A} = T\mathbf{B}$ implies $T(\mathbf{A} - \mathbf{B}) = \mathbf{0}$, which implies in turn that $\mathbf{A} - \mathbf{B} = \mathbf{0}$. This is the same as

$\mathbf{A} = \mathbf{B}$. Thus, T is one-to-one if and only if $\mathbf{0}$ is the only vector whose image is zero. We can also say that T is one-to-one if and only if it is one-to-one at $\mathbf{0}$.

Suppose now that T is not one-to-one. Then there exist $\mathbf{A}$ and $\mathbf{B}$ such that $T\mathbf{A} = T\mathbf{B}$. From this we can see that the nonzero vector $\mathbf{A} - \mathbf{B}$ must be such that $T(\mathbf{A} - \mathbf{B}) = \mathbf{0}$. There is thus a very close relationship between the behavior of the transformation and the set of vectors which map to the zero vector. We find it useful to investigate this set more carefully.

Definition 2–6. Let $T: V \to W$ be a linear transformation. Then by the *kernel* of T we mean the set

$$\ker T = \{\mathbf{X} \in V \mid T\mathbf{X} = \mathbf{0}\}.$$

Note that the kernel of a linear transformation must always contain the vector $\mathbf{0}$. The comments made in the first paragraph of this section constitute the proof of the following theorem.

▶ **Theorem 2–8.** A linear transformation $T: V \to W$ is one-to-one if and only if $\ker T = \{\mathbf{0}\}$.

A most important property of the kernel of a linear transformation is that it is a subspace of the domain.

▶ **Theorem 2–9.** Let $T: V \to W$ be a linear transformation. Then $\ker T$ is a subspace of V.

Proof. Let $\mathbf{A}$ and $\mathbf{B}$ be in $\ker T$ and let t be any scalar. Then

$$T(\mathbf{A} + \mathbf{B}) = T\mathbf{A} + T\mathbf{B} = \mathbf{0} + \mathbf{0} = \mathbf{0}$$

and

$$T(t\mathbf{A}) = tT(\mathbf{A}) = t\mathbf{0} = \mathbf{0}.$$

Hence $\mathbf{A} + \mathbf{B}$ and $t\mathbf{A}$ are also in $\ker T$. Therefore $\ker T$ is closed under vector addition and scalar multiplication and is a subspace. ▮

Since the kernel of a linear transformation is a subspace of the domain V, we can use it to make a direct sum decomposition of V. When we do so, we find that a most remarkable thing happens. The restriction of T to the other direct summand is one-to-one. That is:

▶ **Theorem 2–10.** Let $T: V \to W$ be a linear transformation. Let $K = \ker T$. Let L be a subspace of V such that $V = K \oplus L$. Then T restricted to L is one-to-one.

Proof. To show that a linear transformation is one-to-one, it suffices to show that its kernel consists of the zero vector alone. Let $T': L \to W$ be the restriction of T to L and suppose that $\mathbf{X} \in \ker T'$. Then $\mathbf{X} \in L$ and $T'\mathbf{X} = \mathbf{0}$. However, T' is the restriction of T to L, and hence $T'\mathbf{X} = T\mathbf{X} = \mathbf{0}$. Therefore $\mathbf{X} \in \ker T$ also. The first property of the direct sum decomposition was that K and L had only the vector $\mathbf{0}$ in common. Therefore $\mathbf{X} = \mathbf{0}$. That is, $\ker T' = \{\mathbf{0}\}$. ▮

When we have $V = K \oplus L$, then every vector $\mathbf{X}$ in V can be written in a unique way in the form $\mathbf{X} = \mathbf{A} + \mathbf{B}$, where $\mathbf{A} \in K$ and $\mathbf{B} \in L$. But then, since $K = \ker T$, we have $T\mathbf{A} = \mathbf{0}$ and hence

$$T\mathbf{X} = T(\mathbf{A} + \mathbf{B}) = T\mathbf{B}.$$

That is, the restriction of T to L determines completely the behavior of the linear transformation T. In particular, $T(L) = \operatorname{im} T' = \operatorname{im} T$, since K contributes only the zero vector to the image.

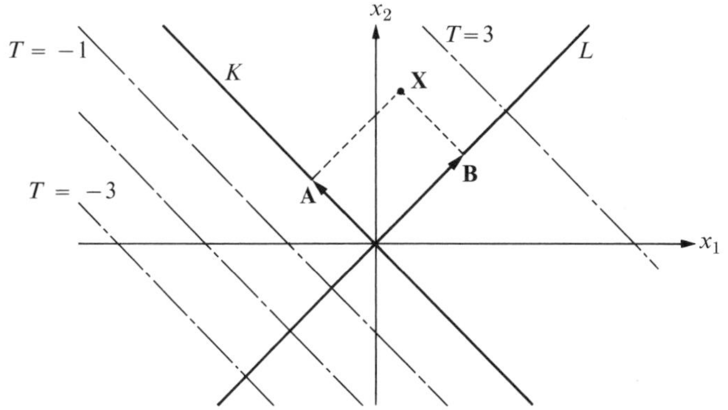

Fig. 2–1

The reader may find it instructive to look at an example. Suppose that we consider the mapping $T: R^2 \to R$ defined by $T[x_1, x_2] = x_1 + x_2$. Here we have $K = \{[x_1, x_2] \mid x_1 + x_2 = 0\}$. It is clear that K is generated by the vector $[1, -1]$. We can let L be the subspace generated by the vector $[1, 1]$. It is helpful to represent these subspaces as lines on the cartesian plane. The space generated by $[1, -1]$ is represented as the line through the origin which passes through the point with these coordinates. This is shown in Fig. 2–1. Note that an arbitrary vector (or point) $\mathbf{X}$ can be expressed as the sum of two vectors, $\mathbf{A} + \mathbf{B}$, with $\mathbf{A} \in K$ and $\mathbf{B} \in L$, as shown. For any such decomposition, the value of $T\mathbf{X} = T(\mathbf{A} + \mathbf{B}) = T\mathbf{B}$. Hence the function is a constant on each of the (dashed) lines parallel to the line representing the subspace K.

Here, we have chosen a subspace L which happens to give a line that is perpendicular to the line representing the subspace K. This is not essential. We could just as well have used the decomposition $R^2 = K \oplus L'$, where L' is the subspace generated by $[1, 0]$ (i.e., is represented by the x_1-axis).

We now prove the following important relation.

▶ **Theorem 2–11.** Let $T: V \to W$ be a linear transformation. Then

$$\dim(\operatorname{im} T) + \dim(\ker T) = \dim V. \tag{2–8}$$

Proof. Suppose that $\dim(\ker T) = k$. Let $\mathbf{B}_1, \ldots, \mathbf{B}_k$ be a basis for $\ker T$. Suppose that $\dim V = n$. Then there will be $n - k$ more vectors needed in a basis for V.

Let these be $\mathbf{A}_1, \ldots, \mathbf{A}_{n-k}$; they form a basis for L such that $V = K \oplus L$. Hence the dimension of L is $n - k$. Let T' be the restriction of T to L. Then as we saw above, $\operatorname{im} T = \operatorname{im} T'$. Theorem 2-10 shows us that T' is one-to-one, and Theorem 2-7 then gives $\dim(\operatorname{im} T) = \dim(\operatorname{im} T') = \dim L = n - k$. Putting this together with the assumptions made above proves the theorem. ▌

Some of these results can be combined to give the following theorem, the proof of which is left as an exercise.

Theorem 2-12. Each of the following conditions is sufficient for a linear transformation $T: V \to W$ to be one-to-one:

1. $\dim(\ker T) = 0$,
2. $\dim(\operatorname{im} T) = \dim V$,
3. T is onto and $\dim V = \dim W$.

To conclude this section, let us make some observations about the geometric picture of a linear transformation. We gave an example of this above for the case where the mapping was from R^2 to R^1. A similar picture can be obtained whenever we have a mapping from R^n to R^1. Except for the trivial case in which T is identically zero, $\operatorname{im} T = R^1$ (since this is the only nontrivial subspace in R^1). Therefore $\dim(\operatorname{im} T) = 1$ and hence $\dim(\ker T) = n - 1$.

Thus, if we have the direct sum decomposition $V = K \oplus L$, where $K = \ker T$, then L will have to be one dimensional also. The geometric picture will be similar to that given in Fig. 2-1 except that K will have to be an $(n - 1)$-dimensional subspace. If $V = R^3$, then L would be represented by a line through the origin and K would be represented by a plane through the origin. The transformation would then be a constant on any plane parallel to this plane. The line representing L cuts each of these planes. The point at which a plane cuts this line determines the value of the transformation on this plane.

Note that when we have a linear transformation to the reals defined on a line through the origin, there must be some vector $\mathbf{B}_1$, represented by a point on the line, such that $T\mathbf{B}_1 = 1$. Then $T(t\mathbf{B}_1) = t$, and hence the values of the transformation will be exactly the coordinate of the point on the line when the origin is used as the zero point and the point $\mathbf{B}_1$ is used as the unit point.

When we have transformations whose images are higher dimensional, the picture becomes more complex. We will illustrate some of the possibilities by giving a single example. Suppose that we have a transformation $T: R^3 \to R^2$ which is onto. Then $\dim(\operatorname{im} T) = 2$, and from Theorem 2-11 we have $\dim(\ker T) = 1$. The kernel can then be represented by a line through the origin in R^3. In the direct sum decomposition $R^3 = K \oplus L$, L will thus have to be two dimensional. It can be represented as a plane. At each point of this plane, the transformation takes on some (vector) value. The transformation will take on the same value at every point of the line that goes through this point and which is parallel to the line K. (See Fig. 2-2.)

Let us consider a numerical example. Let $T: R^4 \to R^3$ have the matrix

$$\begin{bmatrix} 1 & 0 & 1 & 2 \\ -1 & 3 & 2 & -5 \\ 2 & 6 & 8 & -2 \end{bmatrix}$$

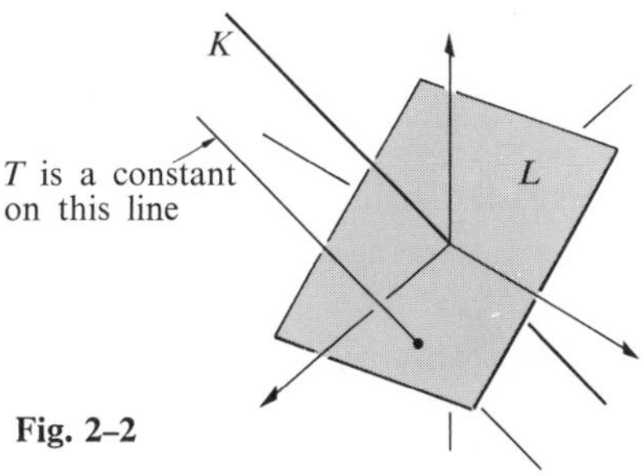

Fig. 2–2

in terms of the standard bases. The four column vectors of this matrix generate the image space. The reduction techniques of the last section can be used to show that $\text{im}\, T = L\{[1, 0, 4], [0, 1, 2]\}$. The dimension of $\text{im}\, T$ is thus 2. Theorem 2–11 tells us that $\dim(\ker T)$ must therefore be 2 also.

In a later section we will develop a method for finding the kernel quite easily. Here we will use the definition directly. A vector $\mathbf{X} = [x_1, x_2, x_3, x_4]$ will be in the kernel of this transformation if and only if the following three equations are satisfied:

$$\begin{aligned} x_1 + x + x_3 + 2x_4 &= 0, \\ -x_1 + 3x_2 + 2x_3 - 5x_4 &= 0, \\ 2x_1 + 6x_2 + 8x_3 - 2x_4 &= 0. \end{aligned} \tag{2–9}$$

Our method is to eliminate the unknowns from these equations, one at a time, so far as is possible. The first equation can be viewed as defining x_1 in terms of the remaining components. We use this equation to eliminate x_1 from the remaining two equations. We find

$$\begin{aligned} 3x_2 + 3x_3 - 3x_4 &= 0, \\ 3x_2 + 3x_3 - 3x_4 &= 0, \end{aligned}$$

which is as far as we can go. (Observe that the method used to eliminate unknowns is exactly the same as the row reduction method applied to the matrix of the coefficients of these equations.)

The three equations (2–9) are therefore equivalent to the two equations

$$\begin{aligned} x_1 &= -x_3 - 2x_4, \\ x_2 &= -x_3 + x_4. \end{aligned}$$

These equations determine x_1 and x_2 once x_3 and x_4 have been determined. We set $x_3 = 1, x_4 = 0$ and $x_3 = 0, x_4 = 1$ successively (why do we know that this will result in two linearly independent vectors?). We then have two vectors which generate the kernel $K = L\{[-1, -1, 1, 0], [-2, 1, 0, 1]\}$. A space L such that $R^4 = K \oplus L$ is easily found to be $L = L\{\mathbf{e}_1, \mathbf{e}_2\}$.

An arbitrary vector $\mathbf{X} = [x_1, x_2, x_3, x_4]$ can be decomposed according to this direct sum decomposition. This vector must be $\mathbf{X} = \mathbf{A} + \mathbf{B}$, where

$$\mathbf{A} = x_3[-1, -1, 1, 0] + x_4[-2, 1, 0, 1] = [-x_3 - 2x_4, -x_3 + x_4, x_3, x_4]$$

and hence

$$\mathbf{B} = [x_1 + x_3 + 2x_4, x_2 + x_3 - x_4, 0, 0].$$

Since $\mathbf{A} \in \ker T$, we must have

$$T\mathbf{X} = T(\mathbf{A} + \mathbf{B}) = T\mathbf{A} + T\mathbf{B} = T\mathbf{B}.$$

The reader should compute this $T\mathbf{B}$ to verify that it does indeed coincide with $T\mathbf{X}$.

PROBLEMS

1. Prove Theorem 2–12.
2. Find the kernels of the transformations given by (a), (b), and (d) of Problem 4 of Section 2–1.
3. Find the kernels of the transformations given by matrices A and B of Problem 5 of Section 2–1.
4. For the transformations of the last problem, find a subspace L of R^3 such that $R^3 = K \oplus L$. Make a sketch showing the behavior of the transformation.
5. Find a basis for the kernel of each of the transformations of Problem 6 in Section 2–2.
6. For each of the following linear transformations, find the kernel K and a complementary subspace L so that $R^4 = L \oplus K$; give the transform of each of the basis elements from L; express an arbitrary vector $[x_1, x_2, x_3, x_4]$ as a linear combination of the basis elements so obtained; and show that the transform of this linear combination gives the same result as the original transformation.

a) $y_1 = x_1 - 4x_2 + x_3 - x_4$

b) $\begin{aligned} y_1 &= x_1 + 2x_2 - x_3 + x_4 \\ y_2 &= 2x_1 + 5x_2 + x_3 + 5x_4 \end{aligned}$

c) $\begin{aligned} y_1 &= x_1 + x_2 \\ y_2 &= x_1 - x_2 + x_3 \\ y_3 &= x_1 - x_2 - x_3 + x_4 \end{aligned}$

d) $\begin{aligned} y_1 &= x_1 + x_2 + 2x_3 \\ y_2 &= x_3 + x_4 \\ y_3 &= x_1 + 2x_3 + x_4 \\ y_4 &= x_2 - x_4 \end{aligned}$

2–4. THE COMPOSITION OF TRANSFORMATIONS

When we have a function $F: V \to W$ and another function $G: W \to U$, we can define the composition of the two functions. For any X in V, $F(X)$ is in W, and hence we can find $G[F(X)]$. This gives rise to a new function whose domain is V and whose range is U. The sets V, W, and U need not be vector spaces in this discussion.

Definition 2–7. Let $F: V \to W$ and $G: W \to U$ be two functions. Then the *composition* of F and G is the function $G \circ F: V \to U$ defined by $(G \circ F)(X) = G[F(X)]$ for every $X \in V$. If F and G are linear transformations, we will write GF instead of $G \circ F$ to represent the composed function.

We remark that there is no standard notation in this field. Some writers indicate the composition by writing the functions in the opposite order. It is common practice in many linear algebra texts to write the function to the right of the variable. When this is done, the composition would have to be written in the opposite order. We find it most convenient to stick to the order given in this definition. The function farthest to the right is the one that is applied first.

Note that the composition of two functions is not always defined. The "center" set must be the same before the composition can exist. For this reason in particular, even if two functions can be composed in one order, they may not lend themselves to composition in the opposite order. Even when both compositions are possible (as, for example, in the case of $F:V \to V$ and $G:V \to V$) it is not necessarily true that $F \circ G = G \circ F$ (see Problem 1 at the end of this section). That is, the composition of functions is not necessarily commutative. Composition is *associative*, however.

▶ **Theorem 2–13.** Let $F:V \to V_1$, $G:V_1 \to V_2$, and $H:V_2 \to W$ be three functions with domain and range as indicated. Then

$$(H \circ G) \circ F = H \circ (G \circ F).$$

Proof. To show that two functions are equal, we merely have to show that the values of both coincide for every $X \in V$. For an arbitrary $X \in V$, set $Y_1 = F(X)$, $Y_2 = G(Y_1)$, and $Z = H(Y_2)$. Then we have

$$\begin{aligned}[(H \circ G) \circ F](X) &= (H \circ G)[F(X)] = (H \circ G)(Y_1) = H[G(Y_1)] \\ &= H(Y_2) = Z.\end{aligned}$$

On the other hand, we also have

$$\begin{aligned}[H \circ (G \circ F)](X) &= H[(G \circ F)(X)] = H[G(F(X))] = H[G(Y_1)] \\ &= H(Y_2) = Z. \ \blacksquare\end{aligned}$$

The proof of this theorem is really quite trivial. It may be useful to see the diagram of the proof.

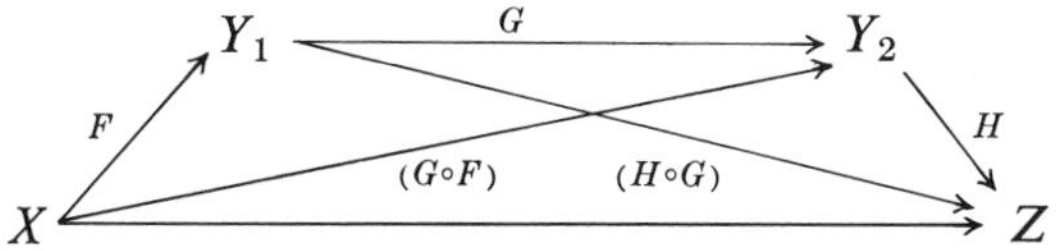

Note that this proof applies to functions defined on any sets. Here, however, we are mainly interested in linear transformations. As always, the first question that must be answered is whether or not the composition of two linear transformations is itself a linear transformation. We certainly expect this to be so, but we must give the actual proof before we can be sure.

Theorem 2–14. Let $T:V \to W$ and $S:W \to U$ be two linear transformations. Then ST, the composed function, is also a linear transformation.

Proof. We will prove that the composed function has the additive property and leave the other property as an exercise. Suppose that **A** and **B** are any two vectors in V.

Then

$$\begin{aligned} ST(\mathbf{A} + \mathbf{B}) &= S[T(\mathbf{A} + \mathbf{B})] \\ &= S[T\mathbf{A} + T\mathbf{B}] \\ &= S(T\mathbf{A}) + S(T\mathbf{B}) \\ &= (ST)\mathbf{A} + (ST)\mathbf{B}. \blacksquare \end{aligned}$$

Can you supply the reason for each step?

At this point we wish to begin a study of the two properties of a function which were given in Definition 2–5. We are particularly interested in functions which are *both* one-to-one and onto. The first properties we are interested in hold for functions in general.

Theorem 2–15. The composition of two functions that are both one-to-one is itself one-to-one,

Proof. First, note that it is implicit in the statement of the theorem that the two functions are such that they *can* be composed. It is not necessary to make an explicit statement of this in the hypotheses of the theorem.

Suppose F and G are the two functions and that $F \circ G$ is the composition of the two. Suppose X and Y are two points in the domain of G (and likewise in the domain of $F \circ G$) such that $(F \circ G)(X) = (F \circ G)(Y)$. That is, $F[G(X)] = F[G(Y)]$. Since F is one-to-one, we have $G(X) = G(Y)$. Since G is itself one-to-one, we conclude that $X = Y$ and hence that $F \circ G$ is one-to-one. ▮

Theorem 2–16. The composition of two functions that are both onto is itself onto.

The proof of this theorem is left as an exercise. A consequence of these two theorems is obviously:

Theorem 2–17. The composition of two functions that are both one-to-one and onto is itself one-to-one and onto.

Why are we interested in functions which are both one-to-one and onto? The answer is that they are exactly the functions which have inverses.

▶ **Theorem 2–18.** Let $F: V \to W$ be a function which is one-to-one and onto. Then there exists a function $F^{-1}: W \to V$, called the *inverse* of F, which is also one-to-one and onto and which is such that

1. for any $X \in V$, $F^{-1}[F(X)] = X$, and
2. for any $Y \in W$, $F[F^{-1}(Y)] = Y$.

Proof. The function F is actually a set of ordered pairs in $V \times W$. The condition that F is onto means that every element in W appears as the second element in at least one of these ordered pairs. The condition that F is one-to-one means that an element of W appears as the second element in at most one of these ordered pairs. We may now define F^{-1} to be the set of ordered pairs in $W \times V$ defined by

$$F^{-1} = \{\langle Y, X\rangle \mid \langle X, Y\rangle \in F\}.$$

To complete the proof we must show that this set is a function which satisfies properties (1) and (2) of the theorem. To show that F^{-1} is a function we must show that for each Y in W there exists one and only one X in V such that $\langle Y, X\rangle \in F^{-1}$. From the definition of F^{-1}, this is the same as saying that for each $Y \in W$, there exists one and only one $X \in V$ such that $\langle X, Y\rangle \in F$, or such that $Y = F(X)$.

Given any Y, the fact that F is onto shows that there is at least one such X. The fact that F is one-to-one shows that there is at most one such X. Thus F^{-1} is a function.

Next we show that properties (1) and (2) are satisfied. Suppose $X \in V$ is given. Let $Y = F(X)$. Then $\langle X, Y\rangle \in F$ and $\langle Y, X\rangle \in F^{-1}$. That is, $F^{-1}(Y) = X$. Hence

$$F^{-1}[F(X)] = F^{-1}(Y) = X.$$

Similarly, given any $Y \in W$, let $X = F^{-1}(Y)$. Then $Y = F(X)$, and hence

$$F[F^{-1}(Y)] = F(X) = Y.$$

Finally, we see that statement (1) implies that F^{-1} is onto and statement (2) implies that F^{-1} is one-to-one. The last assertion follows from the observations that if $F^{-1}(Y_1) = F^{-1}(Y_2)$, then $F[F^{-1}(Y_1)] = Y_1 = F[F^{-1}(Y_2)] = Y_2$. ∎

Observe that there is only one inverse function satisfying the two given properties. Suppose that F^{-1} was the function defined above and G was a different function satisfying the two properties. If $Y \in W$ and $X = F^{-1}(Y)$, we have

$$\begin{aligned} G(Y) &= G[F(X)] \\ &= X && \text{by the assumption of property (1)} \\ &= F^{-1}[F(X)] \\ &= F^{-1}(Y). \end{aligned}$$

The two functions are therefore identical. ∎

What about the inverse of a linear transformation? We know that a linear transformation that is one-to-one and onto must have an inverse. But will this inverse itself be a linear transformation? Fortunately for the theory, the answer is yes.

▶ **Theorem 2–19.** Suppose that $T: V \to W$ is a linear transformation which is one-to-one and onto. Then the inverse function $T^{-1}: W \to V$ is also a linear transformation.

Proof. First let us show that $T^{-1}(t\mathbf{X}) = tT^{-1}(\mathbf{X})$. Since any $\mathbf{X} \in W$ is in $\operatorname{im} T$, there exists an $\mathbf{A} \in V$ such that $\mathbf{X} = T(\mathbf{A})$. This is equivalent to the fact that $\mathbf{A} = T^{-1}(\mathbf{X})$ by the properties of the inverse function. Now, T is linear and hence

$$T(t\mathbf{A}) = tT(\mathbf{A}) = t\mathbf{X}.$$

Therefore

$$T^{-1}(t\mathbf{X}) = T^{-1}[T(t\mathbf{A})] = t\mathbf{A} = tT^{-1}(\mathbf{X}).$$

The reader should supply the reason for each step.

Next, let us prove that $T^{-1}(\mathbf{X} + \mathbf{Y}) = T^{-1}(\mathbf{X}) + T^{-1}(\mathbf{Y})$. Again, given $\mathbf{X}$ and $\mathbf{Y}$, we can set $\mathbf{A} = T^{-1}(\mathbf{X})$ and $\mathbf{B} = T^{-1}(\mathbf{Y})$. We then have $\mathbf{X} = T(\mathbf{A})$ and $\mathbf{Y} = T(\mathbf{B})$. Therefore, from the linearity of T we have

$$T(\mathbf{A} + \mathbf{B}) = T\mathbf{A} + T\mathbf{B} = \mathbf{X} + \mathbf{Y}.$$

Hence

$$T^{-1}(\mathbf{X} + \mathbf{Y}) = T^{-1}[T(\mathbf{A} + \mathbf{B})] = \mathbf{A} + \mathbf{B} = T^{-1}\mathbf{X} + T^{-1}\mathbf{Y}. \blacksquare$$

We should note here that one of the major aims of the next few chapters will be to find methods for finding the matrix of T^{-1}, knowing the matrix of T.

The class of linear transformations that are one-to-one and onto is important enough to deserve a special name.

Definition 2-8. A linear transformation which is one-to-one and onto is called a *nonsingular linear transformation.* A linear transformation which is *not* a nonsingular linear transformation is called *singular.*

With the help of this definition and Theorem 2-14 we can restate Theorem 2-17 in the following useful form.

▶ **Theorem 2-20.** The composition of two nonsingular linear transformations is itself a nonsingular linear transformation.

A nonsingular linear transformation always has an inverse. Suppose that a linear transformation has an inverse. Will it be nonsingular? The answer obviously is yes (see the problems at the end of the section).

Theorem 2-20 shows that the composition of two nonsingular transformations will have an inverse. The next theorem shows us how the inverse of this transformation is related to the inverses of the "factor" transformations.

▶ **Theorem 2-21.** Let T and S be nonsingular linear transformations of a vector space V onto itself. Then

$$S^{-1}T^{-1} = [TS]^{-1}. \tag{2-10}$$

Proof. From the previous theorem we know that if T and S are nonsingular, then so is TS. Therefore TS has an inverse. This inverse is characterized by the fact that $[TS]^{-1}[TS]\mathbf{X} = \mathbf{X}$ for every $\mathbf{X}$. Any function which satisfies this for all $\mathbf{X}$ will therefore have to coincide with $[TS]^{-1}$. We can verify it easily for the function $S^{-1}T^{-1}$, as follows:

$$\begin{aligned}(S^{-1}T^{-1})(TS)\mathbf{X} &= S^{-1}(T^{-1}T)S\mathbf{X} \\ &= S^{-1}S\mathbf{X} \\ &= \mathbf{X}. \blacksquare\end{aligned}$$

The reader should make careful note of Eq. (2-10). The fact that the inverse of the composition of the two functions is the composition of the inverses *in the opposite order* is most important.

PROBLEMS

1. Let $F:R \to R$ and $G:R \to R$ be defined by $F(x) = -x$ and $G(x) = x^2$.
   a) What is $F \circ G$? b) What is $G \circ F$?
2. Complete the proof of Theorem 2–14.
3. Prove Theorem 2–16.
5. Prove that if a linear transformation has an inverse, then it is nonsingular.
4. Let the functions $T:V \to W$ and $S:W \to U$ be given. These need not be linear transformations.
   a) Suppose that $S \circ T$ is onto. Prove that S is onto.
   b) Suppose that $S \circ T$ is one-to-one. Prove that T is one-to-one.
   c) Suppose that $S \circ T$ is onto. Give an example which shows that T need not be onto.
   d) Suppose that $S \circ T$ is one-to-one. Give an example which shows that S need not be one-to-one.
6. Let the function $F:V \to W$ be one-to-one. Prove that there exists a function $G:W \to V$ such that for every $X \in V$,
$$(G \circ F)(X) = X.$$
   Such a function G is called a left-hand inverse of F.
7. Let the function $F:V \to W$ be onto. Prove that there exists a function $G:W \to V$ such that for every $Y \in W$
$$(F \circ G)(Y) = Y.$$
   Such a function G is called a right-hand inverse of F. The proof of its existence requires the assumption that an element can be chosen from every set in a collection of sets.
8. Let the linear transformations S and T be given by
$$S:\quad \begin{aligned} z_1 &= y_1 + 3y_2 - y_3, \\ z_2 &= 2y_1 + y_2 + y_3, \end{aligned}$$
$$T:\quad \begin{aligned} y_1 &= x_1, \\ y_2 &= 2x_1 + x_2, \\ y_3 &= 3x_1 + 2x_2. \end{aligned}$$
   Find the linear transformation $S \circ T$.
9. Compute the inverse of the linear transformation
$$\begin{aligned} y_1 &= x_1 + 3x_2 + x_3 \\ y_2 &= x_2 + 2x_3 \\ y_3 &= -x_2 + x_3. \end{aligned}$$
10. Let S and T be two linear transformations such that the composition ST exists.
    a) Prove that $\text{im}(ST) \subset \text{im } S$. b) Prove that $\ker(ST) \supset \ker T$.
11. Let $T:R^n \to R^m$ be a linear transformation and suppose that $R^n = \ker T \oplus L$. Let T' be the linear transformation $T':L \to \text{im } T$ defined by $T'\mathbf{X} = T\mathbf{X}$ for all $\mathbf{X} \in L$. Prove that T' has an inverse and is one-to-one onto $\text{im } T'$.

2–5. MATRIX ALGEBRA

Now we turn to the behavior of matrices of linear transformations under composition. Let us suppose that we have the linear transformations $T: V \to W$ and $S: W \to U$. Suppose also that bases for these three spaces are given by

$$\begin{aligned}
\mathcal{B} &= \langle \mathbf{B}_1, \mathbf{B}_2, \ldots, \mathbf{B}_n \rangle, && \text{a basis for } V, \\
\mathcal{B}^* &= \langle \mathbf{B}_1^*, \mathbf{B}_2^*, \ldots, \mathbf{B}_m^* \rangle, && \text{a basis for } W, \\
\mathcal{B}^{**} &= \langle \mathbf{B}_1^{**}, \mathbf{B}_2^{**}, \ldots, \mathbf{B}_r^{**} \rangle, && \text{a basis for } U.
\end{aligned}$$

Let $[a_{ij}]$ be the $r \times m$ matrix of the transformation S with respect to the bases $\mathcal{B}^*$ and $\mathcal{B}^{**}$.

Let $[b_{jk}]$ be the $m \times n$ matrix of the transformation T with respect to the bases $\mathcal{B}$ and $\mathcal{B}^*$.

Let $[c_{ik}]$ be the $r \times n$ matrix of the composed transformation ST with respect to the bases $\mathcal{B}$ and $\mathcal{B}^{**}$. What we wish to do is find the c_{ik} in terms of the a_{ij} and b_{jk}. First, we compare with Eq. (2–6) to write the defining equations for these three matrices. We find

$$S\mathbf{B}_j^* = \sum_{i=1}^{r} a_{ij}\mathbf{B}_i^{**}, \tag{2–11}$$

$$T\mathbf{B}_k = \sum_{j=1}^{m} b_{jk}\mathbf{B}_j^*, \tag{2–12}$$

$$ST\mathbf{B}_k = \sum_{i=1}^{r} c_{ik}\mathbf{B}_i^{**}. \tag{2–13}$$

To calculate the c_{ik}, we merely need to apply the transformation S to both sides of (2–12). Using the linearity of S and substituting in the expressions from (2–11) gives us a result which we can compare with (2–13);

$$\begin{aligned}
ST\mathbf{B}_k &= S\left[\sum_{j=1}^{m} b_{jk}\mathbf{B}_j^*\right] = \sum_{j=1}^{m} b_{jk}S\mathbf{B}_j^* = \sum_{j=1}^{m} b_{jk}\sum_{i=1}^{r} a_{ij}\mathbf{B}_i^{**} \\
&= \sum_{j=1}^{m}\sum_{i=1}^{r} b_{jk}a_{ij}\mathbf{B}_i^{**} = \sum_{i=1}^{r}\sum_{j=1}^{m} a_{ij}b_{jk}\mathbf{B}_i^{**}.
\end{aligned}$$

The reversal of order of the summation symbols is valid since these are finite sums and both orders of summation result in the same thing, summation of all of the terms in the rectangular array defined by the subscripts i and j going from 1 to r and 1 to m respectively.

Comparing the last result with (2–13), we find that

$$c_{ik} = \sum_{j=1}^{m} a_{ij}b_{jk}. \tag{2–14}$$

The entry of the matrix $[c_{ik}]$ in the ith row and kth column is found by adding the products of the corresponding entries from the ith row of $[a_{ij}]$ and the kth column of $[b_{jk}]$.

The above discussion motivates the definition of the multiplication of matrices. Putting together the ideas already introduced gives us a complete algebra of matrices.

Definition 2–9. Let $A = [a_{ij}]$ and $B = [b_{ij}]$ be two $n \times m$ matrices. Then by the *sum* of A and B we mean the matrix

$$A + B = [(a_{ij} + b_{ij})],$$

that is, the matrix whose entry in the i, j position is the sum of the entries in the same position of A and B.

Definition 2–10. Let $A = [a_{ij}]$ be an $n \times m$ matrix and let t be a real number. Then by the *scalar multiple* of t and A we mean the matrix

$$tA = [ta_{ij}],$$

each of whose entries are t times the corresponding entry of A.

Definition 2–11. Let $A = [a_{ij}]$ be an $r \times m$ matrix and let $B = [b_{jk}]$ be an $m \times n$ matrix. Then by the *product* of A and B, in that order, we mean the $r \times n$ matrix

$$AB = [c_{ik}]$$

where the c_{ik} are defined by Eq. (2–14).

Note that in this definition, we multiply an $r \times m$ matrix by an $m \times n$ matrix to get an $r \times n$ matrix. The following symbolic equation is useful to help remember how these sizes are related

$$(r \times m) \cdot (m \times n) = (r \times n).$$

The numbers in the center must coincide.

The definitions given here are all motivated by the properties of linear transformations. In fact, we clearly have

▶ **Theorem 2–22.** In terms of fixed bases, the matrix of the sum of two linear transformations is the sum of the two matrices of the individual transformations. The matrix of the scalar multiple of a transformation is the scalar multiple of the matrix of that transformation. The matrix of the composition of two transformations is the product of the matrices of the two transformations.

An important property of this identification of linear transformations is that it is unique (so long as the bases are fixed). This property is stated more accurately in the following theorem, the proof of which is left to the reader.

Theorem 2–23. Let $S: V \to W$ and $T: V \to W$ be two linear transformations which have the matrices A and B, respectively, with respect to the fixed bases $\mathcal{B}$ for V and $\mathcal{B}^*$ for W. Then S and T are identical if and only if A and B are identical.

What are the basic algebraic properties of matrix addition and matrix multiplication? Strangely enough, they are very similar to the algebraic properties of the real number system. We will investigate the matrix analogs of the nine field axioms for the real numbers. We will find only one complete failure (although some axioms hold only in a limited sense). We start by looking at matrix addition. The sum of two arbitrary matrices is not defined in general. Matrix addition is defined only when the two matrices have the same dimensions. However, whenever the sum is defined, the following two properties hold.

A1. *Matrix addition is commutative.*

A2. *Matrix addition is associative.*

These two properties are obviously true since they hold for each entry in the resulting matrix. The next property concerns the existence of an identity for addition.

A3. *For any n and m, there exists an $n \times m$ matrix $0_{n,m}$ such that for any $n \times m$ matrix A,*

$$A + 0_{n,m} = A.$$

The matrix required to satisfy this property is given in the following definition.

Definition 2–12. For any n and m, the $n \times m$ *zero matrix* is the matrix $0_{n,m}$ all of whose entries are zero. Where there is no possibility of confusion in the number of rows and columns, this matrix will be denoted by just 0, without the subscripts.

Since addition is defined only between two matrices having the same number of rows and columns, we can usually omit the subscripts on the zero vector. Its "dimensions" will be determined by the context.

Observe that the zero matrix is the matrix of the "degenerate" linear transformation which maps every vector to the zero vector. Can you show that this is indeed a linear transformation? What is the kernel of this transformation?

Next, we turn to the additive inverse of a matrix.

A4. *Given any matrix A, there exists a matrix $-A$ such that*

$$A + (-A) = 0.$$

The required matrix is given by the following definition.

Definition 2–13. The *negative* of a matrix A, is the matrix $-A = (-1)A$, that is, the matrix which results from multiplying every entry of A by -1. Given two $n \times m$ matrices A and B, the *difference* of these is $A - B = A + (-B)$.

The entire set of axioms for real number addition thus have their analogs for matrix addition. The only real difference is that addition is defined only for matrices of the same dimension. However, if we restricted ourselves to a fixed size, the analogy would be complete.

It is when we turn to matrix multiplication that we find the first failure.

M1. *Matrix multiplication is not commutative.*

To prove this, all we need is one example in which the commutative property fails:

$$\begin{bmatrix} 1 & -1 \\ 2 & 0 \end{bmatrix}\begin{bmatrix} 1 & 1 \\ 0 & 1 \end{bmatrix} = \begin{bmatrix} 1 & 0 \\ 2 & 2 \end{bmatrix}, \qquad \begin{bmatrix} 1 & 1 \\ 0 & 1 \end{bmatrix}\begin{bmatrix} 1 & -1 \\ 2 & 0 \end{bmatrix} = \begin{bmatrix} 3 & -1 \\ 2 & 0 \end{bmatrix}.$$

We have success with the next property however.

M2. *Matrix multiplication is associative.*

A direct proof of this would be very difficult. However, because of the relation between matrix multiplication and the composition of linear transformations, there is a very simple proof available. Given three matrices which can be multiplied together, they define three linear transformations (between R^n, R^m, and R^r). Since the composition of these linear transformations is associative, as we saw in Theorem 2–13, the corresponding matrix multiplication must be associative also.

Next, we turn to the problem of the existence of a multiplicative identity. Again, we find that there would have to be more than one.

M3. *For any n there exists an $n \times n$ matrix I_n such that if A is any $k \times n$ matrix, then $AI_n = A$, and if B is any $n \times m$ matrix, then $I_nB = B$.*

It is easily verified that the required matrix is given by

Definition 2–14. For any n, the $n \times n$ *identity matrix* is the matrix which has all of its entries zero, except for those on the *major diagonal*, which are 1. That is, $I_n = [\delta_{ij}]$, where

$$\delta_{ij} = \begin{cases} 0 & \text{if } i \neq j, \\ 1 & \text{if } i = j. \end{cases}$$

The symbol δ_{ij} with these properties is called the *Kronecker delta*.

The identity matrix I_n is the matrix of the identity transformation $I: R^n \to R^n$ (in terms of the standard bases). This transformation maps each vector to itself, i.e., $I\mathbf{X} = \mathbf{X}$ for every $\mathbf{X}$. If any other basis is used for both the domain and range, the matrix of this transformation remains unchanged. However, if different bases are used for the domain and the range, then the matrix of the identity transformation will not be I_n.

The next property we wish to study is the existence of a multiplicative inverse. Given an $n \times m$ matrix, we could look for a right-hand inverse or a left-hand inverse. A right-hand inverse, if it existed, would have to be an $m \times n$ matrix. A left-hand inverse would have to be an $m \times n$ matrix also, but the product in the latter case would be I_m instead of I_n. Matters will be greatly simplified if we look only at square matrices. An $n \times n$ matrix A has an inverse if and only if the associated linear transformation has an inverse. We saw that this is true if and only if the linear transformation is nonsingular. If a linear transformation is nonsingular, then it has an inverse which is both a right-hand and a left-hand inverse (Theorem 2–18). Hence, if an $n \times n$ matrix A has an inverse A^{-1}, then we must have $AA^{-1} = A^{-1}A = I_n$. Note however that not all square matrices have inverses. For example, the matrix

$$\begin{bmatrix} 0 & 0 \\ 0 & 1 \end{bmatrix}$$

cannot possibly have an inverse, as the reader can easily prove.

Definition 2–15. An $n \times n$ matrix which is the matrix of a nonsingular linear transformation is called a *nonsingular matrix.*

M4. *A nonsingular matrix A has an inverse A^{-1} for which*

$$AA^{-1} = A^{-1}A = I.$$

Note that "nonsingular" replaces nonzero when this property is applied to the set of matrices instead of the real numbers. Note also that we use I to represent the identity matrix instead of I_n. The subscript can be suppressed since it is usually obvious from the context. It is worth knowing that this result has a converse.

Theorem 2–24. If A is an $n \times n$ matrix and there exists an $n \times n$ matrix B such that $BA = I$, then A is nonsingular and $B = A^{-1}$.

Proof. Let T be the linear transformation of R^n to R^n defined by A and let S be the linear transformation defined by B. Then we have $ST = I$ (the identity transformation) and hence we can conclude that T must be nonsingular since otherwise there would be some nonzero $\mathbf{X}$ with $T\mathbf{X} = \mathbf{0}$. However, we would then have $\mathbf{X} = ST\mathbf{X} = S\mathbf{0} = \mathbf{0}$, which is a contradiction. Therefore T is a nonsingular and hence A is nonsingular. ▮

In later sections we will look into the problem of the existence of inverses more closely, but we can find one simple test which can be applied with the theory we have developed so far.

Theorem 2–25. An $n \times n$ matrix A is nonsingular if and only if its column vectors are linearly independent.

Proof. This follows from the fact that the image of the basis vectors under the corresponding transformation are exactly the column vectors of the matrix. That is, the column vectors generate the image space. Hence dim (im T) = dim V if and only if the column vectors are linearly independent. In this case, it follows from (2–8) in Theorem 2–11 that dim(ker T) = 0. Hence ker $T = \{\mathbf{0}\}$ and im $T = V$. This means that T is onto. On the other hand, it follows from (1) in Theorem 2–12 that T is also one-to-one. Therefore T and hence A is nonsingular. In the other direction, it is easily seen that if A is nonsingular then dim(im T) = dim V. ▮

There is still one remaining analog to the field axioms. This is the distributive property.

D1. *If the matrices A, B, and C are such that all of the required sums and products exist, then*

$$A(B + C) = AB + AC \tag{2–15}$$

and

$$(B + C)A = BA + CA. \tag{2–16}$$

This result could be proved by direct application of the definitions, or by use of the fact that matrix multiplication and addition are equivalent to composition and addition of linear transformations. Let us prove (2–15) by the latter method. The proof of (2–16) would be similar and can be left to the reader.

We start by introducing a notation for a linear transformation which may be associated with a particular matrix.

Definition 2–16. Given a matrix A, let T_A be the linear transformation $T_A : R^n \to R^m$ which has A as its matrix, in terms of the standard bases for R^n and R^m.

With this notation, we have from Theorem 2–22 that

$$\begin{aligned} T_{A(B+C)} &= T_A T_{(B+C)} = T_A[T_B + T_C] \\ &= T_A T_B + T_A T_C = T_{AB} + T_{AC} \\ &= T_{(AB+AC)}. \end{aligned}$$

Hence $A(B + C) = AB + AC$. The reader should have no trouble in supplying a reason for each step except one. The proof of this step is simple and is left as an exercise. Try to find which step it is before checking the problems below.

Property D1 completes the list of the basic algebraic properties of addition and multiplication of matrices. Matrices therefore behave very much like the real numbers except that multiplication is not commutative and only nonsingular matrices have inverses.

As mentioned before, one of the main purposes of the next few sections will be to develop methods for obtaining the inverse of a matrix. This is an important problem in many different fields. Even many disciplines other than the physical sciences are finding these methods useful. For example, an important tool in modern economics is the "input-output matrix," whose entries give the amounts of the products of one industry which are used in another. The inverse of this matrix must be computed in order to determine the direct and indirect requirements for the changes in each industry to produce a desired change in the output of one industry.

PROBLEMS

1. Prove Theorem 2–23.
2. Prove that the identity transformation $I : R^n \to R^n$ has the matrix I_n whenever the same basis is used in both the domain and the range spaces but will *not* have the matrix I_n if different bases are used.

3. Prove that the matrix $\begin{bmatrix} 0 & 0 \\ 0 & 1 \end{bmatrix}$ cannot have an inverse.

4. Let A be an $m \times n$ matrix and suppose that there exist matrices B and C such that $AB = I_m$ and $CA = I_n$. With the results of Problem 4 of Section 2–4, show that A must be nonsingular and hence that $m = n$ and $B = C = A^{-1}$.

5. Show that the set of all $m \times n$ matrices is a vector space by showing that matrix addition and scalar multiplication satisfy the P1 through P8 of Theorem 1–1. What is the dimension of this space?

6. If A and B are two nonsingular $n \times n$ matrices, prove that $(AB)(B^{-1}A^{-1}) = I$ and hence that AB is nonsingular with $(AB)^{-1} = B^{-1}A^{-1}$.

7. If T_A, T_B, and T_C are linear transformations for which all of the following sums and compositions are defined, prove that

$$T_A(T_B + T_C) = T_AT_B + T_AT_C.$$

8. Calculate the products of the indicated matrices:

a) $\begin{bmatrix} 3 & -1 & 2 \\ 0 & 4 & -5 \end{bmatrix} \begin{bmatrix} 1 & 6 \\ 5 & -4 \\ 6 & 2 \end{bmatrix}$ b) $\begin{bmatrix} 2 & -3 & 0 & 3 \\ 4 & 2 & 1 & 3 \\ -5 & 0 & 9 & -3 \end{bmatrix} \begin{bmatrix} 3 & -2 & 8 & 0 \\ 3 & 12 & -1 & 5 \\ 5 & 0 & 2 & 4 \\ 7 & 1 & -2 & 10 \end{bmatrix}$

c) $\begin{bmatrix} 1 & 0 & 0 \\ 1 & 1 & 0 \\ -1 & 1 & 1 \end{bmatrix} \begin{bmatrix} 2 & 1 & 5 \\ 3 & -5 & 2 \\ 2 & 4 & -1 \end{bmatrix}$ d) $\begin{bmatrix} 1 & 3 & 7 \\ 3 & -2 & 8 \\ 7 & 8 & 0 \end{bmatrix} \begin{bmatrix} 0 & 2 & 5 \\ 2 & 3 & -4 \\ 5 & -4 & 2 \end{bmatrix}$

9. Determine whether or not the following matrices are nonsingular.

a) $\begin{bmatrix} 1 & 2 \\ 3 & 7 \end{bmatrix}$ b) $\begin{bmatrix} 1 & 0 \\ 1 & 1 \end{bmatrix}$ c) $\begin{bmatrix} -5 & 12 \\ 6 & -8 \end{bmatrix}$

d) $\begin{bmatrix} 12 & -28 \\ -18 & 42 \end{bmatrix}$ e) $\begin{bmatrix} 5 & -3 & 6 \\ -4 & 1 & 2 \\ 1 & -2 & 7 \end{bmatrix}$ f) $\begin{bmatrix} 3 & -1 & -5 \\ 4 & 0 & 2 \\ 1 & 5 & 33 \end{bmatrix}$.

10. Let $A = \begin{bmatrix} a & b \\ c & d \end{bmatrix}$. Prove that if $\Delta = ad - bc \neq 0$, then A has the inverse

$$A^{-1} = \begin{bmatrix} d/\Delta & -b/\Delta \\ -c/\Delta & a/\Delta \end{bmatrix}.$$

11. By Theorem 2–24, if two $n \times n$ matrices, A and B, are such that $BA = I$, then $B = A^{-1}$. However, if BA is "nearly" I, we cannot conclude that B is necessarily nearly A^{-1}. Let

$$A = \begin{bmatrix} 10{,}000 & 3 \\ 3333 & 1 \end{bmatrix}, \qquad B = \begin{bmatrix} 34.33 & -103 \\ -3333 & 10{,}000 \end{bmatrix}.$$

a) Compute BA. In what sense is this "nearly" I?

b) Compute AB. Is this product "nearly" I?

c) Use the formula given in Problem 10 to compute A^{-1}. Compare with B.

2-6. CHANGE OF BASES

The matrix of a linear transformation depends on the bases of the domain and range spaces. Suppose that we are given the matrix of a linear transformation with respect to a particular set of bases. How can we find the matrix of the same linear transformation with respect to a different pair of bases? This is the problem we wish to investigate in this section.

We will start by answering the question for the simplest possible case: when the transformation is the identity. Suppose then we have a space V and a pair of bases

$$\mathcal{B} = \langle \mathbf{B}_1, \mathbf{B}_2, \ldots, \mathbf{B}_n \rangle \quad \text{and} \quad \hat{\mathcal{B}} = \langle \hat{\mathbf{B}}_1, \hat{\mathbf{B}}_2, \ldots, \hat{\mathbf{B}}_n \rangle.$$

We wish to find the matrix of the identity transformation, I, from V with the basis $\hat{\mathcal{B}}$ to V with the basis $\mathcal{B}$. Let the matrix of this transformation be denoted by $P = [p_{jk}]$. Then, comparing with (2–6), we find that

$$I\hat{\mathbf{B}}_k = \hat{\mathbf{B}}_k = \sum_{j=1}^{n} p_{jk}\mathbf{B}_j. \tag{2–17}$$

The way to remember this matrix is to recall that the column vectors of the matrix give the representation of the images of the original basis vectors in terms of the basis vectors in the image space.

Now, suppose that we have a linear transformation $T: V \to W$ which has the matrix A in terms of the basis $\mathcal{B}$ in V and the basis $\mathcal{B}^* = \langle \mathbf{B}_1^*, \ldots, \mathbf{B}_m^* \rangle$ in W. Then the entries of A are determined by

$$T\mathbf{B}_j = \sum_{i=1}^{m} a_{ij}\mathbf{B}_i^*. \tag{2–18}$$

But what is the matrix of the same transformation from V with the basis $\hat{\mathcal{B}}$ to W with the same basis $\mathcal{B}^*$? This matrix can be obtained from a representation of the form corresponding to (2–18), but giving the expansions of $T\hat{\mathbf{B}}_k$ in terms of the vectors $\mathbf{B}_i^*$. We find this representation with the help of (2–17) and (2–18) in the following way:

$$T\hat{\mathbf{B}}_k = T\left[\sum_{j=1}^{n} p_{jk}\mathbf{B}_j\right] = \sum_{j=1}^{n} p_{jk}T\mathbf{B}_j = \sum_{j=1}^{n}\sum_{i=1}^{m} a_{ij}p_{jk}\mathbf{B}_i^*. \tag{2–19}$$

A look at (2–19) shows that the i, k entry in the matrix of the transformation in question is exactly the i, k entry in the matrix AP. This result can be visualized in terms of the following diagram.

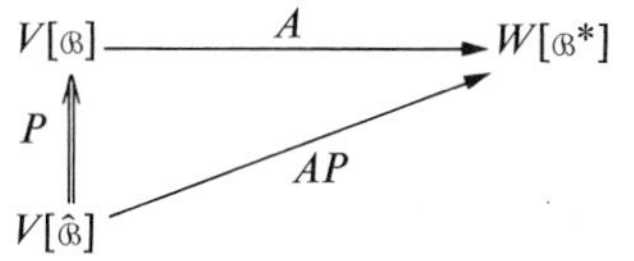

In this diagram, the arrows representing the transformations are marked with the matrix which defines that transformation. The bases are indicated for each space.

A double arrow is used to indicate the identity transformation. It may help to recall that when we write AP we are thinking of P being applied first. Our rule for composition goes from right to left. Hence the product AP should also be viewed from right to left.

Now, what if we also change the basis in W, say to $\hat{\mathcal{B}}^* = \langle \hat{\mathbf{B}}_1^*, \ldots, \hat{\mathbf{B}}_m^* \rangle$? Then the identity transformation from W with the basis $\hat{\mathcal{B}}^*$ to W with the basis $\mathcal{B}^*$ is given by

$$\hat{\mathbf{B}}_h^* = \sum_{i=1}^{m} q_{ih}\mathbf{B}_i^*, \tag{2–20}$$

where the column vectors of the matrix $Q = [q_{ih}]$ are the representations of the new basis vectors $\hat{\mathbf{B}}_h^*$ in terms of the basis $\mathcal{B}^*$. However, to obtain our desired result we must use Q^{-1} instead of Q. That is, we must have expressions for the $\mathbf{B}_i^*$ in terms of the $\hat{\mathbf{B}}_h^*$. Now, the matrix Q is the matrix of the identity transformation, which is most certainly nonsingular. Therefore the inverse $Q^{-1} = [r_{hi}]$ exists and it must satisfy

$$\mathbf{B}_i^* = \sum_{h=1}^{m} r_{hi}\hat{\mathbf{B}}_h^*. \tag{2–21}$$

Putting (2–21) into (2–19) gives us

$$T\hat{\mathbf{B}}_k = \sum_{j=1}^{n}\sum_{i=1}^{m} a_{ij}p_{jk}\mathbf{B}_i^* = \sum_{j=1}^{n}\sum_{i=1}^{m}\sum_{h=1}^{m} r_{hi}a_{ij}p_{jk}\hat{\mathbf{B}}_h^*.$$

From this we can conclude that the matrix of the transformation T in terms of the bases $\hat{\mathcal{B}}$ and $\hat{\mathcal{B}}^*$ is $Q^{-1}AP$. We then have the following diagram.

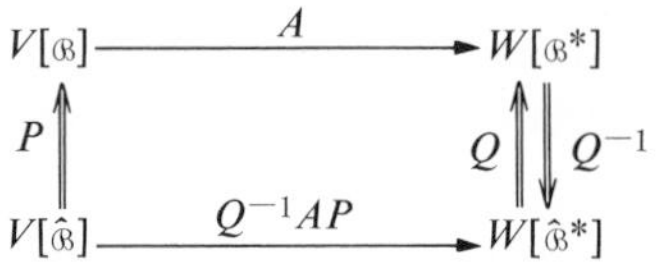

Note that in this diagram, the matrices Q and Q^{-1} are shown attached to arrows pointing in opposite directions. Whenever a transformation (and hence its matrix) has an inverse, this relation exists.

In most cases we will find that the transformation we are working with is between R^n and R^m and given in terms of the standard bases at the start. In the present case, the column vectors of P and Q would be the vectors of the new bases themselves (with their components given in R^n and R^m). Let us look at a particular example to see how this works.

Suppose that we are given the transformation $T: R^3 \to R^2$ defined by

$$T[x_1, x_2, x_3] = [y_1, y_2],$$

where

$$\begin{aligned} y_1 &= x_1 + 3x_2, \\ y_2 &= \phantom{x_1 + {}} x_2 - x_3. \end{aligned}$$

The matrix of this transformation is

$$A = \begin{bmatrix} 1 & 3 & 0 \\ 0 & 1 & -1 \end{bmatrix}.$$

We can see that $T[1, 0, 0] = [1, 0]$, $T[0, 0, -1] = [0, 1]$, and $T[3, -1, -1] = [0, 0]$. (In the next section we will start learning methods of finding such vectors when they are not obvious.) Define a new basis $\mathcal{B}$ for R^3 by setting $\mathbf{B}_1 = [1, 0, 0]$, $\mathbf{B}_2 = [0, 0, -1]$, and $\mathbf{B}_3 = [3, -1, -1]$. Then the matrix of the identity transformation from $R^3[\mathcal{B}]$ to R^3 (with the standard basis when no other is indicated) is given by the matrix P.

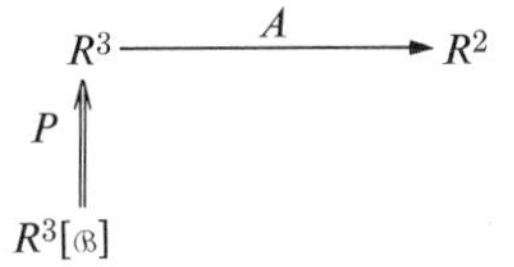

$$P = \begin{bmatrix} 1 & 0 & 3 \\ 0 & 0 & -1 \\ 0 & -1 & -1 \end{bmatrix}.$$

Then the matrix of the transformation $T: R^3[\mathcal{B}] \to R^2$ is given by AP, which is

$$AP = \begin{bmatrix} 1 & 0 & 0 \\ 0 & 1 & 0 \end{bmatrix}.$$

That is, the image of the vector $\mathbf{X} = x_1'\mathbf{B}_1 + x_2'\mathbf{B}_2 + x_3'\mathbf{B}_3$ is $[y_1, y_2]$, where

$$\begin{bmatrix} y_1 \\ y_2 \end{bmatrix} = \begin{bmatrix} 1 & 0 & 0 \\ 0 & 1 & 0 \end{bmatrix} \begin{bmatrix} x_1' \\ x_2' \\ x_3' \end{bmatrix} = \begin{bmatrix} x_1' \\ x_2' \end{bmatrix}.$$

From this representation, it is easy to see that $\mathbf{B}_3$ generates the kernel of the transformation. Indeed, $R^3 = K \oplus L$, where $K = L\{\mathbf{B}_3\}$ and $L = L\{\mathbf{B}_1, \mathbf{B}_2\}$. Furthermore, the behavior of the transformation T on L is quite simple; indeed, it is essentially the identity transformation.

This example illustrates how a transformation can be simplified by the proper choice of a basis.

PROBLEMS

1. What is the matrix which defines the change of basis if two vectors in the basis are interchanged?
2. Let $\mathcal{B}$ be a basis for V and let $\mathcal{B}^*$ be a new basis which is identical to $\mathcal{B}$ except that the ith basis vector of $\mathcal{B}$ has been multiplied by the scalar $c \neq 0$. What is the matrix P giving the change of basis $V[\mathcal{B}^*] \overset{P}{\Rightarrow} V[\mathcal{B}]$?
3. Let $T: R^n \to R^m$ be defined by $T\mathbf{X} = \mathbf{Y}$, where

$$\begin{aligned} y_1 &= a_{11}x_1 + a_{12}x_2 + \cdots + a_{1n}x_n, \\ y_2 &= a_{21}x_1 + a_{22}x_2 + \cdots + a_{2n}x_n, \\ &\vdots \\ y_m &= a_{m1}x_1 + a_{m2}x_2 + \cdots + a_{mn}x_n. \end{aligned}$$

   Prove that the matrix of T is $A = [a_{ij}]$.

4. In each of the following, A is the matrix of a linear transformation of R^n to R^m (with n and m as required). $\mathcal{B}$ is a new basis for R^n, and $\hat{\mathcal{B}}$ is a new basis for R^m. In each case, find the matrix of the transformation $R^n[\mathcal{B}] \to R^m$ and $R^n[\mathcal{B}] \to R^m[\hat{\mathcal{B}}]$, verifying first that the given matrix Q^{-1} is the matrix of the change of basis $R^m[\hat{\mathcal{B}}] \Rightarrow R^m$.

a) $A = \begin{bmatrix} 1 & 3 & -1 & 0 \\ 2 & -2 & 0 & 1 \end{bmatrix}$, $\quad Q^{-1} = \begin{bmatrix} -\frac{1}{2} & 1 \\ \frac{1}{2} & 0 \end{bmatrix}$

$\mathcal{B} = \langle [1, 0, 0, 0], [1, 1, 0, 0], [1, 1, 1, 0], [1, 1, 1, 1] \rangle$, $\quad \hat{\mathcal{B}} = \langle [0, 1], [2, 1] \rangle$.

b) $A = \begin{bmatrix} 3 & 1 & 0 \\ 2 & 2 & 0 \end{bmatrix}$, $\quad Q^{-1} = \begin{bmatrix} \frac{1}{2} & \frac{1}{2} \\ \frac{1}{2} & -\frac{1}{2} \end{bmatrix}$

$\mathcal{B} = \langle [1, -3, 0], [1, -1, 0], [0, 0, 1] \rangle$, $\quad \hat{\mathcal{B}} = \langle [1, 1], [1, -1] \rangle$.

c) $A = \begin{bmatrix} 1 & 0 & 0 \\ 2 & 1 & 0 \\ 3 & 2 & 1 \end{bmatrix}$, $\quad Q^{-1} = \begin{bmatrix} 1 & 0 & 0 \\ -2 & 1 & 0 \\ 1 & -2 & 1 \end{bmatrix}$

$\mathcal{B} = \langle [1, 2, 3], [0, 1, 2], [0, 0, 1] \rangle$, $\quad \hat{\mathcal{B}} = \langle [1, 2, 3], [0, 1, 2], [0, 0, 1] \rangle$

5. For each of the transformations of Problem 4, find a basis for the domain R^n which simplifies the matrix of the transformation $R^n[\mathcal{B}^*] \to R^m$ as much as possible.

2–7. ELEMENTARY MATRICES

In Sections 1–2 and 1–3 we saw that the space generated by a sequence of vectors was not changed by any of the three operations:

1. interchange of two vectors of the sequence;
2. multiplication of a vector of the sequence by a scalar $c \neq 0$;
3. replacing a vector $\mathbf{B}_i$ in the sequence by $\mathbf{B}_i + c\mathbf{B}_j$, where $\mathbf{B}_j$ is any other vector of the sequence and c is any scalar.

The dimension of the space generated by a sequence of vectors is equal to the maximum number of linearly independent vectors contained in the sequence (this follows from Theorem 1–18). In particular, if the above operations are applied to a set of linearly independent vectors, the resulting set will also be linearly independent. That is, if these operations are applied to a basis, then the resulting set is a new basis. Otherwise, the dimension of the space generated would have decreased.

We will now find the matrices which give the change of basis resulting from these operations. These are called the *elementary matrices*. In each case, let V be the given vector space with a basis $\mathcal{B} = \langle \mathbf{B}_1, \mathbf{B}_2, \ldots, \mathbf{B}_n \rangle$ and let the operations result in the new basis $\mathcal{B}^* = \langle \mathbf{B}_1^*, \mathbf{B}_2^*, \ldots, \mathbf{B}_n^* \rangle$. The matrix we seek is the matrix of the transformation

$$V[\mathcal{B}^*] \Rightarrow V[\mathcal{B}].$$

1. Let P_{ij} be the matrix of the change of basis which results when $\mathbf{B}_i$ and $\mathbf{B}_j$ are interchanged. That is,

$$\begin{aligned} \mathbf{B}_i^* &= \mathbf{B}_j, \\ \mathbf{B}_j^* &= \mathbf{B}_i, \\ \mathbf{B}_k^* &= \mathbf{B}_k \qquad \text{for all } k \neq i, j. \end{aligned}$$

The matrix of the change of basis has as its column vectors the components of the $\mathbf{B}_k^*$ in terms of the $\mathbf{B}_i$ [cf. Eq. (2–17)]. The matrix P_{ij} therefore consists entirely of zeros except for a single 1 in each column. There will be a 1 in the ith row of the jth column and one in the jth row of the ith column. The 1 will be in the kth row of the kth column for all other columns. That is, P_{ij} is the matrix which results when the ith and jth columns of the identity matrix I are interchanged. For example, if $n = 4$,

$$P_{23} = \begin{bmatrix} 1 & 0 & 0 & 0 \\ 0 & 0 & 1 & 0 \\ 0 & 1 & 0 & 0 \\ 0 & 0 & 0 & 1 \end{bmatrix}.$$

2. Let $D_i(c)$ be the matrix of the change of basis which results from the multiplication of $\mathbf{B}_i$ by $c \neq 0$. Then

$$\mathbf{B}_i^* = c\mathbf{B}_i,$$
$$\mathbf{B}_j^* = \mathbf{B}_j \qquad \text{for all } j \neq i.$$

Thus the matrix $D_i(c)$ is zero except on the major diagonal. The entries on the major diagonal are all 1, except for the one in the ith column, which is c. That is, the matrix $D_i(c)$ is the matrix which results when the ith column of the identity matrix is multiplied by c. For example,

$$D_3(c) = \begin{bmatrix} 1 & 0 & 0 & 0 \\ 0 & 1 & 0 & 0 \\ 0 & 0 & c & 0 \\ 0 & 0 & 0 & 1 \end{bmatrix}.$$

3. Let $S_{ji}(c)$ be the matrix of the change of basis given by

$$\mathbf{B}_i^* = \mathbf{B}_i + c\mathbf{B}_j,$$
$$\mathbf{B}_k^* = \mathbf{B}_k \qquad \text{for all } k \neq i.$$

Then $S_{ji}(c)$ is exactly the identity matrix except in the ith column. There, it will have a 1 in the ith row and a c in the jth row. The c is thus in the j, i position. This matrix results from the multiplication of the jth column of the identity matrix by c and adding it to the ith column. For example,

$$S_{24}(c) = \begin{bmatrix} 1 & 0 & 0 & 0 \\ 0 & 1 & 0 & c \\ 0 & 0 & 1 & 0 \\ 0 & 0 & 0 & 1 \end{bmatrix}.$$

Definition 2–17. The matrices P_{ij}, $D_i(c)$, and $S_{ji}(c)$ defined above are called the *elementary matrices.*

The elementary matrices actually perform the three basic operations of the first paragraph of this section. It is simple to demonstrate that each of the results of the following theorem hold. This can be done by direct calculation and is left for the reader.

Theorem 2–26. Let A be an $m \times n$ matrix and let B be an $n \times m$ matrix. Let P_{ij}, $D_i(c)$, and $S_{ji}(c)$ be $n \times n$ elementary matrices. Then

1. AP_{ij} is the matrix which results upon interchanging the ith and jth columns of the matrix A.
2. $P_{ij}B$ is the matrix which results upon interchanging the ith and jth rows of the matrix B.
3. $AD_i(c)$ is the matrix which results upon multiplying the ith column of the matrix A by c.
4. $D_i(c)B$ is the matrix which results upon multiplying the ith row of the matrix B by c.
5. $AS_{ji}(c)$ is the matrix which results when the jth column of A is multiplied by c and added to the ith column.
6. $S_{ji}(c)B$ is the matrix which results when the jth row of B is multiplied by c and added to the ith row.

Each of the elementary matrices represents a change of basis, and is therefore nonsingular. What are the inverses of the elementary matrices? From the above results, it is easy to verify that the following theorem holds.

Theorem 2–27

$$\begin{aligned} P_{ij}^{-1} &= P_{ij}, \\ [D_i(c)]^{-1} &= D_i(1/c), \\ [S_{ji}(c)]^{-1} &= S_{ji}(-c). \end{aligned}$$

The inverse of each of the elementary matrices is itself an elementary matrix. In particular, P_{ij} is its own inverse.

Definition 2–18. The operations on the rows and columns of a matrix by the multiplication of that matrix on the left or right by one of the elementary matrices are called *elementary row operations* and *elementary column operations*, respectively.

We saw earlier how any matrix could be brought to *reduced row echelon form* by means of the elementary row operations. Recall that a matrix in reduced row echelon form is of the form (for example)

$$\begin{bmatrix} 0 & 1 & 0 & 4 & 0 & 5 \\ 0 & 0 & 1 & -3 & 0 & 10 \\ 0 & 0 & 0 & 0 & 1 & 7 \\ 0 & 0 & 0 & 0 & 0 & 0 \end{bmatrix}.$$

When a matrix is in reduced row echelon form, each of its rows has a 1 as its first nonzero entry (the last row or rows may be all zeros). Every other entry in the column which contains this 1 is zero. Each row has its first nonzero entry farther to the right than the previous row.

Any matrix can be reduced to this form by means of the elementary row operations. If the first column has any nonzero entries, interchange rcws to bring this entry to the first row. Multiply this row through by the multiplicative inverse of this entry. Use the third row operation to reduce all other entries in the first column to 0. This process can then be repeated on the second column, or the next column which has a nonzero entry in a lower row. The process terminates only when all of the rows have been used (or reduced to all zeros).

By turning the whole process on its side, we see that any matrix could be reduced to *reduced column echelon form* by the use of the elementary column operations. An example of a matrix in reduced column echelon form is

$$\begin{bmatrix} 1 & 0 & 0 & 0 & 0 \\ 2 & 0 & 0 & 0 & 0 \\ 0 & 1 & 0 & 0 & 0 \\ 0 & 0 & 1 & 0 & 0 \\ 7 & -3 & 5 & 0 & 0 \end{bmatrix}.$$

In this form, each *column* has a 1 as its first nonzero entry. All other entries in the row containing this entry are 0. Each column has its first nonzero entry farther down than the previous column.

Suppose that we reduce some *nonsingular* $n \times n$ matrix to reduced column echelon form by means of the elementary column operations. We know that these operations do not change the space generated by the column vectors of the matrix. If we think of the matrix as representing a linear transformation of R^n onto itself, then the column vectors generate the image space, which is R^n itself since we assume that the matrix is nonsingular. Thus the column vectors must be linearly independent.

The elementary column operations will leave the column vectors linearly independent; hence the column vectors in the reduced column echelon form must also be linearly independent and generate R^n. In particular, none of these vectors can be $\mathbf{0}$.

In reduced column echelon form, each column has its lead entry farther down than the previous lead entry. But here there are only n positions in the column vectors. If one of these positions is skipped, we will run out of positions to place a nonzero lead entry. Therefore, the lead entries of the reduced matrix must all be on the major diagonal. Since all the other entries in a row containing one of these entries must be zero, the reduced column echelon form of this matrix must be I_n. Putting this together with Theorem 2–26, we find that we have actually proved the next theorem.

Theorem 2–28. If A is a nonsingular matrix, then there exists a sequence of elementary matrices, $E_1, E_2, \ldots, E_N$, such that

$$AE_1E_2 \cdots E_N = I. \tag{2–22}$$

From this theorem and with the help of Theorem 2–27 we can now prove

Theorem 2–29. Every nonsingular matrix can be written as the product of a sequence of elementary matrices.

Proof. If A is a nonsingular matrix, then by the previous theorem, there exists a sequence of elementary matrices E_i such that

$$AE_1E_2\cdots E_N = I.$$

The elementary matrices are themselves nonsingular, and each has an inverse. Multiply this equality on the right by E_N^{-1}, giving us

$$AE_1E_2\cdots E_{N-1} = E_N^{-1}.$$

This equality can be multiplied again on the right by E_{N-1}^{-1} to give

$$AE_1E_2\cdots E_{N-2} = E_N^{-1}E_{N-1}^{-1}.$$

Continuing in this way, we finally end with

$$A = E_N^{-1}E_{N-1}^{-1}\cdots E_2^{-1}E_1^{-1}. \tag{2-23}$$

Since Theorem 2–27 tells us that the inverse of each elementary matrix is itself an elementary matrix, this proves the theorem. ▮

We are usually not interested in finding the particular sequence of elementary matrices which satisfy the requirements of (2–22) or (2–23). What we wish to find is the resulting product in (2–22), which we identify with A^{-1}. We will use the result of Theorem 2–29 mainly as a theoretical tool and the result of Theorem 2–28 as a practical method for finding the inverse of a matrix.

By successive multiplication on the *left*, Eq. (2–23) can be transformed to

$$E_1E_2\cdots E_NA = I. \tag{2-24}$$

Since multiplication on the right by one of the elementary matrices is equivalent to performing one of the elementary column operations, Eq. (2–22) says that a nonsingular matrix can be reduced to the identity by means of a sequence of elementary column operations. In exactly the same way, (2–24) can be interpreted as saying that the matrix A can be reduced to the identity by a series of elementary row operations.

Most people find it easier to work with the elementary row operations, and we thus prefer to use them whenever possible.

These facts are summarized in Theorem 2–30, stated in the next section. It is these results which will be used to help us in the actual analysis of linear transformations.

PROBLEMS

1. What is the maximum number of elementary row operations which would be required to transform an n-row matrix into reduced row echelon form?
2. A *permutation matrix* is a square $n \times n$ matrix whose entries are all either 0 or 1 and which has exactly n 1's, distributed so that there is exactly one of them in each row and column.

a) How many different $n \times n$ permutation matrices are there?
b) Prove that every permutation matrix is the product of elementary matrices of the form P_{ij}.
c) Prove that every product of elementary matrices of the form P_{ij} is a permutation matrix.
d) Prove that every permutation matrix is nonsingular.
e) Prove that the inverse of a permutation matrix is a permutation matrix.
f) Prove that the product of permutation matrices is a permutation matrix.
g) Let P be a permutation matrix. Define $P^2 = PP$, $P^3 = PP^2$, and so on. Prove that there must be two different powers of P that are identical among the first $n! + 1$ powers, and hence that there must be some power of P which is the identity.

3. Prove that if the elementary column operations are applied so as to bring a *singular* $n \times n$ matrix into reduced column echelon form, at least one of the columns in the reduced form must consist entirely of zeros.

2-8. THE ANALYSIS OF LINEAR TRANSFORMATIONS

In the last section we found that there exist matrices, the elementary matrices, which can be used to perform the elementary row and column operations. Given a nonsingular matrix, it can be reduced to the identity matrix by a sequence of elementary row operations. Each of these operations corresponds to the multiplication on the left by one of the elementary matrices. If the same elementary matrices are multiplied to the identity matrix, the result will be the inverse of the given matrix. However, it is not necessary to actually exhibit the individual elementary matrices. In fact, we have the following theorem.

▶ **Theorem 2-30.** Let A be a nonsingular matrix. Suppose that exactly the same sequence of elementary row operations are applied to the matrix A and the identity matrix I and that the sequence of row operations reduces A to the identity. Then I will be transformed into A^{-1}.

Proof. The elementary row operations are equivalent to the multiplication on the left by one of the elementary matrices. Hence the fact that A can be reduced to the identity is equivalent to the statement that there exist elementary matrices $E_1, E_2, \ldots, E_N$ such that

$$E_N E_{N-1} \cdots E_2 E_1 A = I.$$

The matrix A^{-1} is the unique matrix such that $A^{-1}A = I$. Therefore

$$A^{-1} = E_N E_{N-1} \cdots E_1.$$

Now, suppose we use the first elementary row operation on the matrix A. By Theorem 2-17, the result is the same as multiplying A on the left by E_1. Suppose we perform exactly the same elementary operation on the identity matrix. The result will be the matrix $E_1 I = E_1$. We continue by performing the second operation on both $E_1 A$ and E_1. The results will be $E_2 E_1 A$ and $E_2 E_1$, respectively. Finally, we arrive at I and A^{-1}. ▮

Note that the elementary row operations never mix the different columns. Because of this, we can do the row operations to A and I simultaneously by merely writing the two matrices side by side and treating the result as a larger matrix.

Definition 2–19. Let $A = [a_{ij}]$ be an $n \times m$ matrix and let $B = [b_{ik}]$ be an $n \times r$ matrix. Then by the matrix $[A, B]$ we will mean the $n \times (m + r)$ matrix

$$\begin{bmatrix} a_{11} & \cdots & a_{1m} & b_{11} & \cdots & b_{1r} \\ a_{21} & \cdots & a_{2m} & b_{21} & \cdots & b_{2r} \\ \vdots & & & & & \vdots \\ a_{n1} & \cdots & a_{nm} & b_{n1} & \cdots & b_{nr} \end{bmatrix}.$$

In a similar way, if C is an $n \times m$ matrix and D is an $r \times m$ matrix, we define the matrix $\left[\begin{smallmatrix} C \\ D \end{smallmatrix}\right]$ to be the $(n + r) \times m$ matrix which results when the arrays defining C and D are written one above the other.

Using this definition, we see that to find the inverse of the matrix A, we merely have to perform the elementary row operations on the matrix $[A, I]$ so as to reduce the first n columns (the A part) to I. The remaining n columns will then give A^{-1}.

An example may help make this procedure clearer. Suppose that we want to find the inverse of the matrix

$$A = \begin{bmatrix} 1 & -3 & 2 \\ 3 & -5 & 5 \\ -2 & 9 & -5 \end{bmatrix}.$$

We proceed as follows:

$$\left[\begin{array}{ccc|ccc} 1 & -3 & 2 & 1 & 0 & 0 \\ 3 & -5 & 5 & 0 & 1 & 0 \\ -2 & 9 & -5 & 0 & 0 & 1 \end{array}\right] \to \left[\begin{array}{ccc|ccc} 1 & -3 & 2 & 1 & 0 & 0 \\ 0 & 4 & -1 & -3 & 1 & 0 \\ 0 & 3 & -1 & 2 & 0 & 1 \end{array}\right]$$

$$\to \left[\begin{array}{ccc|ccc} 1 & -3 & 2 & 1 & 0 & 0 \\ 0 & 1 & -\frac{1}{4} & -\frac{3}{4} & \frac{1}{4} & 0 \\ 0 & 3 & -1 & 2 & 0 & 1 \end{array}\right] \to \left[\begin{array}{ccc|ccc} 1 & 0 & \frac{5}{4} & -\frac{5}{4} & \frac{3}{4} & 0 \\ 0 & 1 & -\frac{1}{4} & -\frac{3}{4} & \frac{1}{4} & 0 \\ 0 & 0 & -\frac{1}{4} & \frac{17}{4} & -\frac{3}{4} & 1 \end{array}\right]$$

$$\to \left[\begin{array}{ccc|ccc} 1 & 0 & \frac{5}{4} & -\frac{5}{4} & \frac{3}{4} & 0 \\ 0 & 1 & -\frac{1}{4} & -\frac{3}{4} & \frac{1}{4} & 0 \\ 0 & 0 & 1 & -17 & 3 & -4 \end{array}\right] \to \left[\begin{array}{ccc|ccc} 1 & 0 & 0 & 20 & -3 & 5 \\ 0 & 1 & 0 & -5 & 1 & -1 \\ 0 & 0 & 1 & -17 & 3 & -4 \end{array}\right]$$

It was not necessary to interchange any of the rows in this particular set of calculations. Here we multiplied a row through by a constant to make its lead entry 1 and then used this entry to reduce all other entries in its column to 0. The reader should check through each step of the calculation. Note that several steps can be done at once when they do not mix the rows. In fact, the next to last step need not have been written down at all (why?). The reader should check that we have indeed found

$$A^{-1} = \begin{bmatrix} 20 & -3 & 5 \\ -5 & 1 & -1 \\ -17 & 3 & -4 \end{bmatrix}.$$

After doing such a calculation, it is always important to check your answer, since it is very easy to make a slight slip somewhere along the line.

A nonsingular matrix can be reduced to the identity matrix by using column operations instead of row operations. In order to perform the same operations on the identity at the same time, we can use the matrix $\left[\begin{smallmatrix} A \\ I \end{smallmatrix}\right]$. A column operation performed on this matrix will be performed simultaneously on A and I.

The point to notice here is that a column operation corresponds to multiplication on the left by an elementary matrix E. Hence it can be applied simultaneously to two matrices C and D in the form

$$\begin{bmatrix} C \\ D \end{bmatrix} E = \begin{bmatrix} CE \\ DE \end{bmatrix}.$$

In the case of row operations, multiplication is performed on the left, and we must write

$$E[A, B] = [EA, EB],$$

The reader should find the inverse of the matrix A given above by using column operations on the matrix $\left[\begin{smallmatrix} A \\ I \end{smallmatrix}\right]$ instead of using row operations on $[A, I]$ as was done in the example. The result must of course be the same.

It is most important to observe that while the inverse of the matrix A can be found by doing row operations simultaneously on A and I, or by doing column operations simultaneously on the same two matrices, *the two types of operations cannot be mixed.* If they are, the matrix obtained will not usually be A^{-1}.

For example, suppose we reduce A to B by row operations and B to I by column operations. Then there must exist nonsingular matrices P and Q such that $PA = B$ and $BQ = I$. That is,

$$PAQ = I.$$

Now suppose that the same row and column operations are performed in the same order on the identity matrix. We would obtain first $PI = P$ and then PQ. But since $PAQ = I$,

$$PA = PAQQ^{-1} = Q^{-1}$$

and

$$QPA = QQ^{-1} = I.$$

That is, $A^{-1} = QP$. However, PQ and QP are not in general the same.

The methods discussed in this section can also be used to analyze a linear transformation by obtaining new bases which will simplify the transformation. Given a matrix A, which need be neither nonsingular nor square, we may reduce it to column echelon form by means of a sequence of column operations; and at the same time, operating on I with the same operations, we will obtain a matrix P (which must be nonsingular). That is, we find

$$\begin{bmatrix} A \\ I \end{bmatrix} P = \begin{bmatrix} B \\ P \end{bmatrix}$$

where B is in reduced column echelon form. Looking at this equation from the point of view that $AP = B$ defines a change of basis, we obtain the desired simplification. If necessary, we can find Q^{-1} by using row operations so as to simplify B even further. That is, we can find Q^{-1} such that $Q^{-1}B = C$ is as simple as possible.

The following diagram illustrates this analysis.

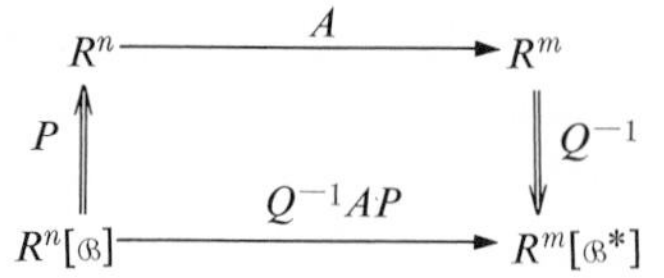

It is useful to recall that the column vectors of P and Q in this diagram are the basis vectors of $\mathcal{B}$ and $\mathcal{B}^*$, respectively. Column operations on A correspond to changing the basis in the domain space of the linear transformation defined by the matrix A, while row operations correspond to the change in the image space. The actual computation we go through produces the matrix Q^{-1}. This matrix must be inverted to give Q before we can identify the new basis.

The methods here are again best illustrated by means of examples. Suppose that we are given the transformation $T: R^4 \to R^3$ which has the matrix

$$A = \begin{bmatrix} 1 & 0 & -2 & 4 \\ 2 & 1 & 4 & 1 \\ -3 & 0 & 2 & 0 \end{bmatrix}.$$

We start by performing the elementary column operations on the matrix $\left[\begin{smallmatrix} A \\ I \end{smallmatrix}\right]$ so as to simplify the A part as much as possible. We will not illustrate the actual calculations here, but the reader should be able to verify that we obtain $\left[\begin{smallmatrix} AP \\ P \end{smallmatrix}\right]$, where

$$AP = \begin{bmatrix} 1 & 0 & 0 & 0 \\ 0 & 1 & 0 & 0 \\ 0 & 0 & 1 & 0 \end{bmatrix},$$

$$P = \begin{bmatrix} -\frac{1}{2} & 0 & -\frac{1}{2} & 2 \\ 4 & 1 & 2 & -17 \\ -\frac{3}{4} & 0 & -\frac{1}{4} & 3 \\ 0 & 0 & 0 & 1 \end{bmatrix}.$$

The columns of the matrix P can be identified as the vectors of a new basis $\mathcal{B}$. If $\mathbf{X} = [x_1, x_2, x_3, x_4]_{\mathcal{B}}$, then $T\mathbf{X} = [x_1, x_2, x_3]$ and hence we find that $\operatorname{im} T = R^3$, while $\ker T = L\{[0, 0, 0, 1]_{\mathcal{B}}\} = L\{[2, -17, 3, 1]\}$.

Let us now look at another example, one in which the column operations fail to reduce the matrix completely. Let us suppose that $T: R^2 \to R^3$ is defined by the matrix

$$A = \begin{bmatrix} 1 & 2 \\ -1 & -3 \\ 1 & -4 \end{bmatrix}.$$

Then we may proceed with column operations on $\left[\begin{smallmatrix} A \\ I \end{smallmatrix}\right]$. We find

$$\left[\begin{array}{rr} 1 & 2 \\ -1 & -3 \\ 1 & -4 \\ \hdashline 1 & 0 \\ 0 & 1 \end{array}\right] \rightarrow \left[\begin{array}{rr} 1 & 0 \\ -1 & -1 \\ 1 & -6 \\ \hdashline 1 & -2 \\ 0 & 1 \end{array}\right] \rightarrow \left[\begin{array}{rr} 1 & 0 \\ 0 & 1 \\ 7 & 6 \\ \hdashline 3 & 2 \\ -1 & -1 \end{array}\right].$$

In this way we have obtained a change of basis matrix P such that

$$AP = \begin{bmatrix} 1 & 0 \\ 0 & 1 \\ 7 & 6 \end{bmatrix},$$

$$P = \begin{bmatrix} 3 & 2 \\ -1 & -1 \end{bmatrix}.$$

Next, we operate on $[AP, I]$ with row operations in the following fashion:

$$\left[\begin{array}{cc:ccc} 1 & 0 & 1 & 0 & 0 \\ 0 & 1 & 0 & 1 & 0 \\ 7 & 6 & 0 & 0 & 1 \end{array}\right] \rightarrow \left[\begin{array}{cc:ccc} 1 & 0 & 1 & 0 & 0 \\ 0 & 1 & 0 & 1 & 0 \\ 0 & 6 & -7 & 0 & 1 \end{array}\right]$$

$$\rightarrow \left[\begin{array}{cc:ccc} 1 & 0 & 1 & 0 & 0 \\ 0 & 1 & 0 & 1 & 0 \\ 0 & 0 & -7 & -6 & 1 \end{array}\right].$$

This gives us a change of basis matrix Q such that

$$Q^{-1}AP = \begin{bmatrix} 1 & 0 \\ 0 & 1 \\ 0 & 0 \end{bmatrix}, \quad Q^{-1} = \begin{bmatrix} 1 & 0 & 0 \\ 0 & 1 & 0 \\ -7 & -6 & 1 \end{bmatrix}, \quad Q = \begin{bmatrix} 1 & 0 & 0 \\ 0 & 1 & 0 \\ 7 & 6 & 1 \end{bmatrix}$$

(cf. the diagram on page 70). The last matrix Q was found by inverting Q^{-1} by the methods described above. The reader should verify this result also.

Now, what information about the transformation have we obtained? Using our knowledge of the change of basis matrices, we introduce the bases

$$\mathcal{B}: \ \mathbf{B}_1 = [3, -1], \quad \mathbf{B}_2 = [2, -1]$$
$$\mathcal{B}^*: \ \mathbf{B}_1^* = [1, 0, 7], \quad \mathbf{B}_2^* = [0, 1, 6], \quad \mathbf{B}_3^* = [0, 0, 1].$$

Then the transformation T has the matrix $Q^{-1}AP$ in terms of these bases. That is,

$$T[x_1, x_2]_{\mathcal{B}} = [x_1, x_2, 0]_{\mathcal{B}^*}.$$

From this equation we can immediately conclude that $\operatorname{im} T = L\{\mathbf{B}_1^*, \mathbf{B}_2^*\}$ and that $\ker T = \{\mathbf{0}\}$.

PROBLEMS

1. If the process described in this section of finding the inverse of a matrix is applied to an $n \times n$ singular matrix, what will happen?
2. Find the inverses of each of the following matrices which are nonsingular:

a) $\begin{bmatrix} 2 & -1 & 3 \\ 4 & -2 & 2 \\ 1 & 1 & 0 \end{bmatrix}$ b) $\begin{bmatrix} 1 & 0 & 1 \\ 1 & 1 & -1 \\ 2 & 1 & 2 \end{bmatrix}$ c) $\begin{bmatrix} 3 & 0 & 0 \\ -1 & 4 & 0 \\ 5 & 7 & -2 \end{bmatrix}$

d) $\begin{bmatrix} -1 & 4 & 2 & -1 \\ 10 & 7 & -1 & -1 \\ -23 & -14 & 3 & 2 \\ -9 & -6 & 1 & 1 \end{bmatrix}$ e) $\begin{bmatrix} 1 & 2 & 0 & -6 \\ -1 & -1 & 1 & 6 \\ 3 & 8 & 3 & -13 \\ 0 & 4 & 3 & -4 \end{bmatrix}$

f) $\begin{bmatrix} 1 & 4 & 3 & -1 \\ 3 & 13 & 9 & -4 \\ 2 & 9 & 7 & -1 \\ -4 & -17 & -10 & 10 \end{bmatrix}$ g) $\begin{bmatrix} 1 & -2 & 2 & -4 \\ -3 & 7 & -7 & 17 \\ 1 & -3 & 4 & -14 \\ -1 & 5 & -7 & 30 \end{bmatrix}$

3. Analyze the linear transformations defined by the given matrices, as was done in the text.

a) $\begin{bmatrix} 1 & 2 & -1 & 5 \\ 1 & 3 & 1 & 8 \\ -1 & -5 & -5 & 14 \end{bmatrix}$ b) $\begin{bmatrix} 1 & -1 & 2 \\ 2 & -1 & 1 \\ 2 & -2 & 4 \\ 5 & -2 & 1 \end{bmatrix}$ c) $\begin{bmatrix} 1 & -2 & -2 & -4 \\ 1 & -1 & -1 & -2 \\ 0 & 2 & 3 & 6 \end{bmatrix}$

d) $\begin{bmatrix} -1 & -3 & 4 & -1 \\ 2 & 3 & -6 & 2 \end{bmatrix}$ e) $\begin{bmatrix} 1 & 1 & -2 & 4 \\ 1 & 2 & -2 & 5 \\ 0 & 2 & 1 & 0 \\ -1 & -1 & 3 & -5 \end{bmatrix}$

2–9. RANK

The elementary row operations cannot change the maximum number of linearly independent rows in a matrix since they do not change the space (and hence its dimension) generated by these row vectors. But what do the row operations do to the set of column vectors? Surprisingly, the answer is that they leave the maximum number of linearly independent vectors unchanged. More precisely:

> **Theorem 2–31.** Let A be an $n \times m$ matrix and let R be a nonsingular $n \times n$ matrix. Then the maximum number of linearly independent column vectors of A is the same as the maximum number of linearly independent column vectors of RA.

Proof. An elementary row operation is equivalent to multiplication on the left by an elementary matrix. Since every nonsingular matrix is the product of elementary matrices, it would be enough to prove that an elementary row operation does not change the number of linearly independent column vectors. However, it is just as easy to prove the theorem as stated.

A nonsingular matrix R can be viewed as representing a change of basis. This is indicated by the diagram.

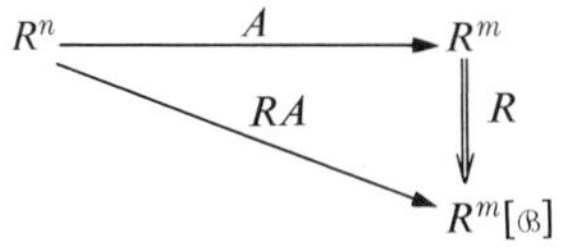

The basis $\mathcal{B}$ is given by the column vectors of R^{-1}. Now what is the dimension of im T_A? Viewing T_A as the mapping from R^n to R^m, we find that im T_A is generated by the column vectors of A and hence dim(im T_A) is the maximum number of linearly independent column vectors of A. On the other hand, the same transformation can also be given by the matrix RA. The column vectors of RA (viewed as vectors whose components are in terms of the basis $\mathcal{B}$) therefore generate the same space. Since the space is the same, the dimension is the same, and the theorem follows. ▌

Definition 2–20. Let T be a linear transformation. Then the *rank* of T is dim(im T). Let A be an $n \times m$ matrix. Then the *rank* of A is the rank of the associated transformation $T_A : R^m \to R^n$. The *row rank* of A is the maximum number of linearly independent row vectors of A, and the *column rank* of A is the maximum number of linearly independent column vectors of A.

As we have observed, the maximum number of linearly independent row vectors is exactly the dimension of the space generated by the row vectors of the matrix. Likewise, the maximum number of linearly independent column vectors is exactly the dimension of the space generated by the column vectors. However, the space generated by the column vectors is exactly the image space of the associated transformation. That is,

Theorem 2–32. For any matrix A

$$\text{rank } A = \text{column rank } A.$$

The comments made in the first paragraph of this section constitute a proof of the fact that the row rank of a matrix is unchanged by one of the elementary row operations. Since the row operations are equivalent to multiplication on the left by elementary matrices and since any nonsingular matrix can be written as the product of elementary matrices, we have as an immediate consequence of Theorem 2–31:

Theorem 2–33. If A is an $n \times m$ matrix and R is any nonsingular $n \times n$ matrix, then

$$\text{row rank } A = \text{row rank } RA,$$
$$\text{column rank } A = \text{column rank } RA.$$

Now, what happens if we speak about column operations instead of row operations? It seems clear that we could repeat the same arguments "turned on their sides" to get exactly similar results. We will find it useful, however, to formalize this idea.

Definition 2–21. Let $A = [a_{ij}]$ be an $n \times m$ matrix. Then by the *transpose* of A we mean the $m \times n$ matrix $A^t = [b_{ij}]$, where for each pair i, j, we have

$$b_{ij} = a_{ji}. \tag{2–25}$$

Loosely speaking, the transpose of a matrix is the matrix obtained by interchanging the rows and columns of the matrix. Do not fall into the trap of thinking that if $A = [a_{ij}]$, then we can write $A^t = [a_{ji}]$. In fact $[a_{ji}] = A$. The subscripts used inside the brackets are "dummy variables" and are used only to indicate that the elements of the matrix are being denoted by the letter a with two subscripts. The first subscript always refers to the row, and the second to the column. Of course, once we have the matrix, we can talk about an individual entry by giving its particular subscripts, as is done in (2–25).

An example of the way we must operate with these ideas is given by the proof of the following theorem.

▶ **Theorem 2–34.** Let A be an $n \times m$ matrix and let B be an $m \times r$ matrix. Then

$$[AB]^t = B^t A^t.$$

Proof. Let $A = [a_{ij}]$, $B = [b_{jk}]$, $AB = [c_{ik}]$, $A^t = [a^*_{jk}]$, $B^t = [b^*_{ij}]$, and $B^t A^t = [c^*_{ik}]$. Then we can compute for any i and k

$$c^*_{ik} = \sum_{j=1}^{m} b^*_{ij} a^*_{jk} = \sum_{j=1}^{m} b_{ji} a_{kj} = \sum_{j=1}^{m} a_{kj} b_{ji} = c_{ki},$$

and this proves the theorem. ▮

Next we observe that

▶ **Theorem 2–35.** The $n \times n$ matrix A^t is nonsingular if and only if A is nonsingular. Furthermore,

$$[A^t]^{-1} = [A^{-1}]^t.$$

Proof. The transpose of any elementary matrix is an elementary matrix. Since a matrix is nonsingular if and only if it is the product of elementary matrices, the first part of the theorem follows from Theorem 2–34. On the other hand, if A is nonsingular, then we can use Theorem 2–34 on the equation $A^{-1}A = I$ in the following way:

$$A^t[A^{-1}]^t = [A^{-1}A]^t = I^t = I.$$

This shows that $[A^{-1}]^t$ must be the inverse of A^t and completes the proof of the theorem. ▮

We will now use these ideas to prove the column operation equivalent of Theorem 2–33.

Theorem 2–36. If A is an $n \times m$ matrix and P is any nonsingular $m \times m$ matrix, then

$$\text{row rank } A = \text{row rank } AP,$$
$$\text{column rank } A = \text{column rank } AP.$$

Proof. We will prove the first of these two results and leave the second as an exercise.

$$\begin{aligned}\text{row rank } A &= \text{column rank } A^t \\ &= \text{column rank } P^tA^t \\ &= \text{column rank } (AP)^t \\ &= \text{row rank } AP. \blacksquare\end{aligned}$$

We will now turn to the proof of the fact that the row rank and column rank of a matrix are the same. The proof is accomplished by using Theorems 2–33 and 2–36 to reduce a matrix to one which we know has its row rank and column rank the same.

Definition 2–22. Let $r \leq \min\{n, m\}$. Then, by the *cannonical $n \times m$ matrix of rank r* we mean the matrix $C_{nm}^r = [c_{ij}]$ defined by

$$c_{ij} = \begin{cases}\delta_{ij} & \text{for all } i \leq r, \\ 0 & \text{for all } i > r.\end{cases}$$

The matrix defined here consists entirely of zeros except for r 1's along the upper end of the major diagonal. For example,

$$C_{34}^2 = \begin{bmatrix}1 & 0 & 0 & 0\\ 0 & 1 & 0 & 0\\ 0 & 0 & 0 & 0\end{bmatrix} \quad\text{or}\quad C_{32}^2 = \begin{bmatrix}1 & 0\\ 0 & 1\\ 0 & 0\end{bmatrix}.$$

By obvious extensions of the conventions introduced in Definition 2–19, we can write

$$C_{nm}^r = \begin{bmatrix}I_r & 0_{r,m-r}\\ 0_{n-r,r} & 0_{n-r,m-r}\end{bmatrix} = \begin{bmatrix}I_r & 0\\ 0 & 0\end{bmatrix}.$$

The second and simpler form requires the reader to fill in the sizes of the zero matrices. This is usually easy to do.

Note that it is obvious that rank C_{nm}^r = column rank C_{nm}^r = row rank $C_{nm}^r = r$, since there are exactly r linearly independent row vectors and as many column vectors. Now we prove

▶ **Theorem 2–37.** Let A be any $n \times m$ matrix. Then there exists an r and nonsingular matrices R and P such that

$$RAP = C_{nm}^r.$$

Proof. Let r be the row rank of the matrix A. We know that there exists a sequence of row operations which will reduce A to reduced row echelon form. This sequence of row operations is equivalent to multiplication of A on the left by a nonsingular matrix R. Since A is of row rank r, and by Theorem 2–33, RA is also of row rank r, we must have exactly r rows of RA with nonzero lead entries. Now we operate on RA with the elementary column operations. Each of the first r rows of RA has a 1 as its first nonzero entry. Interchange columns so as to bring these entries into positions along the main diagonal. Each column that contained one of these entries had all of its other entries 0, and therefore we have already obtained a matrix whose first r columns are identical with C_{nm}^r.

All rows of RA below the first r rows had to consist entirely of 0 since RA was in reduced row echelon form. Therefore the matrix we have just obtained is C^r_{nm} except (possibly) in the upper right-hand corner. But the 1's in the upper-left hand corner can then be used with the elementary column operations to remove all of these entries. Thus we have finally obtained $C^r_{nm} = RAP$, where P is the nonsingular matrix equivalent to this sequence of elementary column operations. This completes the proof. ▌

With this theorem, we can now prove the main result of this section.

▶ **Theorem 2–38.** For any matrix A

$$\text{rank } A = \text{column rank } A = \text{row rank } A.$$

Proof. Theorem 2–32 shows that rank A = column rank A. It remains only to show that column rank A = row rank A. Let R and P be nonsingular matrices as required by Theorem 2–37 such that $RAP = C^r_{nm}$. Then, by Theorems 2–33 and 2–36,

$$\text{row rank } A = \text{row rank } RA = \text{row rank } RAP = r,$$

$$\text{column rank } A = \text{column rank } RA = \text{column rank } RAP = r.$$

Thus the two ranks are the same, and the theorem is proved. ▌

Theorem 2–38 is the first result in the text that is really not obvious. This result is quite deep in the theory of vector spaces. There is certainly no obvious reason for the maximum number of linearly independent row and column vectors of a matrix to be the same.

Note that in order to find the rank of a matrix, it is not necessary to reduce the matrix all the way to the cannonical form of Definition 2–22. It suffices to use the elementary row operations (or column operations if there are fewer columns than rows) just far enough to be able to state with certainty how many linearly independent rows (or columns) there are. In particular, it is not necessary to complete the job of removing all entries in a column with a nonzero lead coefficient. It is enough to remove the entries below that coefficient.

There is another characterization of the rank of a matrix which has useful applications. Suppose that C is an $n \times m$ matrix whose rank is r. Then C has exactly r linearly independent column vectors. That is, the space generated by the column vectors of C is an r-dimensional subspace of R^n. Hence there must be r vectors $\mathbf{A}_1, \mathbf{A}_2, \ldots, \mathbf{A}_r$ in R^n which form a basis for this space, and every column vector $\mathbf{C}_j$ of C must be some linear combination of these. There must exist $b_{1j}, b_{2j}, \ldots, b_{rj}$ for each j such that

$$\mathbf{C}_j = b_{1j}\mathbf{A}_1 + b_{2j}\mathbf{A}_2 + \cdots + b_{rj}\mathbf{A}_r,$$

which is the same as

$$C = AB,$$

where A is the $n \times r$ matrix whose column vectors are the $\mathbf{A}_j$ and $\mathbf{B} = [b_{ij}]$.

The converse of this result is also true. That is,

Theorem 2–39. An $n \times m$ matrix C is of rank r if and only if there is an $n \times r$ matrix A of rank r and an $r \times m$ matrix B of rank r such that $C = AB$.

Proof. Suppose that $C = AB$, where A and B are as in the statement of the theorem. Since A is of rank r, the process of row reduction can be followed to reduce A to reduced row echelon form. Since A has exactly r columns and the reduced row echelon form has exactly r nonzero rows, the reduced form must be of the type C_{nr}^r as in Definition 2–22. That is, there must exist a nonsingular matrix R such that

$$RA = \begin{bmatrix} I_r \\ 0_{n-r,r} \end{bmatrix}.$$

Similarly, since B is also of rank r, there must exist an $m \times m$ nonsingular matrix P such that

$$BP = [I_r, 0_{r,m}].$$

However, we then have

$$RCP = RABP = \begin{bmatrix} I_r \\ 0 \end{bmatrix} [I_r, 0] = C_{nm}^r,$$

which shows that C is of rank r.

The proof in the other direction was given in the discussion before the statement of the theorem. However, we can reverse the above proof to give another proof which is more constructive. The method described can be used to give the actual factorization.

Suppose that C is of rank r. Then, as shown earlier in this section, we can obtain an $n \times n$ nonsingular matrix R and an $m \times m$ nonsingular matrix P such that

$$RCP = C_{nm}^r = \begin{bmatrix} I_r \\ 0_{n-r,r} \end{bmatrix} [I_r, 0_{r,m-r}].$$

The matrices

$$A = R^{-1} \begin{bmatrix} I_r \\ 0_{n-r,r} \end{bmatrix} \quad \text{and} \quad B = [I_r, 0_{r,m-r}]P^{-1}$$

then satisfy the conclusions of the theorem. ▌

The decomposition of this theorem is the basis of a very useful mathematical technique known as "factor analysis." It often happens that in some physical situation, n different quantities can be measured but they depend on only r different factors. It would be most helpful if these "factors" could be separated out, which is precisely what is accomplished by the above theorem.

A commonly given example is the set of scores of m students on a bank of n examinations. It is thought likely that there may be a limited number of factors (such as general intelligence, mathematical ability, geometric visualization, perseverance, etc.) which can be used to account for the differences in the scores of students whose training has been the same. This hypothesis could be tested by the methods of factor analysis.

It should be mentioned however that the actual process of factor analysis is much more complex than given above. In practical problems, the components of the vectors cannot be measured exactly, so we must investigate the possibility of the matrix being "approximately of rank r." Also, the vectors may sometimes lie in an "affine subspace" rather than in a subspace, which means that there is some fixed vector $\mathbf{V}$ such that all $\mathbf{C}_i' = \mathbf{C}_i - \mathbf{V}$ lie in the subspace. Altogether, the matrix C will be of the form

$$C = C_0 + C_1 + D,$$

where C_0 is of rank r, C_1 is an $n \times m$ matrix whose m column vectors are all the same, and D is the matrix of "error terms." The problem would be to find C_1 and a D whose terms were no larger than we were willing to allow so as to reduce the rank of C_0 as low as possible.

The matrix C_0 in this decomposition would then be the one to be factored. The methods used to determine C_1 and D are statistical in nature and are outside the scope of this text.

PROBLEMS

1. Supply reasons for each line of the proof of the first half of Theorem 2–36.
2. Prove the second half of Theorem 2–36.
3. Find the rank of each of the following matrices

a) $\begin{bmatrix} 1 & 3 & -1 & 2 & 0 & 5 \\ 3 & 5 & 0 & 0 & 1 & 0 \\ 2 & 4 & 1 & 1 & 0 & 0 \\ 3 & 2 & 0 & 0 & 1 & 1 \end{bmatrix}$ b) $\begin{bmatrix} 4 & 2 & 4 & 0 & 1 & -1 \\ 1 & 0 & 0 & -5 & 0 & 12 \\ 2 & -5 & 1 & 0 & 3 & 0 \\ 5 & -3 & 5 & 5 & 4 & -13 \\ 2 & -1 & 3 & 3 & 0 & 2 \\ 2 & 3 & 1 & -3 & 1 & -3 \end{bmatrix}$

4. Decompose the two matrices of Problem 3 into the product of two matrices satisfying the conditions of Theorem 2–39.

2–10. SYSTEMS OF LINEAR EQUATIONS

The study of linear algebra essentially began with the study of the solutions of systems of linear equations. This topic still remains one of the major applications of the theory. It is surprising how many different types of problems can be reduced to the problem of finding the solution of a system of linear equations.

By a system of linear equations, we mean a collection of equations of the form

$$\begin{aligned} a_{11}x_1 + a_{12}x_2 + \cdots + a_{1n}x_n &= b_1, \\ a_{21}x_1 + a_{22}x_2 + \cdots + a_{2n}x_n &= b_2, \\ &\vdots \\ a_{m1}x_1 + a_{m2}x_2 + \cdots + a_{mn}x_n &= b_m. \end{aligned} \tag{2–26}$$

This system of equations can be written in the more compact form

$$AX = \mathbf{B}, \tag{2–27}$$

where A is the matrix $[a_{ij}]$, $\mathbf{X}$ is the vector $[x_1, x_2, \ldots, x_n]$ and $\mathbf{B}$ is the vector $[b_1, b_2, \ldots, b_m]$. In the equation shown in (2–27), we think of the vectors $\mathbf{X}$ and $\mathbf{B}$ as column vectors, or $n \times 1$ and $m \times 1$ matrices, in order to make the multiplication meaningful.

The matrix A defines a linear transformation $T_A : R^n \to R^m$. This is exactly the linear transformation defined by Eq. (2–27). A look at this equation shows us that this system of equations will have a solution if and only if $\mathbf{B} \in \operatorname{im} T_A$. A solution, if one exists at all, is unique if and only if T_A is one-to-one. Let us start by discussing some of the possibilities which can occur.

Definition 2–23. A system of equations (2–26) is called a *homogeneous system* if and only if $\mathbf{B} = \mathbf{0}$. The solution $\mathbf{X} = \mathbf{0}$ is called the *trivial solution* of the homogeneous system. If $\mathbf{X} \neq \mathbf{0}$ is a solution of the homogeneous system, then it is called a *nontrivial solution* of this system.

This is the traditional terminology. Note that in terms of the definitions we gave in earlier sections, solutions of the homogeneous system are exactly the vectors $\mathbf{X}$ in the kernel of T_A. There exists a nontrivial solution if and only if the dimension of the kernel is greater than zero.

Since $\dim(\ker T_A) + \dim(\operatorname{im} T_A) = \dim V = n$ (the number of unknowns), we find

Theorem 2–40. If $n > m$, then the homogeneous system of (2–26) has a nontrivial solution. If $n = m$, then the homogeneous system has a nontrivial solution if and only if the matrix A is singular.

The proof of this theorem is left as an exercise. The first statement of the theorem was essentially proved in the course of the proof of Theorem 1–17, but the tools of the last section allow a very short proof to be given at this stage. Note that when $n < m$ (that is, when there are more equations than there are unknowns) it is still possible that A might have rank less than n, and hence there might exist some nontrivial solution of the homogeneous system. This is an unusual case, however.

Theorem 2–41. If the system (2–26) has a solution for some $\mathbf{B} \neq \mathbf{0}$, then that solution is unique if and only if the corresponding homogeneous system has only the trivial solution.

Proof. This theorem is nothing more than a restatement of Theorem 2–8. The uniqueness of the solution requires that the linear transformation be one-to-one, which happens if and only if $\ker T_A = \{\mathbf{0}\}$. ▌

This theorem gives us an answer to the question of whether or not a solution is unique, but it is of no help in answering whether or not a solution exists at all. The existence of a solution depends completely on whether or not $\mathbf{B} \in \operatorname{im} T_A$, and the latter inclusion must be investigated for each individual case. As a matter of probability, it is more likely that a solution exists when $n > m$, but it is easy to give a counterexample. In particular, suppose that two of the equations are identical but the b_i are different?

The case that we are mainly interested in is one where the number of unknowns is the same as the number of equations, that is, when $n = m$. Then we can state the following theorem.

Theorem 2–42. If $n = m$ in (2–26) and the matrix A is nonsingular, then there exists a unique solution of the system for every $\mathbf{B}$.

Proof. The uniqueness comes from the fact that $\dim(\operatorname{im} T_A) = \operatorname{rank} A = n$ and hence that $\dim(\ker T_A) = 0$. Also, $\dim(\operatorname{im} T_A) = n$ means that $\operatorname{im} T_A = R^n$ and hence that every vector $\mathbf{B} \in \operatorname{im} T_A$. ▮

If A is a nonsingular matrix, then it has an inverse A^{-1}. If we multiply Eq. (2–27) on the left by A^{-1}, we find that

$$\mathbf{X} = A^{-1}\mathbf{B}.$$

This gives us the solution of (2–27) for any vector $\mathbf{B}$. However, to obtain a solution in this way, we must know A^{-1}, which is usually more difficult to find than the direct solution of (2–27). If we must solve several equations of the type (2–27), all with the same matrix A but with different vectors $\mathbf{B}$, then it might be worthwhile to find A^{-1} and use this method. We note that any large computer will probably have a program available for the computation of the inverse of a matrix and programs for the direct solution of a system of equations.

Now let us discuss the practical method for solving a system of equations (2–26). By this we mean discovering whether or not a solution exists, and if one does, finding it. When the solution is not unique, we wish to find the set of all solutions. Our method is to reduce the matrix A to reduced row echelon form, which is equivalent to multiplying A on the left by a nonsingular matrix R. Applying the resulting matrix to both sides of (2–27), we would have

$$(RA)\mathbf{X} = R\mathbf{B}. \tag{2–28}$$

When we have the system of equations in this form, it is always easy to see whether or not a solution exists, find one if it does, and find any nontrivial solutions of the homogeneous system. The procedure is best explained by means of an example.

First, however, note that we can find both RA and $R\mathbf{B}$ simultaneously by using the row operations on the "augmented matrix" $[A, \mathbf{B}]$. In reducing this matrix, we are interested only in obtaining the reduced row echelon form for the A part of this matrix. No extra benefit is obtained by making a final reduction in the "$\mathbf{B}$" column.

The row-reduction process is the same one that we have already discussed, so there is no point in repeating it. Suppose, then, that after the reduction process we have the matrix $[RA, R\mathbf{B}]$, for example

$$\left[\begin{array}{ccccc|c} 1 & 0 & 2 & 0 & -5 & 7 \\ 0 & 1 & 4 & 0 & 8 & -2 \\ 0 & 0 & 0 & 1 & -3 & 5 \\ 0 & 0 & 0 & 0 & 0 & 0 \end{array}\right]. \tag{2–29}$$

Here, we might have started with four equations in five unknowns. The row-reduction process has essentially eliminated one of the equations. If a row of RA consists entirely of zeros and the corresponding entry in $R\mathbf{B}$ is nonzero, then there can be no solution. A zero row of RA produces a zero component of $RA\mathbf{X}$. In this example, the nonzero components of $R\mathbf{B}$ occur in rows with nonzero entries of RA, so we still expect a solution. It may be helpful to see what is happening by writing out the set of equations corresponding to the above augmented matrix. These are the equations of (2–28). In the present case, we have

$$\begin{aligned} x_1 + \quad + 2x_3 \quad\quad - 5x_5 &= 7, \\ x_2 + 4x_3 \quad\quad + 8x_5 &= -2, \\ x_4 - 3x_5 &= 5, \\ 0x_1 + 0x_2 + 0x_3 + 0x_4 + 0x_5 &= 0. \end{aligned} \tag{2–30}$$

The rank of RA is the number of nonzero rows, and it is also the same as the number of *principal columns*, that is, columns in which there is a lead entry to some row. In our example, the rank is three. The dimension of the kernel is the dimension of the domain space (the number of columns of RA) minus the dimension of the image space. Hence the dimension of the kernel is exactly the number of nonprincipal columns of RA. In this example, the dimension of the kernel is 2. The first, second, and fourth are the principal columns. The third and fifth are the nonprincipal columns.

One of the x_i is associated with each column of RA. We find our basic solution by setting each x_i associated with one of the nonprincipal columns equal to zero. The remaining x_i will then be exactly the entries of $R\mathbf{B}$. In this example, we set $x_3 = x_5 = 0$, and we find the basic solution $x_1 = 7$, $x_2 = -2$, $x_4 = 5$. That is, we have the solution $[7, -2, 0, 5, 0]$. Now we wish to find the remaining solutions.

If $\mathbf{Y} \in \ker T_A$, then $A\mathbf{Y} = \mathbf{0}$. Thus if $A\mathbf{X} = \mathbf{B}$, then $A(\mathbf{X} + \mathbf{Y}) = \mathbf{B}$ also. In fact, it is easy to see that if $\mathbf{X}_0$ is any one solution of $A\mathbf{X} = \mathbf{B}$, then the set of all solutions is given by $\{\mathbf{X}_0 + \mathbf{Y} \mid \mathbf{Y} \in \ker T_A\}$. Our problem is thus to find the vectors in the kernel of the transformation. We do this with the help of the entries in the nonprincipal columns.

Set all but one of the unknowns associated with the nonprincipal columns equal to zero. Set the remaining one equal to 1. Now adjust the unknowns associated with the principal columns so as to make $RA\mathbf{X} = \mathbf{0}$. Since there is only one nonzero entry in each row associated with a principal column, this is easy to do. In the above example, set $x_5 = 0$ and $x_3 = 1$. Then we have to solve the equations

$$\begin{aligned} x_1 \qquad + 2 \qquad &= 0, \\ x_2 + 4 \qquad &= 0, \\ x_4 &= 0. \end{aligned}$$

We find $[-2, -4, 1, 0, 0]$ to be in the kernel. Similarly, we let $x_3 = 0$ and $x_5 = 1$. Solving $RA\mathbf{X} = \mathbf{0}$ for this case gives the vector $[5, -8, 0, 3, 1]$. Therefore the complete solution of this system of equations is

$$\mathbf{X} = [7, -2, 0, 5, 0] + s[-2, -4, 1, 0, 0] + t[5, -8, 0, 3, 1],$$

where s and t are any scalars. The solution can also be written in the form

$$\begin{aligned} x_1 &= 7 - 2x_3 + 5x_5, \\ x_2 &= -2 - 4x_3 - 8x_5, \\ x_3 &= x_3, \\ x_4 &= 5 + 3x_5, \\ x_5 &= x_5, \end{aligned}$$

where x_3 and x_5 have arbitrary scalar values.

The reader should go through this example carefully, comparing the matrix (2–29) with the set of equations (2–30) and seeing how the basic solution and the vectors in the kernel are obtained. The actual process is easier than the description makes it seem.

Suppose that we were given a system of equations

$$A\mathbf{X} = \mathbf{B}$$

which had no solution. What would happen when we applied the above method? When we had performed the row-reduction technique, we would have the system

$$(RA)\mathbf{X} = R\mathbf{B},$$

where RA is in reduced row echelon form. An examination of the above example should suffice to show that a system such as this always has a solution, unless there is a row of RA consisting entirely of zeros while the corresponding entry of $R\mathbf{B}$ is nonzero. It is the latter conditions which indicate that the original system has no solution.

Finally, note that we cannot use column operations on these matrices. Column operations correspond to changing the basis in the domain space, which is exactly the space of the unknowns. If we make a change of basis here, we will have to change back to find what the solution of the original set of equations was. In the method described here, row operations were used. These operations correspond to a change of basis in the image space. By carrying along $\mathbf{B}$ in this process we avoid having to make any other changes.

PROBLEMS

1. Prove Theorem 2–40.
2. Suppose that the system of (2–24) is such that $m > n$ (i.e., such that there are more equations than unknowns). Prove that if a solution exists, it is not unique.
3. Find the complete solution for each of the following sets of equations.

a)
$$\begin{aligned} x - 2y - 2z - 4w &= 19 \\ 2x - 3y - 6z - 5w &= 25 \\ x + y + 4w &= -15 \\ 2x - 4z + 3w &= -9 \end{aligned}$$

b)
$$\begin{aligned} x - 2y + 4z + 5w &= -1 \\ 3x + y + 5z + w &= 18 \\ 2x - y + 5z + 4w &= 7 \\ x + 3y - z - 5w &= 14 \end{aligned}$$

c)
$$\begin{aligned} x + 2y - z + w &= -3 \\ 2x + 5y + 7z + 10w &= 4 \\ 5x + 10y - 11z - 10w &= -12 \\ 10x + 5w &= -5 \end{aligned}$$

d)
$$\begin{aligned} x_1 + 4x_2 + 4x_3 + 3x_4 &= 1 \\ x_1 + 5x_2 + 7x_3 + 5x_4 &= 0 \\ 2x_1 + 7x_2 + 7x_3 + 2x_4 &= 5 \end{aligned}$$

e) $x - 2y + 5z + w = 3$

f)
$$\begin{aligned} 2x + 10y - 4z &= -6 \\ 3x - 2y + 11z &= 42 \\ 4x + 3y + 9z &= 39 \\ -2x + 5y - 11z &= -39 \\ 2x + 8y - 2z &= 0 \end{aligned}$$

4. Show that each of the following sets of equations has no solution. Find the solution of the corresponding homogeneous set.

a)
$$\begin{aligned} x - 2y + 4z &= -1 \\ 2x - 3y + 7z &= 0 \\ x - 3y + 5z &= -5 \end{aligned}$$

b)
$$\begin{aligned} x + 2y - 5z + 5u &= -3 \\ 2x - y + 5u + 5v &= 14 \\ x + y - 3z + 4u + v &= 3 \end{aligned}$$

c)
$$\begin{aligned} x + 2y - 2z + 4w &= -8 \\ x + y + 2w &= -1 \\ 2x + 3y - z + 6w &= -6 \\ x + 3y + 6w &= -13 \end{aligned}$$

5. For each of the following systems of equations, find the complete solution if one exists. If there is no solution to the given system, find the complete solution of the corresponding homogeneous system. In each case, the system of equations is given by $A\mathbf{X} = \mathbf{B}$ where the given matrix is $[A, \mathbf{B}]$. The last column of the given matrix is the vector $\mathbf{B}$.

a)
$$\left[\begin{array}{rrrrr|r} 3 & 2 & -1 & 2 & 1 & 6 \\ -1 & 4 & 0 & 1 & 1 & 0 \\ 5 & 5 & -7 & 0 & -1 & 6 \\ 3 & 3 & 1 & 2 & 2 & 5 \end{array}\right]$$

b)
$$\left[\begin{array}{rrrr|r} 1 & 3 & -1 & 0 & 4 \\ 5 & 0 & 3 & 3 & -3 \\ 0 & 1 & 1 & 0 & 0 \\ 3 & 4 & 1 & 3 & 3 \end{array}\right]$$

c)
$$\left[\begin{array}{rrr|r} 0 & 0 & -1 & 3 \\ 1 & 7 & 1 & -1 \\ 5 & 2 & 2 & 4 \\ 3 & -4 & -3 & 14 \end{array}\right]$$

d)
$$\left[\begin{array}{rrr|r} 4 & -1 & 2 & 5 \\ 3 & 1 & 0 & 1 \\ 2 & 0 & 1 & 0 \\ 5 & 0 & 1 & 5 \end{array}\right]$$

CHAPTER 3

Determinants

3–1. THE DEFINITION OF A DETERMINANT

We know what it means for a function from one vector space to another to be a linear transformation (linear function). There are two conditions which must be satisfied. A function F is linear if and only if

$$F(\mathbf{X} + \mathbf{Y}) = F(\mathbf{X}) + F(\mathbf{Y})$$

for every pair of vectors **X** and **Y**, and also

$$F(t\mathbf{X}) = tF(\mathbf{X})$$

for every vector **X** and every scalar t. It is sometimes useful to note that these two conditions can be replaced by a single condition. Indeed, the function F is linear if and only if

$$F(s\mathbf{X} + t\mathbf{Y}) = sF(\mathbf{X}) + tF(\mathbf{Y})$$

for every pair of vectors **X** and **Y** and for every pair of scalars s and t. Both of the conditions given first are consequences of this single condition by proper choice of the vectors or scalars.

In this section, we wish to speak of functions defined over the cartesian product of a number of vector spaces, that is, about functions of several vectors. Just as our interest was centered on linear functions of a single vector, now we are most interested in functions of several vectors which are linear functions of each variable separately.

Definition 3–1. Let $F(\mathbf{X}_1, \mathbf{X}_2, \ldots, \mathbf{X}_n)$ be a real-valued function of n vectors. This function is called *multilinear* if and only if it is linear as a function of every variable separately, all others being held fixed.

This definition is not as rigorous as it might be, but it should be clear enough. Actually, we probably should say that the function is multilinear if and only if

$$F(\mathbf{X}_1, \ldots, s\mathbf{X}_i + t\mathbf{Y}_i, \ldots, \mathbf{X}_n) = sF(\mathbf{X}_1, \ldots, \mathbf{X}_i, \ldots, \mathbf{X}_n) + tF(\mathbf{X}_1, \ldots, \mathbf{Y}_i, \ldots, \mathbf{X}_n)$$

for every i, s, t, $\mathbf{X}_i$, $\mathbf{Y}_i$, and set of vectors $\mathbf{X}_1, \mathbf{X}_2, \ldots, \mathbf{X}_{i-1}, \mathbf{X}_{i+1}, \ldots, \mathbf{X}_n$.

The above definition is valid for a function defined over a cartesian product of any set of vector spaces. We will be interested only in the case in which all of the spaces are the same, however. In particular, the case we will consider is the one in which the n vector spaces are all R^n. If V is some vector space, then by V^n we mean $V \times V \times \cdots \times V$, the cartesian product of n copies of this space.

Definition 3–2. Let V be a vector space, and let $F: V^n \to R$ be a multilinear function. Then F is called an *alternating* function if and only if it has the value zero whenever two of the variables have the same value.

That is, if $\mathbf{X}_i = \mathbf{X}_j$ for some $i \neq j$, then $F(\mathbf{X}_1, \ldots, \mathbf{X}_n) = 0$. Note that this definition would be impossible if the spaces were not the same. They must be the same or we could not compare two different vectors.

The reason for the name *alternating function* is not obvious from this definition. This name comes from another property of such functions, stated in Theorem 3–1 below. This theorem concerns what happens to the value of the function when two of its variables are "interchanged." It would be more accurate to say that the values of two of the vectors have been interchanged. Perhaps it is best to state exactly what we mean by this phrase.

If $\langle \mathbf{X}_1, \ldots, \mathbf{X}_n \rangle$ is an element of V^n, then we will say that the vectors $\mathbf{X}_i$ and $\mathbf{X}_j$ have been interchanged when the new n-tuple $\langle \mathbf{Y}_1, \ldots, \mathbf{Y}_n \rangle$ in V^n satisfies the equations

$$\mathbf{Y}_i = \mathbf{X}_j, \qquad \mathbf{Y}_j = \mathbf{X}_i, \qquad \mathbf{Y}_k = \mathbf{X}_k,$$

for all k other than i or j.

Theorem 3–1. A multilinear function $F: V^n \to R$ is alternating if and only if it changes sign whenever the arguments of two vectors are interchanged.

Proof. Suppose first that F is a multilinear function such that it changes sign whenever two of the vectors are interchanged. Suppose two of the vectors $\mathbf{X}_i$ and $\mathbf{X}_j$ are equal. Then, on the one hand, the interchange of these two vectors will change the sign of the value of the function, but, on the other hand, since the two vectors are equal, the function is unchanged. The only real number which is its own negative is zero. Therefore the value of the function must be zero, and we have proved that the function satisfies Definition 3–2.

To prove the other statement of the theorem, suppose that the property of Definition 3–2 holds. We wish to prove that the function changes sign whenever the arguments of two vectors are interchanged. The main difficulty in the proof is the number of variables involved in the expressions of the functions. It is easy to get tangled up in notation. To simplify matters, let us fix all of the vectors except the ith and jth and write a new function which depends on these two vectors alone:

$$G(\mathbf{X}_i, \mathbf{X}_j) = F(\mathbf{X}_1, \ldots, \mathbf{X}_i, \ldots, \mathbf{X}_j, \ldots, \mathbf{X}_n).$$

What we wish to prove is that $G(\mathbf{X}_j, \mathbf{X}_i) = -G(\mathbf{X}_i, \mathbf{X}_j)$. We are given that the function is multilinear and that it is zero whenever the two variables take on the same value. Therefore

$$\begin{aligned} 0 &= G(\mathbf{X}_i + \mathbf{X}_j, \mathbf{X}_i + \mathbf{X}_j) = G(\mathbf{X}_i, \mathbf{X}_i + \mathbf{X}_j) + G(\mathbf{X}_j, \mathbf{X}_i + \mathbf{X}_j) \\ &= G(\mathbf{X}_i, \mathbf{X}_i) + G(\mathbf{X}_i, \mathbf{X}_j) + G(\mathbf{X}_j, \mathbf{X}_i) + G(\mathbf{X}_j, \mathbf{X}_j) \\ &= G(\mathbf{X}_i, \mathbf{X}_j) + G(\mathbf{X}_j, \mathbf{X}_i). \end{aligned}$$

Hence

$$G(\mathbf{X}_j, \mathbf{X}_i) = -G(\mathbf{X}_i, \mathbf{X}_j). \blacksquare$$

We are now ready to define the determinant.

Definition 3-3. The *determinant* of order n is an alternating, multilinear function $\Delta:[R^n]^n \to R$ such that

$$\Delta(\mathbf{e}_1, \mathbf{e}_2, \ldots, \mathbf{e}_n) = 1. \tag{3-1}$$

There are two problems connected with this definition. First, is there any function satisfying this definition? And second, if there is, is it unique? When we write *the* determinant in the first line of the definition we imply that it exists and is unique. The main purpose of the next section will be to prove this.

Here, however, let us assume for the moment that such a function exists and derive some of the properties that it would then have to satisfy.

Theorem 3-2. If the n vectors $\mathbf{X}_1, \mathbf{X}_2, \ldots, \mathbf{X}_n$ are linearly dependent, then $\Delta(\mathbf{X}_1, \mathbf{X}_2, \ldots, \mathbf{X}_n) = 0$.

Proof. If a set of vectors is linearly dependent, then one of them can be written as a linear combination of the others. Suppose, for example, that $\mathbf{X}_n = \sum_{i=1}^{n-1} t_i\mathbf{X}_i$. Then, by using the multilinearity of Δ, we must have

$$\begin{aligned}\Delta(\mathbf{X}_1, \mathbf{X}_2, \ldots, \mathbf{X}_n) &= \Delta\left(\mathbf{X}_1, \mathbf{X}_2, \ldots, \mathbf{X}_{n-1}, \sum_{i=1}^{n-1} t_i\mathbf{X}_i\right) \\ &= \sum_{i=1}^{n-1} t_i\, \Delta(\mathbf{X}_1, \mathbf{X}_2, \ldots, \mathbf{X}_{n-1}, \mathbf{X}_i).\end{aligned}$$

However, in this last sum, the final vector, $\mathbf{X}_i$, in the argument of Δ is the same one that appears at some earlier position in the argument. Hence, since Δ was to be an alternating function, the value of that term is zero. Since all of the terms are zero, $\Delta(\mathbf{X}_1, \ldots, \mathbf{X}_n) = 0$. ▮

Now let us see how the value of the determinant must depend on the individual components of the vectors. The vector $\mathbf{X}_i$ is a linear combination of the coordinate vectors $\mathbf{e}_j$. This linear combination will be different for each of the vectors, so we will have an entire matrix of coefficients. For each i, let

$$\mathbf{X}_i = \sum_{j=1}^{n} a_{ij}\mathbf{e}_j. \tag{3-2}$$

The matrix $A = [a_{ij}]$ is therefore the matrix whose row vectors are the vectors $\mathbf{X}_i$. Now we can use the multilinearity of Δ. In order to help us keep the various summations straight, we can use a different dummy variable for each $\mathbf{X}_i$. We find

$$\begin{aligned}\Delta(\mathbf{X}_1, \mathbf{X}_2, \ldots, \mathbf{X}_n) &= \Delta\left(\sum_{j_1=1}^{n} a_{1j_1}\mathbf{e}_{j_1}, \sum_{j_2=1}^{n} a_{2j_2}\mathbf{e}_{j_2}, \ldots, \sum_{j_n=1}^{n} a_{nj_n}\mathbf{e}_{j_n}\right) \\ &= \sum_{j_1=1}^{n}\sum_{j_2=2}^{n}\cdots\sum_{j_n=n}^{n} a_{1j_1}a_{2j_2}\cdots a_{nj_n}\,\Delta(\mathbf{e}_{j_1}, \mathbf{e}_{j_2}, \ldots, \mathbf{e}_{j_n}). \end{aligned} \tag{3-3}$$

If it exists at all, the determinant must satisfy this relation. Therefore we will have found the determinant when we know its values on every possible ordered n-tuple of the standard coordinate vectors. What we will show in the next section is that given any ordered n-tuple of coordinate vectors $\langle \mathbf{e}_{j_1}, \ldots, \mathbf{e}_{j_n} \rangle$, there is only one possible value for the determinant.

Equation (3–3) contains repeated summation symbols. How many terms are there in the sum altogether? Each sum extends through n terms for each possible value of any of the other indices. Thus the number of terms in each summation multiplies. The right-hand side of (3–3) therefore includes n^n terms.

Not all these terms are meaningful, however. Whenever two of the $\mathbf{e}_{j_i}$ are the same, the value of Δ must be zero. We could therefore eliminate from this expression all terms in which two of the indices are repeated. How many terms will remain? The first index, j_1, can run from 1 to n. For each value of this index, the second, j_2, can take on any of the remaining $n - 1$ values. For any pair, j_1, j_2, there are $n - 2$ values remaining that j_3 can assume. Continuing in this way, we find that when $j_1, \ldots, j_{n-1}$ have been fixed, there remains only a single value that j_n can take on. This means that there are exactly $n!$ terms in the summation of (3–3) which are not automatically zero.

PROBLEMS

1. Write out (3–3) fully for $n = 2$. Two of the resulting terms must be zero. Which two and why? One of the terms is determined from (3–1). The remaining term can be determined with the help of Theorem 3–1. Determine both of these terms. Prove your results.
2. Using Definition 3–2 and Theorem 3–1, together with (3–1), determine the value of $\Delta(\mathbf{e}_{j_1}, \mathbf{e}_{j_2}, \mathbf{e}_{j_3})$ for every possible sequence of the coordinate vectors in R^3. Use the values you find to give the expansion of (3–3) for $n = 3$.

3–2. PERMUTATIONS

We saw that the terms in Eq. (3–3) are zero whenever two of the integers of the sequence $j_1, j_2, \ldots, j_n$ are the same. When none of them are the same, however, this sequence of integers must be exactly a rearrangement of the first n integers.

Definition 3–4. Let $J_n = \{1, 2, \ldots, n\}$ be the set of the first n positive integers. A *permutation* σ of J_n is a function $\sigma : J_n \to J_n$ which is one-to-one and onto. The set of all permutations of J_n is denoted by $\mathcal{P}_n$.

Suppose that σ is a permutation in $\mathcal{P}_n$. Let $\sigma(1) = j_1, \sigma(2) = j_2, \ldots, \sigma(n) = j_n$. Then the same permutation can be defined by merely giving the sequence (that is, the ordered n-tuple) of integers $\langle j_1, j_2, \ldots, j_n \rangle$, because there is a natural one-to-one correspondence between the integers and the position of an element of a sequence. Thus we may write $\sigma = \langle j_1, j_2, \ldots, j_n \rangle$ when we mean that $\sigma(i) = j_i$ for each i.

Another way of looking at the permutation is as follows. The permutation $\sigma = \langle 3, 1, 4, 2\rangle$ could be written in the form

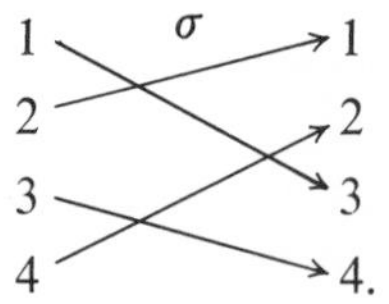

This representation is quite helpful in understanding what happens when two permutations are composed. For example, if $\rho = \langle 1, 3, 4, 2\rangle$ is another permutation, then $\rho \circ \sigma$ is $\langle 4, 1, 2, 3\rangle$ as can be read from the diagram

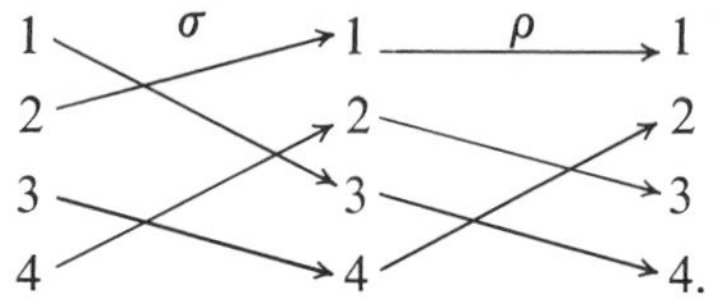

Remember that when we write the composition of two functions, the one written on the right is to be done first. The reader should find the composition of these two permutations in the opposite order. Note that the result is entirely different.

There is still another way in which we can look at permutations. Let $\sigma = \langle j_1, j_2, \ldots, j_n\rangle$ be a permutation. We can associate a sequence of the coordinate vectors with this permutation [motivated by Eq. (3–3)].

Definition 3–5. Let $\sigma = \langle j_1, j_2, \ldots, j_n\rangle$ be a permutation in $\mathcal{P}_n$. Then the matrix $P(\sigma)$ is the matrix whose ith column vector is $\mathbf{e}_{j_i}$.

For example, using the permutations $\sigma = \langle 3, 1, 4, 2\rangle$ and $\rho = \langle 1, 3, 4, 2\rangle$ given above, we have

$$P(\rho) = \begin{bmatrix} 1 & 0 & 0 & 0 \\ 0 & 0 & 0 & 1 \\ 0 & 1 & 0 & 0 \\ 0 & 0 & 1 & 0 \end{bmatrix}, \qquad P(\sigma) = \begin{bmatrix} 0 & 1 & 0 & 0 \\ 0 & 0 & 0 & 1 \\ 1 & 0 & 0 & 0 \\ 0 & 0 & 1 & 0 \end{bmatrix}.$$

In this case, we observe that $P(\rho)P(\sigma) = P(\rho \circ \sigma)$. This result is not confined to the example presented here.

Theorem 3–3. If ρ and σ are any two permutations in $\mathcal{P}_n$, then

$$P(\rho)P(\sigma) = P(\rho \circ \sigma).$$

Proof. $P(\rho \circ \sigma)$ is characterized by the fact that in its ith column, all of the entries are zero except for a 1 in the $\rho(\sigma(i)) = \rho(j_i)$ row. Now, what about the ith column of the product $P(\rho)P(\sigma)$? The ith column of this product comes from the ith column of $P(\sigma)$ which is $\mathbf{e}_{\sigma(i)}$. Therefore the entry in this column of the product will be 0 except for the row in which $P(\rho)$ has a 1 in the $\sigma(i)$ position. That is, there must be a 1 in the

$\sigma(i)$ column of this row. However, matrix $P(\rho)$ has a 1 in the $\rho(\sigma(i))$ row of the $\sigma(i)$ column. Therefore $P(\rho)P(\sigma)$ will have a 1 in the $\rho(\sigma(i))$ row of the ith column and hence it is identical with $P(\rho \circ \sigma)$. ▮

The reader should observe that the above proof can be given in a somewhat different and possibly simpler form by noting that $P(\sigma)$ is the matrix of the change of basis from $\langle \mathbf{e}_1, \mathbf{e}_2, \ldots, \mathbf{e}_n \rangle$ to $\langle \mathbf{e}_{\sigma(1)}, \mathbf{e}_{\sigma(2)}, \ldots, \mathbf{e}_{\sigma(n)} \rangle$.

The matrices of the above definition are called the *permutation matrices*. Among them, in particular, are the elementary matrices P_{ij}. There is a corresponding permutation which is of special interest.

Definition 3–6. A *transposition* is a permutation which interchanges two integers and leaves the rest fixed, that is, a permutation whose matrix is an elementary matrix of the type P_{ij}.

Theorem 3–4. Every permutation can be written as the composition of a sequence of transpositions.

Proof. This theorem amounts to saying that every permutation matrix can be written as the product of elementary matrices of the type P_{ij}—a fact which is almost self-evident. Any permutation matrix can be reduced to the identity by a sequence of interchanges of rows, corresponding to multiplication on the left by elementary matrices of the form P_{ij}. We merely have to interchange row 1 with whichever row has 1 in column 1 [which is, of course, row $\sigma(1)$]. Interchange the new row 2 with whichever row has 1 in the second column, and so on. Some rows will already be in the proper position, and so the interchange will not be needed. This will give a sequence of matrices P_{ik_i} which are either elementary matrices of this form, or are the identity, so that

$$P_{1k_1}P_{2k_2}\cdots P_{n-1,k_{n-1}}P(\sigma) = I.$$

The sequence ends at $n - 1$, since when the first $n - 1$ rows are correct the last is automatically correct. Knowing that each of these elementary matrices is its own inverse, we then have

$$P(\sigma) = P_{n-1,k_{n-1}}\cdots P_{2k_2}P_{1k_1}. \blacksquare$$

We see from the above proof that any permutation σ in $\mathcal{P}_n$ can be expressed as the composition of at most $n - 1$ transpositions. However, the same permutation can usually be expressed in many different ways as the composition of transpositions. For example, the permutation $\langle 2, 3, 1, 4 \rangle$ can be expressed as the composition of either two or four transpositions in the following ways:

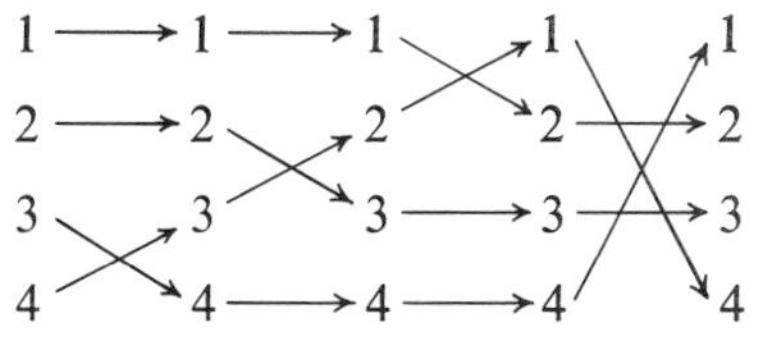

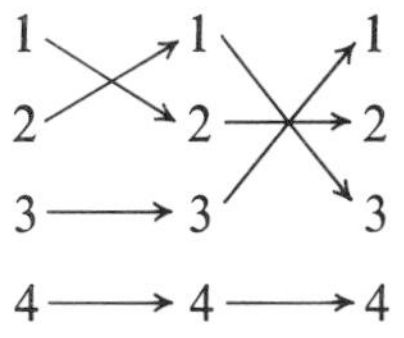

Note that in both of these the number of transpositions is even. It is clear that if a permutation can be written as the composition of a sequence of transpositions, then we can always add two more to the sequence. We merely need to add the same transposition twice. We cannot expect that the number of transpositions needed to express a permutation is uniquely determined. We will find, however, that for a given permutation, this number is always either even or odd.

Theorem 3–5. Let σ_0 be a permutation in $\mathcal{P}_n$. Suppose that there are sequences of transpositions τ_i and τ_i' such that

$$\begin{aligned}\sigma_0 &= \tau_k \circ \tau_{k-1} \circ \cdots \circ \tau_2 \circ \tau_1 \\ &= \tau_j' \circ \tau_{j-1}' \circ \cdots \circ \tau_2' \circ \tau_1'.\end{aligned}$$

Then

$$(-1)^k = (-1)^j.$$

Proof. The proof of this theorem is accomplished with the help of a special trick. The use of this particular method in one form or another seems to be necessary in the proof. We define a function $H : \mathcal{P}_n \to R$ in the following way: For any σ in $\mathcal{P}_n$, let

$$H(\sigma) = \prod_{i<k} [\sigma(k) - \sigma(i)].$$

Let $\sigma(i) = j_i$ for each i. Then this product can be written in the form

$$H(\sigma) = (j_2 - j_1)(j_3 - j_2)(j_3 - j_1)(j_4 - j_3) \cdots (j_n - j_2)(j_n - j_1). \tag{3–4}$$

In particular, for the identity permutation I, $I(i) = i$, then

$$\begin{aligned}H(I) &= (2 - 1)(3 - 2)(3 - 1)(4 - 3)(4 - 2) \cdots (n - 1) \\ &= (1!)(2!)(3!) \cdots [(n - 1)!] \\ &= 1^{n-1} \cdot 2^{n-2} \cdot 3^{n-3} \cdots (n - 2)^2 \cdot (n - 1).\end{aligned} \tag{3–5}$$

How does (3–4) compare with (3–5)? Every pair of indices i and i' appears in one and only one of the factors of the product (3–4). However, given any two integers r and s in J_n, there is a pair of integers i and i' such that $\sigma(i) = r$ and $\sigma(i') = s$. Thus (3–4) contains one (and only one) factor which is the difference of r and s. This factor will be either $(r - s)$ or $(s - r)$ depending on whether $i' < i$ or $i' > i$. Every factor in (3–5) therefore appears once and only once in (3–4), except that it may appear with a negative sign in (3–4). We can conclude that for every σ in $\mathcal{P}_n$

$$H(\sigma) = \pm H(I).$$

To prove the theorem, all we need to do is to prove that for any permutation σ and any transposition τ,

$$H(\tau \circ \sigma) = (-1)H(\sigma).$$

Then

$$H(\sigma_0) = H(\tau_k \circ \tau_{k-1} \circ \cdots \circ \tau_2 \circ \tau_1) = (-1)^k H(I),$$

and also

$$H(\sigma_0) = H(\tau_j' \circ \tau_{j-1}' \circ \cdots \circ \tau_2' \circ \tau_1') = (-1)^j H(I).$$

From these two equations we can obtain the desired relation.

Suppose then that τ is a transposition which interchanges the pair of integers s and t. There exist i and k such that $\sigma(i) = s$ and $\sigma(k) = t$. That is, τ will interchange the integers j_i and j_k. What effect will this transposition have on $H(\sigma)$? All of those factors in $H(\sigma)$ which contain neither j_i or j_k will be unchanged. If r is any integer in J_n other than j_i or j_k, then there will be exactly one factor which contains both r and j_i, and exactly one which contains both r and j_k. The product of these two will be

$$\pm (j_i - r)(j_k - r).$$

Interchanging j_i and j_k will not change this product.

Finally, there is exactly one factor in $H(\sigma)$ which contains both j_i and j_k. The transposition will change the order of these two terms in the factor, and hence will change the sign of that particular factor. Putting these together, we find that $H(\tau \circ \sigma) = (-1)H(\sigma)$. This proves the theorem. ▌

Once we have proved this theorem, we can state the following definition.

Definition 3–7. Let σ be a permutation and suppose that it can be expressed as the composition of k transpositions

$$\sigma = \tau_k \circ \tau_{k-1} \circ \cdots \circ \tau_2 \circ \tau_1.$$

Then the *parity* of the permutation is defined as

$$\epsilon(\sigma) = (-1)^k.$$

Now let us return to the representation of the determinant obtained in Eq. (3–3). There are n^n terms in this expansion, but, as we saw, the only terms which need be considered are those in which the subscripts in $\Delta(\mathbf{e}_{j_1}, \mathbf{e}_{j_2}, \ldots, \mathbf{e}_{j_n})$ are all distinct. That is, we need consider only those terms in which the sequence $j_1, j_2, \ldots, j_n$ represents a permutation of J_n.

Definition 3–8. Let σ be any permutation in $\mathcal{P}_n$. Suppose that for each i, $\sigma(i) = j_i$. Then by the symbol $\mathbf{e}_\sigma$ we shall mean the n-tuple of vectors

$$\langle \mathbf{e}_{j_1}, \mathbf{e}_{j_2}, \ldots, \mathbf{e}_{j_n} \rangle$$

With this definition, we can now restate Eq. (3–3). If $\mathbf{X}_i = \sum_{j=1}^n a_{ij}\mathbf{e}_j$ for each i, then the determinant function must satisfy

$$\Delta(\mathbf{X}_1, \mathbf{X}_2, \ldots, \mathbf{X}_n) = \sum_{\sigma \in \mathcal{P}_n} a_{1j_1} a_{2j_2} \cdots a_{nj_n} \Delta(\mathbf{e}_\sigma).$$

By definition the determinant function is an alternating function. This means that for any transposition τ, $\Delta(\mathbf{e}_{\tau \circ \sigma}) = (-1)\Delta(\mathbf{e}_\sigma)$. We were given in the definition of the determinant that $\Delta(\mathbf{e}_I) = 1$. Therefore, from Definition 3–8, we conclude that

$\Delta(\mathbf{e}_\sigma) = \epsilon(\sigma)$. Furthermore, Theorem 3–5 shows us that this is the only possibility. The assumptions that $\Delta(\mathbf{e}_I) = 1$ and that the determinant function is alternating therefore define $\Delta(\mathbf{e}_\sigma)$ in a unique manner for each σ. We thus have

▶ **Theorem 3–6.** The determinant function is uniquely defined by Definition 3–3. If

$$\mathbf{X}_i = \sum_{j=1}^{n} a_{ij}\mathbf{e}_j$$

for each i, then

$$\Delta(\mathbf{X}_1, \mathbf{X}_2, \ldots, \mathbf{X}_n) = \sum_{\sigma \in \mathcal{P}_n} \epsilon(\sigma) a_{1j_1} a_{2j_2} \cdots a_{nj_n}. \tag{3-6}$$

PROBLEMS

1. Prove that $\sigma: J_n \to J_n$ is one-to-one if and only if it is onto.
2. Given that ρ and σ are permutations in $\mathcal{P}_n$, prove that $\rho \circ \sigma$ is also a permutation.
3. Given that P is a permutation matrix, prove that P^t is also a permutation matrix.
4. If $P(\rho) = [P(\sigma)]^t$, what is ρ in terms of σ? Prove your answer.
5. Let $K = \langle j_1, j_2, \ldots, j_n \rangle$ be an arbitrary n-tuple of integers from J_n. That is, K is an element of $[J_n]^n$. Define $\mathbf{e}_K = \langle \mathbf{e}_{j_1}, \mathbf{e}_{j_2}, \ldots, \mathbf{e}_{j_n} \rangle$. For each K, let A_K be some real number. Prove that

$$F(\mathbf{X}_1, \ldots, \mathbf{X}_n) = \sum_{K \in [J_n]^n} A_K a_{1j_1} a_{2j_2} \cdots a_{nj_n}$$

is a multilinear function and, conversely, that every multilinear function can be expressed in this form.

6. A *cycle* is a permutation which leaves all integers fixed except for $h_1, \ldots, h_k$, for which $\sigma(h_1) = h_2, \sigma(h_2) = h_3, \ldots, \sigma(h_k) = h_1$.
   a) Prove that if two cycles have no integers in common, then they commute.
   b) If a cycle is of length k, what is its parity?
7. Write down all the permutations of $\mathcal{P}_4$. Find the parity of each.
8. For each of the following permutations, give the inverse, write it as a sequence of transpositions, give the parity, and give the result of the composition (in both orders) with $\rho = \langle 2, 3, 4, 5, 6, 1 \rangle$.
   a) $\sigma = \langle 3, 5, 1, 4, 2, 6 \rangle$
   b) $\sigma = \langle 1, 2, 3, 5, 6, 4 \rangle$
   c) $\sigma = \langle 2, 3, 1, 4, 5, 6 \rangle$
   d) $\sigma = \langle 6, 5, 4, 3, 2, 1 \rangle$

3–3. SOME PROPERTIES OF DETERMINANTS

We have defined the determinant as a multilinear function of n vectors in R^n. The reader may be more familiar with the determinant as a function of a matrix. We will now extend our definition to include this case.

Definition 3–9. Let $A = [a_{ij}]$ be an $n \times n$ matrix. Let $\mathbf{A}_1, \mathbf{A}_2, \ldots, \mathbf{A}_n$ be the row vectors of A, that is, $\mathbf{A}_i = [a_{i1}, a_{i2}, \ldots, a_{in}]$. Then by the *determinant of A* we mean

$$\det A = \begin{vmatrix} a_{11} & a_{12} & \cdots & a_{1n} \\ a_{21} & a_{22} & \cdots & a_{2n} \\ \vdots & & & \vdots \\ a_{n1} & a_{n2} & \cdots & a_{nn} \end{vmatrix} = \Delta(\mathbf{A}_1, \mathbf{A}_2, \ldots, \mathbf{A}_n).$$

Now let us state some of the elementary consequences of the properties of determinants as given in Section 3–1. Many of these properties are easier to see when we write them in terms of the determinant of a matrix.

The first property we shall look at is the consequence of the fact that the determinant was defined to be an alternating function.

Theorem 3–7. If two rows of the matrix A are identical, then

$$\det A = 0.$$

Theorem 3–8. If two rows of a matrix A are interchanged, then the value of the determinant is multiplied by -1. That is

$$\det (P_{ij}A) = (-1) \det A,$$

where P_{ij} is the elementary matrix of Definition 2–17.

Next, we observe the consequences of multilinearity. We divide this result into two parts. The first is the result of scalar multiplication of a vector.

Theorem 3–9. If one of the rows of a matrix A is multiplied by a scalar c, then the value of the determinant is multiplied by the same constant. That is,

$$\det [D_i(c)A] = c \det A.$$

Next, we consider the sum of two vectors in one of the rows.

Theorem 3–10. If the matrices A, A', and A'' are identical except for their ith rows, which are $\mathbf{A}_i$, $\mathbf{A}'_i$, $\mathbf{A}''_i$, respectively, and if $\mathbf{A}_i = \mathbf{A}'_i + \mathbf{A}''_i$, then

$$\det A = \det A' + \det A''.$$

The proofs of the above theorems are all trivial as consequences of the quoted properties and can safely be left to the reader. The next property is not quite as trivial, although it is still not difficult.

Theorem 3–11. The determinant of a matrix is unchanged if one of the rows is multiplied by a constant c and added to another row. That is

$$\det [S_{ji}(c)A] = \det A.$$

Proof. Here the jth row of the original matrix is being replaced by $\mathbf{A}_j + c\mathbf{A}_i$. Let A be the original matrix, A' the same matrix except that its jth row is $\mathbf{A}_i$, and A'' the same matrix except that its jth row is $c\mathbf{A}_i$. Let B be the matrix which is identical with A except that its jth row is $\mathbf{A}_j + c\mathbf{A}_i$. Then what we are to prove is that $\det B = \det A$. But

$$\det A' = 0,$$
$$\det A'' = \det [D_j(c)A'] = c \det A' = 0,$$
$$\det B = \det A + \det A'' = \det A. \blacksquare$$

Before we continue, let us note that there is at least one special case in which it is easy to determine the value of a determinant.

Definition 3–10. A matrix $A = [a_{ij}]$ is called an *upper triangular matrix* if and only if $a_{ij} = 0$ for all i and j such that $i > j$.

This condition means that all of the entries below the major diagonal are zero. In an exactly similar way we can define a lower triangular matrix.

Definition 3–11. A matrix $A = [a_{ij}]$ is a *lower triangular matrix* if and only if $a_{ij} = 0$ for all i and j with $i < j$. A matrix is called a *triangular matrix* if it is either an upper triangular matrix or a lower triangular matrix.

▶ **Theorem 3–12.** The value of the determinant of a triangular matrix is the product of the entries on the main diagonal.

Proof. Let us suppose, for example, that the matrix A is a lower triangular matrix. Then $a_{ij} = 0$ when $j > i$. Let us look at the expansion (3–6):

$$\det A = \sum \epsilon(\sigma) a_{1j_1} a_{2j_2} \cdots a_{nj_n}.$$

Which terms in this expansion are nonzero? The factor a_{1j_1} is zero whenever j_1 is greater than 1. This means that j_1 must be equal to 1 in any term which is not zero. Similarly, j_2 must be either 1 or 2, or else a_{2j_2} is equal to 0. However, in order to have a nonzero term, both of the first two factors must be nonzero. Hence we must have $j_1 = 1$. This leaves only 2 for j_2. Continuing in this way, we find that $j_3 = 3, \ldots$, and finally, $j_n = n$ are the only possibilities open if the term is not to be automatically zero. That is, I is the only permutation left in the entire sum. $\epsilon(I) = 1$, and the theorem follows. $\blacksquare$

As a simple consequence of this theorem, we can find the value of the determinants of the elementary matrices. Indeed, it is easy to calculate

$$\det D_i(c) = c \qquad \text{and} \qquad \det S_{ji}(c) = 1.$$

What about the value of the determinant of P_{ij}? We can calculate it in the following way:

$$1 = \det I = \det P_{ij}P_{ij} = -\det P_{ij}.$$

Here we have used the fact that $P_{ij}P_{ij} = I$ and Theorem 3–8. The result is

$$\det P_{ij} = -1.$$

These conclusions can be combined with the results of Theorems 3–8, 3–9, and 3–10 to give the following theorem.

Theorem 3–13. If E is any elementary matrix, then

$$\det EA = (\det E)(\det A).$$

From this theorem it is only a short step to the proof of the next theorem.

▶ **Theorem 3–14.** If A and B are any two $n \times n$ matrices, then

$$\det AB = (\det A)(\det B).$$

Proof. Suppose that A is a singular matrix. Then AB is also a singular matrix. However, the row vectors of a singular matrix must be linearly dependent, and hence we can conclude from Theorem 3–2 that $\det A = \det AB = 0$. The statement of the theorem therefore follows in this case.

Next, suppose that A is nonsingular. Then there exists a sequence of elementary matrices $E_1, E_2, \ldots, E_k$ such that

$$A = E_1 E_2 \cdots E_k.$$

We now use Theorem 3–13 repeatedly, to find

$$\begin{aligned}
\det AB &= \det E_1(E_2 \cdots E_k B) \\
&= (\det E_1)[\det E_2(E_3 \cdots E_k B)] \\
&\;\vdots \\
&= (\det E_1)(\det E_2) \cdots (\det E_{k-1})(\det E_k)(\det B) \\
&= (\det E_1)(\det E_2) \cdots [(\det E_{k-1})(\det E_k)](\det B) \\
&= (\det E_1)(\det E_2) \cdots [(\det E_{k-2})(\det E_{k-1}E_k)](\det B) \\
&\;\vdots \\
&= (\det E_1 E_2 \cdots E_k)(\det B) \\
&= (\det A)(\det B).
\end{aligned}$$

Note how we "peel" the E_i off from the front, and then put them back in the same way, but without the B. This result has a number of corollaries. ▌

▶ **Theorem 3–15.** An $n \times n$ matrix A is nonsingular if and only if $\det A \neq 0$.

Proof. Theorem 3–2 shows that if A is singular, then $\det A = 0$. On the other hand, if A is nonsingular, then it can be represented as the product of elementary matrices. Each elementary matrix has a nonzero determinant. Hence the determinant of their product, which is the product of their determinants, must also be nonzero. ▌

Theorem 3–16. If the $n \times n$ matrix A is nonsingular, then

$$\det A^{-1} = 1/\det A.$$

The proof of this theorem is left as an exercise.

It is interesting to note that we can define the determinant of a linear transformation of a vector space into itself. Suppose, for example, that we are given a linear transformation $T: R^n \to R^n$. This transformation will have a matrix A in terms of the standard basis for R^n. We could then define $\det T = \det A$. But what would happen if we were to use the matrix of T in terms of some other basis? Since the transformation goes from a space into itself, we naturally wish to use the same basis in both the domain and range.

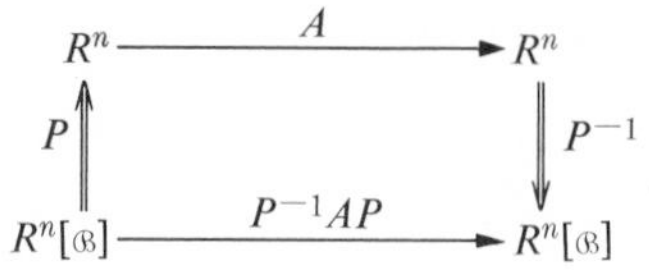

Then if P is the matrix of the change of basis, the matrix of the transformation T in terms of the new basis is $P^{-1}AP$. However,

$$\det P^{-1}AP = (\det P^{-1})(\det A)(\det P) = \det A$$

by Theorems 3–14 and 3–16. Thus the linear transformation has the same value for its determinant, no matter what basis we use.

To close this section, let us describe a method which could be used to find the value of a given determinant. If E is any elementary matrix, then $A = E^{-1}EA$, and hence

$$\det A = (\det E^{-1})(\det EA).$$

Therefore we merely need to apply the elementary row operations to the matrix so as to reduce it to triangular form. As each operation is applied, the determinant of its inverse matrix is written as a factor multiplying the new determinant. For example,

$$\begin{vmatrix} 2 & -1 & 7 & 5 \\ 1 & 3 & 2 & 0 \\ 5 & 10 & 3 & -4 \\ 7 & 22 & 0 & -1 \end{vmatrix} = (-1)\begin{vmatrix} 1 & 3 & 2 & 0 \\ 2 & -1 & 7 & 5 \\ 5 & 10 & 3 & -4 \\ 7 & 22 & 0 & -1 \end{vmatrix} = (-1)\begin{vmatrix} 1 & 3 & 2 & 0 \\ 0 & -7 & 3 & 5 \\ 0 & -5 & -7 & -4 \\ 0 & 1 & -14 & -1 \end{vmatrix}$$

$$= (-1)^2\begin{vmatrix} 1 & 3 & 2 & 0 \\ 0 & 1 & -14 & -1 \\ 0 & -5 & -7 & -4 \\ 0 & -7 & 3 & 5 \end{vmatrix} = \begin{vmatrix} 1 & 3 & 2 & 0 \\ 0 & 1 & -14 & -1 \\ 0 & 0 & -77 & -9 \\ 0 & 0 & -95 & -2 \end{vmatrix}$$

$$= (-77)\begin{vmatrix} 1 & 3 & 2 & 0 \\ 0 & 1 & -14 & -1 \\ 0 & 0 & 1 & \frac{9}{77} \\ 0 & 0 & 0 & \frac{701}{77} \end{vmatrix} = -701.$$

PROBLEMS

1. Prove Theorems 3–7, 3–8, 3–9, and 3–10.
2. Supply reasons for each displayed line in the proof of Theorem 3–11.
3. Prove Theorem 3–12 for upper diagonal matrices.
4. Prove directly from Eq. (3–6) that $\det P_{ij} = -1$.
5. Prove Theorem 3–16.
6. For each step in the evaluation of the determinant at the end of this section, state which row operations were applied.
7. a) Prove that the product of two upper triangular matrices is an upper triangular matrix.
   b) Prove that the inverse of an upper triangular matrix (assuming it has one) is an upper triangular matrix.
   c) Prove that any 2×2 matrix which has a nonzero element in the upper left is the product of two triangular matrices. What can you say if the upper left-hand corner entry is zero?
8. Evaluate the following determinants:

a) $\begin{vmatrix} 1 & 5 & 31 \\ 2 & 9 & -5 \\ 4 & -5 & 0 \end{vmatrix}$ b) $\begin{vmatrix} 2 & -1 & 5 & -3 \\ 0 & 1 & 3 & -1 \\ 1 & -5 & -8 & 10 \\ 3 & -1 & 12 & 2 \end{vmatrix}$ c) $\begin{vmatrix} 1 & 1 & 2 & 2 & 3 \\ 1 & 2 & 3 & 3 & 4 \\ 2 & 2 & 3 & 4 & 4 \\ 3 & 3 & 4 & 4 & 5 \\ 3 & 4 & 5 & 5 & 6 \end{vmatrix}$

3–4. FURTHER PROPERTIES OF DETERMINANTS

There are other ways of defining determinants than the one used in Section 3–1. From a pragmatic point of view, some of these other methods might be considered simpler. In the day when determinants had more use as practical tools, some of these less abstract definitions were preferred.

No matter how determinants are defined, some difficult proofs occur. The particular method we have chosen makes the properties we discussed in the last section quite easy to prove. Of course, we found it difficult to show that the determinant existed so as to satisfy the definition we gave. The properties we prove in this section would be simple to prove with the proper definition for a determinant, but are somewhat deeper using the definition that we have given. This does not mean that the proofs need to be difficult. The following theorem, for example, has a proof which is quite simple, but only because of the power of some of the results we have developed.

▶ **Theorem 3–17.** Let A be an $n \times n$ matrix. Then

$$\det A^t = \det A.$$

Proof, Suppose A is singular. Then we know that the row vectors of A must be linearly dependent (Theorem 2–28), and hence, by Theorem 3–2, $\det A = 0$. However if A is singular, then so is A^t because of Theorem 2–35. It therefore follows that $\det A^t = 0$ also.

On the other hand, if A is nonsingular, then by Theorem 2–29, $A = E_1E_2 \ldots E_N$, where the E_i are all elementary matrices. Theorem 2–34 tells us that

$$A^t = E_N^t E_{N-1}^t \cdots E_1^t.$$

It is easily verified that for any elementary matrix E, $\det E^t = \det E$. Hence, using Theorem 3–14 and the commutativity of multiplication of real numbers, we find the

$$\begin{aligned} \det A^t &= (\det E_N^t)(\det E_{N-1}^t) \cdots (\det E_1^t) \\ &= (\det E_N)(\det E_{N-1}) \cdots (\det E_1) \\ &= (\det E_1)(\det E_2) \cdots (\det E_N) \\ &= \det A. \ \blacksquare \end{aligned}$$

As a consequence of this theorem, the results of the last section concerning elementary row operations will apply equally well to elementary column operations. For example:

Theorem 3–18. For any $n \times n$ matrix A and elementary matrices P_{ij}, $D_i(c)$, and $S_{ji}(c)$, we have

$$\begin{aligned} \det AP_{ij} &= (-1) \det A, \\ \det AD_i(c) &= c \det A, \\ \det AS_{ji}(c) &= \det A. \end{aligned}$$

Proof. These results all follow from Theorem 3–14. However, they can also be proved as consequences of Theorem 3–17. For example,

$$\begin{aligned} \det AP_{ij} &= \det [AP_{ij}]^t = \det P_{ij}^t A^t \\ &= \det P_{ij}A^t = (-1) \det A^t \\ &= (-1) \det A. \ \blacksquare \end{aligned}$$

The method of proof illustrated here can be used to prove the next theorem.

Theorem 3–19. If the matrices A, A', and A'' are identical except for their jth columns, which are $\mathbf{A}_j$, $\mathbf{A}'_j$, and $\mathbf{A}''_j$, respectively, and if $\mathbf{A}_j = \mathbf{A}'_j + \mathbf{A}''_j$, then

$$\det A' + \det A'' = \det A.$$

Proof. The proof is left as an exercise.

The main application of these results is in the simplification of the reduction procedure used in the last section. The methods discussed there involved only the row operations. Here we see that the same results hold for the column operations as well. Sometimes it is more convenient to make use of the column operations. Often, by using a mixture of row and column operations, the value of the determinant can be found very quickly.

When we used the row or column operations to find the inverses of matrices, we could not mix the two because matrix multiplication is not commutative. However, when we calculate determinants, we find that $\det AB = \det BA$, and hence a mixture of row and column methods is allowable.

Now let us turn to the expansion of determinants by cofactors. To start this discussion, we need to extend the ideas of Theorem 3–10.

Let $A = [a_{ij}]$ be any $n \times n$ matrix. Define the matrix A_0 to be the same matrix except that its ith row consists entirely of zeros. For each i and j, let U_{ij} be the matrix all of whose entries are zero except for the one in the i, j place, which is 1. Then we see that

$$A = A_0 + \sum_{j=1}^{n} a_{ij} U_{ij}.$$

From Theorem 3–10, we therefore have

$$\det A = \sum_{j=1}^{n} \det [A_0 + a_{ij} U_{ij}] = \sum_{j=1}^{n} a_{ij} \det [A_0 + U_{ij}].$$

The second form follows from Theorem 3–9. If we know the values of the determinants which appear on the right-hand side of this expression, we can simplify the calculation of the determinant.

Definition 3–12. Let A be an $n \times n$ matrix. Let i and j be given. Let A_0 be the matrix which is identical to A except that its ith row consists entirely of zeros, and let U_{ij} be the matrix which has a 1 in the i, j position and otherwise consists entirely of zeros. Then the *cofactor* of the i, j position in the matrix A is the number

$$C_{ij} = C_{ij}(A) = \det [A_0 + U_{ij}].$$

The calculation made above gives the proof of Theorem 3–20.

Theorem 3–20. Let A be an $n \times n$ matrix and let C_{ij} be the cofactors of the i, j positions in A. Then for any i,

$$\det A = \sum_{j=1}^{n} a_{ij} C_{ij}. \tag{3–7}$$

This theorem is, of course, a fraud. We "proved" it by giving a name to some quantities. The result would be of little or no value if there were not another characterization of the cofactors. We will now turn to the problem of proving that another characterization does indeed exist.

Theorem 3–21. Let $A = [a_{ij}]$ be an $n \times n$ matrix whose last row vector is $\mathbf{e}_n$. Let A' be the $(n - 1) \times (n - 1)$ matrix resulting from the deletion of the last row and column from A (i.e., $a'_{ij} = a_{ij}$ for all $i, j \leq n - 1$). Then

$$\det A' = \det A.$$

Proof. Observe that

$$A = \begin{bmatrix} a_{11} & a_{12} & \cdots & a_{1,n-1} & a_{1n} \\ a_{21} & a_{22} & \cdots & a_{2,n-1} & a_{2n} \\ \vdots & & & & \vdots \\ 0 & 0 & \cdots & 0 & 1 \end{bmatrix}.$$

From (3-6), we have

$$\det A = \sum_{\sigma \in \mathcal{P}_n} \epsilon(\sigma) a_{1j_1} a_{2j_2} \cdots a_{nj_n} \qquad (\sigma(i) = j_i).$$

However, $a_{nj_n} = 0$ except when $j_n = n$. Therefore, the only terms of this summation which will contribute to $\det A$ are those for which $\sigma(n) = n$. Every permutation $\sigma \in \mathcal{P}_n$ which is such that $\sigma(n) = n$ determines (and is determined by) a permutation $\sigma' \in \mathcal{P}_{n-1}$. The relationship is

$$\sigma(i) = \sigma'(i) \qquad \text{for all } i < n,$$
$$\sigma(n) = n.$$

Since $a_{nn} = 1$, we therefore have

$$\det A = \sum_{\sigma' \in \mathcal{P}_{n-1}} \epsilon(\sigma') a_{1,\sigma'(1)} a_{2,\sigma'(2)} \cdots a_{n-1,\sigma'(n-1)} = \det A'. \ ▮$$

Theorem 3-22. Let A be an $n \times n$ matrix. For any i, j let A_{ij} be the $(n-1) \times (n-1)$ matrix which results when the ith row and jth column of A are deleted. Then the cofactor C_{ij} of the i, j position of A is given by

$$C_{ij} = (-1)^{i+j} \det A_{ij}.$$

Proof. We note that the matrix A_{ij} defined in the statement of the theorem is usually called the *minor* of the i, j position. We have $C_{ij} = \det [A_0 + U_{ij}]$ by definition. The matrix $A_0 + U_{ij}$ has the vector $\mathbf{e}_j$ as its ith row vector. Let us make a sequence of interchanges of the rows of $A_0 + U_{ij}$. We successively interchange the ith row with the $(i+1)$th row, then with the $(i+2)$th row, and so on. After $n - i$ interchanges, we will arrive at the matrix A' which has $\mathbf{e}_j$ as its bottom row and the remaining rows of $A_0 + U_{ij}$, in their proper order, in the first $n - 1$ rows. From Theorem 3-8, we have

$$\det A' = (-1)^{n-i} \det [A_0 + U_{ij}] = (-1)^{n-i} C_{ij}.$$

Next, we successively interchange the columns of A'. Interchange the jth column with the $(j+1)$th, then with the $(j+2)$th, and so on. After $n - j$ interchanges, we will arrive at a matrix A'' which has $\mathbf{e}_n$ as its nth row vector. The upper left-hand $(n-1) \times (n-1)$ submatrix of A'' is exactly the matrix A_{ij} of the theorem. From Theorems 3-21 and 3-22, we therefore have

$$\begin{aligned} \det A_{ij} &= \det A'' = (-1)^{n-j} \det A' \\ &= (-1)^{2n-i-j} C_{ij} = (-1)^{-i-j} C_{ij} \\ &= (-1)^{i+j} C_{ij}. \ ▮ \end{aligned}$$

Equation (3–7) is called the expansion of the determinant of A by the cofactor of the ith row. We will obtain exactly similar results for the expansion by cofactors of a column. This can be done with the help of Theorem 3–17. The complete statement and proof of this property is left as an exercise.

Equation (3–7) can be used to derive a formula for the inverse of a matrix.

Definition 3–13. Let A be an $n \times n$ matrix. Let $A^\dagger = [a^\dagger_{ij}]$ be the matrix whose entries are the cofactors of the transpose of A; that is, for any i and j,

$$a^\dagger_{ij} = C_{ji}.$$

The matrix $A^\dagger$ is called the *adjoint* of the matrix A.

▶ **Theorem 3–23.** Let A be an $n \times n$ matrix and let $A^\dagger$ be the adjoint of A. Then

$$AA^\dagger = (\det A)I.$$

Proof. Let $D = [d_{ik}] = AA^\dagger$. Then any element d_{ik} is given by

$$d_{ik} = \sum_{j=1}^{n} a_{ij}a^\dagger_{jk} = \sum_{j=1}^{n} a_{ij}C_{kj}. \tag{3–8}$$

Now if $i = k$, then (3–8) is recognized from Theorem 3–20 as the expansion of the determinant of A. Therefore, for each i, $d_{ii} = \det A$.

Consider (3–8) when $i \neq k$. This equation can be compared with (3–7). It can be viewed as the expansion by cofactors of the kth row of a matrix which is identical to A except that its kth row is $[a_{i1}, a_{i2}, \ldots, a_{in}]$. This matrix has its ith and kth rows identical. Therefore its determinant is equal to zero. Hence $d_{ik} = 0$ when $i \neq k$, and the theorem is proved. ▌

As a corollary, we have

▶ **Theorem 3–24.** Let A be a nonsingular $n \times n$ matrix. Then

$$A^{-1} = \left(\frac{1}{\det A}\right) A^\dagger.$$

The proof of this theorem is left as an exercise.

This result is quite useful in finding the inverse of a 2×2 or 3×3 matrix. Its use would not usually be recommended for a matrix of higher order.

Let us see an example of how this theorem could be used. Suppose we wished to find the inverse of the matrix

$$A = \begin{bmatrix} 1 & 3 & -1 \\ 2 & 0 & -1 \\ -1 & -1 & 0 \end{bmatrix}.$$

In theory, we could write down the adjoint of A directly, but it is safer to proceed in stages.

First we compute the matrix of the determinants of the A_{ij} defined in Theorem 3–22. This would be

$$\begin{bmatrix} \begin{vmatrix} 0 & -1 \\ -1 & 0 \end{vmatrix} & \begin{vmatrix} 2 & -1 \\ -1 & 0 \end{vmatrix} & \begin{vmatrix} 2 & 0 \\ -1 & -1 \end{vmatrix} \\ \begin{vmatrix} 3 & -1 \\ -1 & 0 \end{vmatrix} & \begin{vmatrix} 1 & -1 \\ -1 & 0 \end{vmatrix} & \begin{vmatrix} 1 & 3 \\ -1 & -1 \end{vmatrix} \\ \begin{vmatrix} 3 & -1 \\ 0 & -1 \end{vmatrix} & \begin{vmatrix} 1 & -1 \\ 2 & -1 \end{vmatrix} & \begin{vmatrix} 1 & 3 \\ 2 & 0 \end{vmatrix} \end{bmatrix}.$$

We have written this out in full here so that the reader can see what is being done. In practice we would write down only the resulting matrix:

$$\begin{bmatrix} -1 & -1 & -2 \\ -1 & -1 & 2 \\ -3 & 1 & -6 \end{bmatrix}$$

This is easily done by inspection, using the fact that the determinant of a 2×2 matrix is given by the product of the entries on the principal diagonal, minus the product of the remaining two entries. That is,

$$\begin{vmatrix} a & b \\ c & d \end{vmatrix} = ad - bc.$$

Next, we convert the matrix we have just found to the matrix of cofactors by multiplying each entry by the appropriate factor (positive or negative 1). These factors occur in a checkerboard pattern, starting with a $+1$ in the upper left-hand corner, that is,

$$\begin{bmatrix} +1 & -1 & +1 \\ -1 & +1 & -1 \\ +1 & -1 & +1 \end{bmatrix}.$$

The result in the example above is

$$\begin{bmatrix} -1 & 1 & -2 \\ 1 & -1 & -2 \\ -3 & -1 & -6 \end{bmatrix}.$$

Finally, we obtain the adjoint by transposing this last matrix:

$$A^{\dagger} = \begin{bmatrix} -1 & 1 & -3 \\ 1 & -1 & -1 \\ -2 & -2 & -6 \end{bmatrix}$$

To find A^{-1}, we merely have to divide this matrix by det A. However, it is not necessary to determine the value of det A separately. The value must be the same as any of the diagonal entries of $AA^{\dagger}$. This product should be computed in any case as a check.

For this example, we find that the upper left-hand entry of $AA^{\dagger}$ is $-1 + 3 + 2 = 4$ and hence

$$A^{-1} = \frac{1}{4}\begin{bmatrix} -1 & 1 & -3 \\ 1 & -1 & -1 \\ -2 & -2 & -6 \end{bmatrix}.$$

PROBLEMS

1. Prove Theorem 3–19.
2. State and prove a theorem corresponding to Theorem 3–20 for the expansion by cofactors of a column.
3. Prove Theorem 3–24.
4. Let A be a nonsingular $n \times n$ matrix and let $A\mathbf{X} = \mathbf{B}$ be a system of linear equations
   a) Prove that a solution of the system is given by
   $$\mathbf{X} = \left(\frac{1}{\det A}\right) A^{\dagger}\mathbf{B},$$
   where $A^{\dagger}$ is the adjoint of A.
   b) Prove that for each i, the same solution is given by
   $$x_i = \frac{\det A(i)}{\det A},$$
   where $A(i)$ is the matrix which is identical to A except in its ith column, which is made equal to $\mathbf{B}$. This is known as *Cramer's rule.*
5. The *determinant rank* of a matrix is defined to be the size of the largest square submatrix whose determinant is nonzero which can be obtained from the given matrix by the deletion of rows and columns. Prove that the determinant rank of a matrix equals the rank of the matrix. [*Hint:* Show that the elementary row and column operations will not change the determinant rank of a matrix.]
6. Prove
   $$\begin{vmatrix} x & x^2 & yz \\ y & y^2 & xz \\ z & z^2 & xy \end{vmatrix} = \begin{vmatrix} x^2 & x^3 & 1 \\ y^2 & y^3 & 1 \\ z^2 & z^3 & 1 \end{vmatrix}$$
   and give the value of this determinant in as simple a form as possible.
7. Prove that
   $$\begin{vmatrix} a & b & c & d \\ e & f & g & h \\ 0 & 0 & j & k \\ 0 & 0 & m & n \end{vmatrix} = \begin{vmatrix} a & b \\ e & f \end{vmatrix} \cdot \begin{vmatrix} j & k \\ m & n \end{vmatrix}.$$

8. Find the adjoint of each of the following matrices. Use this to compute the inverse of the matrix if the matrix is nonsingular.

a) $\begin{bmatrix} 1 & 3 & -1 \\ 2 & 0 & 1 \\ 1 & 5 & 3 \end{bmatrix}$ b) $\begin{bmatrix} 1 & 0 & 2 \\ 1 & 1 & -1 \\ 2 & 4 & -2 \end{bmatrix}$ c) $\begin{bmatrix} 3 & 0 & 6 \\ 2 & -1 & 0 \\ 0 & 3 & -4 \end{bmatrix}$

d) $\begin{bmatrix} 1 & 1 & 0 \\ 2 & 2 & 1 \\ -1 & -2 & 3 \end{bmatrix}$ e) $\begin{bmatrix} 3 & 1 & -2 \\ -1 & -2 & 2 \\ 3 & -4 & 2 \end{bmatrix}$

9. For each n, let A_n be the $n \times n$ matrix whose entries are all zeros except for ones on the major diagonal and in the first diagonal above the major diagonal. That is,

$$A_n = \begin{bmatrix} 1 & 1 & 0 & 0 & \cdots & 0 & 0 & 0 \\ 0 & 1 & 1 & 0 & \cdots & 0 & 0 & 0 \\ 0 & 0 & 1 & 1 & \cdots & 0 & 0 & 0 \\ \vdots & & & & & & & \vdots \\ 0 & 0 & 0 & 0 & \cdots & 0 & 1 & 1 \\ 0 & 0 & 0 & 0 & \cdots & 0 & 0 & 1 \end{bmatrix}.$$

a) Prove that $\det A_n = 1$.

b) Find the inverse of A_n. [*Hint: Use induction.*]

c) Suppose that a matrix B is of the same form except that the terms on the major diagonal are all equal to some nonzero number c, while the terms directly above the major diagonal are still ones. Find $\det B$ and B^{-1}.

CHAPTER 4

Metric Properties

4–1. INNER PRODUCTS

In working with three-dimensional vectors, one of the fundamental tools is the "dot product," which is a real-valued function of two vectors, defined by

$$\mathbf{A} \cdot \mathbf{B} = [a_1, a_2, a_3] \cdot [b_1, b_2, b_3] = a_1b_1 + a_2b_2 + a_3b_3.$$

What are the properties of this function? The first thing we notice is that it is a linear function of each vector (separately). This is obvious from the fact that each term in the expansion of the dot product contains a component of each vector as a linear factor. Therefore the dot product is a multilinear function of the two vectors. We have a special name for such a function.

Definition 4–1. A real-valued multilinear function of two vectors is called a *bilinear* function.

As an operation on two vectors, the dot product is obviously commutative. Again, we have a special name for this property when viewed as a property of a function.

Definition 4–2. A real-valued function of two vectors, $F(\mathbf{X}, \mathbf{Y})$, is called *symmetric* if and only if $F(\mathbf{X}, \mathbf{Y}) = F(\mathbf{Y}, \mathbf{X})$ for every pair of vectors $\mathbf{X}$ and $\mathbf{Y}$.

The dot product has still a third property which we wish to generalize. From the definition we see that the dot product of any vector with itself is the sum of the squares of the components of the vector. Therefore the dot product of any vector with itself is always nonnegative. Can you state the conditions under which the dot product could be zero?

Definition 4–3. A bilinear function $F(\mathbf{X}, \mathbf{Y})$ is called *positive* if and only if $F(\mathbf{X}, \mathbf{X}) \geq 0$ for every vector $\mathbf{X}$. The function is called *positive definite* if and only if it is positive and such that $F(\mathbf{X}, \mathbf{X}) = 0$ if and only if $\mathbf{X} = \mathbf{0}$.

Definition 4–4. An *inner product* on R^n is a bilinear, symmetric, positive definite function $F: R^n \times R^n \to R$.

Before discussing the properties of an inner product, we must first make some observations about the properties of bilinear and symmetric functions.

We recall that we write $A\mathbf{X}$, where A is a matrix and $\mathbf{X}$ is a vector, to represent the matrix product which results when we think of $\mathbf{X}$ as an $n \times 1$ matrix (that is, a column vector). Suppose, however, that we wished to multiply the matrix on the left. Then we would have to use a "row vector" in order to have the product defined. We always consider that our vectors are written in column form. This means that we must write X^t to represent the vector X as a $1 \times n$ matrix. (In the text, we usually write the components of the vectors in "row" form to save space.)

Let $A = [a_{ij}]$ be an $n \times n$ matrix and suppose that $\mathbf{X} = [x_1, x_2, \ldots, x_n]$ and $\mathbf{Y} = [y_1, y_2, \ldots, y_n]$ are two vectors in R^n. What is the product $\mathbf{X}^tA\mathbf{Y}$? We see that $\mathbf{X}^tA$ is a $1 \times n$ matrix, and the product of this matrix with $\mathbf{Y}$ is a 1×1 matrix, that is, a single real number. Indeed, it is easy to see that

$$\mathbf{X}^tA\mathbf{Y} = \sum_{i=1}^{n}\sum_{j=1}^{n} x_i a_{ij} y_j. \tag{4–1}$$

Note that we are making an identification of 1×1 matrices with the real numbers.

This matrix product can be viewed as a function of the two vectors $\mathbf{X}$ and $\mathbf{Y}$. The properties of matrix multiplication show that this product is a bilinear function of the two vectors. For example, we have $(\mathbf{X}_1^t + \mathbf{X}_2^t)A\mathbf{Y} = \mathbf{X}_1^tA\mathbf{Y} + \mathbf{X}_2^tAY$, and so on. The interesting thing is that the converse is also true.

▶ **Theorem 4–1.** A real-valued function of two vectors in R^n is a bilinear function if and only if there is an $n \times n$ matrix A such that

$$F(\mathbf{X}, \mathbf{Y}) = \mathbf{X}^tA\mathbf{Y}.$$

Proof. We proved half of this theorem in the discussion above. Suppose, then, that $F(\mathbf{X}, \mathbf{Y})$ is a bilinear function. Setting $\mathbf{X} = \sum_{i=1}^{n} x_i\mathbf{e}_i$ and $\mathbf{Y} = \sum_{j=1}^{n} y_j\mathbf{e}_j$, we find by linearity that

$$F(\mathbf{X}, \mathbf{Y}) = \sum_{i=1}^{n}\sum_{j=1}^{n} x_i y_j F(\mathbf{e}_i, \mathbf{e}_j).$$

Comparing this equation with (4–1), we see that we merely need to set

$$a_{ij} = F(\mathbf{e}_i, \mathbf{e}_j) \tag{4–2}$$

in order to satisfy the requirements of the theorem. ▮

In Definition 4–2 we introduced the concept of a symmetric function. If a bilinear function is symmetric, what property must the matrix of the function have? The answer is trivial. All we have to do is look at (4–2). Since the function must be symmetric for every pair $\mathbf{e}_i$ and $\mathbf{e}_j$ in particular, we must have $a_{ij} = a_{ji}$. This condition is equivalent to the statement that $A = A^t$.

Definition 4–5. An $n \times n$ matrix A is *symmetric* if and only if $A = A^t$.

We saw that a symmetric bilinear function has a symmetric matrix. Again, what about the converse? Suppose that A is a symmetric matrix and that $F(\mathbf{X}, \mathbf{Y}) = \mathbf{X}^tA\mathbf{Y}$. Then $F(\mathbf{Y}, \mathbf{X}) = \mathbf{Y}^tA\mathbf{X}$. This real number can be viewed as a 1×1 matrix.

A 1×1 matrix is its own transpose. Hence

$$\begin{aligned} F(\mathbf{X}, \mathbf{Y}) &= \mathbf{X}^t A \mathbf{Y} = [\mathbf{X}^t A \mathbf{Y}]^t \\ &= \mathbf{Y}^t A^t \mathbf{X} = \mathbf{Y}^t A \mathbf{X} \\ &= F(\mathbf{Y}, \mathbf{X}). \end{aligned}$$

We have therefore proved

Theorem 4–2. A bilinear function whose matrix is A is symmetric if and only if the matrix A is symmetric.

We will now return to the problem of characterizing inner products. The most obvious generalization of the dot product from R^3 to R^n is given by the following definition.

Definition 4–6. The bilinear function defined by

$$\mathbf{X} \cdot \mathbf{Y} = x_1 y_1 + x_2 y_2 + \cdots + x_n y_n$$

is called the *standard inner product* in R^n.

It is easy to see that this dot product is an inner product in the sense of Definition 4–4. Many different notations are used to represent the standard inner product. We will use the "dot" notation, which you are probably already familiar with. The two most common notations which may also be found are $(\mathbf{X}, \mathbf{Y})$ and $\langle \mathbf{X}, \mathbf{Y} \rangle$.

Note that the matrix associated with this inner product is I. Hence we can write

$$\mathbf{X} \cdot \mathbf{Y} = \mathbf{X}^t I \mathbf{Y} = \mathbf{X}^t \mathbf{Y}.$$

The immediate question is, what other inner products could there be? We are not in a position to prove it yet, but the answer is that all inner products on R^n are of the type given in the following Theorem.

Theorem 4–3. Let D be an $n \times n$ matrix which has positive entries on the major diagonal and zero for all other entries. Let P be any nonsingular $n \times n$ matrix. If $A = P^t D P$, then the bilinear function defined by $F(\mathbf{X}, \mathbf{Y}) = \mathbf{X}^t A \mathbf{Y}$ is an inner product.

Proof. The function defined by $\mathbf{X}^t A \mathbf{Y}$ is clearly bilinear and symmetric, since $A^t = [P^t D P]^t = P^t D^t P = P^t D P = A$. Furthermore, it is clear that

$$\mathbf{Y}^t D \mathbf{Y} = \sum_{i=1}^{n} d_{ii} y_i^2 \geq 0,$$

where the sum is equal to zero if and only if $\mathbf{Y} = \mathbf{0}$. Then, if $\mathbf{X} = \mathbf{0}$, we must have $\mathbf{X}^t A \mathbf{X} = 0$, while if $\mathbf{X} \neq \mathbf{0}$, then $\mathbf{Y} = P\mathbf{X} \neq \mathbf{0}$ and hence

$$\mathbf{X}^t A \mathbf{X} = (\mathbf{X}^t P^t) D (P\mathbf{X}) = \mathbf{Y}^t D \mathbf{Y} > 0. \blacksquare$$

From any inner product, and in particular from the standard inner product, we can obtain a "norm," or "magnitude" function.

Definition 4–7. The *magnitude* of a vector in a space with an inner product is the square root of the inner product of a vector with itself. In particular, in R^n, with the standard inner product, the magnitude of a vector **A** is

$$|\mathbf{A}| = (\mathbf{A} \cdot \mathbf{A})^{1/2}.$$

For any scalar t, we can prove that $|t\mathbf{A}| = |t|\,|\mathbf{A}|$. The proof is left as an exercise. We will, however, prove the following most important result.

▶ **Theorem 4–4** (*The Cauchy-Schwarz inequality*). Let **A** and **B** be any two vectors in a space with an inner product. Then

$$|\mathbf{A} \cdot \mathbf{B}| \le |\mathbf{A}|\,|\mathbf{B}|. \tag{4–3}$$

Remark: Equation (4–3) has been written in terms of the standard inner product or "dot product" notation. It applies however in any vector space with an inner product. We will use the "dot product" notation to represent the inner product even in the general case. When any distinction is necessary, it will be made in the text.

Proof. Note first that the vertical bars on the left-hand side of (4–3) mean the absolute value of the real number represented by the inner product. The bars on the right-hand side refer to the magnitude of the vectors, as defined in Definition 4–7.

The zero vector can be written as $\mathbf{0} = 0\mathbf{0}$. Hence, by the linearity of the inner product, $\mathbf{0} \cdot \mathbf{B} = 0(\mathbf{0} \cdot \mathbf{B}) = 0$. Therefore (4–3) holds if $\mathbf{A} = \mathbf{0}$. On the other hand, if $\mathbf{A} \neq \mathbf{0}$, or, equivalently, if $|\mathbf{A}| \neq 0$, we can calculate for any scalar t

$$\begin{aligned}
|t\mathbf{A} + \mathbf{B}|^2 &= (t\mathbf{A} + \mathbf{B}) \cdot (t\mathbf{A} + \mathbf{B}) \\
&= t^2|\mathbf{A}|^2 + 2t(\mathbf{A} \cdot \mathbf{B}) + |\mathbf{B}|^2 \\
&= t^2|\mathbf{A}|^2 + 2t(\mathbf{A} \cdot \mathbf{B}) + \frac{(\mathbf{A} \cdot \mathbf{B})^2}{|\mathbf{A}|^2} + |\mathbf{B}|^2 - \frac{(\mathbf{A} \cdot \mathbf{B})^2}{|\mathbf{A}|^2} \\
&= \left[t|\mathbf{A}| + \frac{(\mathbf{A} \cdot \mathbf{B})}{|\mathbf{A}|}\right]^2 + \frac{1}{|\mathbf{A}|^2}[|\mathbf{A}|^2|\mathbf{B}|^2 - (\mathbf{A} \cdot \mathbf{B})^2].
\end{aligned}$$

The expression $|t\mathbf{A} + \mathbf{B}|^2$ must be greater than or equal to zero for all values of t, even for $t = -(\mathbf{A} \cdot \mathbf{B})/|\mathbf{A}|^2$. But then the first term in the last line above is zero, and hence the second term must be greater than or equal to zero—which is equivalent to the statement of the theorem. ▮

The Cauchy-Schwarz inequality has the following important consequence.

▶ **Theorem 4–5** (*The triangle inequality*). Let **A** and **B** be any two vectors in a space having an inner product. Then

$$|\mathbf{A} + \mathbf{B}| \le |\mathbf{A}| + |\mathbf{B}|.$$

Proof

$$\begin{aligned}
|\mathbf{A} + \mathbf{B}|^2 &= |\mathbf{A}|^2 + 2(\mathbf{A} \cdot \mathbf{B}) + |\mathbf{B}|^2 \\
&\le |\mathbf{A}|^2 + 2|\mathbf{A} \cdot \mathbf{B}| + |\mathbf{B}|^2 \\
&\le |\mathbf{A}|^2 + 2|\mathbf{A}|\,|\mathbf{B}| + |\mathbf{B}|^2 = [|\mathbf{A}| + |\mathbf{B}|]^2. \ ▮
\end{aligned}$$

We find that as a consequence of this theorem, we can define a distance function, or metric, in any vector space having an inner product. Before we prove this, we must define what we mean by a distance function. All we have to do is think of the properties that we wish a distance function to have. The properties listed in the following definition must obviously hold.

Definition 4–8. Let V be any set of elements. Then a function $\delta: V \times V \rightarrow R$ is called a *metric* on V if and only if for every X, Y, and Z in V

1. $\delta(X, Y) = \delta(Y, X)$,
2. $\delta(X, Y) \geq 0$ and $\delta(X, Y) = 0$ if and only if $X = Y$,
3. $\delta(X, Z) \leq \delta(X, Y) + \delta(Y, Z)$.

The first of these is the symmetry condition. It says that the distance from X to Y is the same as the distance from Y to X. The second condition says that the distance between any two different points is always positive. The third condition is the triangle inequality.

We could now prove the desired result immediately. However, for future use we find it useful to introduce one additional step.

Definition 4–9. Let V be a vector space. Then a *norm* on this space is a real-valued function of the vectors in the space, which we denote by $\|\mathbf{X}\|$, such that for any $\mathbf{X}$ and $\mathbf{Y}$ in V and for any scalar t

1. $\|\mathbf{X}\| \geq 0$, and $\|\mathbf{X}\| = 0$ if and only if $\mathbf{X} = 0$;
2. $\|t\mathbf{X}\| = |t|\,\|\mathbf{X}\|$;
3. $\|\mathbf{X} + \mathbf{Y}\| \leq \|\mathbf{X}\| + \|\mathbf{Y}\|$.

Note that the magnitude function as defined in Definition 4–7 satisfies these requirements and hence is a norm.

Theorem 4–6. If $\|\mathbf{X}\|$ is a norm on a vector space V, then the function $\delta(\mathbf{X}, \mathbf{Y}) = \|\mathbf{X} - \mathbf{Y}\|$ is a metric on V.

Proof. The proof that conditions (1) and (2) of Definition 4–8 hold is simple and can be left as an exercise. Let us prove the third condition. We make use of condition (3) in Definition 4–9 to do so. For any $\mathbf{X}$, $\mathbf{Y}$, and $\mathbf{Z}$,

$$\begin{aligned} \delta(\mathbf{X}, \mathbf{Z}) &= \|\mathbf{X} - \mathbf{Z}\| \\ &= \|(\mathbf{X} - \mathbf{Y}) + (\mathbf{Y} - \mathbf{Z})\| \\ &\leq \|\mathbf{X} - \mathbf{Y}\| + \|\mathbf{Y} - \mathbf{Z}\| = \delta(\mathbf{X}, \mathbf{Y}) + \delta(\mathbf{Y}, \mathbf{Z}). \ \blacksquare \end{aligned}$$

From this theorem we have immediately Theorem 4–7.

Theorem 4–7. In any vector space with an inner product, the function $\delta(\mathbf{X}, \mathbf{Y}) = |\mathbf{X} - \mathbf{Y}|$ is a metric on the space.

PROBLEMS

1. Prove that in a space with an inner product, for any vector **A** and any scalar t, $|t\mathbf{A}| = |t|\,|\mathbf{A}|$.
2. Prove parts (1) and (2) of Theorem 4–6.
3. Let J be the interval $a \leq x \leq b$ in R and let $C(J)$ be the set of all real-valued continuous functions on J. For any two such functions, f and g, define

$$(f, g) = \int_a^b f(x)g(x)\,dx.$$

   a) Prove that (f, g) is an inner product on the space $C(J)$.
   b) Write out the Cauchy-Schwarz inequality in terms of the integrals in this case.
   c) Prove that if $f(x)$ is continuous in $a \leq x \leq b$, then

$$\left[\int_a^b f(x)\,dx\right]^2 \leq (b - a)\int_a^b f^2(x)\,dx.$$

   d) Write out the triangle inequality for this space. The result is called Minkowski's inequality
4. Prove that each of the following is a norm on R^n:
   a) $\|\mathbf{X}\|_m = \max\{|x_1|, |x_2|, \ldots, |x_n|\}$ b) $\|\mathbf{X}\|_s = |x_1| + |x_2| + \cdots + |x_n|$
5. Prove that $\|f\| = \max\{|f(x)| \mid x \in J\}$ is a norm on $C(J)$.
6. Prove that $|\mathbf{A} + \mathbf{B}|^2 = |\mathbf{A}|^2 + |\mathbf{B}|^2$ if and only if $\mathbf{A} \cdot \mathbf{B} = 0$.
7. Prove that $|\mathbf{A} + \mathbf{B}| = |\mathbf{A}| + |\mathbf{B}|$ if and only if $\mathbf{A} \cdot \mathbf{B} = |\mathbf{A}|\,|\mathbf{B}|$ (i.e., if and only if **A** and **B** "point in the same direction").

4–2. ORTHOGONAL VECTORS

Any pair of linearly independent vectors in R^n determine a plane in the sense that the subspace $L\{\mathbf{A}, \mathbf{B}\}$ is two dimensional and hence can be identified with R^2, which in turn can be thought of as representing the cartesian plane.

In a plane, we can talk about the angle between two vectors. The angle, however, depends on the choice of an inner product.

Definition 4–10. Let V be a vector space with an inner product (which we represent by the dot product). Let **A** and **B** be two nonzero vectors in V. Then the *cosine of the angle* between these two vectors is defined to be

$$\cos\theta = \frac{\mathbf{A} \cdot \mathbf{B}}{|\mathbf{A}|\,|\mathbf{B}|}\cdot \tag{4–4}$$

In particular, if $\mathbf{A} \cdot \mathbf{B} = 0$, then we say that the vectors **A** and **B** are *orthogonal.*

The reader may find it interesting to investigate what happens to this orthogonality condition when a different inner product is used. For example, in R^2, either of the following operations defines an inner product

$$\mathbf{A} \cdot \mathbf{B} = a_1b_1 + a_2b_2, \quad \mathbf{A} \circ \mathbf{B} = a_1b_1 + 2a_2b_2.$$

What do orthogonal vectors look like in the second case? One way of viewing the difference between these cases is to think of a change of scale on one of the axes.

The important point here is that when we have defined an inner product, we can talk about the angle between vectors. However, it is the inner product that determines this definition. Our customary view of angles in the cartesian plane is based on our standard inner product.

With the standard inner product in R^n, we see that the set of vectors $\mathbf{e}_1, \mathbf{e}_2, \ldots, \mathbf{e}_n$ are all mutually orthogonal, according to the above definition. As we shall see, such a set of vectors is most useful.

Definition 4–11. A set of vectors $\mathbf{u}_1, \mathbf{u}_2, \ldots, \mathbf{u}_k$ in a vector space V with an inner product is called an *orthogonal set* if and only if $\mathbf{u}_i \cdot \mathbf{u}_j = 0$ for every pair with $i \neq j$. The set is called an *orthonormal set* if it is an orthogonal set and $|\mathbf{u}_i| = 1$ for every i. That is, the set is orthonormal if and only if

$$\mathbf{u}_i \cdot \mathbf{u}_j = \delta_{ij} \tag{4–5}$$

for all i and j.

The usefulness of orthogonal and orthonormal sets of vectors is in part explained by the following theorem.

▶ **Theorem 4–8.** Let $\mathbf{u}_1, \mathbf{u}_2, \ldots, \mathbf{u}_n$ be an orthonormal set of vectors which generate the space V. Then:

1. The set $\mathbf{u}_1, \mathbf{u}_2, \ldots, \mathbf{u}_n$ is a basis for V.
2. For every vector $\mathbf{A}$ in V,

$$\mathbf{A} = a_1\mathbf{u}_1 + a_2\mathbf{u}_2 + \cdots + a_n\mathbf{u}_n,$$

where for each i, $a_i = \mathbf{A} \cdot \mathbf{u}_i$.

3. If $\mathbf{A} = \sum_{i=1}^n a_i\mathbf{u}_i$ and $\mathbf{B} = \sum_{i=1}^n b_i\mathbf{u}_i$, then

$$\mathbf{A} \cdot \mathbf{B} = \sum_{i=1}^n a_ib_i.$$

4. If $\mathbf{A} = \sum_{i=1}^n a_i\mathbf{u}_i$, then

$$|\mathbf{A}|^2 = \sum_{i=1}^n a_i^2.$$

Proof. Let us prove property (3) first. From the linearity of the inner product we have

$$\begin{aligned}\mathbf{A} \cdot \mathbf{B} &= \left(\sum_{i=1}^n a_i\mathbf{u}_i\right) \cdot \left(\sum_{j=1}^n b_j\mathbf{u}_j\right)\\ &= \sum_{i=1}^n \sum_{j=1}^n a_ib_j(\mathbf{u}_i \cdot \mathbf{u}_j) = \sum_{i=1}^n \sum_{j=1}^n a_ib_j\,\delta_{ij}\\ &= \sum_{i=1}^n a_ib_i.\end{aligned}$$

The last step follows since all of the terms in the double sum vanish except those for which $i = j$.

Property (4) follows immediately from (3) by putting $\mathbf{B} = \mathbf{A}$.

Next, we prove property (1). We see that it suffices to show that the orthonormal set is linearly independent. To do this, we must show that if

$$x_1\mathbf{u}_1 + x_2\mathbf{u}_2 + \cdots + x_n\mathbf{u}_n = \mathbf{0},$$

then all of the $x_i = 0$. However, from this representation of the zero vector we can conclude that for each i

$$\begin{aligned} 0 &= \mathbf{0} \cdot \mathbf{u}_i \\ &= x_1(\mathbf{u}_1 \cdot \mathbf{u}_i) + x_2(\mathbf{u}_2 \cdot \mathbf{u}_i) + \cdots + x_n(\mathbf{u}_n \cdot \mathbf{u}_i) \\ &= x_i. \end{aligned}$$

Finally, we prove (2). Since the $\mathbf{u}_i$ form a basis, every vector $\mathbf{A}$ can be expressed as a linear combination of the $\mathbf{u}_i$, say $\mathbf{A} = \sum_{j=1}^{n} a_j\mathbf{u}_j$. Then for each i we have

$$\begin{aligned} \mathbf{A} \cdot \mathbf{u}_i = \mathbf{u}_i \cdot \mathbf{A} = \mathbf{u}_i \cdot \sum_{j=1}^{n} a_j\mathbf{u}_j \\ = \sum_{j=1}^{n} a_j(\mathbf{u}_i \cdot \mathbf{u}_j) = \sum_{j=1}^{n} a_j\, \delta_{ij} = a_i. \blacksquare \end{aligned}$$

This theorem has some important consequences. One in particular, which is obvious once it has been pointed out, is the following.

Theorem 4-9. Let $\mathbf{u}_1, \mathbf{u}_2, \ldots, \mathbf{u}_n$ be an orthonormal basis for the vector space V. Given any vector $\mathbf{A}$ in V, the vector $\mathbf{X}$ in $L\{\mathbf{u}_1, \mathbf{u}_2, \ldots, \mathbf{u}_k\}$ which is closest to $\mathbf{A}$ (i.e., such that $|\mathbf{X} - \mathbf{A}|$ is a minimum) is the vector

$$\mathbf{X} = \mathbf{A}_k = \sum_{i=1}^{k} (\mathbf{A} \cdot \mathbf{u}_i)\mathbf{u}_i.$$

Proof. Let $\mathbf{X} = \sum_{i=1}^{n} x_i\mathbf{u}_i$ and set $a_i = \mathbf{A} \cdot \mathbf{u}_i$. By Theorem 4-8, $\mathbf{A} = \sum_{i=1}^{n} a_i\mathbf{u}_i$, and since

$$\mathbf{X} - \mathbf{A} = \sum_{i=1}^{n} (x_i - a_i)\mathbf{u}_i,$$

we have

$$|\mathbf{X} - \mathbf{A}|^2 = \sum_{i=1}^{n} (x_i - a_i)^2.$$

Now $\mathbf{X}$ is in $L\{\mathbf{u}_1, \mathbf{u}_2, \ldots, \mathbf{u}_k\}$ if and only if $x_i = 0$ for $i = k + 1, k + 2, \ldots, n$. Hence, for any $\mathbf{X}$ in this subspace we must have

$$|\mathbf{X} - \mathbf{A}|^2 = \sum_{i=1}^{k} (x_i - a_i)^2 + \sum_{i=k+1}^{n} a_i^2.$$

From this expansion it is obvious that the minimum of $|\mathbf{X} - \mathbf{A}|$ occurs when the first sum vanishes, that is, when $x_i = a_i$ for $i = 1, 2, \ldots, k$. This is the statement of the theorem. ▌

The basic assumption in Theorem 4–8 is that there exists an orthonormal set of vectors which generate the space. This is of course true in R^n, but is it true in general? Also, are there orthonormal sets in R^n other than the set $\mathbf{e}_1, \mathbf{e}_2, \ldots, \mathbf{e}_n$? We now turn to this problem. We first prove a theorem which will help us obtain the desired result. This theorem isolates the basic method we use.

Theorem 4–10. Let $\mathbf{u}_1, \mathbf{u}_2, \ldots, \mathbf{u}_k$ be an orthonormal set in a vector space which has an inner product. Let $\mathbf{B}$ be a vector in the same space which is *not* in $L\{\mathbf{u}_1, \mathbf{u}_2, \ldots, \mathbf{u}_k\}$. Then there exists a vector $\mathbf{u}_{k+1}$ such that the sequence $\mathbf{u}_1, \mathbf{u}_2, \ldots, \mathbf{u}_k, \mathbf{u}_{k+1}$ is an orthonormal set and

$$L\{\mathbf{u}_1, \ldots, \mathbf{u}_k, \mathbf{u}_{k+1}\} = L\{\mathbf{u}_1, \ldots, \mathbf{u}_k, \mathbf{B}\}.$$

Proof. What we do is find a vector

$$\mathbf{U} = \mathbf{B} - \mathbf{X}$$

where $\mathbf{X} \in L\{\mathbf{u}_1, \ldots, \mathbf{u}_k\}$ is so chosen that $\mathbf{U}$ is orthogonal to all of the $\mathbf{u}_i$. For such a $\mathbf{U}$,

$$\mathbf{U} \cdot \mathbf{u}_i = \mathbf{B} \cdot \mathbf{u}_i - \mathbf{X} \cdot \mathbf{u}_i,$$

and hence our desired result will be obtained if we set

$$\mathbf{X} = \sum_{i=1}^{k} (\mathbf{B} \cdot \mathbf{u}_i)\mathbf{u}_i.$$

With this definition of $\mathbf{X}$, $\mathbf{U} \neq \mathbf{0}$ (since otherwise we must have $\mathbf{B} = \mathbf{X} \in L\{\mathbf{u}_1, \ldots, \mathbf{u}_k\}$). Set $\mathbf{u}_{k+1} = \mathbf{U}/|\mathbf{U}|$. Then $|\mathbf{u}_{k+1}| = 1$ and $\mathbf{u}_{k+1} \cdot \mathbf{u}_i = 0$ for all $i \leq k$. Hence the set $\mathbf{u}_1, \ldots, \mathbf{u}_k, \mathbf{u}_{k+1}$ is an orthonormal set.

Finally, we see that $L\{\mathbf{u}_1, \ldots, \mathbf{u}_{k+1}\} = L\{\mathbf{u}_1, \ldots, \mathbf{u}_k, \mathbf{B}\}$ since $\mathbf{u}_{k+1}$ is a linear combination of $\mathbf{B}$ and a vector in $L\{\mathbf{u}_1, \ldots, \mathbf{u}_k\}$ with a nonzero coefficient for $\mathbf{B}$. That is,

$$\mathbf{u}_{k+1} = \frac{1}{c}\mathbf{B} - \frac{1}{c}\mathbf{X},$$

and hence $\mathbf{B} = c\mathbf{u}_{k+1} + \mathbf{X}$, where $\mathbf{X} \in L\{\mathbf{u}_1, \ldots, \mathbf{u}_k\}$ and $c \neq 0$. ▌

Now we can prove the main theorem of this section.

▶ **Theorem 4–11.** Let V be a vector space with an inner product and let $\mathbf{B}_1, \mathbf{B}_2, \ldots, \mathbf{B}_n$ be a basis for V. Then there exists an orthonormal sequence $\mathbf{u}_1, \mathbf{u}_2, \ldots, \mathbf{u}_n$ which is a basis for V and such that for every $k \leq n$,

$$L\{\mathbf{B}_1, \mathbf{B}_2, \ldots, \mathbf{B}_k\} = L\{\mathbf{u}_1, \mathbf{u}_2, \ldots, \mathbf{u}_k\}. \tag{4–6}$$

Proof. We start by setting

$$\mathbf{u}_1 = \mathbf{B}_1/|\mathbf{B}_1|.$$

Then we continue inductively, using Theorem 4–10 at each successive stage. Having found $\mathbf{u}_1, \mathbf{u}_2, \ldots, \mathbf{u}_k$ with $L\{\mathbf{u}_1, \ldots, \mathbf{u}_k\} = L\{\mathbf{B}_1, \ldots, \mathbf{B}_k\}$, we apply Theorem 4–10 to $\mathbf{B}_{k+1}$. We then obtain an orthonormal set $\mathbf{u}_1, \ldots, \mathbf{u}_k, \mathbf{u}_{k+1}$ with

$$\begin{aligned} L\{\mathbf{u}_1, \ldots, \mathbf{u}_k, \mathbf{u}_{k+1}\} &= L\{\mathbf{u}_1, \ldots, \mathbf{u}_k, \mathbf{B}_{k+1}\} \\ &= L\{\mathbf{B}_1, \ldots, \mathbf{B}_k, \mathbf{B}_{k+1}\}. \ \blacksquare \end{aligned}$$

The process by which we obtain the orthonormal set of vectors in this theorem is known as the *Gram-Schmidt* process. It is actually a practical technique for converting a basis into an orthonormal sequence. While special methods are often available which allow us to write down an orthonormal set immediately, when such methods cannot be found, the Gram-Schmidt process will always work. The most important feature of this result is (4–6). If the first k vectors of the basis generated some subspace, then the first k vectors of the set of orthonormal vectors that we obtained would generate the same subspace. This allows us to make the following definition.

Definition 4–12. Let V be a vector space with an inner product, and let L be a subspace of V. Let $\mathbf{B}_1, \mathbf{B}_2, \ldots, \mathbf{B}_n$ be a basis of V such that $\mathbf{B}_1, \mathbf{B}_2, \ldots, \mathbf{B}_k$ is a basis for L. Let $\mathbf{u}_1, \mathbf{u}_2, \ldots, \mathbf{u}_n$ be the orthonormal sequence of vectors obtained from this basis by the method described above. Then the *orthogonal complement* of L is the subspace

$$L^{\perp} = L\{\mathbf{u}_{k+1}, \mathbf{u}_{k+2}, \ldots, \mathbf{u}_n\}.$$

The orthogonal complement has several important properties. In particular, the following two theorems follow immediately from the definition.

Theorem 4–12. Let L be a subset of the vector space V. Then

$$V = L \oplus L^{\perp}.$$

Theorem 4–13. Let L be a subspace of the vector space V. Then

$$L^{\perp} = \{\mathbf{X} \mid \mathbf{X} \cdot \mathbf{Y} = 0 \quad \text{for every } \mathbf{Y} \in L\}.$$

When we discussed the direct sum of subspaces, we observed that the decomposition was not unique. Here, however, we find that the decomposition of a space into a given subspace and its orthogonal complement is unique.

Definition 4–13. Let L and M be two subspaces of a vector space V in which there is an inner product. Then L and M are said to be *orthogonal subspaces* if and only if $\mathbf{A} \cdot \mathbf{B} = 0$ for every $\mathbf{A} \in L$ and every $\mathbf{B} \in M$.

Theorem 4–14. Let M and N be two subspaces of a vector space V which are both orthogonal to another subspace L. If $V = L \oplus M$ and also $V = L \oplus N$, then $M = N$.

Proof. Note that it suffices to prove that $M \subset N$. The hypotheses of the theorem are symmetric with respect to M and N. Hence, if we can prove that $M \subset N$, then we can also prove that $N \subset M$ in the same way. This would then show that $M = N$.

To show that $M \subset N$, let us assume that the vector $\mathbf{X} \in M$. Then $\mathbf{X}$ is orthogonal to every vector in L. On the other hand, $\mathbf{X} \in V = L \oplus N$, and hence $\mathbf{X} = \mathbf{A} + \mathbf{B}$, where $\mathbf{A} \in L$ and $\mathbf{B} \in N$. Since $\mathbf{X}$ is orthogonal to every vector in L, we must have

$$\mathbf{A} \cdot \mathbf{X} = 0 = \mathbf{A} \cdot \mathbf{A} + \mathbf{A} \cdot \mathbf{B} = \mathbf{A} \cdot \mathbf{A}.$$

In the last step, we made use of the fact that L and N are orthogonal. Now we conclude that $\mathbf{A} = \mathbf{0}$. Therefore $\mathbf{X} = \mathbf{B} \in N$. That is, $M \subset N$. ▌

Note that the above theorem says that the orthogonal complement of a given subspace is unique. This is a property that makes the orthogonal complement of a subspace easy to work with.

Let us give an example to show how we can find the orthogonal complement of a given subspace. For example, suppose

$$L = L\{[1, 3, 0, -1, 3], [2, -2, 0, 3, -5], [1, 1, 0, 5, 5]\}.$$

What is $L^{\perp}$?

In order to solve this problem, we proceed in the following way. First, we simplify the basis for L so that we can easily complete it to a basis for R^5. Next, we use the Gram-Schmidt procedure on this basis. The first three vectors in the resulting set will be still another basis for L. The last two will be a basis for $L^{\perp}$.

When the row-reduction method is applied to the three given vectors, we find $L = L\{[1, 0, 0, 0, -2],\ [0, 1, 0, 0, 2],\ [0, 0, 0, 1, 1]\}$. These three vectors can be completed to a basis for R^5 by adding the two vectors $\mathbf{e}_3$ and $\mathbf{e}_5$.

We now wish to use the Gram-Schmidt procedure on this set of vectors. However, it is somewhat easier not to bother with the normalization part of the process. We merely use the method to orthogonalize the vectors. We begin by setting

$$\mathbf{U}_1 = [1, 0, 0, 0, -2].$$

We try to find a second vector $\mathbf{U}_2$ which is orthogonal to $\mathbf{U}_1$ and which is a linear combination of $\mathbf{U}_1$ and the second vector, in the form

$$\mathbf{U}_2 = s[0, 1, 0, 0, 2] + t\mathbf{U}_1.$$

We must have $s \neq 0$ and t such that $\mathbf{U}_2 \cdot \mathbf{U}_1 = -4s + 5t = 0$. This is achieved by setting $s = 5$ and $t = 4$, which gives

$$\mathbf{U}_2 = [4, 5, 0, 0, 2].$$

Next we let

$$\mathbf{U}_3 = s[0, 0, 0, 1, 1] + t_1\mathbf{U}_1 + t_2\mathbf{U}_2.$$

In order for this vector to be orthogonal to both $\mathbf{U}_1$ and $\mathbf{U}_2$ we must have $-2s + 5t_1 = 0$ and $2s + 45t_2 = 0$. These equations are satisfied by $s = 45$, $t_1 = 18$, and $t_2 = -2$. Then we obtain the vector $[10, -10, 0, 45, 5]$. However, we can divide the components of this vector through by 5 without changing the orthogonality, thus obtaining

$$\mathbf{U}_3 = [2, -2, 0, 9, 1].$$

The fourth basis vector, $\mathbf{e}_3$, is already orthogonal to the three vectors above. We thus set

$$\mathbf{U}_4 = [0, 0, 1, 0, 0].$$

Finally, we let

$$\mathbf{U}_5 = s[0, 0, 0, 0, 1] + t_1\mathbf{U}_1 + t_2\mathbf{U}_2 + t_3\mathbf{U}_3 + t_4\mathbf{U}_4.$$

The requirements of orthogonality give us the four equations, $-2s + 5t_1 = 0$, $2s + 45t_2 = 0$, $s + 90t_3 = 0$, and $t_4 = 0$. We let $s = 90$, $t_1 = 36$, $t_2 = -4$, $t_3 = -1$, and $t_4 = 0$. We then find the vector $[18, -18, 0, -9, 9]$. Each component can be divided by 9 to give the vector

$$\mathbf{U}_5 = [2, -2, 0, -1, 1].$$

The space $L^\perp$ is then given by $L^\perp = L\{\mathbf{U}_4, \mathbf{U}_5\}$.

The method described here is generally the most useful one. There are times, however, when a complete orthonormal basis is not needed. We might be interested only in finding a basis for $L^\perp$. In this case, we would start, as before, by simplifying the basis for the given space by the row-reduction method. We then find the vectors required to complete the basis. In the above example we found that

$$L = L\{[1, 0, 0, 0, -2], [0, 1, 0, 0, 2], [0, 0, 0, 1, 1]\},$$

and the two completing vectors were $\mathbf{e}_3$ and $\mathbf{e}_5$. We then set

$$\begin{aligned}\mathbf{U}_4 &= \mathbf{e}_3 + s_1[1, 0, 0, 0, -2] + s_2[0, 1, 0, 0, 2] + s_3[0, 0, 0, 1, 1],\\ \mathbf{U}_5 &= \mathbf{e}_5 + t_1[1, 0, 0, 0, -2] + t_2[0, 1, 0, 0, 2] + t_3[0, 0, 0, 1, 1],\end{aligned}$$

and seek to solve for these scalars so as to make $\mathbf{U}_4$ and $\mathbf{U}_5$ orthogonal to all three of the vectors forming the basis of L. We see that $s_1 = s_2 = s_3 = 0$, while the t_i must satisfy the three equations

$$\begin{aligned}-2 + 5t_1 - 4t_2 - 2t_3 &= 0,\\ 2 - 4t_1 + 5t_2 + 2t_3 &= 0,\\ 1 - 2t_1 + 2t_2 + 2t_3 &= 0.\end{aligned}$$

Solving these equations will allow us to compute the vector $\mathbf{U}_5$ which satisfies the required properties. Again, $L^\perp = L\{\mathbf{U}_4, \mathbf{U}_5\} = L\{[0, 0, 1, 0, 0], [2, -2, 0, -1, 1]\}$.

The last topic that we wish to discuss in this section is the question of the characterization of the matrix which represents an inner product. Suppose that we have an inner-product function satisfying Definition 4–4 on the space R^n, and let A be the matrix which represents this inner product. Then, if $\mathbf{X}$ and $\mathbf{Y}$ are any vectors in R^n, the value of the inner product is given by $F(\mathbf{X}, \mathbf{Y}) = \mathbf{X}^t A\mathbf{Y}$. However, as we have seen, once we have the inner product, we can find an orthonormal basis for the space, say

$\mathcal{B} = \langle \mathbf{u}_1, \mathbf{u}_2, \ldots, \mathbf{u}_n \rangle$. Every vector $\mathbf{X}$ (or $\mathbf{Y}$) can be expressed as a linear combination of these vectors. That is, we may write

$$\begin{aligned} \mathbf{X} &= [x_1, x_2, \ldots, x_n] = \hat{x}_1\mathbf{u}_1 + \hat{x}_2\mathbf{u}_2 + \cdots + \hat{x}_n\mathbf{u}_n \\ &= [\hat{x}_1, \hat{x}_2, \ldots, \hat{x}_n]_{\mathcal{B}}. \end{aligned} \tag{4–7}$$

To simplify our writing, we let $\hat{\mathbf{X}} = [\hat{x}_1, \hat{x}_2, \ldots, \hat{x}_n]$, defined as in (4–7). That is, $\hat{\mathbf{X}}$ is the n-tuple whose components are the components of $\mathbf{X}$ with respect to the basis $\mathcal{B}$. As always, we consider this n-tuple as a column vector or $n \times 1$ matrix. Then, if P is the change of basis matrix from $\mathcal{B}$ to the standard basis, we have

$$P\hat{\mathbf{X}} = \mathbf{X}. \tag{4–8}$$

We recall that the column vectors of P are exactly the expressions of the $\mathbf{u}_j$ in terms of the standard basis. This can be seen most easily from (4–8). We merely need to note that $\hat{\mathbf{u}}_j = [0, 0, \ldots, 0, 1, 0, \ldots, 0]$, where the 1 is in the jth position, and therefore $\mathbf{u}_j$ is exactly the jth column of P.

Now what is the matrix of the inner product in terms of the basis $\mathcal{B}$? Since this basis was chosen to be an orthonormal sequence of vectors with respect to this inner product, $F(\mathbf{u}_i, \mathbf{u}_j) = \delta_{ij}$. Therefore the matrix of the inner product in terms of this basis must be the identity. That is,

$$F(\mathbf{X}, \mathbf{Y}) = \hat{\mathbf{X}}^t I \hat{\mathbf{Y}}.$$

The matrix P is a change of basis matrix and hence must be nonsingular. Let $Q = P^{-1}$. Then we have

$$\hat{\mathbf{Y}} = Q\mathbf{Y}, \qquad \hat{\mathbf{X}} = Q\mathbf{X}, \qquad \hat{\mathbf{X}}^t = \mathbf{X}^t Q^t.$$

Therefore

$$F(\mathbf{X}, \mathbf{Y}) = \hat{\mathbf{X}}^t I \hat{\mathbf{Y}} = \mathbf{X}^t Q^t I Q \mathbf{Y}.$$

Comparing this equation with $F(\mathbf{X}, \mathbf{Y}) = \mathbf{X}^t A \mathbf{Y}$, we conclude that

$$A = Q^t Q.$$

We have actually proved the following theorem. (Compare Theorem 4–3.)

Theorem 4–15. $F(\mathbf{X}, \mathbf{Y}) = \mathbf{X}^t A \mathbf{Y}$ is an inner product function on R^n if and only if there is some nonsingular matrix Q such that $A = Q^t Q$.

PROBLEMS

1. The functions $1, x, x^2$, and x^3 are linearly independent and generate a subspace of $C(J)$ where $J = \{x \mid -1 \leq x \leq 1\}$. Using the inner product defined in Problem 3 of the last section, follow the Gram-Schmidt process to construct an orthonormal set of functions from these.
2. Using the inner product of Problem 3 of the last section, prove that the functions 1, $\sin\theta$, $\cos\theta$, $\sin 2\theta$, $\cos 2\theta$, $\sin 3\theta$, $\cos 3\theta$, ... are all orthogonal to one another in $C[-\pi, \pi]$. Find the normalizing factors needed to make these functions an orthonormal set.

3. Let F_n be the subspace of $C[-\pi, \pi]$ generated by the functions 1, $\cos k\theta$, and $\sin k\theta$, $k = 1, 2, \ldots, n$. Let $f(\theta)$ and $g(\theta)$ be any functions in F_n. Restate all of the parts of Theorem 4–8 in terms of the particular orthonormal basis found in Problem 2.
4. Prove that if $F(\mathbf{X}, \mathbf{Y}) = \mathbf{X}^t A \mathbf{Y}$ is an inner product function in R^n, then there is some nonsingular matrix P such that $P^t A P = I$.
5. Use the Gram-Schmidt procedure to orthogonalize the following sequences of vectors. Use the standard inner product.
   a) $[1, 0, 0, 3]$, $[0, 1, -2, -5]$, $[0, -4, 13, 0]$, $[0, 0, 1, 0]$
   b) $[1, 0, 1, 0]$, $[0, 1, -4, 0]$, $[0, 0, 2, -1]$, $[0, 0, 0, 1]$
   c) $[1, 0, 5, 0]$, $[4, 1, -6, 1]$, $[0, 1, 0, 27]$, $[0, 1, 0, 0]$
   d) $[1, 1, 0, 0, 0]$, $[0, 1, 1, 0, 0]$, $[0, 0, 6, 1, 0]$, $[0, 0, 0, 1, -2]$, $[0, 0, 0, 0, 1]$
6. Find the orthogonal complement of the subspace of R^4 generated by each of the following sets of vectors (using the standard inner product)
   a) $[1, -10, 4, 2]$, $[1, -12, 0, 0]$, $[1, 0, 14, 32]$
   b) $[54, -12, 3, -3]$, $[1, 4, -1, 1]$
   c) $[15, -2, 1, 5]$

4–3. ORTHOGONAL MATRICES

Orthonormal bases are the most useful type of bases. In this section we will discuss the characteristics of the matrix representing a change of orthonormal basis.

Let us begin with an intuitive discussion of the geometry of orthonormal sets of vectors. In three-dimensional space, an orthonormal basis would be a set of three vectors, each of unit length, and each orthogonal to the other two. These vectors could be used to define a new coordinate system, which would be either a right-handed or left-handed coordinate system, depending on the particular set of vectors. If it is a right-handed system, then the new coordinate system can be thought of as the result of a rotation in three-dimensional space. A left-handed system would be the result of a rotation followed by a reflection. (Here we think of three-dimensional space as starting with a right-handed coordinate system.)

Similarly, the change of orthonormal basis in R^n can be viewed as either a rotation or a rotation plus a reflection in R^n. We will call the matrix of such a change in basis an orthogonal matrix. In the next section, we will consider these ideas more carefully.

From now on, we will consider only the standard model of a vector space with an inner product. This is the space R^n with the inner product defined as in Definition 4–6. We saw in the last section that we can always find a basis which behaves exactly like this (i.e., has the identity matrix) in any space with an inner product.

Consider then the matrix of the change of some orthonormal basis to the standard basis in R^n. The column vectors of this matrix will then be the vectors of the orthonormal basis.

Definition 4–14. An $n \times n$ matrix $U = [u_{ij}]$ is called an *orthogonal matrix* if and only if the column vectors $\mathbf{u}_j = [u_{1j}, u_{2j}, \ldots, u_{nj}]$, $j = 1, \ldots, n$, form an orthonormal set.

The next theorem characterizes these matrices in several different ways.

▶ **Theorem 4–16.** The following four conditions on an $n \times n$ matrix U are all equivalent:

1. U is an orthogonal matrix.
2. $U^{-1} = U^t$.
3. For every vector $\mathbf{X} \in \mathbf{R}^n$,

$$|U\mathbf{X}| = |\mathbf{X}|. \tag{4–9}$$

4. For every pair of vectors $\mathbf{X}$ and $\mathbf{Y}$ in R^n,

$$(U\mathbf{X}) \cdot (U\mathbf{Y}) = \mathbf{X} \cdot \mathbf{Y}. \tag{4–10}$$

Remarks. Before proving this theorem, let us note what these conditions are. The first is the definition. It amounts to saying that the column vectors form an orthonormal set. If we consider the matrix U as defining a linear transformation, then condition (3) amounts to saying that the transformation preserves the length of all vectors. Thinking of an orthogonal matrix as being the matrix of a rotation or a rotation plus reflection makes this assertion seem reasonable. But it is not clear that the condition would imply that the matrix is orthogonal. Condition (4) is equivalent to the statement that the associated transformation preserves lengths and angles between vectors. It seems to be much stronger than (3) and it seems obvious that a transformation satisfying this condition would have to transform an orthonormal set into an orthonormal set.

Condition (2) appears to be the least likely. The requirement that the transpose of a matrix be its inverse is quite severe; it seems to have nothing to do with the other conditions. As we shall see in the proof, however, this condition is equivalent to the matrix being an orthogonal matrix.

We will prove this theorem by showing the following chain of implications: (1) $\Rightarrow$ (2) $\Rightarrow$ (3) $\Rightarrow$ (4) $\Rightarrow$ (1). When we have proved the last implication, we will have shown that all four conditions are equivalent.

Proof. First, we prove that (1) implies (2). We suppose that $U = [u_{ij}]$ is an orthogonal matrix, that is, its column vectors form an orthonormal set. Now we compute $U^tU = [c_{ij}]$. According to the definition of matrix multiplication, an element c_{ij} in this product is exactly the inner product of the ith row vector of U^t with the jth column vector of U. But this product is nothing more than $\mathbf{u}_i \cdot \mathbf{u}_j = \delta_{ij}$ since the row vectors of U^t are the same as the column vectors of U. Therefore $U^tU = I$, so that $U^t = U^{-1}$, which is what we wished to prove.

Next, we prove that (2) implies (3). We assume that $U^{-1} = U^t$ and try to show that $|U\mathbf{X}| = |\mathbf{X}|$. We note that $|\mathbf{X}|^2 = \mathbf{X} \cdot \mathbf{X} = \mathbf{X}^t\mathbf{X}$, and similarly that

$$|U\mathbf{X}|^2 = (U\mathbf{X})^t(U\mathbf{X}) = \mathbf{X}^tU^tU\mathbf{X} = \mathbf{X}^tU^{-1}U\mathbf{X} = \mathbf{X}^t\mathbf{X} = |\mathbf{X}|^2,$$

which is the desired result.

Although (3) appears to be a weaker condition than (4), we can prove (4) from (3). To do so we proceed as follows. By our assumption of (3), we have for any **X** and **Y**

$$|U(\mathbf{X} + \mathbf{Y})|^2 = |U\mathbf{X} + U\mathbf{Y}|^2 = |\mathbf{X} + \mathbf{Y}|^2.$$

Expand the second and third expressions, giving us the equation

$$|U\mathbf{X}|^2 + 2(U\mathbf{X}) \cdot (U\mathbf{Y}) + |U\mathbf{Y}|^2 = |\mathbf{X}|^2 + 2(\mathbf{X} \cdot \mathbf{Y}) + |\mathbf{Y}|^2.$$

Again, by assumption, $|U\mathbf{X}| = |\mathbf{X}|$ and $|U\mathbf{Y}| = |\mathbf{Y}|$. Therefore the last equation can be simplified to give $(U\mathbf{X}) \cdot (U\mathbf{Y}) = \mathbf{X} \cdot \mathbf{Y}$, which is the desired result.

Finally, to complete the proof of the theorem we must show that condition (4) implies (1). That is, assuming (4), we must show that the column vectors of U form an orthonormal set. Let $\mathbf{u}_j$, $j = 1, 2, \ldots, n$, be the column vectors of U. Then for each j, $\mathbf{u}_j = U\mathbf{e}_j$. Hence, using condition (4), we have

$$\mathbf{u}_j \cdot \mathbf{u}_k = (U\mathbf{e}_j) \cdot (U\mathbf{e}_k) = \mathbf{e}_j \cdot \mathbf{e}_k = \delta_{jk}. \blacksquare$$

If A is the matrix of a linear transformation and P is the matrix of a change of basis, then the matrix of the same linear transformation in terms of the new basis is $P^{-1}AP$.

Theorem 4–17. If P is an orthogonal matrix and A is a symmetric matrix, then $P^{-1}AP$ is also symmetric.

Proof

$$(P^{-1}AP)^t = (P^tAP)^t = P^tA^tP = P^{-1}AP. \blacksquare$$

We saw in a previous section that a bilinear function $F(\mathbf{X}, \mathbf{Y})$ is symmetric if and only if there is some symmetric matrix A such that $F(\mathbf{X}, \mathbf{Y}) = \mathbf{X}^tA\mathbf{Y}$. This gave us our motivation for considering symmetric matrices. In the remainder of this section we wish to look at some of the properties of a linear transformation $T: R^n \to R^n$ which has a symmetric matrix. Theorem 4–17 shows that this property is preserved under orthonormal changes of bases.

The following theorem actually characterizes such transformations.

Theorem 4–18. An $n \times n$ matrix A is symmetric if and only if

$$\mathbf{X} \cdot (A\mathbf{Y}) = (A\mathbf{X}) \cdot \mathbf{Y}$$

for every pair of vectors **X** and **Y**.

Proof. First, suppose that A is a symmetric matrix. Then

$$\mathbf{X} \cdot (A\mathbf{Y}) = \mathbf{X}^tA\mathbf{Y} = (\mathbf{X}^tA)\mathbf{Y} = (A^t\mathbf{X})^t\mathbf{Y} = (A\mathbf{X})^t\mathbf{Y} = (A\mathbf{X}) \cdot \mathbf{Y}.$$

Next, suppose that $\mathbf{X} \cdot (A\mathbf{Y}) = (A\mathbf{X}) \cdot \mathbf{Y}$ for every **X** and **Y**. Let i and j be given. Set $\mathbf{X} = \mathbf{e}_i$ and $\mathbf{Y} = \mathbf{e}_j$. Then, letting $\mathbf{A}_j$ be the jth column vector of A, we can compute

$$\mathbf{X} \cdot (A\mathbf{Y}) = \mathbf{e}_i \cdot (A\mathbf{e}_j) = \mathbf{e}_i \cdot \mathbf{A}_j = a_{ij}.$$

On the other hand, letting $\mathbf{A}_i$ be the ith column vector of A, we find

$$(A\mathbf{X}) \cdot \mathbf{Y} = (A\mathbf{e}_i) \cdot \mathbf{e}_j = \mathbf{A}_i \cdot \mathbf{e}_j = a_{ji}.$$

But then, our hypothesis tells us that $a_{ij} = a_{ji}$, and we conclude that A is a symmetric matrix. ▮

If $\mathbf{U}$ and $\mathbf{V}$ are two vectors, then $\mathbf{U} \cdot \mathbf{V} = \mathbf{U}^t\mathbf{V}$, where we interpret a vector as an $n \times 1$ matrix. The condition of Theorem 4–18 can therefore be written in the form

$$\mathbf{X}^t A \mathbf{Y} = \mathbf{Y}^t A \mathbf{X}, \tag{4–11}$$

where we have also made use of the commutativity of the inner product. This is probably the more natural form for the symmetry condition.

We have seen that any bilinear function can be represented with the help of a matrix, $F(\mathbf{X}, \mathbf{Y}) = \mathbf{X}^t A \mathbf{Y}$. Note that this formula could also be written $F(\mathbf{X}, \mathbf{Y}) = \mathbf{X} \cdot (A\mathbf{Y})$. We can evaluate the function by taking the inner product of one vector with the image of the other under the transformation induced by A. The bilinear function is symmetric if and only if the matrix A is symmetric. If it is, then the last theorem shows that the order in which we take this inner product (that is, which vector is operated on by A) does not matter.

To conclude this section, let us observe that real-valued linear functions can be identified in a natural way with vectors.

▶ **Theorem 4–19.** Let $F: R^n \to R$ be a linear function. Then there exists a vector $\mathbf{A} \in R^n$ such that

$$F(\mathbf{X}) = \mathbf{A} \cdot \mathbf{X}$$

for every $\mathbf{X} \in R^n$.

Proof. All we have to do is define $\mathbf{A} = [a_1, a_2, \ldots, a_n]$, where $a_i = F(\mathbf{e}_i)$ for every i. Then, for any $\mathbf{X} = [x_1, x_2, \ldots, x_n]$,

$$F(\mathbf{X}) = F\left(\sum_{i=1}^{n} x_i \mathbf{e}_i\right) = \sum_{i=1}^{n} x_i F(\mathbf{e}_i) = \sum_{i=1}^{n} x_i a_i = \mathbf{A} \cdot \mathbf{X}.$$ ▮

The vector $\mathbf{A}$ that appears in this theorem stands on a different footing from the vector $\mathbf{X}$. From the matrix point of view, the two are of course different. Our vectors are "column vectors," while $\mathbf{A}$ must be a "row vector." The vector $\mathbf{A}$ is really a representation of a linear transformation and as such should be distinguished from the vectors proper. If we wished to make a complete study of the properties of vector spaces and linear transformations, we would distinguish between vectors $\mathbf{X}$ and these representations of linear transformations. The latter would then be called *covectors.* We will not find it necessary to make such a careful distinction in this text, but the reader should be aware that such a distinction could be made. We will discuss this problem further in the next section.

PROBLEMS

1. Suppose that P and Q are orthogonal matrices. Prove that PQ is an orthogonal matrix.
2. Given that P is an orthogonal matrix, prove that P^{-1} is an orthogonal matrix.
3. Prove the converse of Theorem 4–19.
4. Prove that the inverse of any nonsingular symmetric matrix must be symmetric.
5. Supply a reason for each step of the proof of Theorem 4–17.
6. Prove that the determinant of any orthogonal matrix must be either $+1$ or -1.
7. What is the matrix representing the change of basis in R^2 which results from a rotation of the plane through an angle θ?
8. What is the matrix representing a reflection in the x_1-axis in R^2?
9. What is the general orthogonal 2×2 matrix? Show that it will always be of the type of Problem 7 or the product of this with the matrix of Problem 8.

4–4. COORDINATE SYSTEMS

A basis in a vector space can be thought of as defining a coordinate system in that space. If $\mathcal{B} = \langle \mathbf{B}_1, \mathbf{B}_2, \ldots, \mathbf{B}_n \rangle$ is a basis for the n-dimensional vector space L, then each vector $\mathbf{X}$ in L has a unique representation in terms of this basis,

$$\mathbf{X} = x_1\mathbf{B}_1 + x_2\mathbf{B}_2 + \cdots + x_n\mathbf{B}_n = [x_1, x_2, \ldots, x_n]_{\mathcal{B}}. \tag{4–12}$$

(See Definition 1–15.) We can associate a vector in R^n with this vector. Namely, for any vector $\mathbf{X} \in L$, we may let

$$\mathbf{V}(\mathbf{X}, \mathcal{B}) = [x_1, x_2, \ldots, x_n], \tag{4–13}$$

where the x_i satisfy Eq. (4–12).

For a given basis $\mathcal{B}$, the mapping which carries $\mathbf{X}$ into $\mathbf{V}(\mathbf{X}; \mathcal{B})$ is actually a linear transformation of L onto R^n. The reader can easily verify this fact. It should be observed that such cumbersome notation would rarely be used in practice. We introduce it here only because we wish to discuss some very delicate questions. It is necessary to use a very complete notation to avoid any possibility of confusion.

If T is a linear transformation of the vector space L into the vector space L^*, then we can define the matrix of T in terms of a basis for L and a basis for L^*. Indeed, if L has the basis $\mathcal{B} = \langle \mathbf{B}_1, \mathbf{B}_2, \ldots, \mathbf{B}_n \rangle$ and L^* has the basis $\mathcal{B}^* = \langle \mathbf{B}_1^*, \mathbf{B}_2^*, \ldots, \mathbf{B}_m^* \rangle$, and if for each j,

$$T\mathbf{B}_j = \sum_{i=1}^{m} a_{ij}\mathbf{B}_i^*, \tag{4–14}$$

then $[a_{ij}]$ is called the matrix of T with respect to these two bases.

Definition 4–15. Let $\mathcal{B} = \langle \mathbf{B}_1, \mathbf{B}_2, \ldots, \mathbf{B}_n \rangle$ be a basis for the n-dimensional vector space L. For any vector $\mathbf{X} \in L$, let

$$\mathbf{V}(\mathbf{X}; \mathcal{B}) = [x_1, x_2, \ldots, x_n],$$

where the x_i satisfy Eq. (4–12). This vector, which is a vector in R^n, is called *the coordinate vector of* $\mathbf{X}$ *with respect to* $\mathcal{B}$. The x_i are called *the coordinates of* $\mathbf{X}$ *with respect to the basis* (or *coordinate system*) $\mathcal{B}$.

Let $\mathcal{B}$ and $\mathcal{B}^*$ be bases for the vector spaces L and L^*, respectively. Let T be a linear transformation from L to L^*. Suppose that (4–14) holds. Then the matrix $[a_{ij}]$ defined in (4–14) will be denoted by

$$M(T;\,\mathcal{B}^*,\,\mathcal{B}) = [a_{ij}].$$

Next, suppose that we introduce new bases $\mathcal{B}'$ and $\mathcal{B}^{*\prime}$ in L and L^*, respectively. We have the situation indicated by the following diagram:

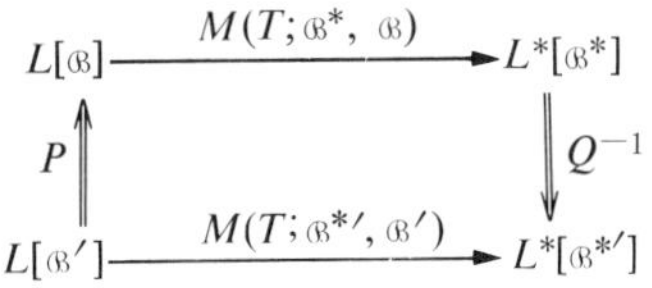

In terms of the notation introduced in this section, the matrices P and Q of the change of basis are given by

$$P = M(I;\,\mathcal{B},\,\mathcal{B}'), \qquad Q = M(I;\,\mathcal{B}^*,\,\mathcal{B}^{*\prime}),$$

where I is the identity transformation. Notice that $Q^{-1} = M(I;\,\mathcal{B}^{*\prime},\,\mathcal{B}^*)$.

The results of Section 2–6 can be summarized in the following two formulas

$$\begin{aligned} M(T;\,\mathcal{B}^{*\prime},\,\mathcal{B}') &= Q^{-1}M(T;\,\mathcal{B}^*,\,\mathcal{B})P,\\ &= M(I;\,\mathcal{B}^{*\prime},\,\mathcal{B}^*)M(T;\,\mathcal{B}^*,\,\mathcal{B})M(I;\,\mathcal{B},\,\mathcal{B}'),\\ \mathbf{V}(\mathbf{X};\,\mathcal{B}) &= P\mathbf{V}(\mathbf{X};\,\mathcal{B}') \qquad\qquad (4\text{–}15)\\ &= M(I;\,\mathcal{B},\,\mathcal{B}')\mathbf{V}(\mathbf{X};\,\mathcal{B}') \end{aligned}$$

In particular, we see that the jth column vector of the matrix P is exactly the vector $\mathbf{V}(\mathbf{B}_j';\,\mathcal{B})$.

When we have a linear transformation $T{:}L \to R$, whose range is the real numbers, we are in a somewhat special situation. The one-dimensional vector space R is best left alone. The set of real numbers has a natural basis, 1, which we would seldom wish to change. Let us denote this standard basis by $\mathcal{B}_0$. Then (4–15) for this case reduces to

$$\begin{aligned} M(T;\,\mathcal{B}_0,\,\mathcal{B}') &= M(T;\,\mathcal{B}_0,\,\mathcal{B})P\\ &= M(T;\,\mathcal{B}_0,\,\mathcal{B})M(I;\,\mathcal{B},\,\mathcal{B}'). \end{aligned}$$

The special results concerning a change of basis and a linear transformation $T{:}L \to R$ can be stated in the following theorem.

▶ **Theorem 4–20.** Suppose that L is a vector space of dimension n with the two bases $\mathcal{B}$ and $\mathcal{B}'$. Let T be a linear transformation of L into R, i.e., $T{:}L \to R$, and let $\mathbf{Y}$ be some vector in L. Let $\mathbf{X}$ and $\mathbf{X}'$ be the coordinate vectors of $\mathbf{Y}$ with respect to the bases $\mathcal{B}$ and $\mathcal{B}'$, respectively; that is,

$$\mathbf{X} = \mathbf{V}(\mathbf{Y};\,\mathcal{B}) \qquad \text{and} \qquad \mathbf{X}' = \mathbf{V}(\mathbf{Y};\,\mathcal{B}').$$

Let A and A' be the matrices of T with respect to $\mathcal{B}$ and $\mathcal{B}'$, respectively; that is,

$$A = M(T; \mathcal{B}_0, \mathcal{B})$$

and

$$A' = M(T; \mathcal{B}_0, \mathcal{B}').$$

Finally, let $P = M(I; \mathcal{B}, \mathcal{B}')$. Then

$$\mathbf{X}' = P^{-1}\mathbf{X} \tag{4-16}$$

and

$$A' = AP. \tag{4-17}$$

Observe that A and A' are $1 \times n$ matrices. Their transposes can be identified with vectors. That is, if we let $\mathbf{A} = A^t$ and $\mathbf{A}' = A'^t$, then we have

$$T\mathbf{Y} = A\mathbf{X} = A'\mathbf{X}' = \mathbf{A} \cdot \mathbf{X} = \mathbf{A}' \cdot \mathbf{X}'.$$

(See also Theorem 4–19.) In terms of these vectors, (4–17) can be rewritten as

$$\mathbf{A}' = P^t\mathbf{A}. \tag{4-18}$$

Note the difference between the behaviors of the vector $\mathbf{X}$ and the vector $\mathbf{A}$ under this coordinate transformation. Since a vector must satisfy (4–16), the $\mathbf{A}$ defined here satisfying (4–18) must be something different; as was mentioned in the last section, it is often called a *covector* instead of a vector. The difference is that a covector is really a representation of a linear transformation. One is a column vector, while the other is a row vector.

Another terminology is also used. A vector $\mathbf{X}$ satisfying (4–16) is often called a covariant vector, while a covector $\mathbf{A}$ satisfying (4–18) is called a contravariant vector. (The opposite terminology is also sometimes used.)

The gradient of a scalar function will be defined in Section 5–4. The gradient sees a great deal of application in the sciences. It is usually called the "gradient vector," but in fact it is not a vector at all. It is a covector. It is represented by a row matrix rather than a column matrix.

The distinction between vectors and covectors is usually ignored in elementary courses. The reason is that (4–16) and (4–18) are actually identical when $P^t = P^{-1}$. This case occurs whenever P is an orthogonal matrix. Most transformations of coordinates that are used in practice are orthogonal transformations, in which case there is no real difference between the behaviors of the two types of vectors.

In this text, we will usually ignore this distinction also. We merely warn the reader that under certain circumstances the difference must be taken into account.

Now let us turn to the example of the coordinate change which results from a rotation of the coordinate system in R^2. A point with coordinates (x, y) can be identified with the vector $[x, y] = x\mathbf{e}_1 + y\mathbf{e}_2$. The coordinates of the same point in the system after rotation will be given by $[x', y'] = x'\mathbf{e}_1' + y'\mathbf{e}_2'$.

From Figure 4–1 it is easy to see that a rotation through the angle θ will result in the vectors $\mathbf{e}_1' = [\cos\theta, \sin\theta]$ and $\mathbf{e}_2' = [-\sin\theta, \cos\theta]$. Therefore the matrix

$P = M(I; \mathcal{B}_0, \mathcal{B}')$, where $\mathcal{B}_0$ is the standard basis in R^2, is given by

$$P = R(\theta) = \begin{bmatrix} \cos\theta & -\sin\theta \\ \sin\theta & \cos\theta \end{bmatrix}. \qquad (4\text{–}19)$$

From this we obtain the usual formulas for the rotation of coordinates. Comparing with (4–16), we have $\mathbf{X}' = P^{-1}\mathbf{X}$, or

$$\begin{bmatrix} x' \\ y' \end{bmatrix} = \begin{bmatrix} \cos\theta & \sin\theta \\ -\sin\theta & \cos\theta \end{bmatrix} \begin{bmatrix} x \\ y \end{bmatrix}, \qquad (4\text{–}20)$$

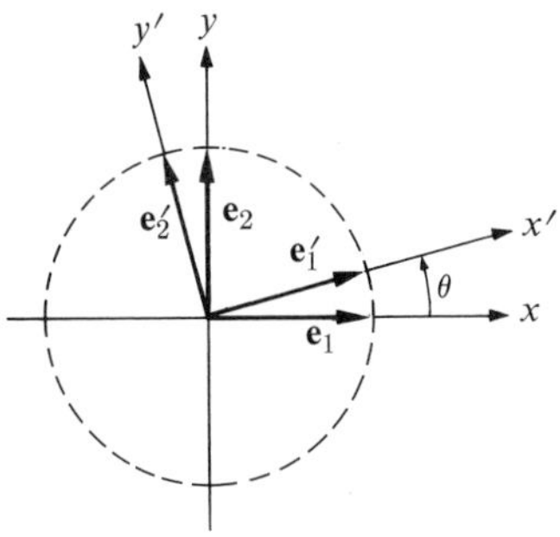

Fig. 4–1

which can also be written in the nonmatrix form found in most older analytic geometry texts

$$x' = x\cos\theta + y\sin\theta,$$
$$y' = -x\sin\theta + x\cos\theta.$$

It is important to observe that it is the set of basis vectors (i.e. the coordinate axes) which have been rotated here. The vector $\mathbf{X}$ is not changed, merely its representation. That is, the vector $[x', y']$ of (4–20) is $\mathbf{X}' = \mathbf{V}(\mathbf{X}; \mathcal{B}')$.

Every matrix $R(\theta)$ of the form (4–19) is an orthogonal matrix. Are all 2×2 orthogonal matrices of the same form? The answer is no, since $\det R(\theta) = +1$, while it is easily seen that the matrix

$$\begin{bmatrix} \cos\theta & -\sin\theta \\ -\sin\theta & -\cos\theta \end{bmatrix}$$

has determinant -1 and yet is still an orthogonal matrix. This particular matrix is exactly

$$\begin{bmatrix} 1 & 0 \\ 0 & -1 \end{bmatrix} R(\theta),$$

a fact which is no coincidence. Every orthogonal 2×2 matrix must be of one of these two forms.

▶ **Theorem 4–21.** Every 2×2 orthogonal matrix is either of the form $R(\theta)$ as given in (4–19) for some θ, or else it is of the form

$$\begin{bmatrix} 1 & 0 \\ 0 & -1 \end{bmatrix} R(\theta)$$

for some θ.

Proof. First, let us observe that every orthogonal matrix has a determinant which is either $+1$ or -1. This follows from the fact that $U^t = U^{-1}$ if U is an orthogonal matrix. Hence

$$1 = \det I = \det U^tU = [\det U^t][\det U] = [\det U]^2.$$

However, if U is a 2×2 orthogonal matrix with $\det U = -1$, then the matrix

$$U' = \begin{bmatrix} 1 & 0 \\ 1 & -1 \end{bmatrix} U$$

is an orthogonal matrix with determinant $+1$. This relation is equivalent to

$$U = \begin{bmatrix} 1 & 0 \\ 0 & -1 \end{bmatrix} U',$$

so either matrix can be recovered from the other.

Suppose that

$$\begin{bmatrix} a & b \\ c & d \end{bmatrix}$$

is an orthogonal matrix. Then $a^2 + c^2 = 1$ and hence the point $[a, c]$ is on the unit circle; that is, there must exist some θ such that $a = \cos\theta$, $b = \sin\theta$. The remaining conditions for the matrix to be orthogonal will require that

$$ab + cd = b\cos\theta + d\sin\theta = 0,$$
$$b^2 + d^2 = 1.$$

Both a and c cannot be zero. Hence, in order that the first equation be satisfied, there must exist some λ such that $b = -\lambda\sin\theta$ and $c = \lambda\cos\theta$. The second condition then requires that $\lambda^2 = 1$. That is, $\lambda = +1$ or -1. If $\lambda = +1$, then the matrix is of the form $R(\theta)$, while if $\lambda = -1$, then it is of the form

$$\begin{bmatrix} 1 & 0 \\ 0 & -1 \end{bmatrix} R(\theta). \blacksquare$$

In a similar way, we can classify all 3×3 orthogonal matrices.

▶ **Theorem 4-22.** Every 3×3 orthogonal matrix is of the form $R(\psi, \theta, \phi)$ or of the form $I'R(\psi, \theta, \phi)$, where

$$I' = \begin{bmatrix} 1 & 0 & 0 \\ 0 & 1 & 0 \\ 0 & 0 & -1 \end{bmatrix}$$

and

$R(\psi, \theta, \phi) =$

$$\begin{bmatrix} \cos\psi\cos\phi - \sin\psi\cos\theta\sin\phi & \cos\psi\sin\phi + \sin\psi\cos\theta\cos\phi & \sin\psi\sin\theta \\ -\sin\psi\cos\phi - \cos\psi\cos\theta\sin\phi & -\sin\psi\sin\phi + \cos\psi\cos\theta\cos\phi & \cos\psi\sin\theta \\ \sin\theta\sin\phi & -\sin\theta\cos\phi & \cos\theta \end{bmatrix}, \tag{4-21}$$

ψ, θ, and ϕ being any three angles such that

$$0 \le \psi < 2\pi, \qquad 0 \le \theta \le \pi, \qquad 0 \le \phi < 2\pi.$$

Proof. If U is an orthogonal matrix with det $U = -1$, then by multiplying it by I' we can convert it into a matrix whose determinant is $+1$. It therefore suffices to assume that

$$U = \begin{bmatrix} a_{11} & a_{12} & a_{13} \\ a_{21} & a_{22} & a_{23} \\ a_{31} & a_{32} & a_{33} \end{bmatrix}$$

is an orthogonal matrix with det $U = +1$. We must show that in this case, U is of the form (4–21).

Since the third column vector of U is of magnitude 1, we must have $|a_{33}| \leq 1$. There must exist a unique θ with $0 \leq \theta \leq \pi$ such that $\cos\theta = a_{33}$. Set $a_{13} = \alpha_1 \sin\theta$ and $a_{23} = \alpha_2 \sin\theta$. Since the magnitude of the third column vector of U is 1, we must then have $\alpha_1^2 + \alpha_2^2 = 1$. Thus, there exists a unique ψ, with $0 \leq \psi < 2\pi$, such that $\alpha_1 = \sin\psi$ and $\alpha_2 = \cos\psi$. We now compute the product:

$$\begin{bmatrix} 1 & 0 & 0 \\ 0 & \cos\theta & -\sin\theta \\ 0 & \sin\theta & \cos\theta \end{bmatrix} \begin{bmatrix} \cos\psi & -\sin\psi & 0 \\ \sin\psi & \cos\psi & 0 \\ 0 & 0 & 1 \end{bmatrix} \begin{bmatrix} a_{11} & a_{12} & \sin\psi\sin\theta \\ a_{21} & a_{22} & \cos\psi\sin\theta \\ a_{31} & a_{32} & \cos\theta \end{bmatrix} = \begin{bmatrix} b_{11} & b_{12} & 0 \\ b_{21} & b_{22} & 0 \\ b_{31} & b_{32} & 1 \end{bmatrix},$$

where the b_{ij} are numbers determined from the a_{ij} which we do not need to compute explicitly at this stage.

The product of three orthogonal matrices is still orthogonal. Likewise, the determinant of the product is still $+1$ as is easily seen because each of the factors has a determinant $+1$.

The bottom row of the new matrix has magnitude 1. Hence we must have $b_{31} = 0$ and $b_{32} = 0$. It is then easy to see that the submatrix

$$\begin{bmatrix} b_{11} & b_{12} \\ b_{21} & b_{22} \end{bmatrix}$$

must itself be an orthogonal matrix with determinant $+1$. That is, it must be of the form given by (4–19). Let ϕ be such that $0 \leq \phi < 2\pi$ and

$$\begin{bmatrix} b_{11} & b_{12} \\ b_{21} & b_{22} \end{bmatrix} = R(-\phi) = \begin{bmatrix} \cos\phi & \sin\phi \\ -\sin\phi & \cos\phi \end{bmatrix}.$$

We then see that we must have

$$U = \begin{bmatrix} \cos\psi & \sin\psi & 0 \\ -\sin\psi & \sin\psi & 0 \\ 0 & 0 & 1 \end{bmatrix} \begin{bmatrix} 1 & 0 & 0 \\ 0 & \cos\theta & \sin\theta \\ 0 & -\sin\theta & \cos\theta \end{bmatrix} \begin{bmatrix} \cos\phi & \sin\phi & 0 \\ -\sin\phi & \cos\phi & 0 \\ 0 & 0 & 1 \end{bmatrix}, \tag{4–22}$$

which is of the form asserted in the theorem when multiplied out. ▌

The form of U given in (4–22) shows how we can identify the meaning of the angles ϕ, θ, and ψ in this expansion. The matrix U defines a change of coordinates which gives

$$\begin{bmatrix} x' \\ y' \\ z' \end{bmatrix} = U \begin{bmatrix} x \\ y \\ z \end{bmatrix}.$$

The form given in (4–22) shows this matrix factored into three successive transformations. Comparing with (4–20), we see that the first of these transformations leaves z unchanged and is a rotation through ϕ in the xy-plane. That is, it is a rotation through the angle ϕ about the z-axis.

Similarly, the second transformation is a rotation through the angle θ about the (new) x-axis. The final transformation rotates the resulting configuration through the angle ψ about the new z-axis, that is, about the z'-axis. Figure 4–2 indicates the geometric character of the resulting transformation. The angles ϕ, θ, and ψ are usually called Euler's angles. (Again, remember that it is the set of basis vectors which is being rotated in each case.)

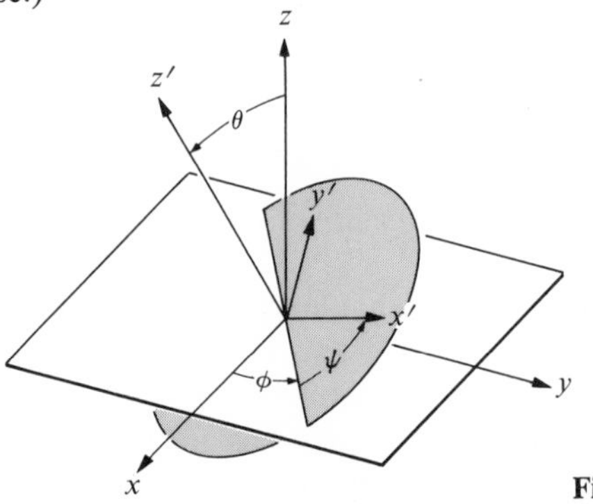

Fig. 4–2

Every rotation of the euclidean 3-space must be of this form. We cannot give a complete proof of this statement since we do not really know what such rotations are. Such a proof belongs to the theory of euclidean geometry, which we are not considering here. However, if we assume that we have an intuitive idea of such rotations, we can give an intuitive proof.

Suppose that we wish some rotation. Consider the ray which is to be rotated into the position originally occupied by the positive z-axis. First, rotate the coordinates about the z-axis through an angle ψ with $0 < \psi \leq \pi$ so as to bring this ray into the plane $x = 0$. A rotation about the x-axis through an angle θ can then be performed to bring this ray to the positive z-axis. Finally a rotation about the z-axis will give the complete rotation in the same representation as given above.

The matrix

$$\begin{bmatrix} 1 & 0 \\ 0 & -1 \end{bmatrix}$$

corresponds to a reflection in the x-axis in R^2. In R^3 the matrix

$$\begin{bmatrix} 1 & 0 & 0 \\ 0 & 1 & 0 \\ 0 & 0 & -1 \end{bmatrix}$$

corresponds to a reflection also. This matrix gives a reflection in the xy-plane. Thus what we have shown in the above theorems can be restated loosely as: Any 2×2 or 3×3 orthogonal matrix represents a reflection, a rotation, or a combination of the two.

Transformations of this type, together with another special type of transformation, the translations, make up a group of transformations which are called the euclidean motions. Let us give a formal definition before starting the discussion of the meaning of these.

Definition 4–16. A function T which maps R^n onto itself and which is defined by

$$T(\mathbf{X}) = \mathbf{X} + \mathbf{A}$$

for every $\mathbf{X} \in R^n$, where $\mathbf{A}$ is some constant vector, is called a *translation.* A function $R: R^n \to R^n$ defined by

$$R(\mathbf{X}) = U\mathbf{X},$$

where U is an orthogonal $n \times n$ matrix, is called a *general rotation* in R^n. If $\det U = +1$, then R is called a *proper rotation* (or merely a *rotation*). If $\det U = -1$, then R is called an *improper rotation.* An improper rotation which leaves a hyperplane fixed is called a *reflection.* A *euclidean motion* of R^n is a mapping of R^n onto itself which is a translation, a general rotation, or the composition of a translation and a general rotation.

The euclidean motions of R^n preserve the metric of R^n. That is, if $M: R^n \to R^n$ is a euclidean motion, then for any $\mathbf{X}$ and $\mathbf{Y}$ in R^n, $|M(\mathbf{X}) - M(\mathbf{Y})| = |\mathbf{X} - \mathbf{Y}|$. This is obvious for translations and follows from Theorem 4–16 for rotations. In fact, Theorem 4-16 shows that the only distance-preserving *linear* transformations of R^n are the general rotations. It can be shown that every distance-preserving transformation of R^n which leaves the origin fixed must be linear, but we will not do so here. Some of the major ideas of the proof of this fact are given in the problem set at the end of this section.

In the remainder of this section, we would like to give an intuitive discussion of the relationship between the vector space R^n, cartesian n-space, and euclidean n-space. The formal definition of a rotation is given in Definition 4–16, but we feel that we know more than this about rotations. Our ideas of rotations are based on what we understand of euclidean space. Euclidean n-space, E^n, is an abstract concept which is usually defined axiomatically (at least in dimensions two and three), but which can also be explained in terms of what we know about n-dimensional vector space R^n plus the concept of euclidean motions.

Let us start by describing n-dimensional cartesian space, CR^n, which consists of a set of abstract elements, called points. Each point P in this set has associated with it a unique ordered n-tuple of real numbers $\langle x_1, x_2, \ldots, x_n \rangle$, called the coordinates of the point. The point P is often identified completely with this n-tuple. Following standard usage, the n-tuple is usually enclosed in parentheses. The same n-tuple can also be identified with the corresponding vector in R^n. If $P = (x_1, x_2, \ldots, x_n)$ is the point in CR^n, we denote the corresponding vector in R^n by $\mathbf{P} = [x_1, x_2, \ldots, x_n]$. The resulting mapping from CR^n to R^n is one-to-one and onto. In cartesian n-space we also have the concepts of lines, angles, and distances between points. These notions coincide with the same concepts in R^n. Thus, for example, the distance between the points P and Q in CR^n is given by $|\mathbf{Q} - \mathbf{P}|$. In fact, n-dimensional cartesian space and the space R^n are essentially the same. However, we normally do not use the concepts of vector addition and scalar multiplication in CR^n.

Euclidean n-space, E^n, is somewhat more difficult to explain. Roughly, it consists of an abstract set of elements, called points, and certain subsets called lines, circles, etc. There exists a notion of congruence, which allows subsets to be compared. A collection of axioms relate these concepts. However, starting with a fixed line segment as unit length, it is possible to use the notion of congruence to develop a metric in the space. Similarly, starting with a "straight angle," one can develop the measurement of angles.

The properties of E^n can be discussed in terms of the spaces R^n and CR^n. Given a point and a set of n mutually orthogonal directions, one can introduce a coordinate system (in the way familiar to anyone who has studied analytic geometry). When this has been done, the points of E^n can be associated with the points of CR^n or R^n. The properties of the space are then the same as those of R^n (including the metric and the measurement of angles). The point is that there is no unique coordinate system in E^n. If we introduce another coordinate system in E^n, we will have a different mapping of E^n onto R^n. These two mappings induce a mapping from R^n onto itself. That is, if $f_1 : E^n \to R^n$ and $f_2 : E^n \to R^n$, then $f_2 f_1^{-1} : R^n \to R^n$. This last mapping must preserve distances, and hence must be one of the euclidean motions.

Thus we will content ourselves with studying the vector spaces R^n. Any properties of these spaces which are invariant under euclidean motions will then be understood to be properties of euclidean space.

As a final remark in this section, let us note that the "real space" we live in is not necessarily the same as E^3. Although we feel that E^3 is a good approximation to this real space, it is not completely accurate. In fact, according to the theory of general relativity, the space we live in can be represented by E^3 with an entirely different metric such that the distance between two points need not be invariant under translation.

Questions such as these are quite delicate and deserve more than the superficial treatment we can give them here. Some of their problems belong to the fields of physics, some to mathematics, and some to the philosophy of science. Let us only say that the role of the mathematician is to develop the theory of the abstract spaces, R^n, E^n and so on, while the physicist must investigate the nature of the approximation of such spaces to "real space."

PROBLEMS

1. Let $\mathcal{B} = \langle \mathbf{B}_1, \mathbf{B}_2, \ldots, \mathbf{B}_n \rangle$ be a basis for R^n. Let P be the matrix whose column vectors are $\mathbf{B}_1, \mathbf{B}_2, \ldots, \mathbf{B}_n$. Let $\mathbf{B}_1^*, \mathbf{B}_2^*, \ldots, \mathbf{B}_n^*$ (in order) be the row vectors of the matrix P^{-1}, and let $\mathcal{B}^*$ be the basis $\langle \mathbf{B}_1^*, \ldots, \mathbf{B}_n^* \rangle$. The basis $\mathcal{B}^*$ is then called the *dual basis* or *reciprocal basis* to $\mathcal{B}$.

   a) Show that for any $\mathbf{X} \in R^n$
$$P\mathbf{V}(\mathbf{X}; \mathcal{B}) = \mathbf{X}.$$
   b) Prove that for any $\mathbf{X} \in R^n$
$$\mathbf{X} = u_1\mathbf{B}_1 + u_2\mathbf{B}_2 + \cdots + u_n\mathbf{B}_n,$$
   where, for each i,
$$u_i = \mathbf{B}_i^* \cdot \mathbf{X}.$$
   (This shows the usefulness of a dual basis.)

2. The matrix
$$\begin{bmatrix} 1 & 0 \\ 0 & -1 \end{bmatrix}$$
defines a reflection across the x-axis. Prove that the transformation
$$\begin{bmatrix} x' \\ y' \end{bmatrix} = \begin{bmatrix} \cos 2\theta & \sin 2\theta \\ -\sin 2\theta & \cos 2\theta \end{bmatrix} \begin{bmatrix} 1 & 0 \\ 0 & -1 \end{bmatrix} \begin{bmatrix} x \\ y \end{bmatrix}$$
represents a reflection across the line through the origin which makes an angle θ with the positive x-axis.

3. With the help of Problem 2, prove that every 2×2 orthogonal matrix with determinant -1 represents a reflection across some line through the origin.

4. Show that two consecutive reflections of R^2 are the same as a rotation if the two axes of reflection intersect, and that they are equivalent to a translation if the two axes are parallel.

5. The reflection defined by
$$\begin{bmatrix} -1 & 0 & 0 \\ 0 & 1 & 0 \\ 0 & 0 & 1 \end{bmatrix}$$
is the same as
$$R \begin{bmatrix} 1 & 0 & 0 \\ 0 & 1 & 0 \\ 0 & 0 & -1 \end{bmatrix}$$
where R is some rotation. What rotation is required?

6. The matrix $-I$ defines a euclidean motion called an *inversion*.

   a) Show that an inversion is a proper rotation in an even-dimensional space.
   b) Prove that the matrix of an inversion is unchanged under a coordinate change.
   c) In R^3, we have the inversion
$$-I = R \begin{bmatrix} 1 & 0 & 0 \\ 0 & 1 & 0 \\ 0 & 0 & -1 \end{bmatrix}$$
   where R is some rotation. What is the rotation R in this case?

7. Prove that an arbitrary distance-preserving mapping of R^n onto itself must map straight lines onto straight lines and must be a linear mapping on each of these lines. [*Hint:* See Problem 7 of Section 4–1.]
8. Prove that a distance-preserving mapping of R^n onto itself maps two lines which intersect at right angles to two lines which also meet at right angles. [*Hint*: See Problem 6 of Section 4–1.]

4–5. DIAGONALIZATION

A linear transformation whose matrix has zeros everywhere except on the major diagonal is exceptionally simple. Each of the standard basis vectors is merely multiplied by a constant. The general case is much more complex. However, it is sometimes possible to make a change of basis which will diagonalize the matrix. We saw in an earlier section that this could always be done if we changed the bases in both the domain and range. When we have a linear transformation of a space onto itself, however, we are naturally interested in changing the basis only once. If A is the matrix of the transformation and P is the matrix of the change of basis, then the matrix in terms of the new basis will be $P^{-1}AP$. Unfortunately, it is not always possible to find a P which will make the resulting matrix a diagonal matrix.

If there is a matrix of change of basis which changes the original matrix to diagonal form, then there are some vectors (the new basis vectors) which are merely multiplied by scalars under the transformation. We find it of value to give such vectors a special name.

Definition 4–17. Let $T: V \to V$ be a linear transformation of a vector space V into itself. Then a number λ is called a *characteristic value* of the transformation if and only if there exists some *nonzero* vector $\mathbf{X}$ in V such that

$$T\mathbf{X} = \lambda\mathbf{X};$$

a vector $\mathbf{X}$ for which this relation holds is called a *characteristic vector* of the transformation, belonging to the characteristic value λ.

Note that 0 is a characteristic value of the transformation T if and only if $\ker T$ contains some nonzero vector. If it does, then every nonzero vector in $\ker T$ is a characteristic vector belonging to the characteristic value 0.

Indeed, it is also clear that λ is a characteristic value of T and $\mathbf{X}$ is a characteristic vector belonging to this value if and only if $\mathbf{X} \neq \mathbf{0}$ and $\mathbf{X} \in \ker (T - \lambda I)$. Thus λ is a characteristic value of T if and only if $T - \lambda I$ is singular. Next, we prove the following theorem.

Theorem 4–23. If the vectors $\mathbf{X}_1, \mathbf{X}_2, \ldots, \mathbf{X}_m$ are all characteristic vectors of the transformation T belonging to different characteristic values, then the $\mathbf{X}_i$ are linearly independent.

Proof. Suppose to the contrary that the vectors $\mathbf{X}_1, \mathbf{X}_2, \ldots, \mathbf{X}_m$ are linearly dependent. Then by Theorem 1–12 there exists a vector $\mathbf{X}_{k+1}$ in this sequence such that the sequence of vectors

$$\mathbf{X}_1, \mathbf{X}_2, \ldots, \mathbf{X}_k$$

is linearly independent, and there exist scalars $t_1, t_2, \ldots, t_k$ such that

$$\mathbf{X}_{k+1} = t_1\mathbf{X}_1 + t_2\mathbf{X}_2 + \cdots + t_k\mathbf{X}_k. \tag{4–23}$$

Apply the transformation T to both sides of this equation. Since each of the $\mathbf{X}_i$ is a characteristic vector, we find that

$$\lambda_{k+1}\mathbf{X}_{k+1} = t_1\lambda_1\mathbf{X}_1 + t_2\lambda_2\mathbf{X}_2 + \cdots + t_k\lambda_k\mathbf{X}_k.$$

Next, we multiply Eq. (4–23) through by λ_{k+1} and subtract from the last result. We obtain

$$\mathbf{0} = t_1(\lambda_1 - \lambda_{k+1})\mathbf{X}_1 + \cdots + t_k(\lambda_k - \lambda_{k+1})\mathbf{X}_k,$$

which contradicts the assumption that the first k vectors are linearly independent since no t_i can be zero [the characteristic vector $\mathbf{X}_{k+1}$ in (4–23) is nonzero] and none of the factors $(\lambda_i - \lambda_{k+1})$ are zero (the characteristic vectors were assumed different). ∎

Now we turn to the definition of the characteristic values of a matrix. The motivation is to think of the matrix as representing a linear transformation of R^n into itself. A characteristic value of A is a scalar λ such that the matrix $A - \lambda I$ is singular. However, a matrix is singular if and only if its determinant is zero (Theorem 3–15).

Definition 4–18. Let A be an $n \times n$ matrix. Then the *characteristic polynomial* of A is the polynomial

$$f_A(\lambda) = \det(A - \lambda I).$$

The *characteristic values* of the matrix are the roots of the characteristic polynomial (which may be real or complex). The *characteristic vectors* of A are the vectors $\mathbf{X}$ in R^n such that $\mathbf{X} \neq 0$ and $A\mathbf{X} = \lambda\mathbf{X}$ for the characteristic value λ.

Note that for each *real* characteristic value λ of the matrix A, the matrix $A - \lambda I$ must be singular and hence there is some nonzero vector $\mathbf{X} \in \ker(A - \lambda I)$. The complex characteristic values will have complex characteristic vectors, and cannot have a (real) characteristic vector in the sense of this definition. We do not wish to discuss complex vector spaces (vector spaces in which the scalars are complex numbers) yet, however.

What happens to the characteristic polynomial of a matrix if there is a change in basis? Recall that the matrix of the linear transformation whose matrix is A becomes $P^{-1}AP$ where P is the (nonsingular) matrix of the change in basis.

Definition 4–19. A matrix A is *similar* to a matrix B if and only if there exists a nonsingular matrix P such that

$$B = P^{-1}AP.$$

If the matrix P in this relation is orthogonal, then A is said to be *orthogonally similar* to B.

Theorem 4–24. Two similar matrices have the same characteristic polynomials and the same characteristic values.

Proof. Since the characteristic values are the roots of the characteristic polynomial, it is sufficient to prove that two similar matrices have the same characteristic polynomials. Let $B = P^{-1}AP$. Then

$$\begin{aligned} f_B(\lambda) &= \det(P^{-1}AP - \lambda I) \\ &= \det(P^{-1}AP - P^{-1}\lambda IP) \\ &= \det P^{-1}(A - \lambda I)P \\ &= (\det P^{-1})(\det[A - \lambda I])(\det P) \\ &= (\det P^{-1})(\det P)f_A(\lambda) \\ &= f_A(\lambda). \blacksquare \end{aligned}$$

Although two similar matrices may have the same characteristic values, their characteristic vectors are usually different. The relation between the characteristic vectors of two similar matrices will be found in a problem at the end of this section. Note also, that two non-similar matrices can have the same characteristic polynomial. For example, the matrices

$$I = \begin{bmatrix} 1 & 0 \\ 0 & 1 \end{bmatrix}, \qquad B = \begin{bmatrix} 1 & 0 \\ 1 & 1 \end{bmatrix}$$

both have the same characteristic polynomial, $(1 - \lambda)^2$, but they cannot be similar. Since $P^{-1}IP = I$ for every P, there is no possible way for I to be similar to B.

Definition 4–20. A matrix $D = [d_{ij}]$ is called a *diagonal matrix* if and only if $d_{ij} = 0$ for all i and j with $i \neq j$. That is, the matrix D has zero entries everywhere except possibly on the major diagonal. In this case we write

$$D = \text{diag}\,[d_{11}, d_{22}, \ldots, d_{nn}].$$

In terms of the definitions we have given, we see that the discussion at the beginning of this section was concerned with the possibility of an arbitrary square matrix being similar to a diagonal matrix. In one respect, we find it easy to answer this question.

Theorem 4–25. An $n \times n$ matrix A is similar to a diagonal matrix D if and only if A has n linearly independent characteristic vectors.

Proof. Suppose first that A is similar to the diagonal matrix D, that is, $D = P^{-1}AP$ for some matrix P. Now, we know that $P^{-1}P = I$. Hence, if $\mathbf{P}_i$ is the ith column vector of P, then $P^{-1}\mathbf{P}_i$ is the same as the ith column vector of I, that is, $P^{-1}\mathbf{P}_i = \mathbf{e}_i$. Similarly, we know that $P\mathbf{e}_i = \mathbf{P}_i$. Since $D = P^{-1}AP$ is equivalent to $A = PDP^{-1}$, we have for each i

$$\begin{aligned} A\mathbf{P}_i &= (PDP^{-1})\mathbf{P}_i = (PD)(P^{-1}\mathbf{P}_i) = PD\mathbf{e}_i \\ &= P(d_{ii}\mathbf{e}_i) = d_{ii}P\mathbf{e}_i \\ &= d_{ii}\mathbf{P}_i; \end{aligned}$$

that is, each $\mathbf{P}_i$ is a characteristic vector of A (with characteristic value d_{ii}). But the column vectors of a nonsingular matrix are linearly independent. This proves the first half of the theorem.

To prove the second half of the theorem, suppose that $\mathbf{P}_1, \mathbf{P}_2, \ldots, \mathbf{P}_n$ is a sequence of n linearly independent characteristic vectors of A. Let λ_i be the characteristic value associated with $\mathbf{P}_i$ for each i. Then $A\mathbf{P}_i = \lambda_i\mathbf{P}_i$. Let P be the matrix whose ith column vector is $\mathbf{P}_i$ for each i. Then P is a nonsingular matrix. Set $D = [d_{ij}] = P^{-1}AP$. We will now show that D is a diagonal matrix. The ith column of D is exactly

$$P^{-1}A\mathbf{P}_i = P^{-1}\lambda_i\mathbf{P}_i = \lambda_i P^{-1}\mathbf{P}_i = \lambda_i\mathbf{e}_i.$$

The last equality holds because $P^{-1}\mathbf{P}_i$ is exactly the ith column of $P^{-1}P = I$. We have therefore proved that $d_{ij} = \lambda_i\,\delta_{ij}$ and hence that D is a diagonal matrix. ∎

Unfortunately, the condition of this theorem is not very useful. If we are given a matrix, it is not very easy to find its characteristic vectors. By the time we have found them and checked to see that they are linearly independent, we have done quite a bit of work. Of course, we then have the matrix P (as in the above proof) required to reduce A to diagonal form, but we would really like to have some conditions telling us before we start whether or not we are going to be successful. That is, we would like to find some fairly simple *sufficient* conditions for a matrix to be similar to a diagonal matrix.

There is one such condition which is very simple. As it happens, it is quite useful also. A great many of the cases which appear in practice are of this form. What we shall prove is that every symmetric matrix is similar to a diagonal matrix. The rest of this section is devoted to proving this remarkable result. We must first prove some preliminary results.

Theorem 4–26. If two characteristic vectors of a symmetric matrix belong to different characteristic values, then they are orthogonal.

Proof. Suppose A is a symmetric matrix, $A\mathbf{X} = \lambda\mathbf{X}$, and $A\mathbf{Y} = \mu\mathbf{Y}$, where $\lambda \neq \mu$. Then

$$\begin{aligned} (\lambda - \mu)(\mathbf{X}\cdot\mathbf{Y}) &= \lambda(\mathbf{X}\cdot\mathbf{Y}) - \mu(\mathbf{X}\cdot\mathbf{Y}) \\ &= (\lambda\mathbf{X}\cdot\mathbf{Y}) - (\mathbf{X}\cdot\mu\mathbf{Y}) \\ &= (A\mathbf{X}\cdot Y) - (\mathbf{X}\cdot A\mathbf{Y}) \\ &= 0. \end{aligned}$$

The last step follows from Theorem 4–18. Since $\lambda \neq \mu$, we conclude that $\mathbf{X}\cdot\mathbf{Y} = 0$. ∎

Theorem 4–27. Let $c_0, c_1, \ldots, c_k$ be k scalars. If λ is a characteristic value of the matrix A, then

$$\mu = c_k\lambda^k + c_{k-1}\lambda^{k-1} + \cdots + c_1\lambda + c_0$$

is a characteristic value of the matrix

$$B = c_kA^k + c_{k-1}A^{k-1} + \cdots + c_1A + c_0I.$$

Proof. Note that the matrix B can be considered as having been obtained by "substituting" the matrix A into the polynomial which gave the value of μ. We consider I to be the 0th power of A, and by A^j we mean $AA \cdots A$ (j factors). This product is well defined because of the associative law for matrix multiplication.

First, we observe that for any positive integer j,

$$A^j - \lambda^jI = (A - \lambda I)(A^{j-1} + \lambda A^{j-2} + \cdots + \lambda^{j-2}A + \lambda^{j-1}I),$$

as can be proved by multiplying out the two factors on the right. But then, using this fact, we can calculate

$$\begin{aligned} B - \mu I &= \sum_{j=1}^{k} c_j(A^j - \lambda^jI) \\ &= \sum_{j=1}^{k} c_j(A - \lambda I)(A^{j-1} + \cdots + \lambda^{j-1}I) \\ &= (A - \lambda I)\sum_{j=1}^{k} c_j(A^{j-1} + \cdots + \lambda^{j-1}I) \\ &= (A - \lambda I)C. \end{aligned}$$

Here the summation extends only from 1 to k, since the 0th power terms cancel immediately. The matrix C in the last line is the matrix represented by the entire summation in the line above. But if λ is a characteristic value of A, then

$$\det(B - \mu I) = [\det(A - \lambda I)][\det C] = 0.$$

Hence μ is a characteristic value for B. ▌

There is nothing in the proof of this theorem that requires λ to be real. It could just as well be complex. Therefore we can prove the following theorem.

Theorem 4–28. All of the characteristic values of a real $n \times n$ symmetric matrix are real.

Proof. We prove this by contradiction. Suppose that the characteristic polynomial of the symmetric matrix A has the complex root

$$\lambda = a + ib \qquad (b \neq 0).$$

Then we know that

$$(\lambda - a)^2 + b^2 = 0.$$

Hence by Theorem 4–27 the matrix

$$B = (A - aI)^2 + b^2 I$$

has 0 as a characteristic value. This means that there must be some nonzero vector $\mathbf{X}$ such that $B\mathbf{X} = \mathbf{0}$. (Note that the matrix B has all of its entries real. The complex values have already been eliminated from the problem.) Now, $A^t = A$, and hence $(A - aI)^t = (A - aI)$. Therefore

$$\begin{aligned} 0 = \mathbf{X} \cdot B\mathbf{X} &= \mathbf{X}^t[(A - aI)^2 + b^2 I]\mathbf{X} \\ &= \mathbf{X}^t(A - aI)^2\mathbf{X} + b^2\mathbf{X}^t\mathbf{X} \\ &= [\mathbf{X}^t(A - aI)][(A - aI)\mathbf{X}] + b^2\mathbf{X}^t\mathbf{X} \\ &= [(A - aI)\mathbf{X}]^t[(A - aI)\mathbf{X}] + b^2\mathbf{X}^t\mathbf{X} \\ &= |(A - aI)\mathbf{X}|^2 + b^2|\mathbf{X}|^2. \end{aligned}$$

In the last line, the first term is greater than or equal to zero. The second term, however, must be actually greater than zero since $b \neq 0$ and $\mathbf{X} \neq \mathbf{0}$. This contradicts the fact that their sum is zero. Therefore $b = 0$, and the proof is complete. ▌

▶ **Theorem 4–29.** Let A be an $n \times n$ symmetric matrix. Then there exists an $n \times n$ orthogonal matrix P such that $P^{-1}AP = P^tAP$ is a diagonal matrix. That is, every $n \times n$ symmetric matrix is orthogonally similar to an $n \times n$ diagonal matrix.

Remarks. In view of the theorems of this section, Theorem 4–29 says that an $n \times n$ symmetric matrix has n different characteristic vectors which form an orthonormal basis.

Note also that Theorem 4–28 does *not* tell us that a symmetric matrix has n distinct characteristic values. It says only that the matrix has n real characteristic values (counting multiplicity). We know that each *different* characteristic value must have at least one corresponding characteristic vector. However, it could happen that the matrix A has only one (n-fold) characteristic value, in which case we are guaranteed of only one characteristic vector. This is all we will need in the following proof however. Theorem 4–28 tells us that a symmetric matrix has all real characteristic values and hence that it has *at least one* characteristic vector.

Proof. The proof proper will proceed by induction on n, the size of the matrix. The theorem is clearly true for a 1×1 matrix, if for no other reason than that such a matrix is already in diagonal form.

Make the inductive hypothesis that the theorem is true for all symmetric $(n - 1) \times (n - 1)$ matrices, and let A be an $n \times n$ symmetric matrix. Then we know that A has at least one characteristic vector, which we can just as well take to be of magnitude 1 (multiplication of a characteristic vector by a scalar leaves it a characteristic vector). Let this vector be $\mathbf{B}_1$. Complete $\mathbf{B}_1$ to an orthonormal basis

$\mathbf{B}_1, \mathbf{B}_2, \ldots, \mathbf{B}_n$ for R^n. Let B be the orthogonal matrix which has these vectors as its column vectors. Now $A\mathbf{B}_1 = \lambda_1\mathbf{B}_1$, and hence a simple computation shows that

$$B^tAB = \begin{bmatrix} \lambda_1 & 0 & 0 & \cdots & 0 \\ 0 & & & & \\ 0 & & A_1 & & \\ \vdots & & & & \\ 0 & & & & \end{bmatrix}$$

where A_1 is an $(n-1) \times (n-1)$ submatrix. However, by Theorem 4–17, A_1 must also be a symmetric matrix. By the inductive hypothesis, therefore, there must exist an $(n-1) \times (n-1)$ orthogonal matrix C_1 such that $C_1^tA_1C_1 = D_1$, where D_1 is an $(n-1) \times (n-1)$ diagonal matrix.

Let

$$C = \begin{bmatrix} 1 & 0 & 0 & \cdots & 0 \\ 0 & & & & \\ 0 & & C_1 & & \\ \vdots & & & & \\ 0 & & & & \end{bmatrix}$$

and set $P = BC$. It is clear that C is an orthogonal matrix (its column vectors form an orthonormal set), and hence so is P. But then

$$\begin{aligned} P^tAP &= C^tB^tABC \\ &= C^t\begin{bmatrix} \lambda_1 & 0 & \cdots & 0 \\ 0 & & & \\ \vdots & & A_1 & \\ 0 & & & \end{bmatrix}C \\ &= \begin{bmatrix} 1 & 0 & \cdots & 0 \\ 0 & & & \\ \vdots & & C_1^t & \\ 0 & & & \end{bmatrix}\begin{bmatrix} \lambda_1 & 0 & \cdots & 0 \\ 0 & & & \\ \vdots & & A_1 & \\ 0 & & & \end{bmatrix}\begin{bmatrix} 1 & 0 & \cdots & 0 \\ 0 & & & \\ \vdots & & C_1 & \\ 0 & & & \end{bmatrix} \\ &= \begin{bmatrix} \lambda_1 & 0 & \cdots & 0 \\ 0 & & & \\ \vdots & & D_1 & \\ 0 & & & \end{bmatrix}. \end{aligned}$$

This completes the proof. The reader will find it easy to verify all of these products. They are easier to see than to explain. ▌

Let us give an example showing how a symmetric matrix can be diagonalized. Suppose we have the matrix

$$A = \begin{bmatrix} 1 & 1 & 0 \\ 1 & 0 & 1 \\ 0 & 1 & 1 \end{bmatrix}.$$

We first compute the characteristic polynomial

$$\det(A - \lambda I) = \begin{bmatrix} 1-\lambda & 1 & 0 \\ 1 & -\lambda & 1 \\ 0 & 1 & 1-\lambda \end{bmatrix} = -2 + \lambda + 2\lambda^2 - \lambda^3$$
$$= -(1 - \lambda)(2 - \lambda)(1 + \lambda).$$

The characteristic roots of this matrix are thus 1, 2, and -1.

The characteristic vectors are most easily found as vectors in the kernel of $A - \lambda I$ for the characteristic roots λ. For example, the characteristic vector belonging to $\lambda = 1$ in this example is a vector in the kernel of

$$A - I = \begin{bmatrix} 0 & 1 & 0 \\ 1 & -1 & 1 \\ 0 & 1 & 0 \end{bmatrix}.$$

The kernel of the transformation defined by this matrix can be found by the methods of the earlier sections or more simply by noting that

$$[A - I]\mathbf{X} = [x_2, x_1 - x_2 + x_3, x_2]$$

and that this is the zero vector for $\mathbf{X} = [1, 0, -1]$.

Similarly, the characteristic vectors belonging to 2 and -1 are $[1, 1, 1]$ and $[1, -2, 1]$, respectively. These three vectors can be used to form the column vectors of an orthogonal matrix once they are normalized. In the present case, we would have

$$P = \begin{bmatrix} 1/\sqrt{2} & 1/\sqrt{3} & 1/\sqrt{6} \\ 0 & 1/\sqrt{3} & -2/\sqrt{6} \\ -1/\sqrt{2} & 1/\sqrt{3} & 1/\sqrt{6} \end{bmatrix}.$$

This matrix can be used, as in Theorem 4–29, to diagonalize the matrix A.

If a given matrix was not symmetric, we could still find its characteristic polynomial and any real characteristic roots. For each characteristic root, we could find a set of vectors forming the basis of ker $(A - \lambda I)$. While these vectors might not be orthogonal, they must be linearly independent. The task of diagonalizing the matrix would usually be much more complicated, but a good start in the simplification of the matrix would be to compute $P^{-1}AB$ where P was the matrix whose column vectors were the characteristic vectors plus any other vectors required to complete the basis for R^n. Note that in this case there is no reason for P to be an orthogonal matrix. Hence P^{-1} might not be the same as P^t.

By following the method of proof of the last theorem, we can obtain a simplification of any matrix whose characteristic values are all real.

Theorem 4–30. Let A be an $n \times n$ matrix whose characteristic values are all real. (A need not be symmetric.) Then A is orthogonally similar to an upper triangular matrix.

The proof of this theorem follows precisely the proof of the last theorem. It can therefore be left as an exercise for the reader.

Most of the material in these first four chapters has been concerned with the fundamental concepts of linear algebra. Some of this material has application in "real problems," while most of it constitutes the background needed to understand more advanced techniques which are used in practice. What has been given in this section is particularly important for applications.

Let us give one simple example showing such applications. Several times before we mentioned the problem of the motion of a set of n masses separated by springs (see Fig. 1–1 on page 7). Suppose all of the masses are the same, all the springs have the same constant, and there is no damping. Then the system must satisfy the system of differential equations

$$\begin{aligned}
m\frac{d^2x_1}{dt^2} &= -kx_1 + k(x_2 - x_1),\\
m\frac{d^2x_2}{dt^2} &= -k(x_2 - x_1) + k(x_3 - x_2),\\
&\vdots\\
m\frac{d^2x_n}{dt^2} &= -k(x_n - x_{n-1}) - kx_n,
\end{aligned}$$

where m is the mass and k the spring constant.

If we assume that the masses are given an initial displacement and released with no initial velocity, then it can be shown that the motion must be of the form $x_i = y_i \cos \omega t$, $i = 1, 2, \ldots, n$, where the y_i are constants determined by the initial displacement, or the linear combination of such solutions. If we set each $x_i = y_i \cos \omega t$, we find easily that the system of equations can be satisfied if and only if

$$m\omega^2\mathbf{Y} = kA\mathbf{Y},$$

where

$$A = \begin{bmatrix} 2 & -1 & 0 & 0 & \cdots & 0 & 0\\ -1 & 2 & -1 & 0 & \cdots & 0 & 0\\ 0 & -1 & 2 & -1 & \cdots & 0 & 0\\ \vdots & & & & & & \vdots\\ 0 & 0 & 0 & 0 & \cdots & 2 & -1\\ 0 & 0 & 0 & 0 & \cdots & -1 & 2 \end{bmatrix}. \tag{4-24}$$

This equation can also be written as

$$A\mathbf{Y} = \lambda\mathbf{Y},$$

where we have put $\lambda = m\omega^2/k$. Any solution of the set of linear differential equations must therefore be of the form

$$\mathbf{X} = \sum_{i=1}^{n} c_i(\cos \omega_i t)\mathbf{Y}_i,$$

where the c_i are constants, each $\lambda_i = m\omega_i^2/k$ is a characteristic value of A, and $\mathbf{Y}_i$ is the corresponding characteristic vector.

PROBLEMS

1. Prove: The set of all vectors in the space V which have a given characteristic value λ with respect to a given linear transformation T, plus the vector $\mathbf{0}$, is a subspace of V.
2. Prove:
   a) If A is similar to B (Definition 4–19), then B is similar to A.
   b) Any $n \times n$ matrix A is similar to itself.
   c) If A is similar to B and B is similar to C, then A is similar to C.
3. Let $\mathbf{X}$ (in R^n) be a characteristic vector of the matrix A with characteristic value λ. Let B be similar to A with $B = P^{-1}AP$. Prove that $\mathbf{Y} = P^{-1}\mathbf{X}$ is a characteristic vector of B, belonging to the same characteristic value λ.
4. Prove: If A has n distinct real characteristic values, then it is similar to a diagonal matrix.
5. Let
$$A = \begin{bmatrix} a & b \\ b & c \end{bmatrix}.$$
   a) Find the characteristic polynomial of A.
   b) Prove that the characteristic polynomial of A has two real roots.
   c) Suppose that $\mathbf{X} = [x_1, x_2]$ is such that $|\mathbf{X}| = 1$, and $A\mathbf{X} = \lambda\mathbf{X}$. Set
$$P = \begin{bmatrix} x_1 & x_2 \\ x_2 & -x_1 \end{bmatrix}.$$
   What is P^tAP?
6. Prove that the matrix $\begin{bmatrix} 1 & 1 \\ 0 & 1 \end{bmatrix}$ cannot be similar to a diagonal matrix.
7. Let A be an $n \times n$ matrix. The *trace* of A is the sum of the entries on the major diagonal.
   a) Prove that the coefficient of λ^{n-1} in the characteristic polynomial of A is $(-1)^{n-1}$ times the trace of A.
   b) Using (a), prove that if P is a nonsingular matrix, then trace A = trace $P^{-1}AP$.
8. Suppose that A is a symmetric $n \times n$ matrix all of whose characteristic values are the same [i.e., its characteristic polynomial is $f_A(\lambda) = (c - \lambda)^n$]. Prove that $A = cI$. [*Hint:* Use Theorem 4–24.]
9. For each of the following matrices, find the characteristic polynomial, the characteristic values, and the characteristic vectors.

   a) $\begin{bmatrix} 2 & 2 \\ -1 & -1 \end{bmatrix}$ b) $\begin{bmatrix} 2 & -1 \\ 3 & -2 \end{bmatrix}$ c) $\begin{bmatrix} 6 & -2 \\ 5 & -1 \end{bmatrix}$

   d) $\begin{bmatrix} 3 & 0 \\ 7 & -4 \end{bmatrix}$ e) $\begin{bmatrix} 3 & 0 \\ 1 & -4 \end{bmatrix}$ f) $\begin{bmatrix} 2 & -4 \\ 1 & -2 \end{bmatrix}$
10. Do the same as in Problem 9 for the following matrices. (The characteristic values are small integers in each case.)

   a) $\begin{bmatrix} 19 & -20 & -13 \\ -11 & 10 & 7 \\ 42 & -42 & -28 \end{bmatrix}$ b) $\begin{bmatrix} -3 & 12 & 6 \\ 6 & -21 & -10 \\ -15 & 54 & 26 \end{bmatrix}$

   c) $\begin{bmatrix} 0 & -4 & -2 \\ -19 & -21 & -10 \\ 41 & 52 & 25 \end{bmatrix}$ d) $\begin{bmatrix} -3 & -10 & 26 \\ -8 & -9 & 32 \\ -4 & -4 & 15 \end{bmatrix}$

11. Do the same as in Problem 9 for this matrix. Complex numbers will be required in this case.

$$\begin{bmatrix} 2 & -5 \\ 1 & -2 \end{bmatrix}.$$

12. Find the characteristic values and characteristic vectors of the matrix A in (4–24) for $n = 2$ and 3. Describe the modes of motion corresponding to the resulting characteristic vectors.

13. Let A be an $n \times n$ matrix with characteristic values $\lambda_1, \lambda_2, \ldots, \lambda_n$ and let k be a positive integer. Prove that the characteristic values of A^k are $\lambda_1^k, \lambda_2^k, \ldots, \lambda_n^k$.

14. Prove that the result of the last problem holds if $k = -1$ provided that A is nonsingular.

15. Let A and B be two $n \times n$ matrices. Prove that the characteristic polynomials of AB and BA are the same.

16. Prove Theorem 4–30.

17. Let **A** and **B** be two vectors in R^n (or, equivalently, $n \times 1$ matrices). Then $C = \mathbf{AB}^t$ is an $n \times n$ matrix.

    a) Show that **A** is a characteristic vector for C. What is the corresponding characteristic value?

    b) Show that any vector which is orthogonal to **B** is a characteristic vector for C with characteristic value 0.

4–6. FURTHER PROPERTIES OF MATRICES

The expansion of the determinant of an $n \times n$ matrix consists of $n!$ terms. Each term is the product of n of the entries, one factor coming from each row and one from each column. The expansion of the characteristic polynomial of the matrix $A = [a_{ij}]$,

$$f(\lambda) = \det \begin{bmatrix} a_{11} - \lambda & a_{12} & a_{13} & \cdots & a_{1n} \\ a_{21} & a_{22} - \lambda & a_{23} & \cdots & a_{2n} \\ \vdots & & & & \vdots \\ a_{n1} & a_{n2} & a_{n3} & & a_{nn} - \lambda \end{bmatrix}$$

contains one term which is the product of the main diagonal elements:

$$(a_{11} - \lambda)(a_{22} - \lambda) \cdots (a_{nn} - \lambda).$$

If a term contains $n - 1$ factors from the main diagonal, then the remaining factor must be from the main diagonal also. Thus, except for the one term given, every term of the expansion has at most $n - 2$ factors from the main diagonal, and hence is a polynomial in λ of degree at most $n - 2$. Thus

$$f(\lambda) = (-1)^n\lambda^n + (-1)^{n-1}c_{n-1}\lambda^{n-1} + (-1)^{n-2}c_{n-2}\lambda^{n-2} + \cdots + c_1\lambda + c_0,$$

where $c_{n-1} = a_{11} + a_{22} + \cdots + a_{nn}$. The coefficient of λ^{n-1} in the characteristic polynomial is particularly important. We give it a special name.

Definition 4–21. Given an $n \times n$ matrix $A = [a_{ij}]$, the *trace* of A is the quantity

$$\operatorname{tr} A = a_{11} + a_{22} + \cdots + a_{nn}. \tag{4–25}$$

In the problems of the last section, the reader was invited to prove that the traces of two similar matrices are the same. This is easy to show by direct computation, but we can also give the following proof.

Theorem 4–31. If the matrices A and B are similar, then

$$\operatorname{tr} A = \operatorname{tr} B.$$

Proof. By Theorem 4–24, two similar matrices have the same characteristic polynomials. The coefficients of the $(n - 1)$th power of λ must then be the same, that is, the traces must be the same. ▌

In the next theorem, we wish to consider matrices which are themselves polynomials. That is, each entry is a polynomial. For example

$$B(t) = \begin{bmatrix} 3 + 2t - t^2 & 4 + t & -3 + t^2 \\ 1 & t^3 & -2 - t \\ t^2 - 2t^3 & 2 + t^2 & 1 - t^2 \end{bmatrix}.$$

Any such matrix can be decomposed into a polynomial whose coefficients are constant matrices. For example, the above matrix can be written

$$B(t) = \begin{bmatrix} 3 & 4 & -3 \\ 1 & 0 & -2 \\ 0 & 2 & 1 \end{bmatrix} + t\begin{bmatrix} 2 & 1 & 0 \\ 0 & 0 & -1 \\ 0 & 0 & 0 \end{bmatrix} + t^2\begin{bmatrix} -1 & 0 & 1 \\ 0 & 0 & 0 \\ 1 & 1 & -1 \end{bmatrix} + t^3\begin{bmatrix} 0 & 0 & 0 \\ 0 & 1 & 0 \\ -2 & 0 & 0 \end{bmatrix}.$$

Now let us state a most remarkable theorem concerning matrices.

▶ **Theorem 4–32** (*The Cayley-Hamilton theorem*). Any $n \times n$ matrix satisfies its own characteristic equation. That is, if $f(\lambda) = \det [A - \lambda I]$, then $f(A) = 0$.

Proof. Let the characteristic polynomial of the $n \times n$ matrix A be

$$f(\lambda) = c_0 - c_1\lambda + \cdots + (-1)^n c_n \lambda^n \qquad (c_n = 1).$$

Thus

$$f(A) - f(\lambda)I = \sum_{k=1}^{n} (-1)^k c_k [A^k - \lambda^k I]$$

(the constant term is the same in both and hence vanishes in the difference). As in the proof of Theorem 4–27, we have

$$A^k - \lambda^k I = (A - \lambda I)(A^{k-1} + \lambda A^{k-2} + \cdots + \lambda^{k-2}A + \lambda^{k-1}I).$$

Therefore

$$f(A) - f(\lambda)I = [A - \lambda I]C(\lambda), \tag{4-26}$$

where $C(\lambda)$ is a polynomial matrix of degree $n - 1$ or less. That is,

$$C(\lambda) = C_0 + \lambda C_1 + \cdots + \lambda^p C_p, \qquad p \leq n - 1,$$

where $C_0, C_1 \cdots C_p$ are $n \times n$ matrices whose entries are constants.

Next, let $D(\lambda) = [A - \lambda I]^\dagger$ be the formal adjoint of $A - \lambda I$ (Definition 3–13). Each entry of $D(\lambda)$ is a cofactor of the matrix $A - \lambda I$ and hence is the determinant of an $(n - 1) \times (n - 1)$ matrix, each entry of which is at most linear in λ. The entries of $D(\lambda)$ are therefore polynomials of degree $n - 1$ or less. Thus we can write

$$D(\lambda) = D_0 + \lambda D_1 + \cdots + \lambda^q D_q, \qquad q \leq n - 1.$$

From Theorem 3–23, we have

$$[A - \lambda I]D(\lambda) = (\det[A - \lambda I])I = f(\lambda)I.$$

Therefore, starting from Eq. (4–26), and letting $B_i = C_i + D_i$ for each i (putting C_i or $D_i = 0$ if not otherwise defined), we compute

$$\begin{aligned} f(A) &= f(\lambda)I + [A - \lambda I]C(\lambda) \\ &= [A - \lambda I][D(\lambda) + C(\lambda)] \\ &= [A - \lambda I][B_0 + \lambda B_1 + \cdots + \lambda^r B_r] \qquad (r \leq n - 1) \\ &= AB_0 + \lambda[AB_1 - B_0] + \lambda^2[AB_2 - B_1] + \cdots + \lambda^r[AB_r - B_{r-1}] - \lambda^{r+1}B_r. \end{aligned}$$

This equation is valid for all real λ. One side of it is a constant, while the other side is a polynomial. Looking at each individual entry, we have a polynomial which is identically a constant. This can be true only if all of the coefficients of positive powers of λ are zero. Thus we must have $B_r = 0$, $AB_r - B_{r-1} = -B_{r-1} = 0$, and so on to $B_1 = 0$, $AB_1 - B_0 = -B_0 = 0$. Thus all of the $B_i = 0$, and hence $f(A) = 0$, which is what we wished to prove. ▮

At first glance, one might think that the Cayley-Hamilton theorem might be useful in calculating the inverse of a matrix. That is, with the characteristic polynomial of the matrix A as given above, we would have from the Cayley-Hamilton theorem

$$A^{-1} = \frac{(-1)^n}{c_0} A^{n-1} + \frac{(-1)^{n-1}c_{n-1}}{c_0} A^{n-2} + \cdots + \frac{c_1}{c_0} I.$$

Observe that A is nonsingular if and only if $f(0) = c_0 \neq 0$.

The difficulty with this formula is that by the time we have calculated the characteristic polynomial and the first $n - 1$ powers of A, we have already done more work than is involved in one of the more usual methods for finding A^{-1}.

Next, we wish to consider a special class of matrices which are connected with projections. First, however, let us give a precise definition of what we mean by a projection.

Definition 4–22. Let V be a vector space with subspaces L and M such that $V = L \oplus M$. Then by the *projection of V onto L along M* we mean the linear transformation $\pi: V \to V$ defined by $\pi\mathbf{X} = \mathbf{X}_L$, where $\mathbf{X} = \mathbf{X}_L + \mathbf{X}_M$, $\mathbf{X}_L \in L$, $\mathbf{X}_M \in M$. By the *orthogonal projection of V onto a subspace L* we mean the projection of V onto L along $L^{\perp}$.

The transformation π is uniquely defined in this way since every $\mathbf{X}$ has a unique decomposition with respect to the given direct-sum decomposition. It may not be completely obvious that π is a linear transformation. The proof is easy, however, and is left for the reader.

Observe that the projection mapping π has the property that $\pi \circ \pi = \pi$. This property actually characterizes the projections. We give it a special name.

Definition 4–23. A function T mapping a set V into itself, $T: V \to V$, is called *idempotent* if and only if $T \circ T = T$. An $n \times n$ matrix A is called *idempotent* if and only if $A^2 = A$.

We may now prove the assertion made above.

Theorem 4–33. Let T be a linear transformation of the vector space V into itself which is idempotent. Then T is the projection of V along $\ker T$ onto $\operatorname{im} T$.

Proof. We first show that $\operatorname{im} T \cap \ker T = \{\mathbf{0}\}$. Let $\mathbf{X} \in \operatorname{im} T \cap \ker T$. Then we must have $T\mathbf{X} = \mathbf{0}$, and also there must exist a $\mathbf{Y} \in V$ such that $\mathbf{X} = T\mathbf{Y}$. Using the fact that T is idempotent, we then find that

$$\mathbf{X} = T\mathbf{Y} = T^2\mathbf{Y} = T(T\mathbf{Y}) = T\mathbf{X} = \mathbf{0}.$$

Since $\dim(\operatorname{im} T) + \dim(\ker T) = n$ (the dimension of V), it then follows that $V = \operatorname{im} T \oplus \ker T$.

Let T_0 be the linear transformation T restricted to $\operatorname{im} T$. Then T_0 is one-to-one (Theorem 2–10). We next show that T_0 is indeed the identity.

Let $\mathbf{X} \in \operatorname{im} T$ and $\mathbf{Y}$ be such that $\mathbf{X} = T\mathbf{Y}$. Then

$$T_0\mathbf{X} = T\mathbf{X} = T^2\mathbf{Y} = T\mathbf{Y} = \mathbf{X}.$$

Thus T_0 is the identity, and the theorem is proved. ▌

Suppose that A is an $n \times n$ idempotent matrix. Then it defines an idempotent linear transformation $T_A: R^n \to R^n$. By the above theorem, T_A must be the projection of R^n onto the subspace $L = \operatorname{im} T$ along $K = \ker T$. Choose a basis $\mathcal{B} = \langle \mathbf{B}_1, \mathbf{B}_2, \ldots, \mathbf{B}_n \rangle$ such that $L = L\{\mathbf{B}_1, \mathbf{B}_2, \ldots, \mathbf{B}_k\}$ and $K = L\{\mathbf{B}_{k+1}, \mathbf{B}_{k+2}, \ldots, \mathbf{B}_n\}$. Then the matrix of the transformation T_A in terms of the basis $\mathcal{B}$ must be C_{nn}^k (Definition 2–22). We have the following diagram:

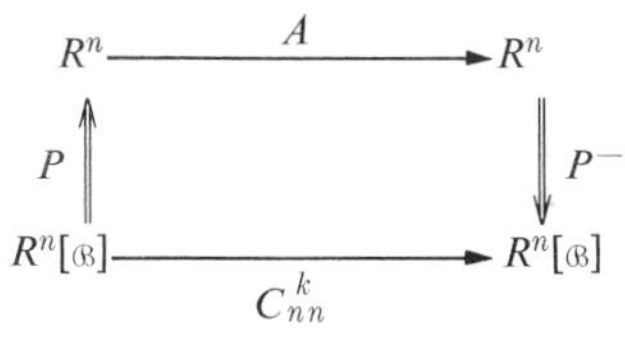

That is, if P is the change of basis matrix, then $P^{-1}AP = C^k_{nn}$. We have therefore proved:

Theorem 4–34. Let A be an $n \times n$ idempotent matrix. Then A is similar to the matrix C^k_{nn} for some k.

We can calculate the powers of square matrices. Can we also take roots? We will not consider all of the possibilities here, but restrict our attention to the problem of taking the square root of a symmetric matrix. This important special case has a number of practical applications.

The first thing that we observe is that by Theorem 4–27, the characteristic values of a matrix B^2 is the squares of the characteristic values of the matrix B. Hence there is no hope of finding the square root of a matrix which has any negative characteristic values (unless we go to the complex case).

Suppose that A is a symmetric matrix with nonnegative characteristic values $\lambda_1, \lambda_2, \ldots, \lambda_n$. Then there exists an orthogonal matrix P such that

$$P^tAP = D = \text{diag}[\lambda_1, \lambda_2, \ldots, \lambda_n].$$

Given a vector $\mathbf{X}$, let $\mathbf{Y} = [y_1, y_2, \ldots, y_n] = P^t\mathbf{X}$. Then $\mathbf{X} = P\mathbf{Y}$ and

$$\mathbf{X}^tA\mathbf{X} = \mathbf{Y}^tP^tAP\mathbf{Y} = \mathbf{Y}^tD\mathbf{Y} = \sum_{i=1}^{n} \lambda_i y_i^2.$$

The last expression must always be greater than or equal to zero since we assumed the λ_i to be nonnegative.

Definition 4–24. An $n \times n$ matrix A is called *positive* if and only if $\mathbf{X}^tA\mathbf{X} \geq 0$ for every vector $\mathbf{X} \in R^n$. It is called *positive definite* if and only if it is positive and $\mathbf{X}^tA\mathbf{X} = 0$ only for $\mathbf{X} = \mathbf{0}$.

From the above discussion, we see that we actually proved:

Theorem 4–35. A symmetric $n \times n$ matrix is positive (positive definite) if and only if its characteristic values are all nonnegative (positive).

Next, we prove:

Theorem 4–36. A symmetric $n \times n$ positive matrix A possesses a symmetric $n \times n$ positive square root, i.e., a matrix $A^{1/2}$ which is symmetric and positive and such that $A^{1/2}A^{1/2} = A$.

Proof. Let P be the orthogonal matrix such that

$$P^tAP = D = \text{diag}[\lambda_1, \lambda_2, \ldots, \lambda_n],$$

where the λ_i are the characteristic values of A. Let $D^{1/2}$ be the diagonal matrix, $D^{1/2} = \text{diag}[\lambda_1^{1/2}, \lambda_2^{1/2}, \ldots, \lambda_n^{1/2}]$, where each $\lambda_i^{1/2}$ is the nonnegative square root of the corresponding λ_i. Set

$$A^{1/2} = PD^{1/2}P^t.$$

Then $A^{1/2}A^{1/2} = PD^{1/2}P^tPD^{1/2}P^t = PD^{1/2}D^{1/2}P^t = PDP^t = A$. Therefore $A^{1/2}$ is a square root of A.

Since $A^{1/2}$ is similar to $D^{1/2}$, its characteristic values are nonnegative, and it is therefore also a positive matrix. To see that it is symmetric, we merely compute

$$(A^{1/2})^t = (PD^{1/2}P^t)^t = P(D^{1/2})^tP^t = PD^{1/2}P^t = A^{1/2}. \blacksquare$$

To close this section, we give a condition which is quite useful in identifying positive matrices.

Theorem 4–37 (*The Jacobi criterion*). Let A be a symmetric $n \times n$ matrix whose characteristic polynomial is

$$f(\lambda) = c_0 - c_1\lambda + c_2\lambda^2 - \cdots + (-1)^{n-1}c_{n-1}\lambda^{n-1} + (-1)^n c_n\lambda^n$$

(where $c_n = 1$). Then A is positive definite if and only if all of the $c_i > 0$. It is positive but not positive definite if and only if there is some $k \geq 0$ such that $c_0 = c_1 = \cdots = c_k = 0$ and all of the remaining $c_i > 0$.

Proof. Let $\lambda_1, \lambda_2, \ldots, \lambda_n$ be the characteristic values of A. Then

$$f(\lambda) = (\lambda_1 - \lambda)(\lambda_2 - \lambda)\cdots(\lambda_n - \lambda).$$

Comparing the expansion of this product with the form given in the theorem, we see that c_{n-1} is the sum of all of the λ_i; c_{n-2} is the sum of all products of distinct pairs of the λ_i, i.e.,

$$c_{n-2} = \sum_{i=1}^{n-1} \sum_{j=i+1}^{n} \lambda_i\lambda_j;$$

c_{n-3} is the sum of all distinct products of three different λ_i, and so on down to $c_0 = \lambda_1\lambda_2\cdots\lambda_n$.

Now suppose that A is positive definite. Then all of the $\lambda_i > 0$, and hence all of the $c_i > 0$ also. The condition of the theorem therefore holds.

Suppose that A is positive but not positive definite. Then some $k + 1$ of the λ_i are $= 0$, where $k \geq 0$. Every product of $n - k$ or more of the λ_i must then vanish. Hence $c_0 = c_1 = \cdots = c_k = 0$. Since all the remaining $\lambda_i > 0$, all of the other $c_i > 0$ also. The condition of the theorem thus holds in this case also.

Next we must prove the converse. We suppose that $f(\lambda)$ is the characteristic polynomial of the symmetric matrix A, and that all the $c_i \geq 0$. We shall show that if $c_0 > 0$, then A is positive definite, while if $c_0 = 0$, then A is positive but not positive definite. This then proves the theorem.

Since A is symmetric, it has n real-characteristic values. That is, all n of the roots of $f(\lambda)$ must be real. Consider now the form of the characteristic polynomial together with the assumption that all of the c_i are greater than or equal to zero. This means that the coefficients of each even power of λ in the characteristic polynomial is positive, while the coefficient of each odd power is negative. It follows that every term of the characteristic polynomial will be non-negative when λ is negative. In particular, the term

$$(-1)^n c_n \lambda^n = (-1)^n \lambda^n$$

will be strictly positive for a negative λ. Thus, $f(\lambda)$ is strictly positive for negative λ and we can conclude that A has no negative characteristic values.

Suppose now that $c_0 > 0$. Then $f(0) = c_0 > 0$ and hence 0 is not a characteristic value for A. All roots of $f(\lambda)$ are then positive and A must be positive definite.

If $c_0 = 0$, then at least one of the λ_i must be zero. Hence A cannot be positive definite. Suppose that c_{k+1} is the first of the c_i which is nonzero. Then

$$\frac{f(\lambda)}{\lambda^{k+1}} = (-1)^{k+1} c_{k+1} + (-1)^{k+2} c_{k+2} \lambda + \cdots + (-1)^n \lambda^{n-k-1}.$$

Exactly the same reasoning as above then shows that all the roots of this polynomial must be positive. We therefore have $k + 1$ of the roots zero and the remaining positive. A is therefore positive, but not positive definite. ▮

PROBLEMS

1. Prove that the trace of an idempotent matrix must be an integer.
2. An $n \times n$ matrix is *nilpotent* if and only if there is some integer p such that $A^p = 0$. Prove that the trace of a nilpotent matrix must be zero.
3. Prove that all the characteristic values of a nilpotent matrix must be zero.
4. Let A be an $n \times n$ matrix all of whose characteristic values are zero. Prove that A is nilpotent. [*Hint:* Use the Cayley-Hamilton theorem.]
5. Let A be an $n \times n$ matrix. Prove that $B = A^tA$ is symmetric and positive, and is positive definite if A is nonsingular.
6. Prove that every nonsingular $n \times n$ matrix A has a *polar decomposition*, $A = RS$, where R is an orthogonal matrix and S is symmetric and positive definite. [*Hint:* Set $S = (A^tA)^{1/2}$, $R = AS^{-1}$.]
7. Show that a positive definite symmetric $n \times n$ matrix has 2^n distinct square roots.
8. Prove that π of Definition 4–21 is a linear transformation.
9. A matrix A is an *involution matrix* if $A^2 = I$.
   a) Show that a symmetric orthogonal matrix is an involution matrix.
   b) Show that a symmetric involution matrix is orthogonal.
   c) Show that an orthogonal involution matrix is symmetric.
10. Let A and B be two $n \times n$ matrices such that $A + I = 2B$. Prove that A is an involution matrix if and only if B is idempotent.
11. Let A and B be two $n \times n$ matrices. Prove that tr AB = tr BA.
12. Let $\mathbf{A}$ and $\mathbf{B}$ be two linearly independent vectors in R^n. Prove that the matrix $C = k\mathbf{A}\mathbf{B}^t$ (see Problem 16 of the last section) is idempotent for a suitable choice of k.

4-7. THE COMPLEX CASE

In this section we will outline some of the major results concerning complex vector spaces and matrices with complex entries. These results will be stated mostly without proof, but enough indication will be given so that the reader should find no difficulty in supplying the complete proof.

In Chapter 1 we introduced the n-dimensional vector space R^n. This space consists of all ordered n-tuples of real numbers. Instead we could just as well have considered all ordered n-tuples of complex numbers. The result would have been a vector space over the complex numbers.

In this latter space, we would make use of the same definition for vector addition and scalar multiplication, except that the scalars would be complex numbers instead of real numbers. The ideas of linear independence remain the same. The row-reduction process proceeds in exactly the same way. Matrices whose entries are complex numbers would be introduced in the same way and used just as in the real case. The development of the theory of determinants would not be changed. Indeed, we would find no need to make any changes until we reached Chapter IV.

Definition 4-25. The vector space C^n is the set of all ordered n-tuples of complex numbers, with vector addition, scalar multiplication, the zero vector, and the negative of a vector defined as in Definition 1-3 with the set of complex numbers C replacing R throughout. In particular, *scalars* are the complex numbers in C. A vector space over the complex numbers is defined exactly as in Definition 1-5 with C replacing R.

A vector space over the complex field C behaves very much like a vector space of twice the dimension over the reals. We can define a mapping from C^n to R^{2n} in the following way: If $\mathbf{Z} = [z_1, z_2, \ldots, z_n]$ is in C^n and if each $z_k = x_k + iy_k$, where x_k and y_k are both real, then we have $\mathbf{Z} = \mathbf{X} + i\mathbf{Y}$ where $\mathbf{X} = [x_1, x_2, \ldots, x_n]$ and $\mathbf{Y} = [y_1, y_2, \ldots, y_n]$. These last two vectors are actually in R^n. The vector $\mathbf{Z}' = [\mathbf{X}, \mathbf{Y}] = [x_1, x_2, \ldots, x_n, y_1, y_2, \ldots, y_n]$ is thus in R^{2n}. The mapping $T: C^n \to R^{2n}$ defined by $T\mathbf{Z} = \mathbf{Z}'$ is clearly linear, one-to-one, and onto.

The set of complex numbers C, is a one-dimensional space over C. It is identified in this way with R^2. The usual identification is given by $z = x + iy \to [x, y]$. This identification of course ignores the multiplicative structure of the complex field.

A similar result holds for any finite-dimensional vector space over C. Thus it might seem that there would be no advantage in considering vector spaces over C. Such a space could always be replaced by a space over R with twice the dimension. However, there is some extra structure imparted by the complex field which often has some significance. The spaces C^n often appear in practice. When they do, there is usually some extra connection between the basis elements which is indicated by the multiplication by i. It is thus often more natural to use C^n instead of R^{2n}.

It is when we introduce the inner product that we must make a fundamental change. Definition 4-6 is not well suited for an inner product on C^n since the inner product of a nonzero vector with itself could be zero using this definition. This situation can be corrected by taking the complex conjugate of one set of components.* We will define the new inner product here, along with another useful device.

Definition 4–26. Let $A = [a_{ij}]$ be an $n \times m$ matrix over C (i.e., a matrix whose entries are complex numbers). Then by the *conjugate transpose* of A we mean the $m \times n$ matrix $A^* = [b_{ij}]$ which is defined by $b_{ij} = \bar{a}_{ji}$ for every i and j.
The *standard inner product* on C^n is the function from $C^n \times C^n$ to C defined by

$$\langle \mathbf{Z}, \mathbf{W} \rangle = \mathbf{W}^*\mathbf{Z} = z_1\bar{w}_1 + z_2\bar{w}_2 + \cdots + z_n\bar{w}_n, \tag{4–27}$$

where $\mathbf{Z} = [z_1, z_2, \ldots, z_n]$ and $\mathbf{W} = [w_1, w_2, \ldots, w_n]$.

The *magnitude* of a vector $\mathbf{Z}$ is

$$|\mathbf{Z}| = \langle \mathbf{Z}, \mathbf{Z} \rangle^{1/2} = [|z_1|^2 + |z_2|^2 + \cdots + |z_n|^2]^{1/2}.$$

The conjugate transpose takes the place of the transpose in the real case. If the matrix is real, the conjugate transpose is in fact the same as the transpose. Observe that whenever the products are defined, $(AB)^* = B^*A^*$.

We introduce a different notation for the inner product here because we do not want to confuse it with the earlier inner product. The notation used here is the same as that used for an ordered pair. The context will always distinguish between the two. The notation $\langle \mathbf{Z}, \mathbf{W} \rangle$ is now the most commonly used in mathematics books. Other notations for the same thing that are often used are $(\mathbf{Z}, \mathbf{W})$ or $\langle \mathbf{Z} \mid \mathbf{W} \rangle$. Again, note that if the vectors are real, then this inner product coincides with the one introduced for R^n.

The reader will find it easy to show that the inner product satisfies the following conditions

Theorem 4–38. The standard inner product on C^n has the following properties:

1. It is a bilinear function of $C^n \times C^n$ onto C, except that $\langle \mathbf{Z}, t\mathbf{W} \rangle = \bar{t}\langle \mathbf{Z}, \mathbf{W} \rangle$.
2. It is Hermitian, that is,
$$\langle \mathbf{W}, \mathbf{Z} \rangle = \overline{\langle \mathbf{Z}, \mathbf{W} \rangle}.$$
3. It is positive definite, that is, $\langle \mathbf{Z}, \mathbf{Z} \rangle \geq 0$ for any $\mathbf{Z} \in C^n$ with equality holding if and only if $\mathbf{Z} = \mathbf{0}$.

The main difference between this inner product and the real inner product is that one must be careful that for any complex scalar t, $t\langle \mathbf{Z}, \mathbf{W} \rangle = \langle t\mathbf{Z}, \mathbf{W} \rangle = \langle \mathbf{Z}, \bar{t}\mathbf{W} \rangle$. The expansion of $|\mathbf{Z} + \mathbf{W}|^2 = \langle \mathbf{Z} + \mathbf{W}, \mathbf{Z} + \mathbf{W} \rangle$ is also somewhat different. It is

$$|\mathbf{Z}|^2 + \langle \mathbf{Z}, \mathbf{W} \rangle + \overline{\langle \mathbf{Z}, \mathbf{W} \rangle} + |\mathbf{W}|^2.$$

---

* If $z = x + iy$ is a complex number with x and y real, then the complex conjugate of z is $\bar{z} = x - iy$. Then $z\bar{z} = x^2 + y^2$.

With these few minor changes, one finds that the Cauchy-Schwarz inequality (Theorem 4–4) can be proved in almost exactly the same way as it was in Section 4–1. That is,

$$|\langle \mathbf{Z}, \mathbf{W} \rangle| \leq |\mathbf{Z}|\, |\mathbf{W}|.$$

Similarly, the proof of the triangle inequality

$$|\mathbf{Z} + \mathbf{W}| \leq |\mathbf{Z}| + |\mathbf{W}|$$

is almost exactly the same as the proof given for Theorem 4–5.

In the real case, transformations which preserved the length of vectors were characterized by having orthogonal matrices. The corresponding situation in the complex case gives rise to *unitary matrices.*

Definition 4–27. An $n \times n$ matrix over the complex field is called *unitary* if and only if its column vectors form an orthonormal set in C^n with respect to the inner product (4–27).

Clearly, a unitary matrix whose entries are all real must be an orthogonal matrix. Hence this matrix is a generalization of orthogonal matrices. Unitary matrices are characterized by an entire set of properties just as the orthogonal matrices are. The reader can easily adapt the proof of Theorem 4–16 to prove:

Theorem 4–39. The following four conditions on an $n \times n$ matrix U over the complex field are all equivalent:

1. U is a unitary matrix.
2. $U^{-1} = U^*$.
3. For every vector $\mathbf{Z} \in C^n$, $|U\mathbf{Z}| = |\mathbf{Z}|$.
4. For every pair of vectors $\mathbf{Z}, \mathbf{W} \in C^n$, $\langle U\mathbf{Z}, U\mathbf{W} \rangle = \langle \mathbf{Z}, \mathbf{W} \rangle$.

The only difficulty that arises in the proof of this theorem is in proving (4) from (3). Since $z + \bar{z} = 2x$ when $z = x + iy$, the proof as given for Theorem 4–16 would only show that the real part of $\langle U\mathbf{Z}, U\mathbf{W} \rangle$ equals the real part of $\langle \mathbf{Z}, \mathbf{W} \rangle$. However, by considering the expansion of $|U(\mathbf{Z} + i\mathbf{W})|^2$ the rest can be easily proved.

Condition (2) shows the difference between orthogonal and unitary matrices. An orthogonal matrix satisfies $P^{-1} = P^t$, while a unitary matrix satisfies $Q^{-1} = Q^*$. (We sometimes wish to speak of orthogonal matrices over the complex field. A complex matrix P is called orthogonal if and only if $P^{-1} = P^t$.)

The reader can easily show that the product of two unitary matrices must be unitary and that the inverse of a unitary matrix is unitary.

Any $n \times n$ matrix with real or complex entries has a characteristic polynomial of degree n with (possibly) complex coefficients. By the fundamental theorem of algebra, this polynomial has n (complex) roots; they are the characteristic values of the matrix. Each distinct characteristic value must have a corresponding characteristic vector (which is usually in C^n even if the original matrix is real). Then, exactly as in the proof of Theorem 4–29 (or perhaps Theorem 4–30 would be better), one proves:

Theorem 4–40. Any $n \times n$ matrix is similar to an upper triangular matrix T under unitary transformations. That is, there exists a unitary matrix U such that

$$U^*AU = T.$$

In the proof of Theorem 4–29, the symmetry of the given matrix served two purposes. First, it ensured that the matrix had n (real) characteristic values. This was taken care of by hypothesis in Theorem 4–30 and in Theorem 4–40 by the fact that *every* $n \times n$ matrix has n (complex) characteristic values.

The second use of symmetry in Theorem 4–29 was to show that a triangular matrix was actually diagonal, a fact which was neglected in Theorem 4–30 and in the last theorem. In the proof of Theorem 4–29, it was important to know that a matrix which is orthogonally similar to a symmetric matrix is itself symmetric. In unitary transformations, this property is lacking, but we can define a suitable substitute.

Definition 4–28. An $n \times n$ (complex) matrix A is called *Hermitian* if and only if $A^* = A$.

Theorem 4–41. All the characteristic values of a Hermitian matrix are real.

Proof. We can give a much simpler proof for this theorem than that given for Theorem 4–28. Let λ be a characteristic value for the Hermitian matrix A and suppose that $\mathbf{X}$ is a characteristic vector with this characteristic value. Then

$$A\mathbf{X} = \lambda\mathbf{X},$$

and hence

$$\mathbf{X}^*A\mathbf{X} = \lambda|\mathbf{X}|^2.$$

Now take the conjugate transpose of both sides of this equation. We get

$$\mathbf{X}^*A^*\mathbf{X} = \bar{\lambda}|\mathbf{X}|^2.$$

Since $A = A^*$, the last equation means that $\lambda = \bar{\lambda}$, and hence λ is real. ▌

We can now prove the following theorems exactly as we proved Theorems 4–17, 4–26, and 4–29.

Theorem 4–42. If A is an $n \times n$ Hermitian matrix and U is an $n \times n$ unitary matrix, then U^*AU is Hermitian.

Theorem 4–43. If $\mathbf{X}_1$ and $\mathbf{X}_2$ are characteristic vectors of a Hermitian matrix A belonging to different characteristic values, then $\langle \mathbf{X}_1, \mathbf{X}_2 \rangle = 0$.

Theorem 4–44. If A is an $n \times n$ Hermitian matrix, then there exists an unitary matrix U such that U^*AU is a diagonal matrix.

We end this section with the following theorem which is of considerable value in the theory of complex matrices.

Theorem 4–45. The determinant of a unitary matrix is a complex number whose absolute value is 1.

Proof. Let U be a unitary matrix and set $d = \det U$. Then $\det U^* = \det (\bar{U})^t = \det \bar{U} = \overline{\det U} = \bar{d}$. However,

$$|d|^2 = d\bar{d} = \det UU^* = \det I = 1. \blacksquare$$

Note that since an orthogonal matrix is real and unitary, this result implies that the determinant of a real orthogonal matrix is $+1$ or -1. In the proof, we needed to know that $\det \bar{U} = \overline{\det U}$. This follows from the fact that conjugation is a linear operation. That is, $\overline{(z + w)} = \bar{z} + \bar{w}$ and $\overline{(zw)} = \bar{z} \cdot \bar{w}$.

PROBLEMS

1. Prove that $(AB)^* = B^*A^*$ whenever the matrix product AB is defined.
2. Prove that the product of two unitary matrices is unitary and that the inverse of a unitary matrix is unitary.
3. Prove that (3) implies (4) in Theorem 4–39.
4. Prove Theorem 4–42.
5. Prove Theorem 4–43.
6. Prove that the determinant of a Hermitian matrix is real.
7. Let A be an $n \times n$ Hermitian matrix. Prove that $\mathbf{X}^*A\mathbf{X}$ is real for any vector $\mathbf{X} \in C^n$
8. Prove that every 2×2 unitary matrix is of the form
$$e^{i\alpha}\begin{bmatrix} e^{i\beta}\cos\theta & e^{i\gamma}\sin\theta \\ -e^{-i\gamma}\sin\theta & e^{-i\beta}\cos\theta \end{bmatrix}$$
where α, β, γ, and θ are real.
9. Let A be an $n \times n$ matrix. Prove that A^*A is Hermitian.
10. An $n \times n$ matrix A is called *normal* if and only if $A^*A = AA^*$. Prove that if A is normal, then there exists a unitary matrix U such that U^*AU is diagonal.

4–8. GROUPS*

A group is a set of elements on which is defined a binary operation which satisfies certain properties. To be precise:

Definition 4–29. Let G be a set of elements, $a, b, c, \ldots$, on which is defined a binary operation, μ. That is, μ is a function

1. $\mu : G \times G \to G$.

---

* These last three sections in this chapter are distinct from the earlier material. The discussion of group theory is not needed in the remainder of the text. It is included only so that the definition of the matrix groups will make sense. These sections may be omitted.

We will write $\mu(a, b) = ab$. Then, G is called a *group* (with respect to this operation) if and only if the following properties hold:

2. μ is associative, that is $a(bc) = (ab)c$ for every a, b, c, in G;
3. there exists an element e in G (called the *identity* of G) such that $ae = ea = a$ for every element a in G;
4. every element G has an *inverse*, that is, given any $a \in G$, there is some element a^{-1} in G such that $a^{-1}a = aa^{-1} = e$.

If μ is commutative, that is, if $ab = ba$ for every a and b in G, then G is called an *abelian group.*

The properties listed here could be weakened somewhat. That is, some of what is required in this definition could be proved from the rest. However, we are not interested in such niceties at this time.

Note that if a is any element of the group, then we can take the "product" of a with itself any number of times. Because of the associative property, it does not matter how the product is grouped. We can thus write the successive "powers" of a: $a = a^1, a^2, a^3, \ldots$ In the same way, we can start with a^{-1} and obtain the successive "negative powers," $a^{-1}, a^{-2}, \ldots$ If we add the convention $a^0 = e$, then we have all integral powers of the element a. It is easily seen that we have $a^j a^k = a^{j+k}$ for any integers (positive, negative, or zero) j and k.

Obviously, the properties listed above in the definition of group are important. We find groups in many places. For example, the set of all real numbers is a group with respect to the operation of addition (do not be confused by the fact that the group operation was written in multiplicative form in the definition). The set of all nonzero real numbers is a group with respect to multiplication. The set of positive real numbers is also a group with respect to multiplication. The set of all complex numbers is a group with respect to addition. The set of nonzero complex numbers is a group with respect to multiplication. A vector space is a group with respect to vector addition. The set of all nonsingular $n \times n$ matrices is a group with respect to matrix multiplication (this is our first example of a nonabelian group).

The fact that this particular set of properties occurs so often should be enough to make us interested in studying the properties of groups. In addition, however, the theory of group structure turns out to be most useful in many applications (including, it seems, the theory of elementary particles). In this and the next section, we will study some of the elementary properties of groups.

First, let us observe that we often find that two different groups are really identical, or at least can be considered so. The group of all real numbers under addition and the group of all positive reals under multiplication are an example. How is it that we can say these two groups are the same? Because they have the same structure. If x is any real number, set $x' = e^x$. This defines a one-to-one mapping of the set of all reals onto the set of all positive reals. But this mapping preserves the group structure. That is, if $x + y = z$, then $x'y' = z'$. The identity in the set of all reals (0) maps to the multiplicative identity, 1, and so on. We say that the two groups are *isomorphic.*

Definition 4–30. Let G and H be two groups and let ϕ be a mapping of G into H, that is $\phi: G \to H$. Then:

1. ϕ is called a *homomorphism* if and only if $\phi(ab) = \phi(a)\phi(b)$ for every a and b in G.
2. ϕ is called an *isomorphism* if it is a homomorphism and, in addition, is one-to-one.
3. The *image* and *kernel* of ϕ are defined by $\text{im}\,\phi = \{\phi(x) \mid x \in G\}$ and $\ker \phi = \{x \in G \mid \phi(x) = e\}$.
4. If ϕ is an isomorphism and $H = \text{im}\,\phi$, then G and H are called *isomorphic.*

(Two isomorphic groups are essentially the same and will be said to be representatives of the same abstract group.)

The reader can easily prove

Theorem 4–46. Let $\phi: G \to H$ be a homomorphism between the groups G and H. Then $\phi(e) = e$, $\phi(a^{-1}) = [\phi(a)]^{-1}$, and ϕ is an isomorphism if and only if $\ker \phi$ consists of the identity alone.

Note that we use the same symbol, e, to represent the identity in either group. Also we use the same multiplicative notation for the group operation in both groups. Only in rare cases do we need to make a more careful distinction.

Let us start by discussing some properties of finite groups.

Definition 4–31. A group which contains only a finite number of elements is called a *finite group*, and the number of elements in the group is called the *order* of the group.

A group can be defined by giving its multiplication table. If we have two elements a and b, we can indicate the "product" ab in such a table by placing ab in the row whose first element is a and the column whose top element is b. That is:

$$\begin{array}{ccc} & & b \\ & & \vdots \\ a & \cdots & ab. \end{array}$$

There is a group of order one. It consists of the identity alone. A group of order two contains only one element besides the identity. The only possible group table is thus:

$$\begin{array}{c|c} e & a \\ \hline a & e \end{array}\,. \tag{4–28}$$

It is simple to verify that this table does indeed define a group. Properties (1), (3), and (4) of Definition 4–29 are trivial. Property (2) takes some checking, but this is easily done.

A nonabelian group must contain the identity, two distinct elements to be multiplied, and the two distinct products. The reader can easily verify that if any two of the five elements e, a, b, ab, ba were the same, we must have $ab = ba$. Thus a nonabelian group must contain at least five elements. We will see later that there is only one possible abstract group of order five and it is abelian.

A nonabelian group of order six does exist. Its multiplication table is:

e	a	b	f	g	h
a	b	e	g	h	f
b	e	a	h	f	g
f	h	g	e	b	a
g	f	h	a	e	b
h	g	f	b	a	e

(4-29)

How can we verify that this table does indeed define a group? Property (1) of the definition is automatic. Just writing down a table gives it. Property (3) holds because e is the "upper left-hand corner" of the table. It is therefore an identity on both the right and the left.

Property (4) follows from the fact that an e appears in each row and column and all the e's are symmetrically located with respect to the major diagonal (so if $ab = e$, then $ba = e$ also; hence b is both a right and left inverse of a).

Given any a and b, we must be able to solve $ax = b$ for x (in fact $x = a^{-1}b$). Thus each row of the table must contain every element of the group exactly once. The same is true for the columns.

Property (2) is the one which cannot be verified easily from the group table. The reader is invited to verify it for this case to see how tedious it is.

These groups are "abstract groups." Each is a set of elements with a group operation. They have no "physical meaning." Nevertheless, like a great many groups of interest, they arise naturally in some "physical way." When they do, they usually arise as groups of "operators" rather than as groups of "objects." A group operation then is usually a composition of two operations. We will give two examples to illustrate this.

The first example is the group of rotations of the plane (about the origin) through multiples of $2\pi/n$, where n is some positive integer. This group is called the cyclic group of order n, and is symbolized (as an abstract group) by Z_n. The elements of this group are the identity e (no rotation), another element a (rotation through $2\pi/n$), and all possible powers of a. Thus a^k represents the rotation through $2\pi k/n$ for any integer k.

The powers of a commute, and we have $a^k a^j = a^{k+j}$ for any integers k and j. However, $a^n = e$. Thus we can remove (or add) multiples of n so as to leave only powers between 0 and $n - 1$ ($a^0 = a^n = e$). Note that the inverse of an element a^k is $a^{-k} = a^{n-k}$.

The group Z_n is completely characterized by saying that it is generated by the element a with the relation $a^n = e$. When the group contains an element a, it must contain all powers of that element. The relation $a^n = e$ then reduces the group to exactly n elements.

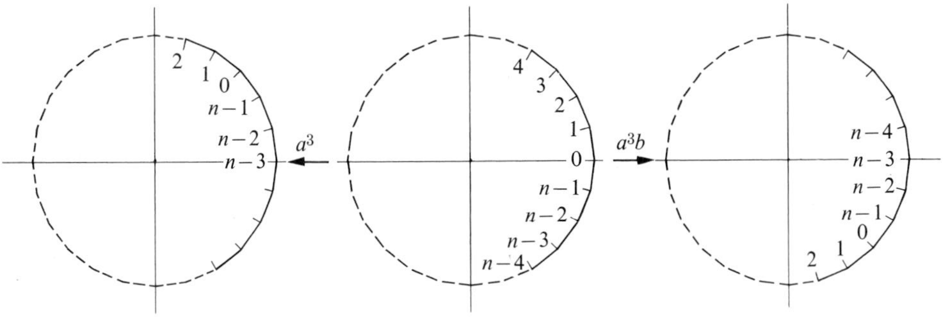

Fig. 4–3

This group Z_n is a group of proper rotations. We can also define a group which contains reflections; this is the dihedral group of order $2n$, which we denote by D_{2n}. This group consists of the rotations of the plane (about the origin) through all possible multiples of $2\pi/n$ together with possible reflections. It suffices to consider the single reflection about the x-axis. Let b denote this reflection and a denote the rotation through $2\pi/n$, as before. Then the group is easily seen to consist of the $2n$ elements $e, a, a^2, \ldots, a^{n-1}, b, ab, a^2b, \ldots, a^{n-1}b$. Here, since the elements of the group are being thought of as operators (i.e., mappings), we consider a^kb to mean reflection followed by rotation. Figure 4–3 indicates the nature of these operations, when applied to a regular polygon with n sides whose vertices have been numbered.

The dihedral group is related to the cyclic group exactly as the group of all rotations of the plane is related to the group of proper rotations.

Every element of the group D_{2n} must be the product of finite powers of a and b. However, $b^2 = e$ and $a^n = e$. Hence we need only consider powers of b which are either 0 or 1 and powers of a which are between 0 and $n - 1$. Thus any element must be of the form $a^{k_1}ba^{k_2}b \cdots ba^{k_n}$ (where the first or last power can be a zero).

We can simplify this list even further. It is easy to verify from the definition in terms of the rotations, that $ba^k = a^{-k}b$. All of the b's can thus be "worked through" until they reach the right-hand end. There they combine to give either $b^0 = e$ or b. Thus the group is generated by the two elements a and b with the relations

$$a^n = e, \qquad b^2 = e, \qquad ba^k = a^{-k}b,$$

and consists of the $2n$ elements listed earlier.

It is easy to see that $D_2 = Z_2$. This is the group of (4–28). However, D_4 differs from Z_4. The group tables of these two groups are:

Z_4: e	a	a^2	a^3
a	a^2	a^3	e
a^2	a^3	e	a
a^3	e	a	a^2

D_4: e	a	b	ab
a	e	ab	b
b	ab	e	a
ab	b	a	e

Any rearrangement of the order of elements will change the group table around. But the number of e's on the major diagonal is unchanged. Therefore these two groups are different. In D_4 the square of every element is e. The reader can easily verify that (4–29) is the group table for the dihedral group D_6.

The general form of the group table for a dihedral group is:

$$
D_{2n}:\quad
\begin{array}{c|cccccccc}
e & a & a^2 & \cdots & b & ab & a^2b & \cdots \\
\hline
a & a^2 & a^3 & \cdots & ab & a^2b & a^3b & \cdots \\
a^2 & a^3 & a^4 & \cdots & a^2b & a^3b & a^4b & \cdots \\
\vdots & \vdots & \vdots & & \vdots & \vdots & \vdots & \\
b & a^{n-1}b & a^{n-2}b & \cdots & e & a^{n-1} & a^{n-2} & \cdots \\
ab & b & a^{n-1}b & \cdots & a & e & a^{n-1} & \cdots \\
a^2b & ab & b & \cdots & a^2 & a & e & \cdots \\
\vdots & \vdots & \vdots & & \vdots & \vdots & \vdots &
\end{array}
$$

Now we wish to turn to the investigation of the structure of groups. For this purpose, we must give some definitions.

Definition 4–32. Let H be a subset of the group G. Then H is called a *subgroup* of G if and only if it is itself a group with respect to the operation defined on G.

Note that to show that a subset is a subgroup, it suffices to show that it is closed under the group operation and under inversion; that is, if a and b are any elements in H then a^{-1} and ab are also in H. If this is true, then e is automatically in H (so long as H contains any element at all) and the associative property is satisfied.

Definition 4–33. Let G be a group and let A be a subgroup of G. For any element $b \in G$, define

$$
\begin{aligned}
Ab &= \{x \in G \mid x = ab,\, a \in A\}, \\
bA &= \{x \in G \mid x = ba,\, a \in A\}.
\end{aligned}
$$

These sets are called *right* and *left cosets* of A, respectively.

Theorem 4–47. Any two right (left) cosets of a subgroup A of a group G are either disjoint or identical.

Proof. We will prove this theorem only for right cosets. The proof for left cosets is essentially the same. Suppose that Ab and Ac are not disjoint. Then there is some element d common to both, that is, $d = a_1b = a_2c$, where we use a's with subscripts to denote different elements of A. Then, since A is a subgroup, $a_1^{-1}a_2 = a_3$, some element in A, and hence

$$b = a_1^{-1}a_2c = a_3c.$$

Now suppose that $x \in Ab$. Then $x = a_4b = a_4a_3c = a_5c$. Hence $x \in Ac$. Thus $Ab \subset Ac$. In the same way, we can show that $Ac \subset Ab$. Hence the two cosets must be the same. ∎

Theorem 4–48. Let A be a subgroup of the finite group G. Then the order of A is a divisor of the order of G.

Proof. Since any element b of the group G is in the coset Ab, G is the union of all of its cosets. However, by the last theorem, G must be the union of some number (say k) of disjoint cosets. Now, the mapping $\phi : A \to Ab$ defined by $\phi(a) = ab$ is onto (by definition of the coset Ab), and one-to-one since $a_1 b = a_2 b$ implies $a_1 bb^{-1} = a_2 bb^{-1}$. Hence, if m is the order of A, then every coset contains exactly m elements. G therefore contains exactly mk elements. ▌

Definition 4–34. Let a be an element of the group G. Then the set of all integral powers of a is called *the cyclic subgroup of G generated by a*. The order of this subgroup is called the *order* of the element a.

Thus the order of an element a is the smallest positive integer m such that $a^m = e$. The reader should verify that the set of all integral powers of the element a does form a subgroup.

By Theorem 4–48, the order of an element must be a divisor of the order of the group. If the group is of prime order p, then the only divisors of p are 1 and p itself. e is the only element with order 1. If an element has order p, then it must generate the entire group. That is:

Theorem 4–49. The only abstract group of prime order p is Z_p.

We note that every group of composite order must contain a proper subgroup (that is, a subgroup which is not the entire group or the element e alone). Suppose that G is of order $n = rs$, $1 < r < n$, $1 < s < n$. Then if G contains an element of order less than n, this result is obvious. On the other hand, if the element a is of order n, then the element a^r is of order s, or less. Thus in either case G must contain a cyclic subgroup of lower order than n.

PROBLEMS

1. Find all the subgroups of D_6.
2. Construct the group table for the set of all proper rotations in R^3 (about the origin) which carry the coordinate axes into one another. (This is called the group of proper rotations of the cube.)
3. Repeat Problem 2 for the set of rotations plus reflections which satisfy the same properties.
4. The set of all permutations of the first n positive integers forms a group, called the *permutation* or *symmetric group* of degree n, and denoted by S_n. (See Section 3–2.) This group has a subgroup consisting of all the even permutations, which is called the *alternating group* of degree n and is denoted by A_n.
   a) Construct the group table for S_3 and A_3. Identify these.
   b) Construct the group tables for S_4 and A_4.
5. Given that ϕ is a homomorphism of the group G into the group H, prove that $\phi(e) = e$.

4–9. FACTOR GROUPS

Given any two groups, we can construct a new group out of them.

Definition 4–35. Let A and B be two groups. Then the *direct product* of A and B is the group of all ordered pairs of elements from A and B, that is,

$$A \times B = \{\langle a, b\rangle \mid a \in A, b \in B\},$$

where the group operation in $A \times B$ is defined by

$$\langle a, b\rangle\langle c, d\rangle = \langle ac, bd\rangle.$$

The reader can easily verify that the direct product is a group. The identity is the element $\langle e, e\rangle$. There are two natural subgroups of the direct product:

$$A' = \langle A, e\rangle = \{\langle a, e\rangle \mid a \in A\},$$
$$B' = \langle e, B\rangle = \{\langle e, b\rangle \mid b \in B\}.$$

The subgroup A' is isomorphic to A, and the subgroup B' is isomorphic to B. For this reason, one sometimes finds references to A being a subgroup of $A \times B$, despite the fact that it could not possibly be so, according to the definition given here.

Note that every element of A' commutes with every element of B'. Furthermore, every element of $A \times B$ is the product of an element of A' with an element of B'.

Thus, we could say that the group $A \times B$ is generated by the elements of the group A and the elements of the group B, together with the relations between the elements of A, the relations between the elements of B, and the one further relation that every element of A commutes with every element of B. From this point of view, we see that A and B are subgroups of $A \times B$.

This last method of describing $A \times B$ is sometimes used as a definition. It may even be better than the definition given in some contexts, but this description can lead to difficulties. An operation may already be defined between the elements of A and B. We must then distinguish carefully between this operation and the "new" operation which defines the elements of $A \times B$.

This difficulty arises particularly when we consider the direct product of a group with *itself*. In order to give a proper definition, we must then use different symbols in the two "copies" of the group. Thus $Z_3 \times Z_3$, for example, can be viewed as the group generated by the two elements a and b with the three relations, $a^3 = e$, $b^3 = e$ and $ab = ba$.

Many times, a group can be decomposed into the direct product of two subgroups (or, rather, it is isomorphic to the direct product of two subgroups). When this situation occurs, we know a great deal about the structure of the group. For example,

Theorem 4–50. If n and m have no common factors other than 1, then $Z_{nm} = Z_n \times Z_m$.

Proof. Let a generate Z_n and b generate Z_m. Then every element of $Z_n \times Z_m$ can be written in the form $a^k b^j$, where we have the relation $ab = ba$. Consider the element $c = ab$. Then $c^k = a^k b^k$. This will be the identity if and only if k is a multiple of both n and m. Since m and n are given as relatively prime, the smallest common multiple of these two is nm. Therefore we easily see that c is of order nm and generates $Z_n \times Z_m$. ▮

Another result along these lines is the following The proof is left as an exercise.

Theorem 4–51. If n is odd, then $D_{4n} = D_{2n} \times Z_2$.

For every n we have the group Z_n. For every even n we also have the dihedral group D_n. There are at least two groups of every even order (except for order two, since $Z_2 = D_2$). Are there any others? The answer is yes. There are a great many groups of some orders. The reader may be interested in seeing a list of all of the groups of order 16 or less.

Order	Groups	Order	Groups
1	Z_1	9	$Z_9, Z_3 \times Z_3$
2	Z_2	10	Z_{10}, D_{10}
3	Z_3	11	Z_{11}
4	$Z_4, D_4 (= Z_2 \times Z_2)$	12	$Z_{12}, Z_6 \times Z_2, D_{12}, Q_{12}, A_4$
5	Z_5	13	Z_{13}
6	Z_6, D_6	14	Z_{14}, D_{14}
7	Z_7	15	Z_{15}
8	$Z_8, Z_4 \times Z_2,$ $Z_2 \times Z_2 \times Z_2,$ D_8, Q_8	16	$Z_{16}, Z_4 \times Z_4, Z_8 \times Z_2,$ $Z_4 \times Z_2 \times Z_2,$ $Z_2 \times Z_2 \times Z_2 \times Z_2,$ $D_{16}, Q_{16}, D_8 \times Z_2, Q_8 \times Z_2$

The last two theorems show that some of these groups have more than one representation. For example, Z_{14} could be represented as $Z_7 \times Z_2$, and Z_{12} as $Z_3 \times Z_4$. Similarly, $D_{12} = D_6 \times Z_2$.

In this table, the group A_4 is the alternating group of degree 4 of Problem 4 of the last section. The Q_{4n} listed here are the *quaternion groups*. The quaternion group Q_{4n} is generated by the two elements a and b with the relations

$$a^{2n} = e, \qquad b^2 = a^n, \qquad ba = a^{-1}b.$$

The problem of discovering all the groups of a given order is extremely difficult. A general solution has not yet been found. We cannot even show that the above table contains all of the groups of order 16 or less without a great deal more theory.

The symmetric group of degree n, S_n, was mentioned in Problem 4 of the last section. It is the group of all permutations of the first n positive integers (see Section

3–2). The group S_n is of order $n!$. These groups are quite important in the theory of groups; they are especially rich in subgroups. A surprising fact is that every finite group of order n must be a subgroup of S_n. We will prove this here. The proof we give is quite important since it offers an introduction to the idea of matrix representations for groups.

Let P_n be the set of all $n \times n$ permutation matrices (Definition 3–5). With the help of Theorem 3–3 one can easily show that P_n is actually isomorphic to S_n, the group operation in P_n being matrix multiplication. In fact, we could have used this criterion to define the symmetric group. Note that the alternating group A_n is then isomorphic to the subgroup of P_n consisting of those matrices with positive determinant.

Theorem 4–52. Any finite group of order n is isomorphic to a subgroup of the symmetric group S_n,

Proof. Let G be a group containing n elements, $b_1, b_2, \ldots, b_n$ (one of these will be e, but it is not necessary to distinguish it at this time). For each i, j, and k define

$$\gamma_{ijk} = \begin{cases} 1 & \text{if } b_i b_j = b_k, \\ 0 & \text{otherwise.} \end{cases}$$

For each μ, define the matrix

$$\Gamma(b_\mu) = [\gamma_{i\mu j}]_{i,j},$$

where the subscript i, j outside the brackets indicates that the subscript i identifies the row while j identifies the column.

For each fixed μ and each i, there is exactly one j such that $b_i b_\mu = b_j$. Hence, the ith row of $\Gamma(b_\mu)$ contains one and only one 1. Indeed, this row is merely the (vector) representation of $b_i b_\mu$ in terms of the basis $b_1, b_2, \ldots, b_n$. As i runs from 1 through n, $b_i b_\mu$ runs through all the b_j without any repetition. We conclude that $\Gamma(b_\mu)$ is a permutation matrix. We have therefore constructed a mapping from G to P_n. We next wish to show that this mapping is an isomorphism. Then we can conclude that G is isomorphic to im Γ, which must be a subgroup of P_n.

We begin by proving that Γ is a homomorphism. Let

$$\Gamma(b_\mu)\Gamma(b_\nu) = [\gamma_{i\mu j}][\gamma_{j\nu k}] = [c_{ik}].$$

Fix i. Let $b_i b_\mu = b_{j_0}$ and $b_{j_0} b_\nu = b_{k_0}$. The only nonzero element in row i of $\Gamma(b_\mu)$ is in column j_0. The element c_{ik} is nonzero only for that k for which $\gamma_{j_0 \nu k} \neq 0$, i.e., for $k = k_0$. Thus

$$c_{ik_0} = 1,$$
$$c_{ik} = 0 \quad \text{for} \quad k \neq k_0.$$

However, $b_i(b_\mu b_\nu) = b_{j_0} b_\nu = b_{k_0}$. It thus follows that $\Gamma(b_\mu)\Gamma(b_\nu) = [c_{ik}] = \Gamma(b_\mu b_\nu)$.

To complete the proof, we must show that Γ is one-to-one. To do this, it suffices to prove that the kernel of Γ consists of the element e alone. This is left as an exercise. ▌

The collection of all right cosets (or of all left cosets) of a group sometimes form a group themselves. In order to do so, a group operation must be defined. If A is a subgroup and $Ae = A, Ab_1, \ldots, Ab_k$ are all of the right cosets of a group G, then the obvious way to try to define a group operation on the cosets is to set

$$(Ab_i)(Ab_j) = A(b_ib_j). \tag{4–30}$$

Is this a valid definition? To show that it is, we must show that if $Ab = Ab'$ and $Ac = Ac'$, then $A(bc) = A(b'c')$. In view of Theorem 4–47, it is enough to prove that $b'c' \in A(bc)$.

The assumptions $Ab = Ab'$ and $Ac = Ac'$ imply that $a_1b = a_2b'$ and $a_3c = a_4c'$, where we let a_i represent arbitrary elements in A. Hence $b' = a_2^{-1}a_1b = a_5b$, and similarly $c' = a_6c$. Then

$$b'c' = a_5ba_6c.$$

This is not necessarily an element of $A(bc)$. However, if we knew that for any b, and any $a_6 \in A$ there existed an element $a_7 \in A$ such that $ba_6 = a_7b$, then $b'c' = a_5a_7bc = a_8bc$, and the desired result would be proved.

Definition 4–36. A subgroup A of a group G is called a *normal subgroup* if and only if $Ab = bA$ for every $b \in G$. If A is a normal subgroup of G, then the group whose elements are the cosets of A and whose group operation is defined by (4–30) is called the *factor group* of G modulo A and is denoted by G/A.

It is often quite difficult to tell whether a given subgroup is normal or not. There are, however, some cases in which it is relatively easy.

Theorem 4–53. A is a normal subgroup of the finite group G if any of the following conditions hold:

1. The order of A is one-half of the order of G.
2. A is the only subgroup of G with its order.
3. A is a subgroup of the abelian group G.

Proof. 1. If b is any element of A, then $Ab = bA = A$. If $b \notin A$, then there is only one remaining coset, $A' = \{x \mid x \notin A\}$. Thus $Ab = bA = A'$ in this case also.

2. If A is a subgroup of G and b is any element of G, then $b^{-1}Ab$ is also a subgroup of G, as can be easily verified. If A is *not* a normal subgroup of G, then $Ab \neq bA$ for some $b \in G$. Suppose, for example, that the element $c \in Ab$ but not in bA. Then $b^{-1}c \in b^{-1}Ab$ but is not in A. Hence $b^{-1}Ab \neq A$. However, the order of these two subgroups is the same. Hence, if A is the only subgroup of this order, it must be a normal subgroup.

The reader is asked to prove part (3) as an exercise. ▮

If G is the direct product of two groups, that is, if $G = A \times B$, then $\langle A, e\rangle = A'$ is a normal subgroup of G since every element of B' commutes with every element of A'.

In this case, G/A' is essentially the same as B. That is:

Theorem 4–54. Let $G = A \times B$. Then $A' = \langle A, e\rangle$ is a normal subgroup of G, and G/A' is isomorphic to B.

Proof. For any $\langle a, b\rangle \in G$,

$$\langle A, e\rangle\langle a, b\rangle = \langle A, b\rangle = \langle a, b\rangle\langle A, e\rangle.$$

Hence A' is a normal subgroup. Every coset of A' is of the form $\langle A, b\rangle$, and each $b \in B$ gives rise to a distinct coset. The mapping $\tau : B \to G/A'$ defined by $\tau(b) = \langle A, b\rangle$ is easily shown to be an isomorphism. ▮

Unfortunately the converse of this theorem is not true in all cases. Even if A is a normal subgroup of G, G may not be isomorphic to $(G/A) \times A$. The example of Z_4 with its subgroup Z_2 shows this. The concept of a factor group is very useful in some situations, however. One of the most important results concerns the decomposition of homomorphisms.

Theorem 4–55. If K is a normal subgroup of G, then there exists a homomorphism π of G onto G/K whose kernel is K.

Define the function $\pi : G \to G/K$ by $\pi(a) = Ka$. The proof that this is the desired homomorphism is left as an exercise.

Theorem 4–56. If ϕ is a homomorphism of the group G onto the group H, $\phi : G \to H$, then $K = \ker \phi$ is a normal subgroup of G, and G/K is isomorphic to H.

Proof. First, we show that $K = \ker \phi$ is a subgroup of G. If a and b are in K, then $\phi(a) = \phi(b) = e$. Hence $\phi(ab) = \phi(a)\phi(b) = e$, and K is closed under the group product. Also, $\phi(a^{-1}) = e\phi(a^{-1}) = \phi(a)\phi(a^{-1}) = \phi(e) = e$. Hence a^{-1} is in K also.

Next, we show that K is a normal subgroup. We show first that

$$Ka = \{x \mid \phi(x) = \phi(a)\}.$$

If $x \in Ka$, then $x = ka$ for some $k \in K$, and $\phi(x) = \phi(k)\phi(a) = \phi(a)$. On the other hand, if $\phi(x) = \phi(a)$, then $\phi(xa^{-1}) = e$, and hence $xa^{-1} = k \in K$. But then $x = ka$. In exactly the same way we can show that $aK = \{x \mid \phi(x) = \phi(a)\}$. Hence $aK = Ka$, and K is a normal subgroup.

Finally, we define the function $\bar{\phi} : G/K \to H$ by $\bar{\phi}(Ka) = \phi(a)$. The reader can easily establish that this is the desired isomorphism. Observe in this regard that $\bar{\phi} \circ \pi = \phi$:

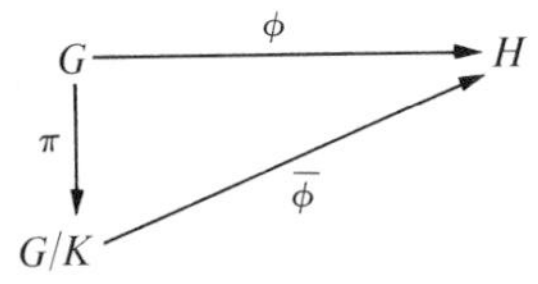

PROBLEMS

1. Make a table of all of the groups of order eight or less, listing the number of elements for each order in the group. For example, the groups of orders nine and ten give the table:

Group	Number of elements of order 1	2	3	5	9	10
Z_9	1		2		6	
$Z_3 \times Z_3$	1		8			
Z_{10}	1	1		4		4
D_{10}	1	5		4		

2. Complete the proof of Theorem 4–52.
3. Let A be a subgroup of the group G and let b be an element of G. Prove that the mapping $\phi: A \to b^{-1}Ab$ defined by $\phi(a) = b^{-1}ab$ is an isomorphism.
4. Prove part (3) of Theorem 4–53.
5. Provide the details of the argument for the proof of Theorem 4–54.
6. Prove Theorem 4–55.
7. Complete the proof of Theorem 4–56.

4–10. MATRIX GROUPS

In this section we wish to give a very brief introduction to certain classes of matrix groups. We will define the standard types and show something about how some groups can be represented by groups of matrices. We cannot, however, go very deeply into this theory here.

There are many different types of infinite groups. For example, there is the obvious extension of the cyclic groups of Section 4–8 to the infinite cyclic group Z. This is the additive group of all integers. Another infinite group is the additive group of all rational numbers, which differs from Z in that it is not generated by a single element as Z is; still a third distinct group is the group of all real numbers under the operation of addition. These are particularly simple types of groups. More interesting are the various classes of matrix groups.

The product of any two nonsingular matrices is also a nonsingular matrix. The inverse of a nonsingular matrix is also nonsingular. Thus the set of all nonsingular $n \times n$ matrices forms a group under the operation of matrix multiplication. This is not the only group of $n \times n$ matrices, however. There are a large number of these groups which can be considered. Here we will merely list nine of the most important. The main reason we restrict ourselves to these nine is that they involve only concepts we have already introduced. In each case, we give the commonly used name for the group, the symbol which is used to denote it, and the defining property. The reader should have no trouble showing that each is a group. In fact, it is easy to see that each of (3) through (9) is a subgroup of either (1) or (2). [Note that (2) is itself a subgroup of (1).]

For each n we have the following types of matrix groups.

1. *The general linear group*, $GL(n, C)$: all nonsingular $n \times n$ (complex) matrices.
2. *The general real group*, $GL(n, R)$: all nonsingular $n \times n$ real matrices.
3. *The special linear group*, $SL(n, C)$: all matrices in $GL(n, C)$ whose determinant is equal to 1.
4. *The special real group*, $SL(n, R)$: all matrices in $GL(n, R)$ whose determinant is equal to 1.
5. *The unitary group*, $U(n)$: all matrices A in $GL(n, C)$ such that $A^{-1} = A^*$.
6. *The orthogonal group*, $O(n, C)$: all matrices A in $GL(n, C)$ such that $A^{-1} = A^t$.
7. *The real orthogonal group*, $O(n)$: all matrices A in $GL(n, R)$ such that $A^{-1} = A^t$.
8. *The special orthogonal group*, $SO(n)$: all matrices in $O(n)$ such that $\det A = +1$.
9. *The special unitary group*, $SU(n)$: all matrices A in $U(n)$ such that $\det A = +1$.

We recall that the group $O(n)$ can be identified with the group of all (general) rotations in R^n and $SO(n)$ with all the proper rotations. Interpretations of some of these groups are also possible, but others are difficult (or impossible) to visualize.

This list by no means exhausts the supply of matrix groups. Many other types are possible. For example, we can even identify the multiplicative group of all nonzero complex numbers with a group of real matrices.

Let the complex number $z = x + iy$ correspond to the matrix

$$\begin{bmatrix} x & y \\ -y & x \end{bmatrix}.$$

It can be verified without difficulty that multiplication of two complex numbers corresponds to the multiplication of the two matrices. Note also that the determinant of this matrix is the square of the magnitude of the complex number. Thus under this association the set of all complex numbers with magnitude 1 corresponds to $SO(2)$. Therefore, the group of proper rotations of the plane is isomorphic to the group of all complex numbers whose magnitude is 1 (multiplication being the group operation).

In the above representation of C, we can write

$$\begin{bmatrix} x & y \\ -y & x \end{bmatrix} = x\begin{bmatrix} 1 & 0 \\ 0 & 1 \end{bmatrix} + y\begin{bmatrix} 0 & 1 \\ -1 & 0 \end{bmatrix}$$

using the addition and scalar multiplication of matrices. The set of all such matrices is then formally a vector space with the two basis vectors I and

$$I' = \begin{bmatrix} 0 & 1 \\ -1 & 0 \end{bmatrix}.$$

(This is of course exactly the additive structure of the complex numbers.) Thus we have a vector space on which is imposed a multiplicative structure. Such structures are important enough to deserve a special name.

Definition 4-37. Let $\mathcal{A}$ be a vector space and suppose that a binary operation of multiplication exists in $\mathcal{A}$, that is, a function $\mu:\mathcal{A} \times \mathcal{A} \to \mathcal{A}$, which we write in the form $\mu(\mathbf{X}, \mathbf{Y}) = \mathbf{XY}$. Suppose that this multiplication satisfies the properties:

1. μ is associative, i.e., $(\mathbf{XY})\mathbf{Z} = \mathbf{X}(\mathbf{YZ})$ for every $\mathbf{X}$, $\mathbf{Y}$, and $\mathbf{Z}$ in $\mathcal{A}$.
2. $\mathbf{X}(\mathbf{Y} + \mathbf{Z}) = (\mathbf{XY}) + (\mathbf{XZ})$ and $(\mathbf{Y} + \mathbf{Z})\mathbf{W} = (\mathbf{YW}) + (\mathbf{ZW})$ for any vectors $\mathbf{X}$, $\mathbf{Y}$, $\mathbf{Z}$, and $\mathbf{W}$ in $\mathcal{A}$.
3. $t(\mathbf{XY}) = (t\mathbf{X})\mathbf{Y} = \mathbf{X}(t\mathbf{Y})$ for all vectors $\mathbf{X}$ and $\mathbf{Y}$ and all scalars t.

Then $\mathcal{A}$ is called an (associative) *algebra* over the scalar field of the vector space $\mathcal{A}$. If there exists an element $\mathbf{e}$ in $\mathcal{A}$ such that $\mathbf{eX} = \mathbf{Xe} = \mathbf{X}$ for every $\mathbf{X}$ in $\mathcal{A}$, then $\mathcal{A}$ is called an algebra with a *unit*.

Nonassociative algebras can also be considered, but their theory is quite difficult. Note that we did not assume that the multiplication in the algebra was commutative.

The algebras that we are particularly interested in are those in which the multiplicative structure gives rise to a group. However, even without this assumption, we can show that if the algebra is finite dimensional (as a vector space), then it always has a representation as a set of matrices. Matrix addition, matrix multiplication, and scalar multiplication correspond to vector addition, the algebra multiplication, and the scalar multiplication in the algebra, respectively.

Theorem 4-57. Let $\langle \mathbf{B}_1, \mathbf{B}_2, \ldots, \mathbf{B}_n \rangle$ be a basis for the algebra $\mathcal{A}$. For every i and j, let the scalars γ_{ijk} be defined by

$$\mathbf{B}_i\mathbf{B}_j = \sum_{k=1}^{n} \gamma_{ijk}\mathbf{B}_k.$$

for each ν, define the matrix

$$\Gamma(\mathbf{B}_\nu) = [\gamma_{i\nu j}]_{i,j}.$$

Then the $n \times n$ matrices $\Gamma(\mathbf{B}_\nu)$, $\nu = 1, 2, \ldots, n$, form a basis for the representation of $\mathcal{A}$ in which matrix addition and multiplication correspond to vector addition and multiplication in $\mathcal{A}$.

Proof. The following proof is merely a generalization of the proof of Theorem 4-52. Because of the linearity conditions, we can extend the definition of the mapping Γ to all vectors in $\mathcal{A}$. That is, given any $\mathbf{X} = \sum_{\nu=1}^{n} x_\nu \mathbf{B}_\nu$, we can define

$$\Gamma(\mathbf{X}) = \Gamma\left(\sum_{\nu=1}^{n} x_\nu \mathbf{B}_\nu\right) = \sum_{\nu=1}^{n} x_\nu \Gamma(\mathbf{B}_\nu) = \left[\sum_{\nu=1}^{n} x_\nu \gamma_{i\nu j}\right]_{i,j}.$$

It is clear that to prove the theorem, it suffices to prove that, for any ν and μ,

$$\Gamma(\mathbf{B}_\nu)\Gamma(\mathbf{B}_\mu) = \Gamma(\mathbf{B}_\nu\mathbf{B}_\mu).$$

The right-hand side of this equation is

$$\Gamma(\mathbf{B}_\nu\mathbf{B}_\mu) = \Gamma\left(\sum_{k=1}^{n} \gamma_{\nu\mu k}\mathbf{B}_k\right) = \left[\sum_{k=1}^{n} \gamma_{\nu\mu k}\gamma_{ikj}\right]_{i,j}.$$

The left-hand side is

$$\Gamma(\mathbf{B}_\nu)\Gamma(\mathbf{B}_\mu) = [\gamma_{i\nu k}]_{i,k}[\gamma_{k\mu j}]_{k,j} = \left[\sum_{k=1}^{n} \gamma_{i\nu k}\gamma_{k\mu j}\right]_{i,j}.$$

Thus in order to prove the theorem, we must show that for every i, j, ν, and μ

$$\sum_{k=1}^{n} \gamma_{\nu\mu k}\gamma_{ikj} = \sum_{k=1}^{n} \gamma_{i\nu k}\gamma_{k\mu j}. \tag{4–31}$$

This is proved by considering

$$\mathbf{B}_i(\mathbf{B}_\nu\mathbf{B}_\mu) = \mathbf{B}_i \sum_{k=1}^{n} \gamma_{\nu\mu k}\mathbf{B}_k = \sum_{k=1}^{n} \gamma_{\nu\mu k}\mathbf{B}_i\mathbf{B}_k = \sum_{k=1}^{n}\sum_{j=1}^{n} \gamma_{\nu\mu k}\gamma_{ikj}\mathbf{B}_j$$

and

$$(\mathbf{B}_i\mathbf{B}_\nu)\mathbf{B}_\mu = \sum_{k=1}^{n} \gamma_{i\nu k}\mathbf{B}_k\mathbf{B}_\mu = \sum_{k=1}^{n}\sum_{j=1}^{n} \gamma_{i\nu k}\gamma_{k\mu j}\mathbf{B}_j.$$

The associative property shows that these two expressions are the same, and hence (4–31) must hold since the coefficients of $\mathbf{B}_j$ must be the same in each. The theorem then follows. ▌

The representation obtained in this way is clearly not unique. It depends on the choice of the basis. If we change to another basis, we will obtain another representation. We can easily find the relation between the two representations, however.

Suppose that we have an algebra $\mathcal{A}$ with basis $\langle \mathbf{B}_1, \mathbf{B}_2, \ldots, \mathbf{B}_n \rangle$ as above and that $\langle \mathbf{B}'_1, \mathbf{B}'_2, \ldots, \mathbf{B}'_n \rangle$ is another basis for $\mathcal{A}$. Let $P = [p_{ij}]$ be the change of basis matrix and $Q = [q_{ij}]$ its inverse. That is,

$$\mathbf{B}_j = \sum_{i=1}^{n} p_{ij}\mathbf{B}'_i, \qquad \mathbf{B}'_j = \sum_{i=1}^{n} q_{ij}\mathbf{B}_i.$$

Now let us compute the representation of a vector $\mathbf{X}$ with respect to the two different bases. Because of linearity, it is enough to let $\mathbf{X}$ be one of the basis vectors, say $\mathbf{X} = \mathbf{B}_\mu$. The general $\mathbf{X}$ is a linear combination of these basis vectors.

Suppose then that we compute the two representations of $\mathbf{B}_\mu$. In terms of the first basis, it is simply

$$\Gamma(\mathbf{B}_\mu) = [\gamma_{i\mu j}]_{i,j}.$$

In terms of the second basis, we find

$$\Gamma'(\mathbf{B}_\mu) = \Gamma'\left(\sum_{\nu=1}^{n} p_{\nu\mu}\mathbf{B}'_\nu\right) = \sum_{\nu=1}^{n} p_{\nu\mu}\Gamma'(\mathbf{B}'_\nu) = \sum_{\nu=1}^{n} p_{\nu\mu}[\gamma'_{i\nu j}]_{i,j},$$

where

$$\mathbf{B}'_i\mathbf{B}'_\nu = \sum_{j=1}^{n} \gamma'_{i\nu j}\mathbf{B}'_j.$$

However,

$$\mathbf{B}'_i\mathbf{B}'_\nu = \left(\sum_{\lambda=1}^{n} q_{\lambda i}\mathbf{B}_\lambda\right)\left(\sum_{\rho=1}^{n} q_{\rho\nu}\mathbf{B}_\rho\right) = \sum_{\lambda=1}^{n}\sum_{\rho=1}^{n}\sum_{l=1}^{n} q_{\lambda i}q_{\rho\nu}\gamma_{\lambda\rho l}\mathbf{B}_l$$

$$= \sum_{\lambda=1}^{n}\sum_{\rho=1}^{n}\sum_{l=1}^{n}\sum_{j=1}^{n} q_{\lambda i}q_{\rho\nu}\gamma_{\lambda\rho l}p_{jl}\mathbf{B}'_j.$$

Therefore,

$$\gamma'_{i\nu j} = \sum_{\lambda=1}^{n}\sum_{\rho=1}^{n}\sum_{l=1}^{n} p_{jl}q_{\lambda i}q_{\rho\nu}\gamma_{\lambda\rho l}.$$

Putting this into the expression computed above, we find

$$\Gamma'(\mathbf{B}_\mu) = \left[\sum_{\nu=1}^{n}\sum_{\lambda=1}^{n}\sum_{\rho=1}^{n}\sum_{l=1}^{n} p_{\nu\mu}p_{jl}q_{\lambda i}q_{\rho\nu}\gamma_{\lambda\rho l}\right]_{i,j}.$$

However,

$$\sum_{\nu=1}^{n} p_{\nu\mu}q_{\rho\nu} = \delta_{\mu\rho}$$

since P and Q are inverses of each other. Thus the terms in the above multiple summation must vanish except when $\mu = \rho$. Therefore

$$\Gamma'(\mathbf{B}_\mu) = \left[\sum_{\lambda=1}^{n}\sum_{l=1}^{n} q_{\lambda i}\gamma_{\lambda\mu l}p_{jl}\right]_{i,j} = Q^t\Gamma(\mathbf{B}_\mu)P^t$$
$$= R^{-1}\Gamma(\mathbf{B}_\mu)R,$$

where $R = P^t$. That is, any two representations of the algebra are related by a similarity transformation. However, note that the same vector always gives rise to a matrix with the same trace. (This fact is very useful in studying groups by means of their representations.)

Many groups which are of considerable interest are (or can be represented as) the multiplicative part of a subset of some algebra. For example $GL(n, C)$ consists of all nonsingular $n \times n$ matrices. These matrices constitute a subset of the algebra of dimension n^2 whose basis elements are the matrices E_{ij} which have a single 1 in the position i, j and all other entries zero. It is easily verified that this algebra is its own representation. To do this, it helps to observe that

$$E_{ij}E_{kl} = \begin{cases} 0 & \text{if } j \neq k, \\ E_{il} & \text{if } j = k. \end{cases}$$

Any group of $n \times n$ matrices is a subgroup of $GL(n, C)$. While there are many of these, the most important have been defined in this section. The determination of the structure of these and other groups is a very important problem. We have not been able to go into this question here. All that we have been able to do in these sections is give a brief introduction to the very beginnings of the subject.

CHAPTER 5

Scalar-Valued Functions of Vectors

5–1. EUCLIDEAN n-DIMENSIONAL SPACE

As we saw in Section 4–4, ordinary three-dimensional space can be identified with R^3. The norm and the associated metric obtained from the standard inner product correspond exactly to the standard metric that we use in E^3. In exactly the same way, E^n can be identified with R^n. Any property of R^n that is invariant under euclidean motions is then a property of E^n.

Most students think of vectors as "being" directed line segments. For many purposes, there is little harm in holding this point of view, but such a feeling makes it hard to think of vectors as also representing "points" in our space. In our subsequent work in this book we will use the elements of R^n to represent both n-dimensional vectors and points in n-dimensional space. A particular element of R^n will be spoken of as a *point* or a *vector*, depending on the point of view needed at the time. These elements will always be represented by boldface letters. The components of a given n-tuple will be thought of interchangeably as the coordinates of the point (in some fixed cartesian coordinate system) or the components of the vector. The metric defined by the standard inner product will give us a distance function in this space; that is, the distance between two points **X** and **Y** will be $|\mathbf{X} - \mathbf{Y}|$. Observe that the triangle inequality holds for this metric (see Section 4–1).

We will now proceed to make a study of the space R^n. We will start by considering some of the geometric aspects of this space. As we proceed, you will find that the more familiar three-dimensional space offers a good guide to the geometry of R^n.

First, what do we mean by a line in R^n? We model our ideas on what we know about lines in R^3. There a line is determined by a point and a direction. Suppose then that **A** and **B** are any two elements of R^n, with $\mathbf{B} \neq \mathbf{0}$. We think of **A** as a point and **B** as a vector which defines a direction. Then the line through **A** with the direction determined by **B** is

$$\{\mathbf{X} \mid \mathbf{X} = \mathbf{A} + t\mathbf{B}, -\infty < t < \infty\}. \tag{5–1}$$

Note that this line does *not* in general pass through the point **B**. Actually it is the line which passes through the two distinct points **A** and $\mathbf{A} + \mathbf{B}$. (Here we see the justification for the identifying the vector and point aspects of R^n. We usually do not speak of the sum of two *points*, but we see in Eq. (5–1) that it can be useful to do so.)

In a similar way, we can define a plane in R^n. Let **A** be any point, and let **B** and **C** be two linearly independent vectors. Then the set

$$\{\mathbf{X} \mid \mathbf{X} = \mathbf{A} + t\mathbf{B} + s\mathbf{C}, -\infty < t < \infty, -\infty < s < \infty\} \tag{5–2}$$

defines a plane in R^n. The same visualization that is used for R^3 will be valid for R^n. The plane itself is strictly two dimensional. It is the embedding of the plane in R^n that is different.

Look at the line defined in (5–1). Here we see a fixed vector plus the vectors in a one-dimensional subspace. Similarly, in (5–2) we have the sum of a fixed vector plus the vectors in a two-dimensional subspace. We will find it useful to introduce formal notation for this and similar expressions.

Definition 5–1. Let S and T be subsets of R^n and let **A** be a point in R^n. Then we define

$$S + T = \{\mathbf{X} + \mathbf{Y} \mid \mathbf{X} \in S, \mathbf{Y} \in T\},$$
$$\mathbf{A} + T = \{\mathbf{A} + \mathbf{Y} \mid \mathbf{Y} \in T\}.$$

If we have the direct sum $L \oplus M$ of two subspaces, then according to this definition, $L \oplus M = L + M$. The circle around the plus sign in the direct sum notation tells us that L and M have only the vector **0** in common. When we write $L + M$, there is no implication that a given vector (or point) has a *unique* expression as the sum of a vector from L plus a vector from M.

Definition 5–2. Let L be a k-dimensional subspace of R^n and let **A** be a fixed point in R^n. Then the set

$$\mathbf{A} + L$$

is called a *k-dimensional affine subspace* of R^n. In particular, if $k = 1$, it is called a *line* in R^n. If $k = 2$, it is called a *plane*; and if $k = n - 1$, it is called a *hyperplane*.

We will find that the three special cases named in this definition occur more often than others. Lines and planes occur frequently since they are the simplest sets containing two and three given points, respectively (and which still have the character of a subspace). Hyperplanes occur often because they are of exactly one dimension fewer than the dimension of the space. In R^3, the concept of plane and hyperplane coincide, but in higher-dimensional spaces they are different.

Observe that an *affine subspace* is not necessarily a *subspace;* it is a subspace if and only if it contains **0**. It is the translate of a subspace and hence has many of the properties of a subspace. In particular, if it contains two distinct points, then it contains all points of the line through those points (see the problems at the end of this section).

A hyperplane is determined by a point and an $(n - 1)$-dimensional subspace. This subspace, in turn, is determined by $n - 1$ linearly independent vectors. There is, however, a much more interesting characterization of a hyperplane. This other point of view helps explain why hyperplanes are found to be so useful.

▶ **Theorem 5–1.** A set H is a hyperplane in R^n if and only if there exists a nonconstant linear function $F: R^n \to R$ and a constant c such that $H = \{\mathbf{X} \mid F(\mathbf{X}) = c\}$.

Proof. First, suppose that F is a nonconstant linear function and that

$$H = \{\mathbf{X} \mid F(\mathbf{X}) = c\}.$$

Let $L = \ker F$. Then, since

$$\dim(\ker F) + \dim(\operatorname{im} F) = \dim R^n,$$

and $\operatorname{im} F = R$, we must have $\dim L = n - 1$. Since F is nonconstant, there must exist some vector $\mathbf{B}$ such that $F(\mathbf{B}) = k \neq 0$. Set $\mathbf{A} = ck^{-1}\mathbf{B}$. Then $F(\mathbf{A}) = c$ and so $\mathbf{A} \in H$. Now, having $\mathbf{A}$, we can prove that $H = \mathbf{A} + L$.

Let $\mathbf{X} \in H$. Then $F(\mathbf{X} - \mathbf{A}) = F(\mathbf{X}) - F(\mathbf{A}) = c - c = 0$ and hence $\mathbf{X} - \mathbf{A} \in L$. But this means that $\mathbf{X} \in \mathbf{A} + L$.

On the other hand, let $\mathbf{X} \in \mathbf{A} + L$. Then $\mathbf{X} - \mathbf{A} \in L$ and hence $F(\mathbf{X} - \mathbf{A}) = 0$. Since $F(\mathbf{A}) = c$, we conclude that $F(\mathbf{X}) = c$ also, and hence that $\mathbf{X} \in H$. This completes the first half of the proof.

Next, suppose that H is a hyperplane, say

$$H = \mathbf{A} + L,$$

where $\mathbf{A}$ is a fixed point in R^n and L is an $(n - 1)$-dimensional subspace. We must produce a linear function which will satisfy the requirements of the theorem. Let $\mathbf{B}_1, \ldots, \mathbf{B}_{n-1}$ be a basis for L. We may as well assume this basis to be an orthonormal basis. Complete it to be an orthonormal basis for R^n, letting the last basis vector be $\mathbf{B}_n$. Then we see that

$$L^{\perp} = L\{\mathbf{B}_n\}.$$

We define the linear function F by $F(\mathbf{X}) = \mathbf{B}_n \cdot \mathbf{X}$ for every $\mathbf{X}$. Then $F(\mathbf{X}) = 0$ for every $\mathbf{X} \in L$. Indeed, $L = \ker F$. Now set $c = F(\mathbf{A}) = \mathbf{B}_n \cdot \mathbf{A}$. We will now prove that $H = \{\mathbf{X} \mid F(\mathbf{X}) = c\}$.

Suppose that $\mathbf{X} \in H$. Then $\mathbf{X} = \mathbf{A} + \mathbf{Y}$, where $\mathbf{Y} \in L$. But then

$$F(\mathbf{X}) = F(\mathbf{A} + \mathbf{Y}) = F(\mathbf{A}) + F(\mathbf{Y}) = c$$

since $\mathbf{Y} \in L = \ker F$.

On the other hand, suppose that $F(\mathbf{X}) = c$. Set $\mathbf{Y} = \mathbf{X} - \mathbf{A}$. Then

$$F(\mathbf{Y}) = F(\mathbf{X} - \mathbf{A}) = F(\mathbf{X}) - F(\mathbf{A}) = c - c = 0.$$

Hence $\mathbf{Y} \in L$, so that $\mathbf{X} = \mathbf{A} + \mathbf{Y} \in \mathbf{A} + L = H$. We have therefore proved the theorem. ▌

Definition 5–3. Let $\mathbf{A}$ be a point in R^n and let δ be a positive real number. Then by the *open ball with center A and radius* δ we mean the set

$$S_\delta(\mathbf{A}) = \{\mathbf{X} \mid |\mathbf{X} - \mathbf{A}| < \delta\}.$$

By the *closed ball* with the same center and radius we mean the set

$$\bar{S}_\delta(\mathbf{A}) = \{\mathbf{X} \mid |\mathbf{X} - \mathbf{A}| \leq \delta\}.$$

When we use the term *ball* alone, we mean an open ball, unless otherwise specified.

The term "sphere" is often used to mean what we have defined here as a "ball." In modern mathematical usage, the term *sphere* is reserved for the "surface" of the ball defined here, so that to refer to the "inside" we would have to use another term such as "solid sphere." The word "ball" is simpler.

Many of the properties which are obvious in two or three dimensions also hold in an arbitrary space R^n. For example,

Theorem 5–2. Let $\mathbf{B} \in S_r(\mathbf{A})$. Then there exists a $\delta > 0$ such that

$$S_\delta(\mathbf{B}) \subset S_r(\mathbf{A}).$$

Proof. The following proof can be obtained by drawing a picture in two dimensions. The proof turns out to be valid for any number of dimensions (see Fig. 5–1).

Since $\mathbf{B} \in S_r(\mathbf{A})$, we must have $|\mathbf{B} - \mathbf{A}| < r$. Set

$$\delta = r - |\mathbf{B} - \mathbf{A}|.$$

We now prove that this is the δ required by the theorem. It is certainly greater than 0. It remains only to show that $S_\delta(\mathbf{B}) \subset S_r(\mathbf{A})$.

Let $\mathbf{X} \in S_\delta(\mathbf{B})$. Then

$$\begin{aligned} |\mathbf{X} - \mathbf{A}| &\leq |\mathbf{X} - \mathbf{B}| + |\mathbf{B} - \mathbf{A}| \\ &< \delta + |\mathbf{B} - \mathbf{A}| = r - |\mathbf{B} - \mathbf{A}| + |\mathbf{B} - \mathbf{A}| \\ &= r. \end{aligned}$$

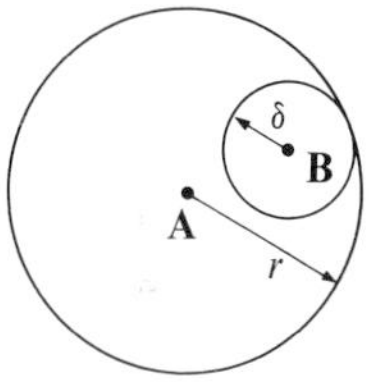

Fig. 5–1

Therefore $\mathbf{X} \in S_r(\mathbf{A})$. Note that the triangle inequality is crucial here. ▌

It is of some interest to observe how "thin" a hyperplane is with respect to these n-dimensional balls.

Theorem 5–3. Let $H = \mathbf{A} + L$ be a hyperplane in R^n and let δ be any positive number. Then there exists a point $\mathbf{C} \in S_\delta(\mathbf{A})$ such that $\mathbf{C} \notin H$; that is, no ball, no matter how small, can be contained in a hyperplane.

Proof. Let $H = \{\mathbf{X} \mid F(\mathbf{X}) = c\}$, where F is a nonconstant linear function. Since F is nonconstant, there exists some nonzero vector $\mathbf{B}$ such that $F(\mathbf{B}) \neq 0$. Set

$$\mathbf{C} = \mathbf{A} + \frac{\delta}{2|\mathbf{B}|}\mathbf{B}.$$

Then $|\mathbf{C} - \mathbf{A}| = \delta/2$ and hence $\mathbf{C} \in S_\delta(\mathbf{A})$. However

$$F(\mathbf{C}) = c + \frac{\delta}{2|\mathbf{B}|} F(\mathbf{B}) \neq c,$$

so that $\mathbf{C} \notin H$. ▌

Next, we wish to generalize the concept of a rectangle in two dimensions or a parallelepiped in three dimensions. For simplicity, we choose to call the generalization an n-dimensional rectangle.

Definition 5–4. Let $\mathbf{A} = [a_1, a_2, \ldots, a_n]$ and $\mathbf{B} = [b_1, b_2, \ldots, b_n]$ be two points in R^n. We write $\mathbf{A} < \mathbf{B}$ if and only if $a_i < b_i$ for every i. Suppose that $\mathbf{A} < \mathbf{B}$. Then by the *n-dimensional* (*closed*) *rectangle* determined by $\mathbf{A}$ and $\mathbf{B}$ we mean the set

$$R[\mathbf{A}, \mathbf{B}] = \{\mathbf{X} \mid a_i \leq x_i \leq b_i, i = 1, 2, \ldots, n\}.$$

By the *n-dimensional open rectangle* we mean the set

$$R(\mathbf{A}, \mathbf{B}) = \{\mathbf{X} \mid a_i < x_i < b_i, i = 1, 2, \ldots, n\}.$$

Unless otherwise specified, a *rectangle* means a closed rectangle.

Note that these rectangles are generalizations of closed and open intervals on the real line. The use of brackets or parentheses corresponds to similar usage in the case of intervals.

It is instructive to observe some of the relations between balls and rectangles.

Theorem 5–4. Let $\mathbf{C} \in R(\mathbf{A}, \mathbf{B})$. Then there exists a δ such that

$$S_\delta(\mathbf{C}) \subset R(\mathbf{A}, \mathbf{B}).$$

Proof. If you think of this theorem in two or three dimensions, it is easy to see that the required radius is merely the shortest distance from $\mathbf{C}$ to one of the faces of $R(\mathbf{A}, \mathbf{B})$. Therefore, we set

$$\delta = \min \{(b_1 - c_1), (b_2 - c_2), \ldots, (b_n - c_n), (c_1 - a_1), (c_2 - a_2), \ldots, (c_n - a_n)\}.$$

The requirement that $\mathbf{C} \in R(\mathbf{A}, \mathbf{B})$ means that all of these quantities are positive. Hence their minimum must also be positive. Thus $\delta > 0$. Let $\mathbf{X} \in S_\delta(\mathbf{C})$. We must show that $\mathbf{X} \in R(\mathbf{A}, \mathbf{B})$. This is easy to do. Since

$$|\mathbf{X} - \mathbf{C}|^2 = \sum_{i=1}^{n} (x_i - c_i)^2 < \delta^2,$$

we must have $|x_i - c_i| < \delta$ for every i. But then, for every i,

$$a_i - c_i \leq -\delta < x_i - c_i < \delta \leq b_i - c_i.$$

Therefore we can conclude that $a_i < x_i < b_i$ and hence that $\mathbf{X} \in R(\mathbf{A}, \mathbf{B})$. ▌

This theorem can be turned around, and we find it as easy to prove the following theorem.

Theorem 5–5. Let $\mathbf{D}$ be a point in the ball $S_r(\mathbf{C})$. Then there exists some n-dimensional open rectangle $R(\mathbf{A}, \mathbf{B})$ such that

$$\mathbf{D} \in R(\mathbf{A}, \mathbf{B}) \subset S_r(\mathbf{C}).$$

Proof. Let

$$\delta = r - |\mathbf{D} - \mathbf{C}|,$$

and set

$$s = \delta/2\sqrt{n}.$$

Let $\mathbf{S} = [s, s, \ldots, s]$ and define

$$\mathbf{A} = \mathbf{D} - \mathbf{S}, \qquad \mathbf{B} = \mathbf{D} + \mathbf{S}.$$

It is clear that $\mathbf{A} < \mathbf{B}$ in the sense of Definition 5–4 and that $\mathbf{D} \in R(\mathbf{A}, \mathbf{B})$. (In fact, $\mathbf{D}$ is the "center" of the rectangle.) It remains to be shown that $R(\mathbf{A}, \mathbf{B}) \subset S_r(\mathbf{C})$,

Let $\mathbf{X} \in R(\mathbf{A}, \mathbf{B})$. Then for every i,

$$a_i < d_i < b_i, \qquad a_i < x_i < b_i.$$

Hence $|x_i - d_i| < b_i - a_i = 2s = \delta/\sqrt{n}$. But this means that

$$|\mathbf{X} - \mathbf{D}| = \left[\sum_{i=1}^{n} (x_i - d_i)^2\right]^{1/2} < \left[\sum_{i=1}^{n} \frac{\delta^2}{n}\right]^{1/2} = \delta.$$

Hence

$$\begin{aligned}|\mathbf{X} - \mathbf{C}| &\leq |\mathbf{X} - \mathbf{D}| + |\mathbf{D} - \mathbf{C}| \\ &< \delta + |\mathbf{D} - \mathbf{C}| = r.\end{aligned}$$

Therefore $\mathbf{X} \in S_r(C)$ and the theorem is proved. ▌

Definition 5–5. Let $\mathbf{P}$ be any point in R^n. Then by a *neighborhood* of $\mathbf{P}$ we mean any ball $S_\delta(\mathbf{P})$ with positive radius.

The term *neighborhood* is meant to signify those points which are "close" to the given point. But, how close is "close"? We avoid this sticky question by defining a neighborhood to be a ball of *any* radius. This suffices for our needs, as we shall see.

In modern mathematics, the term neighborhood usually has a much wider meaning than we give it here. The result is exactly the same, however. Neighborhoods are used to define a *topology*, that is, a collection of sets which are called *open*. The neighborhoods of Definition 5–5, or any of the wider classes which might be called neighborhoods, give rise to the same open sets according to the following definition.

Definition 5–6. A set U in R^n is called an *open set* if and only if, given any point $\mathbf{X} \in U$, there exists a neighborhood $S_\delta(\mathbf{X})$ of $\mathbf{X}$ which is contained in U. A set V in R^n is called closed if and only if its complement $\complement V$ (the set of all points not in V) is open.

According to this definition, the entire space R^n is open. On the other hand, so is the empty set $\emptyset$, which satisfies the definition by virtue of the fact that is contains no points and hence every point that it does contain satisfies the required property. We can therefore conclude that R^n is both an open and a closed set. Likewise $\emptyset$ is both an open and a closed set. However, these two, R^n and $\emptyset$, are the only sets which are both open and closed.

This definition does not classify all sets. Many sets are neither open nor closed, though most of the sets we are interested in are one or the other. For example, an open ball is an open set; Theorem 5–2 shows this. An open rectangle is also an open set; Theorem 5–4 says this.

The reader should be able to show that the theorems of this section are sufficient to prove that we would have obtained exactly the same open sets if we had defined a neighborhood of a point **P** to be any open rectangle which contains **P**. This shows how the neighborhood concept could be widened. We will find, however, that for the work done in this text it will be sufficient to use the somewhat old-fashioned definition as given in Definition 5–5. If the reader goes on, he will find it necessary to enlarge his concept of neighborhoods, but he will find it unnecessary to unlearn anything.

PROBLEMS

1. Given that K is a k-dimensional affine subspace of R^n and if **A** and **B** are two distinct points of K, prove that every point of the line through **A** and **B** is contained in K.
2. Prove that if the intersection of two affine subspaces is not empty, then this intersection will itself be an affine subspace.
3. Suppose that $\mathbf{C} \in S_r(\mathbf{A}) \cap S_{r'}(\mathbf{B})$. Prove that there exists a $\delta > 0$ such that
$$S_\delta(\mathbf{C}) \subset S_r(\mathbf{A}) \cap S_{r'}(\mathbf{B}).$$
4. Prove that the intersection of any two open sets is open.
5. Prove that the union of any number of open sets is open.
6. Let **A** and **B** be two distinct points of R^n. Prove that there exist neighborhoods $S_r(\mathbf{A})$ and $S_{r'}(\mathbf{B})$ such that $S_r(\mathbf{A}) \cap S_{r'}(\mathbf{B}) = \emptyset$.
7. Prove that the set consisting of a single point is closed.
8. Prove that a closed ball is closed.
9. Prove that a closed rectangle is closed.
10. Prove that the intersection of two n-dimensional open rectangles is itself an n-dimensional open rectangle if it is nonempty.
11. Let **A** and **B** be any two points with $|\mathbf{A} - \mathbf{B}| = \delta > 0$. Prove that there exists a hyperplane H which contains **B** and which is such that $H \cap S_\delta(\mathbf{A}) = \emptyset$.
12. Prove that any k-dimensional affine subspace of R^n is closed.
13. Prove that a set V is closed if and only if: given any $\mathbf{X} \notin V$, there is a neighborhood $S_\delta(\mathbf{X})$ of $\mathbf{X}$ which has no points in common with V.

14. Let K be a k-dimensional affine subspace of R^n and suppose that $\mathbf{P} \notin K$. Prove that there exists a unique $(k + 1)$-dimensional affine subspace of R^n which contains both K and $\mathbf{P}$.

15. Prove that there is a unique k-dimensional affine subspace of R^n containing any given set of $k + 1$ distinct points which are such that they are not contained in an affine subspace of dimension lower than k.

16. How many vertices does an n-dimensional rectangle have? How many $(n - 1)$-dimensional "faces"?

5–2. SCALAR-VALUED FUNCTIONS IN R^n

In this section we start the discussion of functions whose domain is some subset D of R^n and whose range is R. Such a function, $f: D \to R$, can be thought of as assigning a real number to each point of D. In physics, a function like this would be called a *scalar field.* An example might be the function defined in R^3 whose value at a given point is the temperature at that point. Another example might be the function which assigns the value of the air pressure at each point in the atmosphere. An example with a higher-dimensional space might be the function whose value was the force of attraction (the magnitude of this force) between two point charges. This function could be defined in R^6; three of the components would correspond to the location of one of the charges, and the other three components would locate the other charge. Hence, instead of having two points in R^3, we would have a single point in R^6.

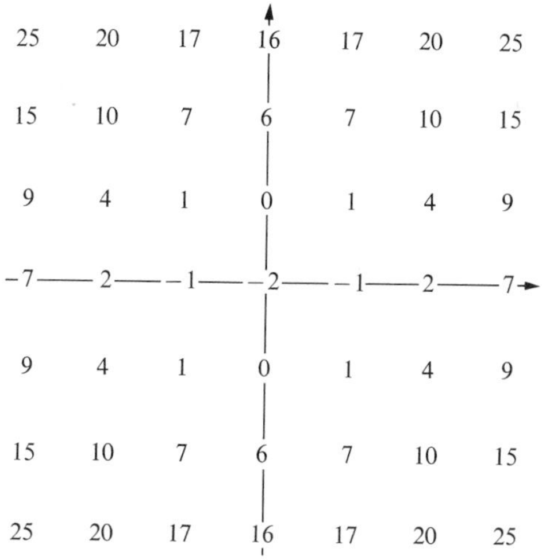

Fig. 5–2

Before going into the discussion of continuity of such functions, we should make a few remarks about the representations that can be made of them. It will help here to consider an actual simple example. Let us consider the function $f: R^2 \to R$ defined by $f(x, y) = x^2 + 2y^2 - 2$. [Note that we follow the custom of letting $[x, y]$

represent an arbitrary point in R^2. Similarly, we usually let $[x, y, z]$ represent a point in R^3.] At each point of the plane, this function takes on some value. We could picture this function by writing the value of the function at a set of selected points in the plane, as in Fig. 5-2. It is not very easy to picture the behavior of the function from such a chart, however. It helps if we draw instead a set of curves such that the function is constant along each curve. We can then get some idea of the values of the function at various points, where the function is increasing, and where it is decreasing. Local maxima and minima show up as systems of closed curves converging to a point.

In this particular example, we set $f(x, y) = x^2 + 2y^2 - 2 = c$ for various values of c. There can be no points satisfying this relation if $c < -2$. For any c greater than this, the set of points satisfying the relation will be an ellipse. Some of these ellipses are sketched in Fig. 5-3. The fact that the outer ellipses are getting closer together means that the values of the function are changing faster. From the diagram in Fig. 5-3 it is clear that this function takes on its minimum value (which is -2) at $[0, 0]$.

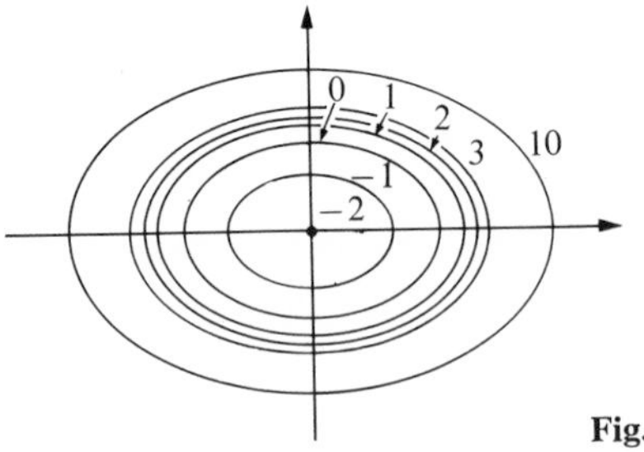

Fig. 5-3

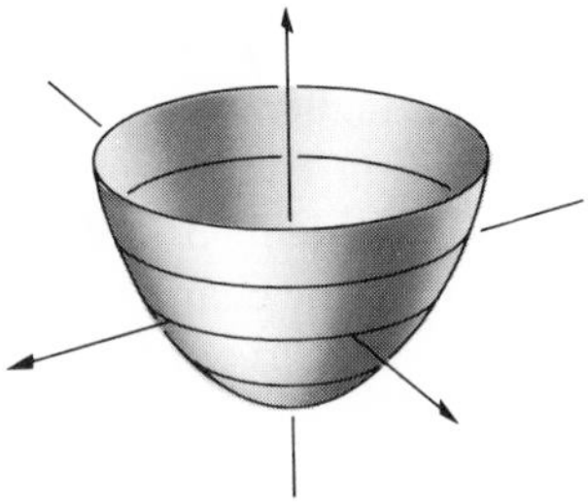

Fig. 5-4

There is still a third way of picturing this function. Although the function is defined in the plane, we can add a third dimension, and for each point $[x, y]$ in the plane we can use the point $[x, y, z]$ in R^3, where we set $z = f(x, y)$. This defines a surface in R^3. For this example, we get a picture like that shown in Fig. 5-4.

This last method works well when we are talking about a function defined in R^2, but it cannot be used in higher dimensions. The method of Fig. 5-3 can still be used to make sketches in R^3, but it too fails if we try to make a picture of a function in a higher number of dimensions. Much of the difficulty in working with functions in several variables is the inability to make meaningful sketches. If we cannot sketch a function, we find it difficult to understand its behavior. Much of our work in this text will be devoted to finding ways of approximating arbitrary functions in a neighborhood of a given point by a simpler function (usually a linear function). This will allow us to think about the general behavior of a function, even if we cannot sketch it.

Definition 5-7. Let D be a subset of R^n and let $f\colon D \to R$. Then by a *level surface* of f, we mean the set

$$\{\mathbf{X} \mid f(\mathbf{X}) = c\}$$

for a constant c.

When we are working in R^2, we usually prefer to refer to level *curves* rather than level surfaces.

Let us consider the relationship between the concept of level surfaces and the methods of illustrating the function that we gave in Figs. 5–3 and 5–4. Suppose that f is a function defined in R^n. By adding another dimension, we can think of the values of f as being the $(n + 1)$th coordinate in R^{n+1}. That is, we can set

$$x_{n+1} = f(\mathbf{X}).$$

But then the function is completely defined by the level surface $g(\mathbf{X}') = 0$, where $\mathbf{X}' \in R^{n+1}$, and the function g is defined by

$$g(\mathbf{X}') = g(x_1, x_2, \ldots, x_n, x_{n+1}) = f(x_1, x_2, \ldots, x_n) - x_{n+1}.$$

It would be valuable to consider this situation carefully. Figures 5–3 and 5–4 illustrate the device that is employed here. In Figure 5–3, we illustrated the function $f(x, y)$ by showing its level curves in R^2. In Figure 5–4, we illustrated the same function by sketching the level surface of $g(x, y, z) = f(x, y) - z = 0$.

A function is a set of ordered pairs. A function $f: R^n \to R$ is a set of ordered pairs of the form $(\mathbf{X}, u)$, where $\mathbf{X}$ is a point in R^n and u is the value of the function at that point. For the above discussion, we merely made the natural identification of the ordered pair $(\mathbf{X}, u)$ with a point $\mathbf{X}' \in R^{n+1}$, defined by

$$\begin{aligned}(\mathbf{X}, u) &= ([x_1, x_2, \ldots, x_n], u) \\ &\to [x_1, x_2, \ldots, x_n, u].\end{aligned}$$

The same identification is just as valid in the other direction. A set in R^{n+1} can be identified with a set of ordered pairs $(\mathbf{X}, x_{n+1})$, where $\mathbf{X} \in R^n$. It sometimes happens that the resulting set of ordered pairs define a function. Thus a given level surface of a function $g: R^{n+1} \to R$ might define a function f: $R^n \to R$. If this happens, we usually say that we can "solve" $f(\mathbf{X}') = c$ for the "variable" x_{n+1}. In later sections we will investigate the conditions under which this can be done.

The word *variable* has long been used in mathematics and its applications. It is in some disfavor in pure mathematics at this time since it seems to imply that something is changing, whereas no such implication is necessary. If we understand this, there is no need for us to avoid using the word. In this text, we will use the word *variable* to mean the unspecified value of a component of a vector (or the vector itself) in the domain of definition or the range of a function.

We now wish to turn to the concept of continuity for functions defined in R^n. The definition is the exact analogue of the definition used in R^1.

Definition 5–8. Let B be a subset of R^n. Let $f: B \to R$ be a function defined on B. Let $\mathbf{A} \in B$. Then f is said to be *continuous* at $\mathbf{A}$ if and only if, given any $\epsilon > 0$ there exists a $\delta > 0$ such that $|f(\mathbf{X}) - f(\mathbf{A})| < \epsilon$ for all $\mathbf{X}$ in $B \cap S_\delta(\mathbf{A})$. If $G \subset B$ and f is continuous at every point of G, then we say that f is *continuous on G*.

If a function is continuous at a point $\mathbf{A}$ then its values are arbitrarily close to $f(\mathbf{A})$ in every sufficiently small neighborhood of that point. This is precisely the same concept of continuity that we have in one dimension. The only difference is that a neighborhood of a point in R^n is a ball rather than an interval. Note, however, that a ball, $S_\delta(c)$, in R^1 is exactly the set $\{x \mid |x - c| < \delta\}$. That is, a one-dimensional ball is an interval.

The reader may wonder about the introduction of the set B into the above definition. Usually we find that our functions are defined in some neighborhood of the point in question. In that case, the set B can be ignored. It may happen, however, that the function is not defined except on some specific set. For example, we may find a function which is defined only on the points of some line. The above definition of continuity takes this case into account. We only require the function to satisfy the requirements of the definition at those points where it is defined.

In particular, note that a function which is defined at some isolated point and nowhere else in some neighborhood of that point must be continuous at that point. The requirements of the definition are satisfied since the only $\mathbf{X} \in B \cap S_\delta(\mathbf{A})$ is the point $\mathbf{A}$ itself.

If we have $B \subset B'$ and $f: B \to R$, $g: B' \to R$ such that $f(\mathbf{X}) = g(\mathbf{X})$ for every point $\mathbf{X}$ in B, then f is called the *restriction* of g to B (or sometimes g is called an extension of f to B'). At first glance, it might seem that since f and g coincide on B, they need not be distinguished. However, it can happen that f is continuous at some point of B while g is not continuous at the same point.

For example, let B be a straight line in R^2 and define f to be identically zero on B. Then f is continuous on B. Define the function g to be zero on B and one everywhere else ($B' = R^2$ in this example). Then g is an extension of f, but is not continuous at any point of B.

It is important to distinguish between continuity in the sense of this definition and continuity of the function in terms of its individual variables. A function can be continuous when considered as a function of each component of $\mathbf{X}$ separately, but not continuous in the sense of this definition. The easiest way of seeing this possibility is to look at an actual example. Let

$$f(x, y) = \begin{cases} \dfrac{2xy}{x^2 + y^2}, & [x, y] \neq [0, 0], \\ 0, & [x, y] = [0, 0]. \end{cases}$$

This function is defined at all points of R^2. Fix $y = y_0$. Then, as a function of x alone, $f(x, y_0)$ is continuous for all x and in particular when $x = 0$. If $y_0 = 0$, then the function is identically zero. If $y_0 \neq 0$, then the function is a rational function of x whose denominator is never zero. Figure 5-5 shows the behavior of this function. In an exactly similar way, we can see that the function is continuous as a function of y for all fixed $x = x_0$. However, this function is not continuous at $[0, 0]$ with respect to $[x, y]$ jointly, as required by Definition 5-8. Indeed, if we look at any point $[x, y]$

other than the origin and use the polar coordinates of that point, $x = r\cos\theta$ and $y = r\sin\theta$, then

$$f(x, y) = \frac{2r^2 \sin\theta\cos\theta}{r^2\sin^2\theta + r^2\cos^2\theta} = \sin 2\theta.$$

In particular, along the line $x = y$, the function is always equal to one (except at the origin). Hence, no matter how small δ may be, there always exists an $[x, y] \in S_\delta(0, 0)$ such that $|f(x, y) - f(0, 0)| = 1$. Therefore, if ϵ is chosen to be less than 1, the condition of Definition 5–8 cannot possibly be satisfied.

We note that it is even possible to find a function which is continuous along every line through the point but which is not continuous at that point. These examples are mentioned only as warnings however. In this book, we are mainly interested in the simple cases. Pathological cases such as this occur only rarely in practice. All we ask is that the reader be aware that we must be careful so that our intuition does not lead us astray.

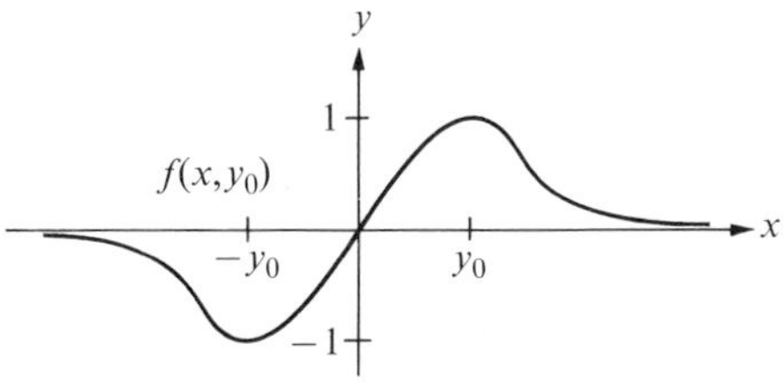

Fig. 5–5

The concept of continuity is closely linked with the concept of *limit*. We wish to define the limit of a function now. However, in order to be able to do so, we must first introduce an important topological concept.

Definition 5–9. By a *deleted neighborhood* of radius δ of a point $\mathbf{A}$ we mean the set $\hat{S}_\delta(\mathbf{A})$ which consists of all the points of $S_\delta(\mathbf{A})$ with the exception of the point $\mathbf{A}$ itself.

Definition 5–10. Let B be a set of points in R^n. Then a point $\mathbf{A}$ is called a *limit point* of the set B if and only if every deleted neighborhood of $\mathbf{A}$ contains at least one point of B.

A point $\mathbf{A}$ is a limit point of a set B if and only if every neighborhood of $\mathbf{A}$ contains an infinite number of points of B (see the problems at the end of this section). For this reason, a limit point is often called an *accumulation point* of the set.

Definition 5–11. Let B be a subset of R^n. Let $f: B \to R$. Let $\mathbf{A}$ be a limit point of B. Then we say $\lim_{\mathbf{X}\to\mathbf{A}} f(\mathbf{X}) = a$ if and only if for any $\epsilon > 0$ there exists a $\delta > 0$ such that $|f(\mathbf{X}) - a| < \epsilon$ for all $\mathbf{X} \in \hat{S}_\delta(\mathbf{A}) \cap B$. This will also be indicated by writing

$$f(\mathbf{X}) \to a \quad \text{as} \quad \mathbf{X} \to \mathbf{A}.$$

There are several things to notice about this definition. The first is that the definition would be without meaning if the point **A** were not a limit point of the set on which the function is defined. The second is that the value of the function at the point **A** has nothing to do with the value of the limit. The function may or may not be defined at the point **A**. If it is, its value there does not enter into the definition. Next, observe that the limit points of a set and the limit of a function are distinct concepts. While there is some connection between them, they are different. Do not let the similarity in names confuse you.

Finally, we see that the concept of continuity and the concept of the limit of a function are closely related. By comparing the two definitions, we see that the following theorem holds.

▶ **Theorem 5–6.** Let B be a subset of R^n, $f\colon B \to R$, and let $\mathbf{A} \in B$ be a limit point of B. Then f is continuous at $\mathbf{A}$ if and only if $\lim_{\mathbf{X}\to\mathbf{A}} f(\mathbf{X}) = f(\mathbf{A})$.

There is still another limit concept that we must introduce. That is the limit of a sequence.

Definition 5–12. A *sequence* in R^n is a function $\sigma\colon J \to R^n$, where J is the set of all positive integers. We usually denote the sequence by a notation such as $\{\mathbf{A}_k\}$, where we understand that $\mathbf{A}_k = \sigma(k)$.

The set of points determined by a sequence could possibly consist of a single point. All of the $\mathbf{A}_k$ could be identical. Such a sequence is called a *stationary sequence*.

There is nothing special about using the set of all positive integers to define the sequence. We could just as well (and sometimes will) use all of the nonnegative integers or the set of all integers greater than or equal to some fixed N. When we do so, we will wish to indicate the exact range of the subscript. We do this by writing the range of the indices immediately to the right of the symbol for the sequence. For example, we would write $\{\mathbf{A}_k\}_{k=N}^{\infty}$ to indicate a sequence in which the index runs from N to ∞.

Definition 5–13. A point $\mathbf{A}$ is called the *limit* of the sequence $\{\mathbf{A}_k\}$, and we write $\mathbf{A} = \lim_{k\to\infty} \mathbf{A}_k$ or $\mathbf{A}_k \to \mathbf{A}$, if and only if, given any $\epsilon > 0$, there exists an N such that $\mathbf{A}_k \in S_\epsilon(\mathbf{A})$ for all $k > N$.

The concept of the limit point of a set which we introduced above allows us to give another characterization of closed sets. A set was defined to be closed if its complement was open. While this is the definition, it does not give us a very good picture of the type of set which is closed. The following theorem helps to fill this gap.

▶ **Theorem 5–7.** A set B in R^n is closed if and only if it contains all of its limit points.

Proof. Suppose first that B is a closed set. Then $\complement B$ is open. Let $\mathbf{X}$ be in $\complement B$. Then there exists some neighborhood of $\mathbf{X}$ which is contained completely in $\complement B$. This neighborhood has no point in common with B, and hence $\mathbf{X}$ cannot be a limit point of B. This proves that every limit point of B has to be in B.

In the other direction, let us suppose that B contains all of its limit points. We wish to prove that B is therefore closed. Let $\mathbf{X} \in \mathbf{C}B$. Then $\mathbf{X}$ is not a limit point of B, and thus there must exist some neighborhood of $\mathbf{X}$ which has no points in common with B ($\mathbf{X}$ itself was chosen not to be in B). Therefore we conclude that $\mathbf{C}B$ is open and hence that B is closed. ▌

We now turn to some of the fundamental topological properties of R^n.

Definition 5–14. A set G in R^n is called *bounded* if and only if there exists some closed rectangle $R[\mathbf{A}, \mathbf{B}]$ which contains it. A set K in R^n is called *compact* if and only if it is closed and bounded.

The following theorems contain the important properties which we will need in the remainder of the text. Their proofs will be given in the next section.

▶ **Theorem 5–8** (*The Bolzano-Weierstrass theorem*). An infinite set of points which is contained in a compact set K has a limit point which is also in K.

▶ **Theorem 5–9** (*The Heine-Borel theorem*).* Let K be a compact set. Let $\mathfrak{N}$ be a collection of neighborhoods such that every point of K is contained in at least one of these neighborhoods (i.e., the neighborhoods in $\mathfrak{N}$ *cover* K). Then there exist a finite number of these neighborhoods which still cover K.

Suppose that a function $f: B \to R$ is continuous at each point of B. Exactly what does this mean? Given any $\epsilon > 0$, there exists a δ for each $\mathbf{X}$ in B such that $|f(\mathbf{X}) - f(\mathbf{Y})| < \epsilon$ for all $\mathbf{Y}$ in $S_\delta(\mathbf{X})$. This δ depends on ϵ, of course, but it also depends on $\mathbf{X}$. We should write $\delta = \delta(\epsilon, \mathbf{X})$ to indicate this dependence. Under special circumstances, it can happen that we could use the same δ at every point of B; that is, δ might be independent of the point $\mathbf{X}$ in B.

Definition 5–15. Let B be a subset of R^n and let $f: B \to R$. Then f is *uniformly continuous* on B if and only if, given any $\epsilon > 0$, there exists a δ, depending on ϵ alone, such that if $\mathbf{X}_1$ and $\mathbf{X}_2$ are any pair of points of B with $|\mathbf{X}_1 - \mathbf{X}_2| < \delta$, then $|f(\mathbf{X}_1) - f(\mathbf{X}_2)| < \epsilon$.

▶ **Theorem 5–10** (*The theorem of uniform continuity*). Let K be a compact subset of R^n. Let $f: K \to R$ be continuous at every point of K. Then f is uniformly continuous on K.

The final theorem in this collection is:

▶ **Theorem 5–11** (*The maximum-value theorem*). Let K be a compact subset of R^n. Let $f: K \to R$ be continuous at every point of K. Then f is bounded on K and assumes its maximum and minimum values at some points of K.

---

*This is also known as the *Borel-Lebesgue Theorem*. There are good arguments for recognizing Lebesgue's contributions, but Heine actually accomplished a great deal more than he is often given credit for. One could, of course, take the irresolute stand and call it the Heine-Borel-Lebesgue Theorem.

PROBLEMS

1. Discuss the following functions by sketching their level curves in the plane and also by making a three-dimensional sketch of each of the surfaces defined by $z = f(x, y)$.
   a) $f(x, y) = x - 2y + 4$ b) $f(x, y) = x^2 - y^2 + 4y$
   c) $f(x, y) = \log(x^2 + y^2)$ d) $f(x, y) = \sin(x + y)$
   e) $f(x, y) = x^2 + 9y^2$ f) $f(x, y) = \dfrac{x^2 + 4y^2}{2x}$
   g) $f(x, y) = e^{xy}$ h) $f(x, y) = \dfrac{y}{x} - x^2$
2. Discuss each of the following functions in terms of their level surfaces in R^3.
   a) $f(x, y, z) = x^2 - 2y^2 + z^2$ b) $f(x, y, z) = x(y^2 - z^2)$
   c) $f(x, y, z) = x^2 + y^2 + z^2$ d) $f(x, y, z) = \dfrac{x^2 + y^2 + z^2}{2z}$
3. For each of the functions in Problems 1 and 2, state where the function is defined and where it is continuous.
4. Prove that every neighborhood of a limit point of a set B contains an infinite number of points of B.
5. Give an example of an infinite set which has no limit points.
6. Prove that $f:B \to R$ is continuous at $\mathbf{A}$ if and only if $\lim_{k\to\infty} f(\mathbf{X}_k) = f(\mathbf{A})$ for every sequence $\{\mathbf{X}_k\}$ such that all of the terms of the sequence are in B and $\lim_{k\to\infty} \mathbf{X}_k = \mathbf{A}$.
7. Let G be an open set in R^n and let $f:G \to R$. Prove that f is continuous on G if and only if the complete inverse image of every open set in R is open in R^n; that is, if U is an open set in R, then
$$f^{-1}(U) = \{\mathbf{X} \mid f(\mathbf{X}) \in U\}$$
is open in R^n.

5-3. PROOFS OF THE FUNDAMENTAL THEOREMS

In this section we will present the proofs of the theorems which were stated in the last section. These proofs are based on the least upper bound axiom for the real numbers.

Least Upper Bound Axiom. Any nonempty set of real numbers which is bounded above has a least upper bound.

Recall that a number m is the least upper bound of a set S if and only if: 1) $m \geq x$ for every $x \in S$ (thus, m is an upper bound) and 2) if $c < m$, then there exists at least one $x \in S$ for which $x > c$ (and thus m is the *least* upper bound).

A similar axiom holds for the greatest lower bound of a set which is bounded below. Either of these axioms can be proved from the other.

The least upper bound of a set is also called the *supremum* of the set, usually written sup S if S is the set in question. The greatest lower bound of a set S is called the *infimum* of the set and is written inf S. This is the notation that we will use in this text.

If a set S has no upper bound, we write $\sup S = +\infty$. Note that even in this case, the two properties mentioned above will still hold:

1. Every element of S is less than $\sup S$.
2. If $c < \sup S$, then there exists some $x \in S$ with $x > c$.

To start with, let us prove the following theorem.

Theorem 5–12. Suppose that $\{a_n\}$ is a monotone increasing sequence of real numbers and $\{b_n\}$ is a monotone decreasing sequence of real numbers where $a_n < b_n$ for every n. Suppose further that $(b_n - a_n) \to 0$ as $n \to \infty$. Then there exists a unique x which is simultaneously the least upper bound of the set of a_n and the greatest lower bound of the set of b_n.

Proof. For any $n \geq 1$, $a_n < b_n \leq b_1$. The set of a_n is therefore bounded above and has a least upper bound. Let $x = \sup \{a_n\}$.* In a similar way, the set of b_n can be shown to be bounded below. Let $y = \inf \{b_n\}$, the greatest lower bound of the set of b_n. What we must show is that $x = y$.

Let n be any integer and let $k \geq n$. Then

$$a_k < b_k \leq b_n.$$

Therefore b_n is an upper bound for the set of all a_k. The least upper bound of this set must be less than or equal to any other upper bound. Hence

$$x \leq b_n$$

for every n. But this in turn says that x is a lower bound of the set of b_n. Hence we conclude that

$$x \leq y.$$

However, we cannot have $x < y$. If $y - x = d > 0$, then since each $a_n \leq x$ and each $b_n \geq y$, we must have $b_n - a_n \geq y - x = d > 0$. This contradicts the assumption that $b_n - a_n \to 0$. Therefore $x = y$. ▮

Now let us consider the process of subdividing a rectangle. Suppose that we are given a closed rectangle $R[\mathbf{A}, \mathbf{B}]$ in R^n. Let $\mathbf{C} = \frac{1}{2}(\mathbf{A} + \mathbf{B})$ be the center of this rectangle. Then for each i we have $c_i = \frac{1}{2}(a_i + b_i)$ and $a_i < c_i < b_i$.

Let S be any subset of J_n, the set of the first n positive integers. Define the two points $\mathbf{A}(S) = [a'_1, a'_2, \ldots, a'_n]$ and $\mathbf{B}(S) = [b'_1, b'_2, \ldots, b'_n]$ by

$$a'_i = a_i \text{ and } b'_i = c_i \quad \text{if} \quad i \in S,$$
$$a'_i = c_i \text{ and } b'_i = b_i \quad \text{if} \quad i \notin S.$$

---

* Here we see the difficulty with the brace notation for sequences. When we write $\sup \{a_n\}$, we are talking about the *set* of the a_n, not the sequence of the a_n. However, there is still no possibility of confusion about what is meant.

Note that $a_i' < b_i'$ for every i. Thus we have a new rectangle $R[\mathbf{A}(S), \mathbf{B}(S)]$. Each "side" of this new rectangle is exactly half as long as the corresponding side of the original rectangle. If $\mathbf{X}$ is any point in $R[\mathbf{A}, \mathbf{B}]$, then we must have either $a_i \leq x_i \leq c_i$ or $c_i \leq x_i \leq b_i$ (or both) for each i. Letting S be the set of all i for which $a_i \leq x_i \leq b_i$, we see that $\mathbf{X} \in R[\mathbf{A}(S), \mathbf{B}(S)]$; that is, the union of all of the new rectangles contains all of the points of the original rectangle.

How many of these new rectangles are there? Since each of the first n integers is either in, or not in, the set S, there are 2^n such subsets. This means that the original rectangle has been divided into 2^n rectangles, each of which is half the length of the original rectangle in every dimension (see Fig. 5-6). The original rectangle has not been divided up without overlap; there is a common "face" to two adjacent rectangles. This overlap will not matter to us. The important thing is that every point of the original rectangle is contained in *at least one* of the new rectangles.

In the proofs of the theorems which follow, we will decompose a rectangle this way into 2^n smaller rectangles. Then we choose one of these, which in turn will be decomposed. We will then obtain a sequence of "nested" rectangles. Each is "half" the size of the previous one. The important thing is that there will exist one, and only one, point common to all of these rectangles.

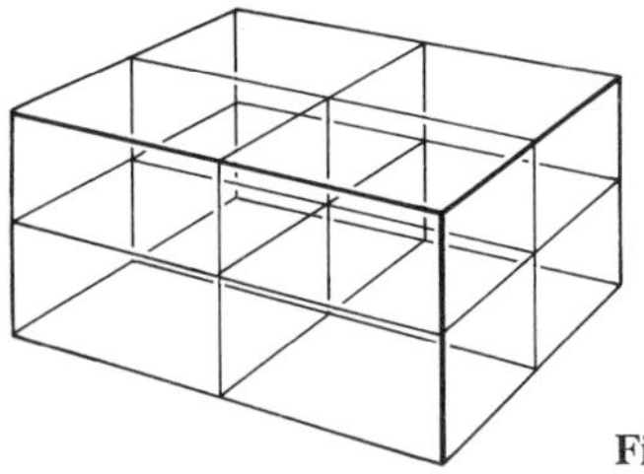

Fig. 5-6

Theorem 5-13. Let $R[\mathbf{A}_i, \mathbf{B}_i]$ be a sequence of rectangles in R^n, each being a subset of the previous one, and each being half as long as the previous one in every dimension, as described above. Then there exists a single unique point $\mathbf{X}_0$ which is common to all of the rectangles of the sequence.

Proof. Let $\mathbf{A}_i = [a_{i1}, a_{i2}, \ldots, a_{in}]$ and $\mathbf{B}_i = [b_{i1}, b_{i2}, \ldots, b_{in}]$ for each i. Then the way in which the successive rectangles have been chosen shows that for each k, $\{a_{ik}\}_{i=1}^{\infty}$ is a monotone increasing sequence, $\{b_{ik}\}_{i=1}^{\infty}$ is a monotone decreasing sequence, $a_{ik} < b_{ik}$, and $b_{ik} - a_{ik} = (b_k - a_k)/2^i$ and hence tends to zero as $i \to \infty$.

Therefore from Theorem 5-12 we have a unique x_k which is the common upper bound of the a_{ik} and lower bound of the b_{ik}. Let $\mathbf{X}_0 = [x_1, x_2, \ldots, x_n]$. Then $\mathbf{X}_0$ is the desired point of the theorem. It is clear that $\mathbf{X}_0$ is common to all the rectangles, since for each coordinate k, $a_{ik} \leq x_k \leq b_{ik}$.

The fact that no other point can be common to all the rectangles follows from the fact that the size of the rectangles tends to zero. The formal proof is left as an exercise for the reader. ▌

We may now proceed to the proofs of the theorems of the last section.

Proof of Theorem 5–8. Let S be an infinite set of points, all contained in the compact set K. Since K is bounded, there must exist some rectangle $R[\mathbf{A}, \mathbf{B}]$ which contains K. We subdivide $R[\mathbf{A}, \mathbf{B}]$ by the method described above. The set S is then contained in the union of the 2^n smaller rectangles. At least one of these must contain an infinite number of points of S, since otherwise S would be the union of 2^n finite sets and hence would have been finite. Choose as the second rectangle of the sequence one which contains an infinite number of points of S. Continue in this way; at every stage, choose a smaller rectangle which contains an infinite number of the points of S.

By Theorem 5–13, there exists a point $\mathbf{X}_0$ which is common to all of these rectangles. This is the desired limit point of the set S. Since the size of the rectangles tends to zero, any neighborhood of $\mathbf{X}_0$ must contain one of these rectangles and hence an infinite number of points of S. This proves the existence of the limit point. The fact that $\mathbf{X}_0 \in K$ follows from the fact that S is a subset of K, hence any limit point of S must be a limit point of K. However, K, being closed, must contain all of its limit points. ▌

Proof of Theorem 5–9. We are given a compact set K and a collection $\mathfrak{N}$ of neighborhoods which cover K. We wish to show that there is a finite subcollection of these neighborhoods which still covers K. We prove this by contradiction.

Suppose that no finite subcollection of $\mathfrak{N}$ covers K. Since K is bounded, there exists a rectangle $R[\mathbf{A}, \mathbf{B}]$ which contains K. We subdivide this rectangle into 2^n smaller rectangles. Choose one of these, $R[\mathbf{A}_1, \mathbf{B}_1]$, such that no finite subcollection of $\mathfrak{N}$ covers $K \cap R[\mathbf{A}_1, \mathbf{B}_1]$. There must be such a subrectangle, since otherwise there would be finite subcollections of $\mathfrak{N}$ covering the parts of K in each of the 2^n rectangles, and together these subcollections would constitute a finite covering of K.

We can continue in this way, at each stage choosing a smaller rectangle such that $K \cap R[\mathbf{A}_k, \mathbf{B}_k]$ cannot be covered by any finite subcollection of $\mathfrak{N}$. By Theorem 5–13, there exists a point $\mathbf{X}_0$ common to all of these rectangles. Since each rectangle must contain points of K, $\mathbf{X}_0$ is a limit point of K. However, K is closed. Hence $\mathbf{X}_0 \in K$.

The collection of neighborhoods $\mathfrak{N}$ covers K. Therefore there will be at least one of the neighborhoods, N_0, which contains $\mathbf{X}_0$. Since $\mathbf{X}_0$ is common to all of the rectangles and the size of the rectangles tends toward zero, there must be one of the rectangles contained in N_0. This is however a contradiction. Each rectangle was supposed to be such that $K \cap R[\mathbf{A}_k, \mathbf{B}_k]$ could not be covered by a finite number of the neighborhoods. This is contradicted if $R[\mathbf{A}_k, \mathbf{B}_k]$ is contained entirely in one of the neighborhoods, N_0. Therefore the original assumption must be incorrect, and the theorem is proved. ▌

Proof of Theorem 5–10. Let f be continuous at every point of the compact set K. Let $\epsilon > 0$ be given. For any point $\mathbf{X}$ in K there exists a $\delta = \delta(\epsilon/2, \mathbf{X})$ such that $|f(\mathbf{Y}) - f(\mathbf{X})| < \epsilon/2$ for all $\mathbf{Y}$ in $S_\delta(\mathbf{X})$. Since ϵ remains fixed until the end of the proof, we suppress the dependence on ϵ and write only $\delta = \delta(\mathbf{X})$.

For each $\mathbf{X}$ let $N(\mathbf{X}) = S_{\delta(\mathbf{X})/2}(\mathbf{X})$. This N is then a neighborhood of the point $\mathbf{X}$. Since there is one such N for each $\mathbf{X}$ in K, the collection of all of them certainly will cover K. By Theorem 5–9 there exists a finite number of these, say $N(\mathbf{X}_1), N(\mathbf{X}_2), \ldots, N(\mathbf{X}_p)$, which cover K. Set

$$\delta = \tfrac{1}{2}\min\{\delta(\mathbf{X}_k) \mid k = 1, 2, \ldots, p\}.$$

Then $\delta > 0$. We will now prove that this is the δ required in the theorem.

Let $\mathbf{X}$ and $\mathbf{Y}$ be any two points of K with $|\mathbf{X} - \mathbf{Y}| < \delta$. Since the neighborhoods $N(\mathbf{X}_k)$ cover K, $\mathbf{X}$ must be in at least one of them. Suppose that $\mathbf{X} \in N(\mathbf{X}_j)$. Then $|\mathbf{X} - \mathbf{X}_j| < \delta(\mathbf{X}_j)/2$. Now $|\mathbf{Y} - \mathbf{X}| < \delta \le \delta(\mathbf{X}_j)/2$, and hence

$$|\mathbf{Y} - \mathbf{X}_j| \le |\mathbf{Y} - \mathbf{X}| + |\mathbf{X} - \mathbf{X}_j| < \delta(\mathbf{X}_j).$$

We therefore have both $\mathbf{X}$ and $\mathbf{Y}$ in $S_{\delta(\mathbf{X}_j)}(\mathbf{X}_j)$. Therefore

$$\begin{aligned}|f(\mathbf{X}) - f(\mathbf{Y})| &\le |f(\mathbf{X}) - f(\mathbf{X}_j)| + |f(\mathbf{X}_j) - f(\mathbf{Y})| \\ &< \epsilon/2 + \epsilon/2 = \epsilon. \ \blacksquare\end{aligned}$$

Proof of Theorem 5–11. We are given that the function f is continuous at every point of the compact set K. We will show that the set of all $f(\mathbf{X})$ is bounded above and that there is some point $\mathbf{X}_0$ in K at which $f(\mathbf{X})$ assumes its maximum value. The proof for the lower bound and the minimum is similar and can be left to the reader.

There are many ways to prove this theorem. The following proof has the advantage of proving both parts at once. Set

$$M = \sup\{f(\mathbf{X}) \mid \mathbf{X} \in K\}.$$

So far as we know at present, this number M could be $+\infty$. The basic property of the least upper bound is that if we choose any number $c < M$, then there must exist some element b of the set such that $b > c$ (this is true whether M is finite or infinite). Choose a sequence of numbers which approach M. Say $c_k = M - 1/k$ if M is finite, or $c_k = k$ if $M = +\infty$. For each c_k there exists an $\mathbf{X}_k$ in K such that $f(\mathbf{X}_k) > c_k$. Therefore $f(\mathbf{X}_k) \to M$.

This sequence must contain an infinite number of points. Let $\mathbf{X}_0$ be a limit point of the sequence (Theorem 5–8). Then $\mathbf{X}_0 \in K$, and since f is continuous at $\mathbf{X}_0$, we must have $f(\mathbf{X}_0) = M$. In particular, we can then conclude that M must be finite since it is the value of the function at the point $\mathbf{X}_0$.

5–4. THE DERIVATIVE

We are familiar with the derivative of a real-valued function of a single real variable. In this section we wish to extend this idea to consider the derivative of a real-valued function of a vector. Obviously we cannot make the simplest possible generalization of the definition of a derivative. If $\mathbf{X}$ is a vector and f is a scalar-valued function of the vector, then the expression $f(\mathbf{X} + h) - f(\mathbf{X})$ is without meaning for a scalar h. In order to consider the difference, we would have to use a vector $\mathbf{H}$. But then

$f(\mathbf{X} + \mathbf{H}) - f(\mathbf{X})$ cannot be used as the numerator of a difference quotient whose denominator is $\mathbf{H}$. There is no useful way to define the quotient of a scalar and a vector.

We must arrange things so that we can consider the function $f(\mathbf{X})$ to be a function of a scalar. Then we will be able to find the difference quotient. We look at the function restricted to a single line passing through the desired point. Thus, if $\mathbf{X}$ is a given point and $\mathbf{Y}$ is any nonzero vector, then the line through $\mathbf{X}$ with direction $\mathbf{Y}$ is the set of all vectors of the form $\mathbf{X} + t\mathbf{Y}$. Along this line the values of the function are values of the variable t alone. Thus, if we define

$$g(t) = f(\mathbf{X} + t\mathbf{Y}), \tag{5–3}$$

then we have obtained a real-valued function of the single real variable t. If f is defined in some neighborhood of $\mathbf{X}$, then g will be defined for all t in some neighborhood of 0. We will now use this new function to define the derivative, which, of course, will depend on $\mathbf{Y}$. Many different ways of denoting the resulting derivative are used. We choose the following one since it seems to be most useful in terms of the linear algebra machinery that we have developed.

Definition 5–16. Let $f: B \to R$ be defined at and in a neighborhood of the point $\mathbf{X} \in B$. Let $\mathbf{Y}$ be a nonzero vector in R^n. Then by the $\mathbf{Y}$-derivative of f at $\mathbf{X}$ we mean the value of

$$D_{\mathbf{Y}}f(\mathbf{X}) = \lim_{h \to 0} \frac{f(\mathbf{X} + h\mathbf{Y}) - f(\mathbf{X})}{h}, \tag{5–4}$$

provided this limit exists.

The derivative defined here is nothing but $g'(0)$ for the function $g(t)$ defined in (5–3). It therefore measures the rate of change of the function along the line through $\mathbf{X}$ with direction $\mathbf{Y}$. This derivative is frequently called the *Fréchet derivative*.

In this book we are interested in discussing the behavior of the derivatives of functions and how they can be used to tell us something about the behavior of the function itself. Concentration on the pathological cases would obscure those basic properties we seek to discover. For this reason, we assume as much continuity of functions and their derivatives as we find useful.

Definition 5–17. Let B be a subset of R^n. Let $f: B \to R$. Let $\mathbf{X}_0$ be a point of B which is such that some neighborhood of $\mathbf{X}_0$ is contained in B. Then we say that f is *continuously differentiable in this neighborhood*, or, for short, that *f is C^1 in this neighborhood* if and only if the limit $D_{\mathbf{Y}}f(\mathbf{X})$ exists and is a continuous function of $\mathbf{X}$ at every point of this neighborhood for each fixed $\mathbf{Y}$.

Note that we do not require $D_{\mathbf{Y}}f(\mathbf{X})$ to be a continuous function of $\mathbf{Y}$, or to be jointly continuous in both $\mathbf{X}$ and $\mathbf{Y}$. While this is not the weakest definition that we could make and still work with, it is really not much stronger than such a definition. The requirements of this Definition 5–17 will make our work much easier, yet they are sufficiently general so that almost every function which we might deal with in practice will satisfy them, except at isolated points. These points will have to be treated on their own merits in any case.

When we apply the mean-value theorem for real-valued functions of a real variable to the function defined in (5–3), we obtain:

▶ **Theorem 5–14** (*The mean-value theorem*). Let $f: B \to R$ be defined and continuously differentiable in a neighborhood of the point $\mathbf{X}_0$. If $\mathbf{Y} \neq \mathbf{0}$ is sufficiently small so that $\mathbf{X} = \mathbf{X}_0 + \theta\mathbf{Y}$ is in this neighborhood for all θ with $0 \leq \theta \leq 1$, then there exists some θ in the interval $0 < \theta < 1$ such that

$$f(\mathbf{X}_0 + \mathbf{Y}) - f(\mathbf{X}_0) = D_{\mathbf{Y}}f(\mathbf{X}_0 + \theta\mathbf{Y}). \tag{5–5}$$

As in the case of the more familiar mean-value theorem, this theorem says that the difference between the values of the function at two points is equal to the value of the derivative at some intermediate point times the distance between the points. The distance between the two points is taken care of by the vector $\mathbf{Y}$ in the symbol for the derivative. Thus in (5–3) t ranges from 0 to 1, hence the t-distance between the points is 1. To prove this result, we only need note that $g'(t_0) = D_{\mathbf{Y}}f(\mathbf{X}_0 + t_0\mathbf{Y})$. The theorem then follows from the definitions.

We now turn to the proof of a most remarkable theorem.

▶ **Theorem 5–15.** Let f be defined and continuously differentiable in a neighborhood of the point $\mathbf{X}$. Then, for fixed $\mathbf{X}$, the function $D_{\mathbf{Y}}f(\mathbf{X})$ is a linear function of the vector $\mathbf{Y}$.

Remarks. If $f(x)$ is a function of the single real variable x, then the vector $\mathbf{Y}$ is also one dimensional, that is, it is a real number y. Then

$$\begin{aligned} D_y f(x) &= \lim_{h\to 0} \frac{f(x + hy) - f(x)}{h} = \lim_{h\to 0} y\left[\frac{f(x + hy) - f(x)}{hy}\right] \\ &= y \lim_{u\to 0} \frac{f(x + u) - f(x)}{u} = yf'(x). \end{aligned}$$

In the course of this calculation, we have put $u = hy$. In the last expression $f'(x)$ is a real number, the usual derivative of f at x. We see that $D_y f(x)$ is indeed a linear function of y for a fixed x. The general proof is much the same.

Proof. First, we prove that if $s \neq 0$ is any scalar, then $D_{s\mathbf{Y}}f(\mathbf{X}) = sD_{\mathbf{Y}}f(\mathbf{X})$:

$$\begin{aligned} D_{s\mathbf{Y}}f(\mathbf{X}) &= \lim_{h\to 0} \frac{1}{h}[f(\mathbf{X} + hs\mathbf{Y}) - f(\mathbf{X})] \\ &= \lim_{h\to 0} \frac{s}{hs}[f(\mathbf{X} + hs\mathbf{Y}) - f(\mathbf{X})] \\ &= \lim_{u\to 0} s\frac{1}{u}[f(\mathbf{X} + u\mathbf{Y}) - f(\mathbf{X})] \\ &= sD_{\mathbf{Y}}f(\mathbf{X}). \end{aligned}$$

Here we merely had to set $u = hs$. Note that although $\mathbf{Y} \neq \mathbf{0}$ is specified in Definition 5–16, if we let $\mathbf{Y} = \mathbf{0}$, then we obtain the value 0 for the derivative. This fits with the result just proved when we set $s = 0$.

Next, we prove that $D_{(\mathbf{Y}+\mathbf{Z})}f(\mathbf{X}) = D_{\mathbf{Y}}f(\mathbf{X}) + D_{\mathbf{Z}}f(\mathbf{X})$. We do this with the help of two applications of the mean-value theorem:

$$\begin{aligned} D_{(\mathbf{Y}+\mathbf{Z})}f(\mathbf{X}) &= \lim_{h\to 0} \frac{1}{h}[f(\mathbf{X} + h\mathbf{Y} + h\mathbf{Z}) - f(\mathbf{X})] \\ &= \lim_{h\to 0} \frac{1}{h}[f(\mathbf{X} + h\mathbf{Y} + h\mathbf{Z}) - f(\mathbf{X} + h\mathbf{Y}) + f(\mathbf{X} + h\mathbf{Y}) - f(\mathbf{X})] \\ &= \lim_{h\to 0} \frac{1}{h}[D_{h\mathbf{Z}}f(\mathbf{X} + h\mathbf{Y} + \theta_1 h\mathbf{Z}) + D_{h\mathbf{Y}}f(\mathbf{X} + \theta_2 h\mathbf{Y})] \\ &= \lim_{h\to 0} [D_{\mathbf{Z}}f(\mathbf{X} + h\mathbf{Y} + \theta_1 h\mathbf{Z}) + D_{\mathbf{Y}}f(\mathbf{X} + \theta_2 h\mathbf{Y})] \\ &= D_{\mathbf{Z}}f(\mathbf{X}) + D_{\mathbf{Y}}f(\mathbf{X}). \end{aligned}$$

In the next to the last line, we made use of the half of the theorem already proved. In the last line, we made use of the continuity of the $\mathbf{Y}$ and $\mathbf{Z}$ derivatives. ▌

Definition 5–18. Let B be a subset of R^n and let $f: B \to R$ be C^1 (continuously differentiable) in a neighborhood of the point $\mathbf{X} \in B$. Then by the *differential* of f at $\mathbf{X}$ we mean the linear transformation $df(\mathbf{X}): R^n \to R$ defined by $[df(\mathbf{X})]\mathbf{Y} = D_{\mathbf{Y}}f(\mathbf{X})$.

The differential represents a linear transformation which is in general different at each point of B. As a function of $\mathbf{X}$, the differential is unlikely to be linear. It is only with respect to $\mathbf{Y}$ that we have linearity.

The differential is a linear transformation for each fixed $\mathbf{X}$. The symbol $df(\mathbf{X})$ taken all together denotes this transformation. Note that it has no "value" until it has operated on some vector in R^n. Later we will see how this differential relates to the "differential" which the reader may have already learned about in earlier courses.

The reader may find it difficult to picture the differential as defined here. However, if we look for the form of the differential we find it to be simpler than it appears at first. The differential is a linear transformation from R^n to R. We saw in Theorem 4–19 that any such transformation could be represented by a vector $\mathbf{A}$ such that $T\mathbf{Y} = \mathbf{A} \cdot \mathbf{Y}$. We give this vector a special name.

Definition 5–19. Let $f: B \to R$ be C^1 in a neighborhood of $\mathbf{X}$. Let $df(\mathbf{X})$ be its differential at $\mathbf{X}$. Then by the *gradient* of f at $\mathbf{X}$ we mean the vector $\operatorname{grad} f(\mathbf{X})$ [also written $\nabla f(\mathbf{X})$] such that for every $\mathbf{Y}$, $[df(\mathbf{X})]\mathbf{Y} = [\operatorname{grad} f(\mathbf{X})] \cdot \mathbf{Y}$.*

* Strictly speaking, the gradient is a covector rather than a vector, and is represented by a row matrix rather than a column matrix. We will not worry about this distinction, however, since the difference does not appear if we restrict ourselves to changes of variable which correspond to euclidean motions on the space.

Thus, the differential of the function f (a scalar field) can be identified with a "vector field," that is, a vector-valued function of $\mathbf{X}$. It remains only to see what the actual value of this gradient is in a specific case.

Suppose that f is a given function. What are the components of grad f in terms of the standard basis? If $\text{grad}\, f = [a_1, a_2, \ldots, a_n]$, then for each i, $a_i = \text{grad}\, f \cdot \mathbf{e}_i = D_{\mathbf{e}_i} f(\mathbf{X})$. But we recognize that

$$\begin{aligned} D_{\mathbf{e}_i} f(\mathbf{X}) &= \lim_{h \to 0} \frac{1}{h} [f(\mathbf{X} + h\mathbf{e}_i) - f(\mathbf{X})] \\ &= \lim_{h \to 0} \frac{1}{h} [f(x_1, \ldots, x_i + h, \ldots, x_n) - f(x_1, \ldots, x_n)] \\ &= \frac{\partial f}{\partial x_i} \end{aligned}$$

in the conventional notation. We therefore have

$$\text{grad}\, f(\mathbf{X}) = \left[\frac{\partial f}{\partial x_1}, \frac{\partial f}{\partial x_2}, \ldots, \frac{\partial f}{\partial x_n}\right]. \tag{5-6}$$

It may help to see an actual example. Suppose we consider the function

$$f(x, y) = x^2 + 2y^2 - 2,$$

which was discussed in Section 5-2. From (5-6) we calculate

$$\text{grad}\, f(x, y) = [2x, 4y]$$

at each point (x, y). Therefore, if $\mathbf{A} = [a_1, a_2]$ is any nonzero vector, then

$$D_{\mathbf{A}} f(x, y) = 2xa_1 + 4ya_2.$$

What does this mean? Looking at Definition 5-16 again, we see that

$$D_{\mathbf{Y}} f(\mathbf{X}) = \frac{d}{dt} f(\mathbf{X} + t\mathbf{Y}) \bigg|_{t=0}.$$

In particular, if $|\mathbf{Y}| = 1$, then t measures the distance along the line from $\mathbf{X}$ to $\mathbf{X} + \mathbf{Y}$. Then $D_{\mathbf{Y}} f(\mathbf{X})$ is the rate of change of f in that direction.

Definition 5-20. Let $f: B \to R$ be C^1 in a neighborhood of the point $\mathbf{X}$ in B. Let $\mathbf{u}$ be a vector whose magnitude is 1. Then by the *directional derivative* of f in the direction $\mathbf{u}$ at $\mathbf{X}$ we mean

$$D_{\mathbf{u}} f(\mathbf{X}) = [df(\mathbf{X})]\mathbf{u} = [\text{grad}\, f(\mathbf{X})] \cdot \mathbf{u}.$$

Any of the following notations are used to represent the particular directional derivatives in the directions of the standard unit coordinate vectors, called the *partial derivatives* of the function

$$D_i f(\mathbf{X}) = \frac{\partial f}{\partial x_i} = f_{,i}(\mathbf{X}) = D_{\mathbf{e}_i} f(\mathbf{X}).$$

The final term in this line uses the notation that was already introduced in Definition 5–16. The first notation given is merely a condensed version of the same one. Observe that (along with the others) it can be used only when we have been given an explicit coordinate system. The ∂-notation in the second term is probably already familiar, but the third form may be new to the reader. The prime is used to indicate that a derivative is being taken, while the subscript indicates the variable with respect to which the differentiation is being performed.

Sometimes we will find it convenient to have a statement of the mean-value theorem (Theorem 5–14) in terms of the gradient. Using Definition 5–19 in (5–5), we find

$$\begin{aligned} f(\mathbf{X}_0 + \mathbf{Y}) - f(\mathbf{X}_0) &= D_{\mathbf{Y}} f(\mathbf{X}_0 + \theta\mathbf{Y}) = [df(\mathbf{X})]\mathbf{Y}, \\ &= [\operatorname{grad} f(\mathbf{X})] \cdot \mathbf{Y}, \end{aligned}$$

where $\mathbf{X} = \mathbf{X}_0 + \theta\mathbf{Y}$ is some point on the line segment between $\mathbf{X}_0$ and $\mathbf{X}_0 + \mathbf{Y}$. A slightly more general form of this result is obtained by setting $\mathbf{Y} = t\mathbf{Z}$. We then have

$$f(\mathbf{X}_0 + t\mathbf{Z}) - f(\mathbf{X}_0) = t[df(\mathbf{X})]\mathbf{Z} = t[\operatorname{grad} f(\mathbf{X})] \cdot \mathbf{Z},$$

where again $\mathbf{X}$ is some point on the line segment joining $\mathbf{X}_0$ and $\mathbf{X}_0 + t\mathbf{Z}$.

The differential has a number of important "linearity properties" which are close analogues of the corresponding properties of the derivative of a function of a single real variable.

▶ **Theorem 5–16.** Let f and g be real-valued functions which are C^1 in a neighborhood of a point $\mathbf{X}_0$ in R^n. Let c be a real number (a constant). Then at $\mathbf{X}_0$

$$\begin{aligned} [d(f + g)] &= [df] + [dg], \\ [d(cf)] &= c[df], \\ [d(fg)] &= f[dg] + g[df]. \end{aligned}$$

The proof of this theorem is quite simple and may be left as an exercise. For the third part, the similar result for functions of a single variable can be assumed to simplify the proof. It should be observed that these results may be viewed as results about linear transformations or about matrices (the expressions in brackets may each be viewed as representing a $1 \times n$ matrix when a specific coordinate system is given).

PROBLEMS

1. Find the gradients of the functions of Problems 1 and 2 of Section 5–2. Find all of the points at which the gradient is the zero vector.
2. Suppose that $f: R \to R$ is a real-valued function of the single real variable x. What is the linear transformation of Definition 5–18 in this case? What is the gradient of f?
3. Prove Theorem 5–16. In proving the third part, the similar result for functions of a single real variable can be assumed. [*Hint:* Consider the directional derivatives derived from expressions such as (5–3).]

4. Let $f(\mathbf{X}) = x^2y + z$. Let $\mathbf{X}_0 = \mathbf{0}$ and $\mathbf{X}_0 + \mathbf{Y} = [1, 1, 1]$. What is the point $\mathbf{X}$ on the line segment joining $\mathbf{X}_0$ and $\mathbf{X}_0 + \mathbf{Y}$ at which the mean-value theorem is satisfied?
5. For a function of a single variable, the mean-value theorem tells us that if $f(a) = f(b)$, then there must be some point between a and b at which $f'(x) = 0$. If $f:B \to R$ is C^1 in the region B in R^n $(n > 1)$ and $f(\mathbf{A}) = f(\mathbf{B})$, is there some point on the line segment between $\mathbf{A}$ and $\mathbf{B}$ at which $\operatorname{grad} f = \mathbf{0}$? What can you conclude from the mean-value theorem about the behavior of $\operatorname{grad} f$ on the line segment between $\mathbf{A}$ and $\mathbf{B}$ in this case?

5-5. TANGENT PLANES AND THE DIFFERENTIAL

The directional derivative introduced in the last section, measures the rate of change of the function in a particular direction. If $\mathbf{u}$ is any vector of unit length, then the directional derivative of a function f at a point $\mathbf{X}_0$ in the direction $\mathbf{u}$ is given by

$$D_{\mathbf{u}}f(\mathbf{X}_0) = [\operatorname{grad} f(\mathbf{X}_0)] \cdot \mathbf{u}.$$

If the gradient vector is not zero, then it points in the direction of maximum increase of the function f. We will now prove this.

From the Cauchy-Schwarz inequality we know that for any unit vector $\mathbf{u}$

$$\begin{aligned} |D_{\mathbf{u}}f(\mathbf{X})| &= |\operatorname{grad} f \cdot \mathbf{u}| \\ &\leq |\operatorname{grad} f|\,|\mathbf{u}| = |\operatorname{grad} f|. \end{aligned}$$

Therefore $|\operatorname{grad} f|$ is the maximum possible value that the directional derivative could assume. If $|\operatorname{grad} f| \neq 0$, then this value is actually assumed if we let

$$\mathbf{u} = (\operatorname{grad} f)/|\operatorname{grad} f|.$$

We thus have

► **Theorem 5-17.** Suppose that $f:B \to R$ is C^1 in a neighborhood of a point $\mathbf{X}_0 \in B$ and that $\operatorname{grad} f(\mathbf{X}_0) \neq \mathbf{0}$. Then the function f increases most rapidly in the direction of $\operatorname{grad} f(\mathbf{X}_0)$, that is, the directional derivative $D_{\mathbf{u}}f(\mathbf{X}_0)$ is a maximum when $\mathbf{u} = (\operatorname{grad} f(\mathbf{X}_0))/|\operatorname{grad} f(\mathbf{X}_0)|$.

While the function increases most rapidly in the direction of grad f, it decreases most rapidly in the opposite direction. The vector grad f points in the steepest "uphill" direction of f. Compare the value of the gradient given in the middle of page 192 with the pictures of the function shown in Figs. 5-3 and 5-4.

Suppose that $\mathbf{u}$ is orthogonal to grad f. Then the directional derivative in the direction of $\mathbf{u}$ must be zero. Thus such a vector can be considered to be tangent to the level surface of f which passes through that point.

Definition 5-21. Let $f: B \to R$ be C^1 in a neighborhood of a point $\mathbf{X}_0 \in B$ Let $\operatorname{grad} f(\mathbf{X}_0) \neq \mathbf{0}$ and set $L = \ker df(\mathbf{X}_0)$. Then the affine hyperplane $\mathbf{X}_0 + L$ is called the tangent hyperplane to the level surface of f at $\mathbf{X}_0$.

The tangent hyperplane approximates the level surface. To see this we note that since

$$\lim_{h\to 0} \frac{1}{h}[f(\mathbf{X}_0 + h\mathbf{Y}) - f(\mathbf{X}_0)] = \operatorname{grad} f \cdot \mathbf{Y}$$

for small enough h, we must have the quantity on the left approximately equal to the expression on the right. That is

$$f(\mathbf{X}_0 + h\mathbf{Y}) - f(\mathbf{X}_0) \doteq \operatorname{grad} f \cdot h\mathbf{Y}.$$

Setting $h\mathbf{Y} = \mathbf{X} - \mathbf{X}_0$, we find that we have shown that if $\mathbf{X}$ is close enough to $\mathbf{X}_0$, then we must have approximately

$$f(\mathbf{X}) \doteq f(\mathbf{X}_0) + [\operatorname{grad} f(\mathbf{X}_0)] \cdot [\mathbf{X} - \mathbf{X}_0]. \tag{5-7}$$

The right-hand side of this equation is an affine linear function of $\mathbf{X}$ approximating the function $f(\mathbf{X})$ near $\mathbf{X}_0$. This approximation is identically equal to $f(\mathbf{X}_0)$ for all $\mathbf{X}$ in the tangent hyperplane of the above definition, and therefore the tangent hyperplane approximates the level surface of f given by $f(\mathbf{X}) = f(\mathbf{X}_0)$.

We can use Eq. (5-7) to give an actual approximation to a given function or to solve for the equation of the tangent hyperplane. For example, if we are given the function $f(x, y, z) = x^2 - xy^2 + 4z^2$ and ask for the equation of the tangent hyperplane to the level surface of f which passes through $[2, 1, 1]$ (i.e., the surface $f = 6$), we may proceed as follows. We compute

$$\operatorname{grad} f = [2x - y^2, -2xy, 8z]\,\big|_{[2,1,1]} = [3, -4, 8].$$

Hence the equation of the tangent hyperplane (plane) is

$$[3, -4, 8] \cdot [x - 2, y - 1, z - 1] = 0,$$

or

$$3x - 4y + 8z = 10.$$

We can use (5-7) to obtain an approximation to the same function in a neighborhood of the point $[2, 1, 1]$. This approximation is given by

$$f(\mathbf{X}) \doteq 6 + [3, -4, 8] \cdot [x - 2, y - 1, z - 1] = 3x - 4y + 8z - 4,$$

which is actually the best possible linear approximation to $f(\mathbf{X}) = x^2 - xy^2 + 4z^2$ in a neighborhood of the point $[2, 1, 1]$.

Equation (5-7) gives us a linear approximation to a function. It does not indicate how good that approximation is. We know that the difference between the two sides must tend to zero as $\mathbf{X}$ tends to $\mathbf{X}_0$, but in fact the approximation is better than that.

▶ **Theorem 5-18.** Let $f: B \to R$ and let f be C^1 in a neighborhood of the point $\mathbf{X}_0 \in B$. Then, setting $\mathbf{A} = \operatorname{grad} f(\mathbf{X}_0)$, we have

$$\lim_{\mathbf{Z}\to 0} \frac{1}{|\mathbf{Z}|} |f(\mathbf{X}_0 + \mathbf{Z}) - f(\mathbf{X}_0) - \mathbf{A} \cdot \mathbf{Z}| = 0. \tag{5-8}$$

Proof. When we say that f is C^1 in a neighborhood of $\mathbf{X}_0$, we mean that $D_{\mathbf{Y}}f(\mathbf{X})$ exists and is a continuous function of $\mathbf{X}$ in a neighborhood of $\mathbf{X}_0$ for each fixed $\mathbf{Y}$. In particular, the partial derivatives $D_i f(\mathbf{X}) = f_{,i}(\mathbf{X})$ must be continuous functions of $\mathbf{X}$. Now from the mean-value theorem we have for any $\mathbf{Z}$ sufficiently close to zero

$$f(\mathbf{X}_0 + \mathbf{Z}) - f(\mathbf{X}_0) = \operatorname{grad} f(\mathbf{X}) \cdot \mathbf{Z},$$

where $\mathbf{X}$ is some point on the line segment between $\mathbf{X}_0$ and $\mathbf{X}_0 + \mathbf{Z}$. In particular, this means that $|\mathbf{X} - \mathbf{X}_0| < |\mathbf{Z}|$. Define $\mathbf{E}(\mathbf{X}) = \operatorname{grad} f(\mathbf{X}) - \operatorname{grad} f(\mathbf{X}_0)$. Then we have [setting $\operatorname{grad} f(\mathbf{X}_0) = \mathbf{A}$]

$$f(\mathbf{X}_0 + \mathbf{Z}) - f(\mathbf{X}_0) = [\mathbf{A} + \mathbf{E}(\mathbf{X})] \cdot \mathbf{Z} = \mathbf{A} \cdot \mathbf{Z} + \mathbf{E}(\mathbf{X}) \cdot \mathbf{Z}.$$

Therefore

$$[f(\mathbf{X}_0 + \mathbf{Z}) - f(\mathbf{X}_0) - \mathbf{A} \cdot \mathbf{Z}] = \mathbf{E}(\mathbf{X}) \cdot \mathbf{Z}.$$

By the Cauchy-Schwarz inequality, $|\mathbf{E}(\mathbf{X}) \cdot \mathbf{Z}| \leq |\mathbf{E}(\mathbf{X})| \cdot |\mathbf{Z}|$, and hence if $\mathbf{Z} \neq \mathbf{0}$ is sufficiently close to zero, we have

$$\frac{1}{|\mathbf{Z}|} |f(\mathbf{X}_0 + \mathbf{Z}) - f(\mathbf{X}_0) - \mathbf{A} \cdot \mathbf{Z}| \leq |\mathbf{E}(\mathbf{X})| = \left(\sum_{i=1}^{n} [f_{,i}(\mathbf{X}) - f_{,i}(\mathbf{X}_0)]^2 \right)^{1/2}.$$

As $\mathbf{Z} \to \mathbf{0}$, we must have $\mathbf{X} \to \mathbf{X}_0$. The continuity of the $f_{,i}(\mathbf{X})$ shows that the last expression must tend to zero. ▮

The assumption of the continuity of the differential that we make is actually stronger than is required for the proof of the theorems we are working toward. Instead, we could get by with the assumption of the property given by (5–8). However, this would complicate our proofs, and the extra generality is probably not worth the effort required at this stage.

An immediate consequence of the last theorem is the next theorem, which gives another form of the same approximation condition as found in (5–8). This version is useful in many cases.

▶ **Theorem 5–19.** Let $f: B \to R$ and let f be C^1 in a neighborhood of the point $\mathbf{X}_0 \in B$. Then, setting $\mathbf{A} = \operatorname{grad} f(\mathbf{X}_0)$, we have

$$f(\mathbf{X}) = f(\mathbf{X}_0) + \mathbf{A} \cdot [\mathbf{X} - \mathbf{X}_0] + \epsilon(\mathbf{X})|\mathbf{X} - \mathbf{X}_0|, \tag{5–9}$$

where $\epsilon(\mathbf{X})$ is a real-valued function of $\mathbf{X}$ such that

$$\lim_{\mathbf{X} \to \mathbf{X}_0} \epsilon(\mathbf{X}) = 0.$$

The differential (or, rather, what we shall call the *total differential*) was introduced into mathematics at the time calculus was first discovered. Much of the work on calculus in the past two hundred years has been devoted to making the concept of a differential satisfactory to the views of mathematics of each age. The concept has always been found to be so useful that attempts to do away with it have always failed. Before giving the exact definition, let us discuss this concept in an intuitive manner.

The idea of the total differential is based on the approximation indicated in Eq. (5–7). Rewriting this equation, we have

$$f(\mathrm{X}) - f(\mathrm{X}_0) \doteq [\operatorname{grad} f(\mathrm{X}_0)] \cdot [\mathrm{X} - \mathrm{X}_0]. \tag{5–10}$$

We know that this approximation gets better as X gets closer to X_0. A common notation for the change in X, that is $\mathrm{X} - \mathrm{X}_0$, is $\Delta\mathrm{X}$. In the early days of calculus, the notation $d\mathrm{X}$ was introduced to represent this change $\Delta\mathrm{X}$, when the change was extremely small; that is, $d\mathrm{X}$ was defined as

$$d\mathrm{X} = [dx_1, dx_2, \ldots, dx_n] = \Delta\mathrm{X} = \mathrm{X} - \mathrm{X}_0.$$

However, the feeling was that X was to be very close to X_0 so that all of the dx_i were very close to zero.

The *total differential* of f was defined to be the right-hand side of (5–10). That is,

$$\begin{aligned} df &= \operatorname{grad} f \cdot d\mathrm{X} \\ &= f'_1(\mathrm{X}_0)dx_1 + f'_2(\mathrm{X}_0)dx_2 + \cdots + f'_n(\mathrm{X}_0)dx_n. \end{aligned}$$

Then if we let Δf represent the actual change in f corresponding to the change in X, i.e., $\Delta f = f(\mathrm{X}) - f(\mathrm{X}_0)$, then Eq. (5–10) is equivalent to

$$\Delta f \doteq df. \tag{5–11}$$

Here we see the reason for the tacit assumption that $d\mathrm{X}$ is always small. The approximation in (5–11) is a good approximation only if $d\mathrm{X}$ is small. But how good is "good"? How small is "small"? These questions are difficult to answer. Instead, we free the total differential from the restriction of having to be small, and merely take note that (5–11) is an approximation which becomes more accurate as $d\mathrm{X}$ tends to zero.

Definition 5–22. Let B be a subset of R^n and let $f: B \to R$ be C^1 in a neighborhood of a point $\mathrm{X}_0 \in B$. Let $df = df(\mathrm{X}_0)$ be the linear transformation which is the differential of f at X_0. We will let $d\mathrm{X}$ denote an arbitrary vector in the domain of the linear transformation df. We will write

$$d\mathrm{X} = [dx_1, dx_2, \ldots, dx_n].$$

By the *total differential of* f at X_0 we mean the corresponding image of $d\mathrm{X}$ under the linear transformation df, i.e.,

$$df = [df]\, d\mathrm{X} = f'_1\, dx_1 + f'_2\, dx_2 + \cdots + f'_n\, dx_n. \tag{5–12}$$

We now seem to have two different meanings for the same notation. In particular, the dx_i introduced here represent real numbers rather than linear transformations as would fit in with the notation introduced in the last section. Similarly, the symbol df in the last line of the definition represents a real number. However, we will not find that this causes any confusion. Later, we will see that when the coordinate variables x_i are themselves functions of other variables, the same formulas hold. Using the same symbol to represent either a function or the value of that function is a common abuse of notation. We can view the expressions (5–12) for the total differential as being a formal expression which defines the linear transformation df in terms of its value for each vector $d\mathbf{X}$.

The total differential can be used to express the approximation property of (5–11), but a more important use is as a representation of the linear transformation df. Note that df is more than just some real number. It is the real number which corresponds to the vector $d\mathbf{X}$ under this particular linear transformation.

Although the discussion we gave above was based on thinking of $d\mathbf{X}$ as representing the change in $\mathbf{X}$, it is better to think of $d\mathbf{X}$, as defined in this definition, as a new vector in an entirely separate vector space—the vector space in which we discuss the linear transformation df.

For simple functions involving a small number of variables, the total differential is often the easiest way to write down the linear transformation df and the approximation property (5–10). The tangent hyperplane to the level surface of f can also be obtained quite easily from the total differential. For example, suppose we are given

$$f(x, y, z, w) = w^3(x^2 + y^2)e^{xz^2}$$

and are interested in the behavior of this function near the point $\mathbf{P} = [0, 1, 0, 1]$, We start by computing the total differential:

$$df = f'_1\,dx + f'_2\,dy + f'_3\,dz + f'_4\,dw = dx + 2\,dy + 3\,dw.$$

From this we can immediately read off the approximation

$$f(x, y, z, w) \doteq 1 + x + 2(y - 1) + 3(w - 1), \qquad [x, y, z, w] \text{ near } \mathbf{P}.$$

This approximation was obtained by (5–11), noting that $\Delta f = f(\mathbf{X}) - f(\mathbf{P})$ and $f(\mathbf{P}) = 1$. Also we set $dx = x - 0 = x$, $dy = y - 1$, $dz = z$, and $dw = w - 1$.

The equation of the tangent hyperplane to the level surface $f(\mathbf{X}) = 1$ (through $\mathbf{P}$) is found by setting $df = 0$. For this example, we find the tangent hyperplane

$$x + 2y + 3w - 5 = 0.$$

The fact that z does not appear in this equation is an accident, meaning that the resulting hyperplane is parallel to the z-axis. The general equation of a hyperplane in four dimensions will be a linear equation in the four variables.

PROBLEMS

1. Prove Theorem 5–18.
2. For each function of Problem 1, Section 5–2, find the equation of the line tangent to the level curve of the function at the point $[2, -5]$.
3. For each of the functions of Problem 2, Section 5–2, find the equation of the plane which is tangent to the level surface of the function at $[1, -1, 4]$.
4. Find the linear approximation to the functions of Problems 1 and 2 of Section 5–2 at the points $[1, 0]$ and $[1, 0, 1]$, respectively.

5. Prove that the hyperplane tangent to the level surface of f at $\mathbf{X}_0$ is obtained by setting $df = 0$.
6. Find the equation of the four-dimensional affine hyperplane which is tangent to the level surface of $f(x, y, z, u, v) = x^2 + xy^2 + yz^2 + 2uv + 3zv$ through the point $[x, y, z, u, v] = [1, -1, 2, 1, -1]$.
7. Let $F(v, V, W, T) = (vR/V)e^{-W/kT}$, where R and k are constants. What is the best linear approximation to F in a neighborhood of $[v, V, W, T] = [v_0, V_0, W_0, T_0]$?
8. Show that the level surfaces of the functions

$$\begin{aligned} f &= xy^2 + x + 2wz + \tfrac{1}{2}w^2, \\ g &= x^2 + y^2 + z^2 + \tfrac{1}{2}w^2, \\ h &= x^2 - y^2 + z^2 + 2xz + w^2 - 8w \end{aligned}$$

through $[x, y, z, w] = [1, 1, -1, 4]$ are orthogonal to one another at that point.

5-6. HIGHER-ORDER DERIVATIVES

If $f: B \to R$, where B is a subset of R^n, then df is a linear transformation which we can identify with the vector $[f_{,1}, f_{,2}, \ldots, f_{,n}]$. In later sections we will consider the problem of differentiating vector-valued functions. Here let us merely consider each of the components of this vector as a new function which can then itself be differentiated. Thus the ith component, $f_{,i}: B \to R$, may have a differential $df_{,i}$. This differential has a representation as a vector also. The components of this vector are the partial derivatives of $f_{,i}$.

Definition 5-23. Let $f: B \to R$ be C^1 in a neighborhood of the point $\mathbf{X}$ in B. Suppose also that each of the partial derivatives, $f_{,i}$, are themselves C^1 in a neighborhood of $\mathbf{X}$. Then we say that f is *twice continuously differentiable*, or that f is C^2 in a neighborhood of $\mathbf{X}$. The *second partial derivatives* of f are defined to be

$$f_{,ij}(\mathbf{X}) = \frac{\partial^2 f}{\partial x_j\, \partial x_i} = D_j f_{,i}(\mathbf{X}).$$

Note that the notation for the second derivative is read from the "inside out." In particular, the notation using the ∂ is to be interpreted as representing

$$\frac{\partial^2 f}{\partial x_j\, \partial x_i} = \frac{\partial}{\partial x_j}\left(\frac{\partial f}{\partial x_i}\right).$$

This definition could be extended to any number of derivatives in an obvious way. In this text, however, we will make use of only the first and second derivatives. In fact, we will only rarely need to consider the second derivatives. In this section we wish to prove the basic result concerning the second derivatives. This is the theorem which states that partial derivatives with respect to two variables are independent of the order in which the differentiations are performed.

▶ **Theorem 5–20.** Let $f\colon B \to R$ be defined and C^2 in a neighborhood of a point $\mathbf{X}_0$ [that is, the partial derivatives $f_{,ij}(\mathbf{X})$ are continuous functions of $\mathbf{X}$]. Then for any i and j

$$f_{,ij}(\mathbf{X}_0) = f_{,ji}(\mathbf{X}_0).$$

Proof. The theorem is obviously true if $i = j$. If $i \neq j$, then it is only the changes in the function due to changes in x_i and x_j that we are interested. All the remaining variables can be held constant throughout the argument. Thus it suffices to prove the theorem for a function of two variables, $f(x_1, x_2)$.

Let $f(\mathbf{X})$ be twice differentiable in a neighborhood $S_\delta(\mathbf{X}_0)$. Let h and k be any two nonzero real numbers with $h^2 + k^2 < \delta^2/4$. Then for any θ_1 and θ_2 with $0 \leq \theta_1, \theta_2 \leq 1$, we have $(\mathbf{X}_0 + \theta_1 h\mathbf{e}_1 + \theta_2 k\mathbf{e}_2) \in S_\delta(\mathbf{X}_0)$.

Let us define the quantity

$$Q(h, k) = \frac{1}{hk}[f(\mathbf{X}_0 + h\mathbf{e}_1 + k\mathbf{e}_2) - f(\mathbf{X}_0 + h\mathbf{e}_1) - f(\mathbf{X}_0 + k\mathbf{e}_2) + f(\mathbf{X}_0)].$$

Define, for any $\mathbf{X} \in S_{\delta/2}(\mathbf{X}_0)$, $g(\mathbf{X}) = f(\mathbf{X} + h\mathbf{e}_1) - f(\mathbf{X})$. Then, with the help of the mean-value theorem, we can compute

$$\begin{aligned}
Q(h, k) &= (1/hk)[g(\mathbf{X}_0 + k\mathbf{e}_2) - g(\mathbf{X}_0)] \\
&= (k/hk)\, D_2 g(\mathbf{X}_0 + \theta_2 k\mathbf{e}_2) \\
&= (1/h)\, D_2[f(\mathbf{X}_0 + \theta_2 k\mathbf{e}_2 + h\mathbf{e}_1) - f(\mathbf{X}_0 + \theta_2 k\mathbf{e}_2)] \\
&= (1/h)[f_{,2}(\mathbf{X}_0 + \theta_2 k\mathbf{e}_2 + h\mathbf{e}_1) - f_{,2}(\mathbf{X}_0 + \theta_2 k\mathbf{e}_2)] \\
&= (h/h)\, D_1 f_{,2}(\mathbf{X}_0 + \theta_2 k\mathbf{e}_2 + \theta_1 h\mathbf{e}_1) \\
&= f_{,21}(\mathbf{X}_0 + \theta_2 k\mathbf{e}_2 + \theta_1 h\mathbf{e}_1).
\end{aligned}$$

In exactly the same way, defining $\phi(\mathbf{X}) = f(\mathbf{X} + k\mathbf{e}_2) - f(\mathbf{X})$, we find that $Q(h, k) = (1/hk)[\phi(\mathbf{X}_0 + h\mathbf{e}_1) - \phi(\mathbf{X}_0)]$; and by use of the mean-value theorem, just as above, we find that

$$Q(h, k) = f_{,12}(\mathbf{X}_0 + \theta_1' h\mathbf{e}_1 + \theta_2' k\mathbf{e}_2).$$

Letting h and k tend toward zero in both these expressions for $Q(h, k)$ and using the continuity of the second derivatives, we find that

$$f_{,21}(\mathbf{X}_0) = f_{,12}(\mathbf{X}_0). \ \blacksquare$$

We remark that the equality of these partial derivatives depends on the continuity of the second derivatives. Just existence would not be enough. Note that in this proof we made use of the results of Problem 3 of Section 5–4.

PROBLEMS

1. Find all the second partial derivatives of the following functions:

   a) $f(x, y) = x^2 - x^3y^2$ b) $f(x, y) = e^{x^2y} \cos x$.

   c) $f(x, y, z) = x^4y^2 \log(x^2 + y^2 + z^2)$ d) $f(x, y, z, w) = e^{y^2}[\cos(x^2 + w^2)] \sec z$

5-7. MAXIMUM AND MINIMUM PROBLEMS

Just as maximum and minimum problems form one of the major applications of the calculus of functions of a single variable, so also they are one of the useful applications of the calculus of functions of vectors. Suppose that f is a function which is defined and continuous on some compact set K in R^n. Then we know that there must exist some point in K at which the function assumes its maximum value. (There is also a point at which it assumes its minimum value.) But how do we go about actually finding this point? We find that there are two distinct cases which must be considered. The function can assume its maximum at some interior point of K or at some boundary point of K. The method of attack on the problem differs in these two cases.

First, let us define exactly what we mean by these terms.

Definition 5-24. Let B be any given set in R^n. Then by an *interior point* of B we mean a point $\mathbf{X} \in B$ such that there is some neighborhood of $\mathbf{X}$ contained entirely in B. The set of all interior points of B is called the *interior* of B. A point $\mathbf{X}$ is called a *boundary point* of B if and only if every neighborhood of $\mathbf{X}$ contains points of both B and $\complement B$. The set of all boundary points of B is called the *boundary* of B.

Note that a boundary point of a set may or may not belong to the set. However, a boundary point of a closed set (and hence also of a compact set) is always in the set. (See the problems at the end of this section.)

▶ **Theorem 5-21.** Let $f: K \to R$ take on its maximum (minimum) value at $\mathbf{X}_0$, an interior point of the compact set K. Let f be C^1 in some neighborhood of $\mathbf{X}_0$. Then $\operatorname{grad} f(\mathbf{X}_0) = \mathbf{0}$.

Proof. If f takes on its maximum at $\mathbf{X}_0$, then for each i the function $f(\mathbf{X}_0 + t\mathbf{e}_i)$ must take on a local maximum at $t = 0$, which is an interior point of the interval in which this function is differentiable. Hence the derivative of this function (with respect to t) must be zero at $t = 0$. But this is exactly $f_{,i}(\mathbf{X}_0)$. Hence the ith component of $\operatorname{grad} f(\mathbf{X}_0)$ is zero. Since this is true for every i, the gradient must be zero. ▮

Note that the converse of this theorem is not necessarily true. The gradient of the function is zero at any point at which the function assumes a local maximum (or minimum) value, but the function need not have a maximum or minimum value at a point at which the gradient vanishes.

For example, the function

$$f(x, y) = x^2 - y^2$$

has as its gradient

$$\operatorname{grad} f = [2x, -2y].$$

This is zero at the point $[0, 0]$, but the function has neither a local maximum or minimum there. As a function of x, with $y = 0$, this point is a local minimum; but as a function of y, it is a local maximum. In every neighborhood of this point, the function takes on values which are larger and also values which are smaller than the value of the function at this point. Such a point is called a *saddle point* for the function. A sketch of the function $z = f(x, y)$ will help explain the reason for this name.

It is much more common to find that the maximum or minimum value of the function is assumed at a boundary point of the set. For example, let us consider the problem of finding the maximum value of the function

$$f(x, y, z) = x^2 + y - z$$

in the closed ball of radius one with center at the origin. Since the gradient of f is $\text{grad}\, f = [2x, 1, -1]$, there is no point at which this gradient is zero, and hence the function will not have a maximum at any interior point of the ball. The maximum value must thus occur at some point of the boundary (surface) of the ball.

The spherical surface in question is the level surface of the function $g(\mathbf{X}) = x^2 + y^2 + z^2$ for $g(\mathbf{X}) = 1$. Thus the problem is reduced to finding the maximum value of $f(\mathbf{X})$ when $\mathbf{X}$ is constrained to lie on the level surface defined by $g(\mathbf{X}) = 1$. Since the set in question is compact, we know that the maximum must actually occur at some point of the surface, say at $\mathbf{X}_0 = [x_0, y_0, z_0]$. We cannot have $\text{grad}\, f = \mathbf{0}$ at this point since its second and third components are never zero. However, as we will show below, the directional derivative of f in every direction tangent to the sphere will have to be zero. Therefore, the directional derivative of f is

$$D_{\mathbf{A}} f(\mathbf{X}_0) = [\text{grad}\, f(\mathbf{X}_0)] \cdot \mathbf{A} = \nabla f \cdot \mathbf{A} = 0 \tag{5–13}$$

for every vector $\mathbf{A}$ which is in the plane tangent to the surface of the sphere at this point. Here we have introduced again the "del" notation for the gradient. We will find that this notation is much more convenient in computations and in complex formulas.

Now if M_0 is the plane which is tangent to the sphere at $\mathbf{X}_0$, then $M_0 = M + \mathbf{X}_0$ where M is exactly that subspace of R^3 consisting of those vectors which are orthogonal to $\text{grad}\, g = \nabla g = [2x_0, 2y_0, 2z_0]$. Let $L = L\{\nabla g(\mathbf{X}_0)\} = \{\mathbf{Y} \mid \mathbf{Y} = t\nabla g(\mathbf{X}_0)\}$. Then $M = L^{\perp}$.

We can now characterize $\text{grad}\, f$ at this point. We do this with the help of the direct-sum decomposition of $R^3 = L^{\perp} \oplus L$. We may write

$$\nabla f = \mathbf{A} + \mathbf{B},$$

where $\mathbf{A} \in L^{\perp} = M$ and $\mathbf{B} \in L$. Since L is the space $L\{\nabla g(\mathbf{X}_0)\}$, we must have $\mathbf{B} = \lambda \nabla g(\mathbf{X}_0)$ for some scalar λ. Since f has a maximum on the surface at $\mathbf{X}_0$, $\nabla f \cdot \mathbf{A} = 0$ for any $\mathbf{A} \in L$. We are thus able to conclude that $\mathbf{A} = \mathbf{0}$ in the decomposition of ∇f. (The easiest way to see this is to compute $\nabla f \cdot \mathbf{A}$. Since $\mathbf{B}$ is orthogonal to $\mathbf{A}$, we find that $0 = \mathbf{A} \cdot \mathbf{A}$.

This shows that there must exist a scalar λ such that $\nabla f(\mathbf{X}_0) = \lambda \nabla g(\mathbf{X}_0)$, or

$$\nabla f - \lambda \nabla g = 0 \tag{5–14}$$

at the point at which the maximum occurs. It should be observed that at this point, $\lambda \nabla g$ is exactly the orthogonal projection of ∇f in the direction of ∇g.

How does this conclusion apply to the example we started with? Here $f = x^2 + y - z$, and $g = x^2 + y^2 + z^2$. Equation (5–14) thus becomes

$$[2x, 1, -1] - \lambda[2x, 2y, 2z] = [2x - 2\lambda x, 1 - 2\lambda y, -1 - 2\lambda y] = \mathbf{0}.$$

From this we have three equations which must hold at the point at which the maximum occurs. There are unfortunately four unknowns, x, y, z, and λ. We do not know λ until we know the coordinates of the point. However, there is still a fourth equation which must be satisfied: $g(x, y, z) = x^2 + y^2 + z^2 = 1$. The required point must be on the sphere. We must therefore solve the equations

$$\begin{aligned} x(1 - \lambda) &= 0, \\ 2\lambda y &= 1, \\ 2\lambda z &= -1, \\ x^2 + y^2 + z^2 &= 1. \end{aligned}$$

From the second and third of these equations we conclude that $y = -z$. The first equation is satisfied if $x = 0$ or $\lambda = 1$.

If $x = 0$, then to satisfy the last equation, we must have $2y^2 = 1$. We find the two possible solutions $\mathbf{X} = [0, 1/\sqrt{2}, -1/\sqrt{2}]$, or $[0, -1/\sqrt{2}, 1/\sqrt{2}]$. On the other hand, if $\lambda = 1$, then from the second and third equations we have $y = \frac{1}{2}$, $z = -\frac{1}{2}$, and hence from the last equation, $x = \pm 1/\sqrt{2}$. This gives us the two more possibilities $\mathbf{X} = [1/\sqrt{2}, \frac{1}{2}, -\frac{1}{2}]$ and $[-1/\sqrt{2}, \frac{1}{2}, -\frac{1}{2}]$.

The values of f at these four points are $\sqrt{2}$, $-\sqrt{2}$, $\frac{3}{2}$, and $\frac{3}{2}$, respectively. The maximum thus is $\frac{3}{2}$, occurring at either of the last two points.

Now let us sketch the proof of the fact which was made use of in the above discussion.

Theorem 5–22. Let $f(\mathbf{X})$ and $g(\mathbf{X})$ be C^1 in a region D of R^n. Let

$$K = \{\mathbf{X} \mid g(\mathbf{X}) = 0\}.$$

Suppose that $f(\mathbf{X})$ attains its maximum value on K at the point $\mathbf{X}_0 \in K \cap D$ and that $\nabla g(\mathbf{X}_0) \neq 0$. Then $\nabla f(\mathbf{X}_0) \cdot \mathbf{A} = 0$ for every vector $\mathbf{A}$ such that $\nabla g(\mathbf{X}_0) \cdot \mathbf{A} = 0$.

Proof. Let $\mathbf{A}$ be any vector with $|\mathbf{A}| = 1$ and $\nabla g(\mathbf{X}_0) \cdot \mathbf{A} = 0$. Set

$$\mathbf{B} = \nabla g(\mathbf{X}_0)/|\nabla g(\mathbf{X}_0)|.$$

$\mathbf{A}$ and $\mathbf{B}$ are therefore an orthogonal pair of unit vectors. The plane N defined by $\mathbf{X} = \mathbf{X}_0 + s\mathbf{A} + t\mathbf{B}$ for all real s and t contains $\mathbf{B}$ which is orthogonal to the surface K. Therefore this plane intersects K in some curve which passes through the point $s = 0$, $t = 0$. That is, given any sufficiently small s, there exists a t such that the point $\mathbf{X} = \mathbf{X}_0 + s\mathbf{A} + t\mathbf{B}$ is on K. Furthermore, as $s \to 0$, we must have the corresponding $t \to 0$. See Fig. 5–7. (A complete proof of these facts, not depending on geometric intuition, requires the implicit-function theorem which will be proved in a later section. However, we do not wish to delay our discussion of maximum and minimum problems.)

Let s be given, let t be such that $\mathbf{X} = \mathbf{X}_0 + s\mathbf{A} + t\mathbf{B}$ is on $K \cap N$. Set $h = [s^2 + t^2]^{1/2} = |\mathbf{X} - \mathbf{X}_0|$. As $s \to 0$, we have $t \to 0$ and also $h \to 0$. Now apply Theorem 5-19. Since $g(\mathbf{X}) = g(\mathbf{X}_0) = 0$, we have

$$\lim_{s \to 0} \frac{1}{h} \nabla g(\mathbf{X}_0) \cdot [s\mathbf{A} + t\mathbf{B}] = 0.$$

Since we are given that $\nabla g(\mathbf{X}_0) \cdot \mathbf{A} = 0$, this tells us that

$$\lim_{s \to 0} \frac{t}{h} \nabla g(\mathbf{X}_0) \cdot \mathbf{B} = \lim_{s \to 0} \frac{t}{h} |\nabla g(\mathbf{X}_0)| = 0.$$

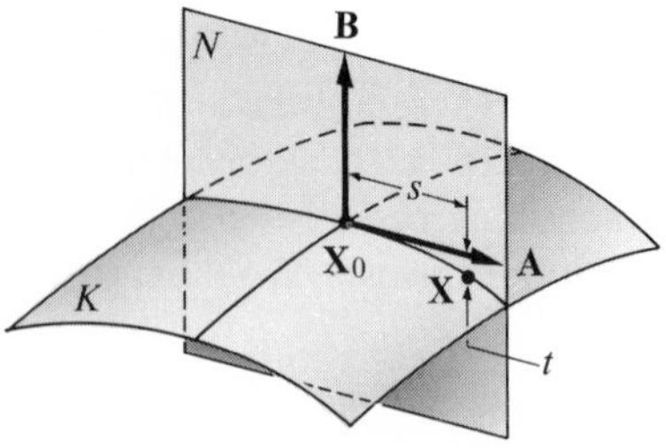

Fig. 5-7

That is, we must have $t/h \to 0$.

Next we apply the approximation theorem, Theorem 5-19, to f to obtain

$$\lim_{s \to 0} \frac{1}{h} [f(\mathbf{X}) - f(\mathbf{X}_0) - \nabla f(\mathbf{X}_0) \cdot (s\mathbf{A} + t\mathbf{B})] = 0.$$

However, the condition that f have a maximum on K at $\mathbf{X}_0$ means that $f(\mathbf{X}) - f(\mathbf{X}_0) \geq 0$ for each such $\mathbf{X}$. Therefore,

$$\lim_{s \to 0} \nabla f(\mathbf{X}_0) \cdot \left[\frac{s}{h}\mathbf{A} + \frac{t}{h}\mathbf{B}\right] \geq 0.$$

Since $h^2 = s^2 + t^2$, and $t/h \to 0$, we must have $s/h \to \pm 1$, depending on which sign of s is chosen originally. Thus we must have both

$$\pm \nabla f(\mathbf{X}_0) \cdot \mathbf{A} \geq 0.$$

The only way in which this can hold is for $\nabla f(\mathbf{X}_0) \cdot \mathbf{A} = 0$. ▮

The methods used here can be generalized. Indeed, we can specify any number of constraints (less than the dimension). The result is called the method of Lagrange multipliers.

Theorem 5-23. Let $f, g_1, g_2, \ldots, g_p$ be functions which are defined and differentiable in some open set B in R^n. Suppose that the set

$$K = \{\mathbf{X} \mid g_1(\mathbf{X}) = 0, g_2(\mathbf{X}) = 0, \ldots, g_p(\mathbf{X}) = 0\}$$

is contained in B, and that f takes on its maximum (or minimum) value on K at the point $\mathbf{X}_0$. Then there exist p scalars, $\lambda_1, \lambda_2, \ldots, \lambda_p$, called *Lagrange multipliers*, such that at $\mathbf{X}_0$

$$\operatorname{grad}\left(f - \sum_{i=1}^{p} \lambda_i g_i\right) = \mathbf{0}. \tag{5-15}$$

Proof. The function f assumes its maximum at some point $\mathbf{X}_0$ of K. At this point we must have $\nabla f \cdot \mathbf{Y} = 0$ for all $\mathbf{Y}$ which are simultaneously in the planes tangent to the level surfaces of all of the g_i, that is, for all $\mathbf{Y}$ which are simultaneously orthogonal to all of the ∇g_i. This can be proved in exactly the same way as Theorem 5–22.

Set $L = L\{\nabla g_1, \nabla g_2, \ldots, \nabla g_p\}$, each gradient being evaluated at the point $\mathbf{X}_0$. Then the required condition is that $\nabla f \cdot \mathbf{Y} = 0$ for every vector $\mathbf{Y} \in L^{\perp}$, the orthogonal complement of L. Having the direct sum decomposition $R^n = L^{\perp} \oplus L$, we can write $\nabla f = \mathbf{A} + \mathbf{B}$, where $\mathbf{A} \in L^{\perp}$ and $\mathbf{B} \in L$.

Suppose that $\mathbf{Y}$ is any vector in $L^{\perp}$. Then since we are assuming that f has a local maximum in K at this point, $\nabla f \cdot \mathbf{Y} = \mathbf{A} \cdot \mathbf{Y} = 0$. In other words, $\mathbf{A} = \mathbf{0}$. Thus at this point ∇f is in the space L. Since L is generated by the ∇g_i, we have the existence of a set of λ_i such that

$$\nabla f = \sum_{i=1}^{p} \lambda_i \nabla g_i. \tag{5–16}$$

This equation is equivalent to Eq. (5–15), and the theorem is proved. ▌

Equation (5–16) gives us the geometric meaning of the Lagrange multipliers. They are merely the coefficients required to find the projection of grad f in the space L (which is the orthogonal complement of the intersection of all of the tangent hyperplanes).

Note also that Eq. (5–15) gives us n equations in the $n + p$ unknowns, $x_1, x_2, \ldots, x_n, \lambda_1, \lambda_2, \ldots, \lambda_p$. There are the additional p equations $g_i(\mathbf{X}) = 0$ which must also be satisfied. Hence it is usually possible to find one or more solutions of this set of equations. By checking the values of the function at all of these *critical points*, it is easy to determine where the maximum or minimum occurs. We know that it must occur at one of these points. An example may help to explain this process.

Suppose that we wish to find the maximum value of the function

$$f(\mathbf{X}) = x^2y + z^2$$

in the cylindrical region $K = \{\mathbf{X} \mid 0 \le z \le 1, x^2 + y^2 \le 1\}$. We may proceed in the following way. First, we check for any possible maxima which may occur in the interior of this region. We set

$$\text{grad} f = [2xy, x^2, 2z] = \mathbf{0},$$

which is true only at the points $[0, y, 0]$. None of these are interior points of the region K, and thus there are no critical points in the interior of K.

Next we look for critical points on the surface of the cylinder. We start by finding the critical points of f which are in the plane $z = 0$ but interior to the circle $x^2 + y^2 = 1$. This time we set

$$\text{grad}\,(f - \lambda z) = [2xy, x^2, 2z - \lambda] = \mathbf{0}$$

along with $z = 0$. We obtain the solutions $[0, y, 0]$. We compute

$$f(0, y, 0) = 0.$$

We now look for critical points on the surface $z = 1$, with $x^2 + y^2 < 1$. With

$$\text{grad}\,[f - \lambda(z - 1)] = [2xy, x^2, 2z - \lambda] = \mathbf{0}$$

along with $z = 1$ the solutions are $[0, y, 1]$. We find that

$$f(0, y, 1) = 1,$$

which is larger than the value found on the bottom face.

On the curved surface of the cylinder we look for critical points with $0 < z < 1$, setting

$$\text{grad}\,[f - \lambda(x^2 + y^2 - 1)] = [2xy - 2\lambda x, x^2 - 2\lambda y, 2z] = \mathbf{0};$$
$$x^2 + y^2 = 1.$$

In order for the third component of the above vector to be zero, we must have $z = 0$. This point is not in the allowable range; hence there are no critical points on this part on the surface. See Fig. 5–8.

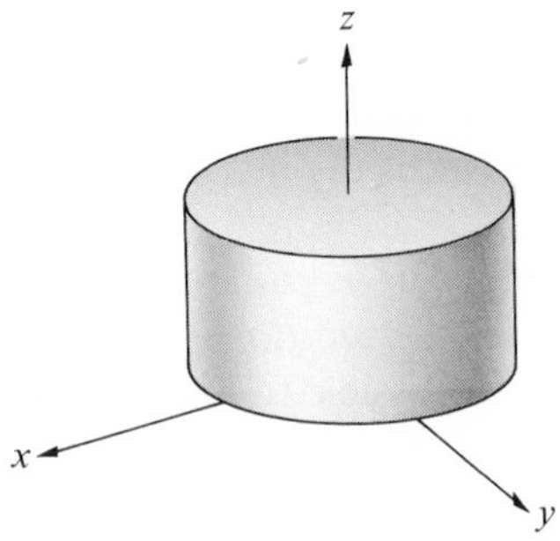

Fig. 5–8

Next we look for critical points on the circle $x^2 + y^2 - 1 = 0, z - 1 = 0$. Here we have two constraints. We set

$$\text{grad}\,[f - \lambda_1(x^2 + y^2 - 1) - \lambda_2(z - 1)] = [2xy - 2\lambda_1 x, x^2 - 2\lambda_1 y, 2z - \lambda_2] = \mathbf{0}$$

and

$$x^2 + y^2 = 1, \qquad z = 1.$$

Since $z = 1$, for the third component of the gradient to be zero we must have $\lambda_2 = 2$. To make the first component zero we must have either $x = 0$ or $\lambda_1 = y$. If $x = 0$, then since $x^2 + y^2 = 1$, we must have either $y = 1$ or $y = -1$, giving us two more critical points. We compute

$$f(0, 1, 1) = 1, \qquad f(0, -1, 1) = 1.$$

If $\lambda_1 = y$, then in order to have the second component of the gradient equal zero we must have $x^2 - 2y^2 = 0$. This, together with $x^2 + y^2 = 1$, gives $3y^2 = 1$, which yields two values of y. With each value of y there are two values of x, and hence we find four critical points. We calculate

$$f(\pm\sqrt{2}/\sqrt{3}, 1/\sqrt{3}, 1) = 1 + 2\sqrt{3}/9,$$
$$f(\pm\sqrt{2}/\sqrt{3}, -1/\sqrt{3}, 1) = 1 - 2\sqrt{3}/9.$$

Finally, we look for the critical points on the bottom circle by setting

$$\text{grad}\,[f - \lambda_1(x^2 + y^2 - 1) - \lambda_2 z] = [2xy - 2\lambda_1 x, x^2 - 2\lambda_1 y, 2z - \lambda_2] = \mathbf{0}$$

along with

$$x^2 + y^2 = 1, \qquad z = 0.$$

Solving these equations in the same way as we did in the last case, we find that we get exactly the same solutions for x and y, but with $z = 0$. We then find

$$f(0, 1, 0) = 0, \qquad f(0, -1, 0) = 0,$$
$$f(\pm\sqrt{2}/\sqrt{3}, 1/\sqrt{3}, 0) = 2\sqrt{3}/9, \qquad f(\pm\sqrt{2}/\sqrt{3}, -1/\sqrt{3}, 0) = -2\sqrt{3}/9.$$

The maximum value of this function is therefore $1 + 2\sqrt{3}/9$. The function f takes on this value at either of the two points $[\pm\sqrt{2}/\sqrt{3}, 1/\sqrt{3}, 1]$. What is the minimum value of this function? Where does this minimum value occur? (These questions refer only to the function in the same region, of course.)

Let us give another example, which shows how such problems can arise. Let us find the shortest distance between the hyperbola

$$xy = 12$$

and the circle

$$(x - 1)^2 + (y + 1)^2 = 1.$$

Let (x, y) be a point on the hyperbola and (u, v) a point on the circle. Then the problem is to minimize the function

$$f(x, y, u, v) = (x - u)^2 + (y - v)^2$$

subject to the constraints

$$g_1(x, y) = xy - 12 = 0,$$
$$g_2(u, v) = (u - 1)^2 + (v + 1)^2 - 1 = 0.$$

Setting the four components of grad $(f - \lambda_1 g_1 - \lambda_2 g_2)$ equal to zero gives

$$\begin{aligned} 2(x - u) - \lambda_1 y &= 0, \\ 2(y - v) - \lambda_1 x &= 0, \\ -2(x - u) - 2\lambda_2(u - 1) &= 0, \\ -2(y - v) - 2\lambda_2(v + 1) &= 0. \end{aligned} \tag{5-17}$$

We wish to solve these four equations simultaneously with the two equations $g_1 = 0$ and $g_2 = 0$. This is not a simple set of equations to solve. There are several methods available, but the following seems to be the simplest. Eliminating λ_1 from the first two equations gives

$$\frac{y}{x} = \frac{x - u}{y - v}.$$

Eliminating λ_2 from the second pair of equations gives

$$\frac{x - u}{y - v} = \frac{u - 1}{v + 1}.$$

Combining the two results gives

$$\frac{y}{x} = \frac{u - 1}{v + 1}.$$

The reader should note that there is no difficulty here even if any of the denominators should happen to be zero. In fact, x cannot be zero since this would make $g_1(x, y) = 0$ impossible to satisfy. The other difficulties arise only by virtue of the way in which we have written these relations. We could also have written them in the "multiplied-out" form, which would not involve the possibility of division by zero. The third equation in the set (5–17) can be written as $x - u = -\lambda_2(u - 1)$. Adding $u - 1$ to both sides of this equation gives $x - 1 = (1 - \lambda_2)(u - 1)$. Similarly, the fourth equation is equivalent to $y - v = -\lambda_2(v + 1)$. Adding $(v + 1)$ to both sides gives $y + 1 = (1 - \lambda_2)(v + 1)$. The two new equations can be combined to give

$$\frac{x - 1}{y + 1} = \frac{u - 1}{v + 1},$$

which, together with the last displayed equation, yields

$$\frac{y}{x} = \frac{x - 1}{y + 1}$$

or $y^2 + y = x^2 - x$. Using $xy = 12$, we thus have

$$y^2 + y = \frac{12^2}{y^2} - \frac{12}{y}$$

or

$$y^4 + y^3 + 12y - 144 = 0.$$

The last equation is equivalent to

$$(y - 3)(y + 4)(y^2 + 12) = 0.$$

From this we find the two critical points

$$[x, y, u, v] = [4, 3, \tfrac{8}{5}, -\tfrac{1}{5}] \quad \text{or} \quad [-3, -4, \tfrac{2}{5}, -\tfrac{9}{5}].$$

Which of these points gives the shortest distance?

Often we want the maximum or minimum of a function in an unbounded region. If this maximum or minimum occurs at all, it occurs at a point where the gradient of the function vanishes. It might be easy to find this point, but how can we tell whether or not this is the desired point? Perhaps the function takes on arbitrarily large positive and negative values at large distances from the origin. Then it has no absolute maximum or minimum.

With some functions it is easy to see by inspection that no absolute maximum or minimum occurs. For example, the function

$$f(x, y, z) = x^2 + y - z$$

becomes arbitrarily large or arbitrarily small if we let $x = 0, z = 0$ and y tend toward positive or negative infinity.

On the other hand, what about a function such as

$$f(x, y, z) = x^4 + y^4 + x^2z^2 + 4xy?$$

This time it is not so obvious. However, if we set $[x, y, z] = t[a, b, c]$, where $[a, b, c] \neq \mathbf{0}$ is any fixed vector, we can study the behavior of this function as we proceed outward along the rays. We find

$$f(x, y, z) = t^4(a^4 + b^4 + a^2c^2) + t^2ac,$$

which obviously becomes nonnegative if we go out sufficiently far along any ray. Thus the function has a minimum somewhere, but it has no absolute maximum. The reader can now show that the minimum occurs at one of the points $[1, -1, 0]$, $[-1, 1, 0]$, or $[0, 0, z]$ for any z. At which of these points is the function a minimum?

More often, the problems which occur are not so trivial. However, if nothing else can be done, one can attempt to find the maximum or minimum of the given function in the region $|\mathbf{X}| \leq R$ and let R tend toward infinity.

The methods described in this section are based on the assumption that the boundaries of the region in question are given by smooth functions. This assumption is usually (but not always) true. However, the real difficulty in the application of these techniques is that the set of equations that must be solved are often difficult or impossible to solve in practice. The methods of this section are of great theoretical importance, however. Many mathematical methods are based on these ideas in one form or another.

PROBLEMS

1. Let F be a closed set in R^n. Prove that $\mathbf{X}_0$ is a boundary point of F if and only if $\mathbf{X}_0 \in F$ and $\mathbf{X}_0$ is not an interior point of F.
2. Suppose $\mathbf{u}_1, \ldots, \mathbf{u}_k$ is an orthonormal set of vectors in R^n where $k \leq n$. Let $\mathbf{A}$ be a vector in R^n. Find the real numbers $x_1, x_2, \ldots, x_k$ which will minimize

$$\left| \mathbf{A} - \sum_{i=1}^{k} x_i \mathbf{u}_i \right|^2.$$

3. Find the critical points and the maxima and minima of the following functions:
   a) $x^4 - 4xy^2 + y^4$
   b) $x^3 + y^3 + 3xyz$
   c) $x^2 - 2xy + 4y^2 - z^2$
   d) $e^x \cos xy$

4. Find the maximum and minimum values of each of the functions in the given region:
   a) $f(x, y, u, v) = x^2 + yu + 6v$ in $K = \{\mathbf{X} \mid x^2 + y^2 + u^2 + v^2 \leq 10\}$
   b) $f = xyz$ in $K = \{\mathbf{X} \mid x^2 + y^2 + z^2 \leq 1, z \geq 0\}$
   c) $f(x, y) = ye^{-x^2 y}$ in $R = \{\mathbf{X} \mid x > 0, y > 0\}$

5. Find the point on the curve

$$z = \sin x, \qquad x^2 + y^2 = 1$$

at which $x^2 - y^2$ is a minimum.

6. Write the equations whose solutions are the critical points in finding the maximum value of $f(x, y, z) = x^2 + 2x + 2yz + z^2$ on the surface of the ellipsoid $4x^2 + 4y^2 + 3z^2 - 20 = 0$. Verify that the points $[\pm\sqrt{5}, 0, 0]$, $[1, 1, 2]$, $[1, -1, -2]$ are critical points. If these are all of the critical points, at what point is f a maximum?

7. Follow the directions of Problem 6 for the problem of maximizing the function

$$f(x, y, z) = x - 8y - z^2$$

on the curve which is the intersection of the cylinder $x^2 + y^2 = 5$ and the sphere $x^2 - 5x + y^2 + z^2 = 0$, using the points $[1, \pm 2, 0]$, $[2, 1, 0]$, $[2, 1, \pm\sqrt{5}]$ as possible critical points.

8. The foci of the ellipse $x^2/a^2 + y^2/b^2 = 1$ $(a > b > 0)$ are at $[\pm c, 0]$ where $c^2 = a^2 - b^2$. Show that if the point $Q = [q, 0]$ is not between the two foci, then the point of the ellipse closest to Q is a vertex.

9. Let $(x_1, y_1), (x_2, y_2), \ldots, (x_n, y_n)$ be n points in the plane. Let

$$\bar{x} = \frac{1}{n}\sum_{i=1}^{n} x_i \quad \text{and} \quad \bar{y} = \frac{1}{n}\sum_{i=1}^{n} y_i.$$

Prove that

$$f(m, b) = \sum_{i=1}^{n} [mx_i + b - y_i]^2$$

is minimized when $b = -m\bar{x} + \bar{y}$ and $m = (\sum x_i y_i - n\bar{x}\bar{y})/(\sum x_i^2 - n\bar{x}^2)$. The quantity $f(m, b)$ is the sum of the squares of the differences between the y_i and the value of y at the point x_i on the line $y = mx + b$. Thus minimizing this quantity corresponds to finding the best fitting line in the sense of least squares.

10. Find the line $y = mx + b$ which best fits the points $(x_1, y_1), (x_2, y_2), \ldots, (x_n, y_n)$, where all the $x_i > 0$ in the sense of minimizing the sum of the squares of the relative errors:

$$g(m, b) = \sum_{i=1}^{n} \frac{[mx_i + b - y_i]^2}{x_i^2}.$$

5-8. TYPES OF CRITICAL POINTS

Suppose that a function $f: B \to R$ is C^2 in the region $B \subset R^n$ and suppose also that $\nabla f(\mathbf{X}_0) = \mathbf{0}$, where $\mathbf{X}_0$ is an interior point of B. The point $\mathbf{X}_0$ is then called an *interior critical point* of f; it may be a local maximum, a local minimum, or, as illustrated in the last section, it may be a saddle point of f.

In the last section we discussed the problem of finding the maximum and minimum values of a function in a compact region. This was done by finding all the critical points of the function on this set and comparing the values of the function at these points. This method is excellent for finding absolute maxima and minima, but it is unnecessarily difficult to apply when we are interested only in identifying interior critical points as to type. To determine whether an interior critical point is a local maximum, a local minimum, or a saddle point using the methods of the last section, we would have to enclose $\mathbf{X}_0$ in a closed ball $\overline{S}_\delta(\mathbf{X}_0) \subset B$ which was small enough not to contain any other interior critical points of f. Then we could find the critical points of f on the surface of the ball. Comparing the values of f at these points with the value at $\mathbf{X}_0$ would then tell us the behavior of the function at $\mathbf{X}_0$.

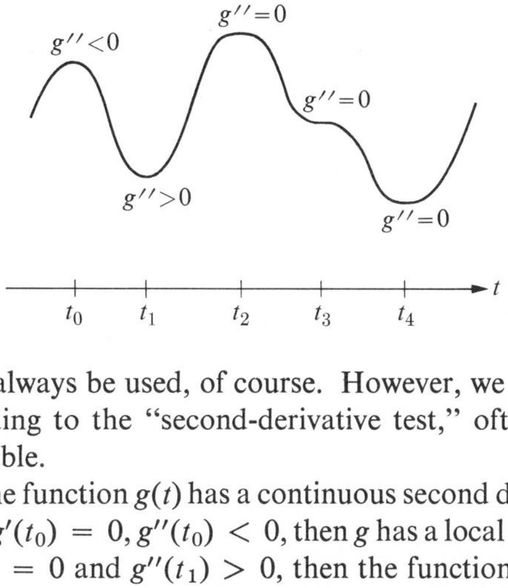

Fig. 5-9

This method can always be used, of course. However, we would prefer to obtain something corresponding to the "second-derivative test," often used in the case of functions of one variable.

We recall that if the function $g(t)$ has a continuous second derivative in a neighborhood of $t = t_0$ and if $g'(t_0) = 0, g''(t_0) < 0$, then g has a local maximum at this point.

Similarly, if $g'(t_1) = 0$ and $g''(t_1) > 0$, then the function has a local minimum. If $g'(t) = 0$ and $g''(t) = 0$, then no conclusion can be drawn; the function may have a local maximum, a local minimum, or a horizontal inflection point, which is neither a local maximum or a local minimum (we will call such a point a saddle point for g in analogy with the higher-dimensional case). Figure 5-9 illustrates these possibilities.

Suppose that $f(\mathbf{X})$ has a local minimum at the interior critical point $\mathbf{X}_0$. Then, if $\mathbf{Y}$ is any nonzero vector (which we can choose to be of unit length for convenience), the function

$$g_{\mathbf{Y}}(t) = f(\mathbf{X}_0 + t\mathbf{Y}) \tag{5-18}$$

is a function of the single real variable t which must also have a minimum at $t = 0$.

Conversely, if the function $g_{\mathbf{Y}}(t)$ in (5–18) has a local minimum at $t = 0$ for every $\mathbf{Y}$ of unit length, then f must have a local minimum at $\mathbf{X} = \mathbf{X}_0$.

Similarly, if every $g_{\mathbf{Y}}(t)$ has a maximum at $t = 0$, then f must have a local maximum at $\mathbf{X}_0$. If some of the $g_{\mathbf{Y}}$ have a maximum while others have a minimum, then $\mathbf{X}_0$ must be a saddle point.

Let us compute the first and second derivatives of the function $g_{\mathbf{Y}}(t)$ defined in (5–18). Clearly

$$g'_{\mathbf{Y}}(t) = D_{\mathbf{Y}}f(\mathbf{X}_0 + t\mathbf{Y}) = \sum_{i=1}^{n} f'_i(\mathbf{X}_0 + t\mathbf{Y})y_i,$$

where $\mathbf{Y} = [y_1, y_2, \ldots, y_n]$. The function $g'_{\mathbf{Y}}(t)$ is then the sum of n functions. The ith function is

$$f'_i(\mathbf{X}_0 + t\mathbf{Y})y_i,$$

and the derivative of this function at $t = 0$ is

$$D_{\mathbf{Y}}f'_i(\mathbf{X}_0)y_i = \sum_{j=1}^{n} f'_{ij}(\mathbf{X}_0)y_iy_j.$$

Therefore

$$g''_{\mathbf{Y}}(0) = \sum_{i=1}^{n}\sum_{j=1}^{n} f'_{ij}(\mathbf{X}_0)y_iy_j = \mathbf{Y}^t\,\Delta_2\mathbf{Y}, \tag{5–19}$$

where

$$\Delta_2 = \begin{bmatrix} f'_{11}(\mathbf{X}_0) & f'_{12}(\mathbf{X}_0) & \cdots & f'_{1n}(\mathbf{X}_0) \\ f'_{21}(\mathbf{X}_0) & f'_{22}(\mathbf{X}_0) & \cdots & f'_{2n}(\mathbf{X}_0) \\ \vdots & & & \vdots \\ f'_{n1}(\mathbf{X}_0) & f'_{n2}(\mathbf{X}_0) & \cdots & f'_{nn}(\mathbf{X}_0) \end{bmatrix} \tag{5–20}$$

is the matrix of the second partial derivatives of f at $\mathbf{X}_0$.

The matrix Δ_2 is a symmetric matrix, as was shown in Section 5–6. Therefore, by Theorem 4–29 there exists an orthogonal matrix P which diagonalizes Δ_2, that is,

$$P^t\,\Delta_2 P = D = \operatorname{diag}\,[\lambda_1, \lambda_2, \ldots, \lambda_n],$$

where $\lambda_1, \lambda_2, \ldots, \lambda_n$ are the n real characteristic values of Δ_2.

If $\mathbf{Y}$ is any vector with $|\mathbf{Y}| = 1$, then

$$\mathbf{W} = P^t\mathbf{Y} \tag{5–21}$$

is also a vector with $|\mathbf{W}| = 1$. Let $\mathbf{W} = [w_1, w_2, \ldots, w_n]$. Then by (5–19) and the fact that $P^t = P^{-1}$,

$$\begin{aligned} g''_{\mathbf{Y}}(0) &= \mathbf{Y}^t\,\Delta_2\mathbf{Y} = (P\mathbf{W})^t\,\Delta_2(P\mathbf{W}) \\ &= \mathbf{W}^tP^t\,\Delta_2P\mathbf{W} = \mathbf{W}^tD\mathbf{W} \\ &= \lambda_1w_1^2 + \lambda_2w_2^2 + \cdots + \lambda_nw_n^2. \end{aligned} \tag{5–22}$$

The transformation (5–21) between **Y** and **W** is nonsingular. (Indeed, it is a general rotation—one of the euclidean motions.) We have therefore almost proved the following theorem.

Theorem 5–24. Let $\mathbf{X}_0$ be an interior point of the region $B \subset R^n$. Let $f: B \to R$ be C^2 in B. Suppose that $\nabla f(\mathbf{X}_0) = 0$ and let Δ_2 be the matrix (5–20) of the second partial derivatives of f at $\mathbf{X}_0$.

1. If all of the characteristic values of Δ_2 are negative, then f has a local maximum at $\mathbf{X}_0$.
2. If all of the characteristic values of Δ_2 are positive, then f has a local minimum at $\mathbf{X}_0$.
3. If Δ_2 has at least one positive characteristic value and at least one negative characteristic value, then f has a saddle point at $\mathbf{X}_0$.

Proof. In case (1), we see from (5–22) that for every $\mathbf{Y}$, $g''_{\mathbf{Y}}(0) < 0$. This means that $g_{\mathbf{Y}}(t)$ has a local maximum at $t = 0$ for every $\mathbf{Y}$. Hence f must have a local maximum at $\mathbf{X}_0$. Similarly, in case (2) we may conclude that f has a local minimum.

Suppose that $\lambda_i > 0$ and $\lambda_j < 0$. Set $\mathbf{W}_i = \mathbf{e}_i$ and $\mathbf{W}_j = \mathbf{e}_j$. If $\mathbf{Y}_i = P\mathbf{e}_i$ and $\mathbf{Y}_j = P\mathbf{e}_j$, then

$$g''_{\mathbf{Y}_i}(0) = \lambda_i > 0,$$

while

$$g''_{\mathbf{Y}_j}(0) = \lambda_j < 0.$$

Then f must have a saddle point at $\mathbf{X}_0$. ▮

Observe that the only case not covered by this theorem is when at least one of the characteristic values of Δ_2 is zero and all of the others are of the same sign. In this case we can draw no conclusion about the nature of the critical point.

We will now consider an example which shows how this theorem can be applied. Suppose that we are given the function

$$f(x, y, z) = 6x + 3y^2 - xyz + \tfrac{1}{12}z^2.$$

We easily compute the gradient

$$\nabla f = [6 - yz, 6y - xz, \tfrac{1}{6}z - xy]$$

and the matrix of second derivatives

$$\Delta_2 = \begin{bmatrix} 0 & -z & -y \\ -z & 6 & -x \\ -y & -x & \frac{1}{6} \end{bmatrix}.$$

To find the critical points, we set $\nabla f = 0$. The three resulting equations are most easily solved if we notice that they imply the further relation $xyz = 6x = 6y^2 = \frac{1}{6}z^2$. It is then simple to show that the only critical points are at $[1, 1, 6]$ and $[1, -1, -6]$.

At [1, 1, 6]

$$\Delta_2 = \begin{bmatrix} 0 & -6 & -1 \\ -6 & 6 & -1 \\ -1 & -1 & \frac{1}{6} \end{bmatrix},$$

and the characteristic polynomial of this matrix is

$$-\lambda^3 + \tfrac{37}{6}\lambda^2 + 37\lambda - 24.$$

Therefore the characteristic values of Δ_2 are the roots of the polynomial

$$P(\lambda) = 6\lambda^3 - 37\lambda^2 - 222\lambda + 144.$$

Note that we do *not* need to solve this equation. All we need to do is locate the roots well enough to tell whether they are positive or negative.

We see that $P(\lambda) \to -\infty$ as $\lambda \to -\infty$ and $P(0) = 144$. Therefore $P(\lambda)$ has at least one negative root. A little experimenting shows that $P(5) = -1141$. Therefore there is a root between 0 and 5, and there must be another between 5 and $+\infty$.

Since Δ_2 has both positive and negative characteristic values, we conclude that f has a saddle point at [1, 1, 6]. A similar argument shows that [1, −1, −6] is also a saddle point (the two characteristic polynomials are the same).

It should be observed that even these few calculations are not needed. The form of the characteristic polynomial tells us immediately that not all of the characteristic values are positive. This can be seen from Theorem 4–37, the Jacobi criterion. See Problem 3 at the end of this section.

The case in which the function f is a function of just two variables occurs quite often in practice. Some simplifications can be made in this case since the characteristic polynomial is quadratic. Indeed, we find

Theorem 5–25. Let $f: B \to R$ be C^2 in the region $B \subset R^2$. Let $\mathbf{X}_0$ be an interior point of B and suppose that $\nabla f(\mathbf{X}_0) = \mathbf{0}$. Let Δ_2 be the matrix of second derivatives evaluated at $\mathbf{X}_0$.

1. If $\det \Delta_2 < 0$, then f has a saddle point at $\mathbf{X}_0$.
2. If $\det \Delta_2 > 0$ and $f_{,11}(\mathbf{X}_0) > 0$, then f has a local minimum at $\mathbf{X}_0$.
3. If $\det \Delta_2 > 0$ and $f_{,11}(\mathbf{X}_0) < 0$, then f has a local maximum at $\mathbf{X}_0$.

Remarks. Since

$$\Delta_2 = \begin{bmatrix} f_{,11}(\mathbf{X}_0) & f_{,12}(\mathbf{X}_0) \\ f_{,21}(\mathbf{X}_0) & f_{,22}(\mathbf{X}_0) \end{bmatrix},$$

we have

$$\det \Delta_2 = f_{,11}(\mathbf{X}_0)f_{,22}(\mathbf{X}_0) - [f_{,12}(\mathbf{X}_0)]^2.$$

Proof. The characteristic polynomial of Δ_2 is

$$\lambda^2 - [f_{,11}(\mathbf{X}_0) + f_{,22}(\mathbf{X}_0)]\lambda + \left(f_{,11}(\mathbf{X}_0)f_{,22}(\mathbf{X}_0) - [f_{,12}(\mathbf{X}_0)]^2\right).$$

The constant term is the product of the two characteristic roots. Hence it is positive or negative according to whether the two roots have the same or opposite signs. Case (1) of the theorem results when the characteristic roots have opposite signs.

In cases (2) and (3) the signs of the characteristic roots are the same. Then it suffices to compute the sign of the second derivative in any one direction. This is easily done by using $f_{11}(\mathbf{X}_0)$, which is the same as $g''_{\mathbf{e}_1}(0)$. ▌

Consider the example

$$f(x, y) = 15xy - x^3 - y^3.$$

Here

$$\nabla f = [15y - 3x^2, 15x - 3y^2] \quad \text{and} \quad \Delta_2 = \begin{bmatrix} -6x & 15 \\ 15 & -6y \end{bmatrix}.$$

Setting $\nabla f = 0$, we have $x^2 = 5y$ and $y^2 = 5x$. That is, $x^4 = 25y^2 = 125x$. Hence the only critical points are [0, 0] and [5, 5].

At [0, 0], det $\Delta_2 = -225$. Hence this is a saddle point.

At [5, 5], det $\Delta_2 = 375$ and $f_{11} = -30$. This point is therefore a local maximum.

Theorem 5–24 cannot be applied when one of the characteristic values of Δ_2 is zero while all the others have the same sign. For example, if the characteristic values of Δ_2 are nonnegative, but one is zero, then we may have either a minimum or a saddle point. The examples

$$f_1 = x^3 + y^2, \qquad f_2 = x^4 + y^2, \qquad f^3 = -x^4 + y^2$$

show that any case is possible.

Sometimes we can make a special analysis to determine the behavior of the function even for this case. Suppose that Δ_2 is a diagonal matrix and that all but one of the characteristic values are positive, the remaining one being zero. Then the function $g_{\mathbf{Y}}(t)$ has a minimum for all $\mathbf{Y}$ except the one in the direction determined by the zero characteristic value. The behavior of f is thus determined by its behavior along this one line. If $\lambda_n = 0$, and if $g_{\mathbf{e}_n}(t)$ has a minimum at $t = 0$, then the function f would also have a local minimum. However, if $g_{\mathbf{e}_n}(t)$ has a local maximum or a saddle point, then f must have a saddle point.

The same reasoning can be used without diagonalizing, provided that the zero characteristic value is "isolated," that is, it would not be changed under diagonalization. This is the case when the entire ith row and ith column of Δ_2 are zero while the submatrix that is obtained by deleting this row and this column has no zero characteristic values.

Another situation which often occurs is that a function has an entire line of critical points. We usually find such a situation when a function is a constant along a line. If this is the case, then the behavior of the function is determined by the remaining characteristic values of Δ_2.

Let us see an example. Consider the function

$$f(x, y, z) = x^3y^2 + x^2z^2,$$

with

$$\nabla f = [3x^2y^2 + 2xz^2, 2x^3y, 2x^2z]$$

and

$$\Delta_2 = \begin{bmatrix} 6xy^2 + 2z^2 & 6x^2y & 4xz \\ 6x^2y & 2x^3 & 0 \\ 4xz & 0 & 2x^2 \end{bmatrix}.$$

If $x = 0$, then $\nabla f = 0$ for any y, z. If $x \neq 0$, then $\nabla f = 0$ only when $y = z = 0$. At each of the latter types of point

$$\Delta_2 = \begin{bmatrix} 0 & 0 & 0 \\ 0 & 2x^3 & 0 \\ 0 & 0 & 2x^2 \end{bmatrix}.$$

Hence, if $x > 0$, then $[x, 0, 0]$ is a local minimum (f is a constant, zero, along this line). If $x < 0$, then $[x, 0, 0]$ is a saddle point.

On the plane $x = 0$, Δ_2 vanishes. However, we can make a direct analysis even here. For fixed y and z, f is a cubic function of x. It is easy to see that if $z \neq 0$, then f has a local minimum at $x = 0$ as a function of x alone. Hence f is positive in some neighborhood of each such point, except for those points on the plane $x = 0$ itself. Therefore each such point is a local minimum. On the other hand, if $z = 0$ and $y \neq 0$, we easily see that f takes on both positive and negative values in each neighborhood of $[0, y, 0]$. The same result holds at $[0, 0, 0]$. Therefore each of these points is a saddle point.

PROBLEMS

1. Find and identify the critical points of each of the following functions.
   a) $xy(10 - x - y)$
   b) $x^2 + xy + y^2 - 3x - 3y$
   c) $\sin x + \sin y + \cos(x + y)$ (in $0 \leqq x \leqq 2\pi, 0 \leqq y \leqq 2\pi$)
   d) $x^3y^3 - 3x - 3y$
   e) $x^4 - 2x^2y^2 + y^4$
   f) $(x + y)e^{-xy}$
2. Determine the nature of the critical point at $[0, 0, 0]$ of each of the following functions:
   a) $4x^2 + 2y^2 + 9z^2 - 6xy - 6yz + 2xy$
   b) $x^4 + 8x^3y - x^2 + 24x^2y^2 + 32xy^3 + 2xz + 16y^4 - 2y^2 + z^4 - 2z^2$
   c) $[1 + y^2]e^{2x^2+z^2}$
   d) $[1 + y^3]e^{2x^2+z^2}$
   e) $x^2 - 4xy^2 + 5y^2 + 6yz + 9z^2$
   f) $x^2 + y^2 + \frac{1}{2}z^2 - 2xy - 4xz$
   g) $x^2 + y^2 + z^2 - 2xy - 4xz$
   h) $zy - \sin x^2$
3. Let f be C^2 in some neighborhood of $\mathbf{X}_0$. Suppose that $\Delta f(\mathbf{X}_0) = \mathbf{0}$. Let $p(\lambda)$ be the characteristic polynomial of Δ_2 defined by (5–20) at $\mathbf{X}_0$. Suppose $p(0) \neq 0$. Prove
   a) If the signs of the coefficients of $p(\lambda)$ are all the same, then $\mathbf{X}_0$ is a local maximum for f.
   b) If the signs of the coefficients of $p(\lambda)$ alternate, then $\mathbf{X}_0$ is a local minimum for f.
   c) If neither case (a) nor (b) holds, then $\mathbf{X}_0$ is a saddle point.

CHAPTER 6

Vector-Valued Functions

6–1. THE DIFFERENTIAL

In the last few sections we were concerned with scalar-valued functions of vectors. In this section we wish to begin our discussion of vector-valued functions of vectors. That is, we will discuss functions of the type $\mathbf{F}: B \to R^m$, where B may be a set in R^n, and n and m are integers, with $n \geq 1$, $m > 1$.

Definition 6–1. Let $\mathbf{F}: B \to R^m$, where B is a set in R^n. Then the functions $f_i: B \to R$ defined by

$$f_i(\mathbf{X}) = \mathbf{F}(\mathbf{X}) \cdot \mathbf{e}_i$$

are called the *component functions* of $\mathbf{F}$, or merely the *components* of $\mathbf{F}$.

Note that in this definition we continue the practice of using the same small roman letters to denote the components of a vector that is represented by a capital letter.

A vector-valued function can thus be represented in the form

$$\mathbf{F}(\mathbf{X}) = [f_1(\mathbf{X}), f_2(\mathbf{X}), \ldots, f_m(\mathbf{X})].$$

Hence such a function can be considered as nothing more than a set of scalar-valued functions. We often find it convenient to think of the function as a single entity, however, and therefore we will find it valuable to study such functions.

The first thing to do is to introduce the notion of continuity for vector-valued functions. The proper definition is merely the obvious extension of the definition given in Section 5–2.

Definition 6–2. Let B be a subset of R^n. Let $\mathbf{A} \in B$ and let $\mathbf{F}: B \to R^m$. Then $\mathbf{F}$ is said to be *continuous* at $\mathbf{A}$ if and only if, given any $\epsilon > 0$, there exists a $\delta > 0$ such that $\mathbf{F}(\mathbf{X})$ is in $S_\epsilon(\mathbf{F}(\mathbf{A}))$ for all $\mathbf{X}$ which are in $B \cap S_\delta(\mathbf{A})$.

The following theorem shows that this definition is really nothing new.

▶ **Theorem 6–1.** A function $\mathbf{F}$ is continuous at a point if and only if all of its component functions are continuous at the same point.

Proof. We have

$$|\mathbf{F}(\mathbf{X}) - \mathbf{F}(\mathbf{A})|^2 = \sum_{i=1}^{m} |f_i(\mathbf{X}) - f_i(\mathbf{A})|^2. \qquad (6\text{–}1)$$

Now, if **F** is continuous at **X** = **A**, then given any $\epsilon > 0$, we know that there exists a δ such that for any **X** in $B \cap S_\delta(\mathbf{A})$ we must have $|\mathbf{F}(\mathbf{X}) - \mathbf{F}(\mathbf{A})|^2 < \epsilon^2$. However, a set of positive terms will have a sum which is less than ϵ^2 only if each of the terms is itself less than ϵ^2. We can therefore conclude that for every **X** in $B \cap S_\delta(\mathbf{A})$ we must have $|f_i(\mathbf{X}) - f_i(\mathbf{A})| < \epsilon$, for every i. That is, each of the component functions f_i is continuous.

To go the other way, let us suppose that each of the component functions f_i is continuous at **A**. Let $\epsilon > 0$ be given. For each i then there exists a $\delta_i > 0$ such that $|f_i(\mathbf{X}) - f_i(\mathbf{A})| < \epsilon/\sqrt{m}$ for all **X** in $B \cap S_{\delta_i}(\mathbf{A})$. Let

$$\delta = \min \{\delta_i \mid i = 1, 2, \ldots, m\}.$$

Then $\delta > 0$ also. If **X** is in $B \cap S_\delta(\mathbf{A})$ then it is in $B \cap S_{\delta_i}(\mathbf{A})$ for every i. Putting the i inequalities into Eq. (6–1), we find that $|\mathbf{F}(\mathbf{X}) - \mathbf{F}(\mathbf{A})|^2 < \epsilon^2$, which is the desired result. ▮

Definition 6–3. Let $\mathbf{F}: B \to R^m$, where B is a subset of R^n. Let **A** be a limit point of B. Then we say that

$$\lim_{\mathbf{X} \to \mathbf{A}} \mathbf{F}(\mathbf{X}) = \mathbf{W}$$

if and only if, given any $\epsilon > 0$, there exists a $\delta > 0$ such that $|\mathbf{F}(\mathbf{X}) - \mathbf{W}| < \epsilon$ for all **X** in $B \cap \hat{S}_\delta(\mathbf{A})$. If this holds, we may also write $\mathbf{F}(\mathbf{X}) \to \mathbf{W}$ as $\mathbf{X} \to \mathbf{A}$.

From this definition the reader should easily be able to prove

Theorem 6–2. Let B be a subset of R^n. Let $\mathbf{A} \in B$ and suppose that **A** is also a limit point of B. Let $\mathbf{F}: B \to R^m$. Then **F** is continuous at **A** if and only if $\lim_{\mathbf{X} \to \mathbf{A}} \mathbf{F}(\mathbf{X}) = \mathbf{F}(\mathbf{A})$.

What can we say about the differentials of vector-valued functions? If we follow the pattern of the last chapter, we find that for any nonzero vector **Y**

$$\lim_{h \to 0} \frac{1}{h} [\mathbf{F}(\mathbf{X} + h\mathbf{Y}) - \mathbf{F}(\mathbf{X})] = [D_{\mathbf{Y}} f_1(\mathbf{X}), D_{\mathbf{Y}} f_2(\mathbf{X}), \ldots, D_{\mathbf{Y}} f_m(\mathbf{X})],$$

provided that all of the derivatives on the right exist. The result is a vector, each of whose components is the **Y**-derivative (see Definition 5–16) of the corresponding component of **F**. Each component of this vector is the value (at **Y**) of the linear transformation df_i. The entire vector is therefore the value of a linear transformation.

Definition 6–4. Suppose that $\mathbf{F}: B \to R^m$, where B is a subset of R^n. Suppose that every component of **F** is C^1 in a neighborhood of the point $\mathbf{X} \in B$. Then **F** is said to be *continuously differentiable*, or C^1, in this neighborhood, and the *differential* of **F** at **X** is the linear transformation $d\mathbf{F}: R^n \to R^m$ defined by

$$[d\mathbf{F}]\mathbf{Y} = [D_{\mathbf{Y}} f_1(\mathbf{X}), D_{\mathbf{Y}} f_2(\mathbf{X}), \ldots, D_{\mathbf{Y}} f_m(\mathbf{X})]. \tag{6–2}$$

The linear transformation defined here has a representation as a matrix in terms of the standard bases for R^n and R^m. If we let $\mathbf{Y} = \mathbf{e}_j$ in (6–2), we obtain the vector

$[f_{1'j}, f_{2'j}, \ldots, f_{m'j}]$ as the jth column vector for this matrix. Here $f_{i'j}$ means $\partial f_i/\partial x_j$, following the notation introduced in the last chapter. Note that the prime now helps us separate the subscript denoting the particular component of $\mathbf{F}$ from the subscript which shows which partial derivative is being taken. The matrix of $d\mathbf{F}$ is $[f_{i'j}]$, i being the row index and j the column index. That is, we have shown:

Theorem 6–3. Let $\mathbf{F}: B \to R^m$, where B is a subset of R^n, be C^1 in a neighborhood of $\mathbf{X} \in B$. Then the matrix of $d\mathbf{F}(\mathbf{X})$ with respect to the standard bases is $[f_{i'j}(\mathbf{X})]$, i being the row index and j being the column index. The ith row vector of this matrix is grad $f_i(\mathbf{X})$.

We shall use the symbol $d\mathbf{F}$ to denote the linear transformation defined above. The symbol $[d\mathbf{F}]$ will be used to denote either the linear transformation or the matrix of the linear transformation. It will always be clear from the context which meaning is desired. Unless otherwise specified, we will always use the standard bases.

The notation that we have set up fits well with our standard uses. We usually write a set of functions one above another. For example, we might have the function $\mathbf{F}(u, v) = [x, y, z]$ defined by

$$\begin{aligned} x &= f_1(u, v) = [a + b \cos u] \sin v, \\ y &= f_2(u, v) = [a + b \cos u] \cos v, \\ z &= f_3(u, v) = b \sin u. \end{aligned}$$

We then find that

$$d\mathbf{F}(u, v) = \begin{bmatrix} -b \sin u \sin v & (a + b \cos u) \cos v \\ -b \sin u \cos v & -(a + b \cos u) \sin v \\ b \cos u & 0 \end{bmatrix}.$$

Definition 6–5. By the $\mathbf{Y}$-*derivative* of $\mathbf{F}$ at $\mathbf{X}$, we mean

$$D_{\mathbf{Y}}\mathbf{F}(\mathbf{X}) = [d\mathbf{F}(\mathbf{X})]\mathbf{Y}.$$

By the jth *partial derivative* of $\mathbf{F}$ at $\mathbf{X}$ we will mean

$$D_j\mathbf{F}(\mathbf{X}) = D_{\mathbf{e}_j}\mathbf{F}(\mathbf{X}) = \frac{\partial \mathbf{F}}{\partial x_j}.$$

Thus the row vectors of $d\mathbf{F}$ are the grad f_i, and the column vectors are the $\partial \mathbf{F}/\partial x_j$. The rows of the matrix correspond to the different lines we use in writing down the list of component functions.

It is important to observe that we do not have a mean-value theorem for vector-valued functions. The mean-value theorem holds for each separate component function, but the points at which the components take on the proper value may differ. For example, suppose that $\mathbf{F}(x, y) = [x^2 + y^2, x^3]$. If the mean-value theorem held, there would be some θ between 0 and 1 such that $\mathbf{F}(1, 0) - \mathbf{F}(0, 0) = D_1\mathbf{F}(\theta, 0)$. However, $\mathbf{F}(1, 0) - \mathbf{F}(0, 0) = [1, 1]$, while $D_1\mathbf{F}(x, y) = [2x, 3x^2]$. Hence to have the mean-value theorem hold we would have to have some θ for which $2\theta = 1$ and $3\theta^2 = 1$. These two equations are incompatible. There can be no single solution.

While we have no mean-value theorem, we do have a local approximation theorem.

▶ **Theorem 6–4.** Let $\mathbf{F}:B \to R^m$ be C^1 in a neighborhood of $\mathbf{X}_0$ in $B \subset R^n$. Then for any $\mathbf{X}$ in some neighborhood of $\mathbf{X}_0$

$$\mathbf{F}(\mathbf{X}) - \mathbf{F}(\mathbf{X}_0) = [d\mathbf{F}(\mathbf{X}_0)][\mathbf{X} - \mathbf{X}_0] + \boldsymbol{\epsilon}(\mathbf{X})|\mathbf{X} - \mathbf{X}_0|,$$

where $\boldsymbol{\epsilon}(\mathbf{X})$ is a vector-valued function of $\mathbf{X}$ such that

$$\lim_{\mathbf{X}\to\mathbf{X}_0} \boldsymbol{\epsilon}(\mathbf{X}) = \mathbf{0}.$$

Proof. For any $\mathbf{X} \neq \mathbf{X}_0$, merely define $\boldsymbol{\epsilon}(\mathbf{X})$ to be the vector which makes the equation given in the theorem hold true. For each component of $\mathbf{F}$, the corresponding component of $\boldsymbol{\epsilon}(\mathbf{X})$ satisfies the requirements of the theorem because of Theorem 5–18. By Theorem 6–2, the requirement is therefore satisfied by $\boldsymbol{\epsilon}(\mathbf{X})$. ∎

This result can be restated in an alternative form:

Theorem 6–5. Let B be a subset of R^n and suppose that $\mathbf{F}:B \to R^m$ is C^1 in a neighborhood of a point $\mathbf{X}_0$ in B. Then there exists a linear transformation

$$T = d\mathbf{F}(\mathbf{X}_0)$$

such that

$$\lim_{\mathbf{Z}\to\mathbf{0}} \frac{1}{|\mathbf{Z}|}[\mathbf{F}(\mathbf{X}_0 + \mathbf{Z}) - \mathbf{F}(\mathbf{X}_0) - T\mathbf{Z}] = \mathbf{0}.$$

The proof of this theorem follows from the last theorem and may be left as an exercise.

Looking at the conclusion of Theorem 6–4, we see that for $\mathbf{X}$ sufficiently close to $\mathbf{X}_0$ we will have the approximation

$$\mathbf{F}(\mathbf{X}) - \mathbf{F}(\mathbf{X}_0) \doteq [d\mathbf{F}(\mathbf{X}_0)][\mathbf{X} - \mathbf{X}_0].$$

That is, $\mathbf{F}(\mathbf{X}) - \mathbf{F}(\mathbf{X}_0)$ behaves locally like a linear transformation. The level surface of $\mathbf{F}$ at this point [the set of all $\mathbf{X}$ for which $\mathbf{F}(\mathbf{X}) = \mathbf{F}(\mathbf{X}_0)$] must therefore be approximated by the kernel of this transformation plus $\mathbf{X}_0$. This affine subspace, $\mathbf{X}_0 + \ker d\mathbf{F}(\mathbf{X}_0)$ is therefore the tangent subspace to the level surface for $\mathbf{F}$.

It is important to notice that the level surface of $\mathbf{F}(\mathbf{X})$ that we are talking about here is a surface *in the domain space*. It is given by

$$\{\mathbf{X} \mid \mathbf{F}(\mathbf{X}) = \mathbf{C}\}$$

for some constant vector $\mathbf{C}$.

It often happens that the image set in the range space can also be interpreted as a surface. We will look into this further in later chapters, but here we are working only with the level surfaces.

Another point to watch out for is that the term "level surface" has only a technical meaning. It need not be an actual surface in our usual meaning of the word. For example, consider the level surfaces of the function $\mathbf{F}(x, y, z) = [u, v, w]$, where

$$u = x^2 + y^2,$$
$$v = x + z,$$
$$w = y - z.$$

One of these, say the surface defined by $\mathbf{F}(x, y, z) = [1, 1, -1]$, is determined by three equations for x, y, and z:

$$x^2 + y^2 = 1,$$
$$x + z = 1,$$
$$y - z = -1.$$

There are only two points which satisfy these three equations. The level surface determined by $\mathbf{F}(\mathbf{X}) = [1, 1, -1]$ is therefore the pair of points

$$[1/\sqrt{2}, -1/\sqrt{2}, 1 - 1/\sqrt{2}]$$

and

$$[-1/\sqrt{2}, 1/\sqrt{2}, 1 + 1/\sqrt{2}].$$

It is of course meaningless to ask for the tangent space to this level surface, but the reader will find it easy to verify that ker $d\mathbf{F}$ is of dimension zero at either of these points.

It may be instructive to take a closer look at this example. The level surface of the function $\mathbf{F}$ is actually the intersection of the three level surfaces of the three given functions defining the components u, v, and w. Let us look at these in order.

Consider first the level surface of the first function alone

$$f(x, y, z) = u = x^2 + y^2.$$

The level surface for which $u = 1$ is a circular cylinder of radius 1. It passes through the point $\mathbf{A} = [1/\sqrt{2}, -1/\sqrt{2}, 1 - 1/\sqrt{2}]$. At the point $\mathbf{A}$, $\nabla f = [\sqrt{2}, -\sqrt{2}, 0]$. Hence the tangent space to this surface at $\mathbf{A}$ is defined by

$$\mathbf{A} + s[1, 1, 0] + t[0, 0, 1].$$

The reader should make a sketch and observe that this plane is indeed tangent to the cylinder in the manner usually understood.

Next, we add a second function and look at the level surface of

$$\mathbf{G}(x, y, z) = \begin{bmatrix} u \\ v \end{bmatrix} = \begin{bmatrix} x^2 + y^2 \\ x + z \end{bmatrix}$$

which passes through the same point $\mathbf{A}$. We easily see that this is the intersection of the cylinder given above and a plane; that is, it is an ellipse in space. At $\mathbf{A}$,

$$[d\mathbf{G}] = \begin{bmatrix} \sqrt{2} & -\sqrt{2} & 0 \\ 1 & 0 & 1 \end{bmatrix}.$$

The kernel of this transformation is the one-dimensional space generated by $[1, 1, -1]$. Hence the tangent space to this level surface (the ellipse) is given by

$$\mathbf{A} + s[1, 1, -1].$$

Again, this defines the line which is tangent to the ellipse in the usual sense.

Finally, when we add the third function to give the function $\mathbf{F}(x, y, z)$ described above, the level surface through $\mathbf{A}$ becomes the pair of points as given, and the tangent space to this level surface at the point $\mathbf{A}$ becomes the point $\mathbf{A}$ alone.

In Problem 3 at the end of this section a characterization of the level surface of a vector-valued function is given. Reference to this problem may help in the understanding of this example.

As in the case of one dimension, we often find it easier to keep track of the linear transformation which represents the differential, together with the above approximation theorem, when we use the total differential of the function.

Definition 6–6. Let B be a subset of R^n. Let $\mathbf{F}: B \to R^m$ be C^1 in a neighborhood of a point $\mathbf{X}_0$ of B. Let $d\mathbf{X}$ represent an arbitrary vector

$$d\mathbf{X} = [dx_1, dx_2, \ldots, dx_n]$$

in the domain of the transformation $d\mathbf{F}(\mathbf{X}_0)$. By the *total differential* of $\mathbf{F}$ at $\mathbf{X}_0$ we mean the corresponding vector which is the image of $d\mathbf{X}$ of this transformation, i.e.,

$$\begin{aligned} d\mathbf{F} &= [d\mathbf{F}(\mathbf{X}_0)]\, d\mathbf{X} \\ &= \begin{bmatrix} df_1(\mathbf{X}_0) \\ df_2(\mathbf{X}_0) \\ \vdots \\ df_m(\mathbf{X}_0) \end{bmatrix} = \begin{bmatrix} f_{1'1}\, dx_1 + f_{1'2}\, dx_2 + \cdots + f_{1'n}\, dx_n \\ f_{2'1}\, dx_1 + f_{2'2}\, dx_2 + \cdots + f_{2'n}\, dx_n \\ \vdots \\ f_{m'1}\, dx_1 + f_{m'2}\, dx_2 + \cdots + f_{m'n}\, dx_n \end{bmatrix}. \end{aligned}$$

For example, the total differential of the function $\mathbf{F}(u, v)$ defined in the middle of page 219 can be given in terms of the total differential of $\mathbf{F}$:

$$d\mathbf{F} = \begin{bmatrix} dx \\ dy \\ dz \end{bmatrix} = \begin{bmatrix} -b \sin u \sin v\, du + (a + b \cos u) \cos v\, dv \\ -b \sin u \cos v\, du - (a + b \cos u) \sin v\, dv \\ b \cos u\, du \end{bmatrix}.$$

When we write $x = f_1(u, v)$, we often find it just as satisfactory to write dx as df_1. The "x" in this case can be thought of as either the value of the function at a specific point or as a shorter symbol to denote the whole function. There are times when using dx in place of df_1 might lead to confusion. If so, this use would have to be avoided. Whenever no confusion can be caused, a shorter notation is usually easier to follow and may well be preferred. Another example of the shorter notation is our use of $d\mathbf{F}$ to stand for $d\mathbf{F}(\mathbf{X}_0)$ when it is clear at which point the matrix is to be evaluated.

PROBLEMS

1. Prove Theorem 6–2.
2. Prove Theorem 6–5.
3. Let $m < n$ and let $\mathbf{F}:B \to R^m$ where B is a subset of R^n. Show that the level surface of $\mathbf{F}$ through a given point is the intersection of the m level surfaces of the component functions of $\mathbf{F}$ through the same point. Show that the tangent space to this level surface is the orthogonal complement of the space generated by the m gradients of the component functions.
4. Let A be an $m \times n$ matrix. Let $\mathbf{F}(\mathbf{X})$ be the linear transformation defined by $\mathbf{F}(\mathbf{X}) = A\mathbf{X}$. Prove that $[d\mathbf{F}] = A$.
5. Prove that $[d(f\mathbf{G})] = \mathbf{G}[df] + f[d\mathbf{G}]$. Here $f: B \to R$ and $\mathbf{G}:B \to R^m$, where B is a subset of R^n. Both functions are assumed to be C^1.
6. Prove that if $\mathbf{F}(\mathbf{X})$ is continuous at $\mathbf{X}_0$, then the function $g(\mathbf{X}) = |\mathbf{F}(\mathbf{X})|$ is also continuous at $\mathbf{X}_0$.
7. Let $B \subset R^k$ and $B' \subset R^m$. Let $\mathbf{A} \in B$ and suppose that $\mathbf{G}:B \to B'$ with $\mathbf{G}(\mathbf{A}) = \mathbf{A}'$. Let $\mathbf{F}:B' \to R^n$ and suppose that $\mathbf{F}$ is continuous at $\mathbf{A}'$ and $\mathbf{G}$ is continuous at $\mathbf{A}$. Prove that the composed function $\mathbf{F}[\mathbf{G}(\mathbf{X})]$ is continuous at $\mathbf{A}$.
8. Give the total differentials of each of the following functions:
   a) $\mathbf{F}(x, y) = [u, v]$, where $u = x^2 - y^2$, $v = 2xy$
   b) $\mathbf{F}(x, y, z) = [u, v]$, where $u = x^2y + y^2z + z^2x$, $v = xyz(1 + x^2 + y^2 + z^2)$
   c) $\mathbf{F}(x, y, z) = [u, v, w]$, where $u = e^{xy}(z + \sin z)$, $v = x^2e^{xyz}$, $w = x^2y \log(1 + z^2)$
   d) $\mathbf{F}(x, y) = [u, v, w]$, where $u = x + y$, $v = xy^2 + x^2y$, $w = x^2y^3 + x^3y^2$
9. Find the tangent space to the level surface of the function of Problem 8(b) at
   a) [0, 0, 1],
   b) [0, 1, 1],
   c) [1, 1, 1].

6–2. THE COMPOSITION OF FUNCTIONS

In this section we wish to prove the formula for the derivative of the composition of two functions. We recall that in the case of functions of a single variable we have the chain rule. That is

$$\frac{d}{dx} f[w(x)] = f'[w(x)]w'(x).$$

We find that a very similar result holds for vector-valued functions. The only difference is that we have the product of two matrices instead of the product of two scalars.

▶ **Theorem 6–6.** Let $\mathbf{F}: D \to R^m$ and $\mathbf{W}:B \to R^n$, where D is a subset of R^n and B is a subset of R^k. Let $\mathbf{X}_0 \in B$ be such that $\mathbf{W}(\mathbf{X}_0) = \mathbf{W}_0 \in D$. Suppose that $\mathbf{W}$ is C^1 in a neighborhood of $\mathbf{X}_0$ and $\mathbf{F}$ is C^1 in a neighborhood of $\mathbf{W}_0$. Then the composite function $\mathbf{G}: B \to R^m$ defined by $\mathbf{G}(\mathbf{X}) = \mathbf{F}[\mathbf{W}(\mathbf{X})]$ is C^1 in a neighborhood of $\mathbf{X}_0$, and its differential is given by

$$d\mathbf{G}(\mathbf{X}_0) = [d\mathbf{F}(\mathbf{W}_0)][d\mathbf{W}(\mathbf{X}_0)]. \tag{6–3}$$

Proof. Note that (6–3) can be interpreted as being either the composition of the two linear transformations or as the product of the two matrices. Since matrix multiplication is not commutative, the order in which the factors are given is important.

To prove this theorem, we must show that for any fixed nonzero vector $\mathbf{Y}$, $D_{\mathbf{Y}}\mathbf{G}(\mathbf{X})$ exists and is equal to $T(\mathbf{X})\mathbf{Y}$, where $T(\mathbf{X}) = [d\mathbf{F}(\mathbf{W})][d\mathbf{W}(\mathbf{X})]$, and further, that $T(\mathbf{X})\mathbf{Y}$ is continuous as a function of $\mathbf{X}$ for all $\mathbf{X}$ in some neighborhood of $\mathbf{X}_0$. However, if we have proved that $T(\mathbf{X})\mathbf{Y} = D_{\mathbf{Y}}\mathbf{G}(\mathbf{X})$, then the continuity of $T(\mathbf{X})\mathbf{Y}$ can be proved quite easily. The existence and continuity of the differential of $\mathbf{W}(\mathbf{X})$ in a neighborhood of $\mathbf{X}_0$ means that all of the partial derivatives, $w_{i'j}(\mathbf{X})$ exist and are continuous. Similarly, all of the partial derivatives $f_{i'j}(\mathbf{W})$ will be continuous (in $\mathbf{W}$). However, a continuous function of a continuous function is continuous (Problem 7 of the last section), and hence each $f_{i'j}[\mathbf{W}(\mathbf{X})]$ will be continuous as a function of $\mathbf{X}$. Therefore every entry of the matrix $T(\mathbf{X})$, as defined above, will be a continuous function of $\mathbf{X}$. This means in turn that $T(\mathbf{X})\mathbf{Y}$ will be continuous for each $\mathbf{Y}$. Therefore it remains only to show that $D_{\mathbf{Y}}\mathbf{G}(\mathbf{X}) = T(\mathbf{X})\mathbf{Y}$.

We will use the approximation theorem. For any $\mathbf{Y}$ and any h sufficiently small, set $\mathbf{U} = \mathbf{W}(\mathbf{X} + h\mathbf{Y}) - \mathbf{W}(\mathbf{X})$. Then by the approximation theorem

$$\mathbf{U} = \mathbf{W}(\mathbf{X} + h\mathbf{Y}) - \mathbf{W}(\mathbf{X}) = [d\mathbf{W}(\mathbf{X})][h\mathbf{Y}] + \boldsymbol{\epsilon}_2(h\mathbf{Y})|h\mathbf{Y}|, \tag{6–4}$$

where $\boldsymbol{\epsilon}_2$ is a vector-valued function which tends to zero as $h\mathbf{Y}$ tends to zero. From this equation we see that $\mathbf{U} \to \mathbf{0}$ as $h \to 0$. We also have the second approximation

$$\mathbf{F}(\mathbf{W} + \mathbf{U}) - F(\mathbf{U}) = [d\mathbf{F}(\mathbf{W})]\mathbf{U} + \boldsymbol{\epsilon}_1(\mathbf{U})|\mathbf{U}|,$$

where $\boldsymbol{\epsilon}_1(\mathbf{U}) \to \mathbf{0}$ as $\mathbf{U} \to \mathbf{0}$ also. But then, letting $\mathbf{W} = \mathbf{W}(\mathbf{X})$, we have

$$\begin{aligned}
\frac{1}{h}[\mathbf{G}(\mathbf{X} + h\mathbf{Y}) - \mathbf{G}(\mathbf{X})] &= \frac{1}{h}[\mathbf{F}(\mathbf{W}(\mathbf{X} + h\mathbf{Y})) - \mathbf{F}(\mathbf{W}(\mathbf{X}))] \\
&= \frac{1}{h}[\mathbf{F}(\mathbf{W} + \mathbf{U}) - \mathbf{F}(\mathbf{W})] \\
&= \frac{1}{h}[d\mathbf{F}(\mathbf{W})]\mathbf{U} + \frac{1}{h}\boldsymbol{\epsilon}_1(\mathbf{U})|\mathbf{U}| \\
&= \frac{1}{h}[d\mathbf{F}(\mathbf{W})]\big([d\mathbf{W}(\mathbf{X})](h\mathbf{Y}) + \boldsymbol{\epsilon}_2(h\mathbf{Y})|h\mathbf{Y}|\big) + \frac{1}{h}\boldsymbol{\epsilon}_1(\mathbf{U})|\mathbf{U}| \\
&= [d\mathbf{F}(\mathbf{W})][d\mathbf{W}(\mathbf{X})]\mathbf{Y} + |\mathbf{Y}|\,[d\mathbf{F}(\mathbf{W})]\boldsymbol{\epsilon}_2(h\mathbf{Y}) + \boldsymbol{\epsilon}_1(\mathbf{U})\left|\frac{1}{h}\mathbf{U}\right|.
\end{aligned}$$

The first term here is independent of h and is exactly the desired quantity. Thus we only need to show that as $h \to 0$ the second and third terms of the last line tend toward zero. From (6–4) we see that

$$\frac{1}{h}\mathbf{U} = [d\mathbf{W}(\mathbf{X})]\mathbf{Y} + \boldsymbol{\epsilon}_2(h\mathbf{Y})|\mathbf{Y}|$$
$$\to [d\mathbf{W}(\mathbf{X})]\mathbf{Y} \quad \text{as} \quad h \to 0.$$

In particular, $\mathbf{U} \to \mathbf{0}$ as $h \to 0$. Therefore, as $h \to 0$, $\mathbf{U} \to 0$, and hence $\boldsymbol{\epsilon}_1(\mathbf{U}) \to \mathbf{0}$. Since $(1/h)\mathbf{U}$ tends to a limit and $\boldsymbol{\epsilon}_1(\mathbf{U}) \to \mathbf{0}$, we must have

$$\boldsymbol{\epsilon}_1(\mathbf{U})\left|\frac{1}{h}\mathbf{U}\right| \to \mathbf{0} \quad \text{as} \quad h \to 0.$$

Now the grad $f_i(\mathbf{W})$ are the row vectors of $d\mathbf{F}(\mathbf{W})$. Let

$$M = \sum_{i=1}^{m} |\text{grad } f_i(\mathbf{W})|.$$

Then for any vector $\mathbf{A}$,

$$|[d\mathbf{F}(\mathbf{W})]\mathbf{A}| \leq M|\mathbf{A}|. \tag{6–5}$$

Hence

$$|[d\mathbf{F}(\mathbf{W})]\boldsymbol{\epsilon}_2(h\mathbf{Y})| \leq M\,|\,\boldsymbol{\epsilon}_2(h\mathbf{Y})| \to 0 \quad \text{as} \quad h \to 0.$$

We therefore conclude that

$$\lim_{h\to 0}\frac{1}{h}[\mathbf{G}(\mathbf{X} + h\mathbf{Y}) - \mathbf{G}(\mathbf{X})] = D_{\mathbf{Y}}\mathbf{G}(\mathbf{X})$$
$$= [d\mathbf{F}(\mathbf{W})][d\mathbf{W}(\mathbf{X})]\mathbf{Y}.$$

This proves the theorem. ▌

Let us see an example of the use of this theorem. Suppose that

$$\mathbf{F}(\mathbf{X}) = \begin{bmatrix} u \\ v \end{bmatrix} = \begin{bmatrix} x^2 + xy \\ x^2 - y^2 \end{bmatrix}, \qquad \mathbf{X}(\mathbf{R}) = \begin{bmatrix} x \\ y \end{bmatrix} = \begin{bmatrix} r\cos\theta \\ r\sin\theta \end{bmatrix}.$$

Then we compute

$$d\mathbf{F} = \begin{bmatrix} 2x + y & x \\ 2x & -2y \end{bmatrix}, \qquad d\mathbf{X} = \begin{bmatrix} \cos\theta & -r\sin\theta \\ \sin\theta & r\cos\theta \end{bmatrix}.$$

Hence, if

$$\mathbf{G}(\mathbf{R}) = \mathbf{F}[\mathbf{X}(\mathbf{R})] = \begin{bmatrix} r^2\cos\theta(\cos\theta + \sin\theta) \\ r^2(\cos^2\theta - \sin^2\theta) \end{bmatrix},$$

then, on the one hand,

$$d\mathbf{G}(\mathbf{R}) = \begin{bmatrix} 2r\cos\theta(\cos\theta + \sin\theta) & r^2(\cos^2\theta - \sin^2\theta - 2\sin\theta\cos\theta \\ 2r(\cos^2\theta - \sin^2\theta) & -4\sin\theta\cos\theta \end{bmatrix}, \tag{6–6}$$

while, on the other hand,

$$[d\mathbf{F}(\mathbf{X})][d\mathbf{X}(\mathbf{R})] = \begin{bmatrix} (2x + y)\cos\theta + x\sin\theta & -r(2x + y)\sin\theta + rx\cos\theta \\ 2x\cos\theta - 2y\sin\theta & -2rx\sin\theta - 2ry\cos\theta \end{bmatrix}. \tag{6–7}$$

Are these two matrices really the same? The reader should verify that they are.

Often it suffices to find only a specific partial derivative of the composite function rather than the entire matrix. For example, suppose that we wish to find $\partial g_i/\partial x_j = g_{i'j}$ [where $\mathbf{G}$, $\mathbf{F}$, and $\mathbf{W} = \mathbf{W}(\mathbf{X})$ are as in Theorem 6–6]. We only have to note that

$$d\mathbf{G} = [g_{i'j}] = [f_{i'k}][w_{k'j}]$$

and hence

$$\begin{aligned} g_{i'j}(\mathbf{X}) &= \sum_{k=1}^{n} f_{i'k}(\mathbf{W})w_{k'j}(\mathbf{X}) \\ &= f_{i'1}w_{1'j} + f_{i'2}w_{2'j} + \cdots + f_{i'n}w_{n'j}. \end{aligned} \tag{6–8}$$

Using the partial derivative "curly *d*" notation, we could write this equation in the form

$$\frac{\partial g_i}{\partial x_j} = \frac{\partial f_i}{\partial w_1}\frac{\partial w_1}{\partial x_j} + \frac{\partial f_i}{\partial w_2}\frac{\partial w_2}{\partial x_j} + \cdots + \frac{\partial f_i}{\partial w_n}\frac{\partial w_n}{\partial x_j}. \tag{6–9}$$

This is the conventional form in which the *chain rule* is written. Either (6–8) or (6–9), which are two representations of the same result, are called the *chain rule*.

A very common practice is to write $\partial g_i/\partial x_j$ as $\partial f_i/\partial x_j$ in order to avoid introducing a notation for the composite function. Since f_i is a function of $\mathbf{W}$, this notation does not have a meaning in terms of the definitions already given. It is thus possible to interpret it in the following way:

$$\frac{\partial f_i}{\partial x_j} = \frac{\partial}{\partial x_j} f_i[\mathbf{W}(\mathbf{X})].$$

This usage causes no confusion *provided that we know the function* $\mathbf{W}(\mathbf{X})$. This function must be known whenever this convention is used. Many of the difficulties that arise in the use of partial derivatives occur because we lose track of the functions which define the "change of variables."

Note that there can be no confusion when we use the subscript notation. When we write $f_{i'j}$ we mean the partial derivative with respect to the "variable" that occurs in the *j*th position of the argument of f_i. Thus $f_{i'j}(\mathbf{W}(\mathbf{X}))$ means $f_{i'j}(\mathbf{W})$ evaluated at $\mathbf{W} = \mathbf{W}(\mathbf{X})$.

Let us remark on the relationship between total differential notation and the above result on the composition of functions. Letting $\mathbf{F}$, $\mathbf{W}$, and $\mathbf{G}$ be as in Theorem 6–6, we see that we can write the differential of $\mathbf{W}(\mathbf{X})$ in the total differential form

$$dw_j = \sum_{i=1}^{k} w_{j'i}\, dx_i. \tag{6–10}$$

Similarly, the total differentials of **F** define the differential of **F**. We have

$$df_r = \sum_{j=1}^{n} f_{r'j}\, dw_j. \tag{6–11}$$

In (6–10) dw_j represents the total differential of the function $\mathbf{W}_j(\mathbf{X})$. In (6–11), the dw_j represent variables in the domain space of $d\mathbf{F}$. The content of Theorem 6–6 can then be interpreted as saying that the expressions in (6–10) can be substituted into (6–11) to yield the total differentials of the f_r in terms of the dx_i. When we perform this substitution, we actually show that $dg_r = df_r$. The total differentials thus offer a convenient way to keep track of the linear transformations which represent the derivatives. If we wish to find $\partial f_r/\partial x_i$, say, we can set all $dx_{i'} = 0$ except for dx_i. Then, after substituting (6–10) into (6–11), we obtain

$$df_r = \sum_{j=1}^{n} f_{r'j} w_{j'i}\, dx_i$$

and hence

$$\frac{\partial f_r}{\partial x_i} = \sum_{j=1}^{n} \left(\frac{\partial f_r}{\partial w_j}\right)\left(\frac{\partial w_j}{\partial x_i}\right).$$

In order to eliminate all differences between the two types of differential, all we need to do is to produce some way of interpreting dx_i as a linear transformation even when x_i is not explicitly given as a function of other variables. Then dx_i could be interpreted either as a linear transformation or as a symbol representing a real number (the value of a linear transformation), whichever seems more convenient.

It is usually said that only functions have differentials. Variables cannot have differentials. However, there is a completely natural way of interpreting a variable as a function. The variable x_i is always a function of **X**, where $\mathbf{X} = [x_1, x_2, \ldots, x_n]$. It is called the ith *component* or *coordinate function*. Let us write this function as

$$x_i = \pi_i(\mathbf{X}).$$

We then have a linear function $\pi_i: R^n \to R$, whose matrix is

$$[\pi_i] = [0\ 0\ \ldots\ 1\ \ldots\ 0] = \mathbf{e}_i^t.$$

Let $\mathbf{Y} = [y_1, y_2, \ldots, y_n]$. Let us now compute $d\pi_i$. We will do this at the point $\mathbf{X} = \mathbf{A} = [a_1, a_2, \ldots, a_n]$, and we start by computing the **Y**-derivative

$$D_{\mathbf{Y}}\pi_i(\mathbf{A}) = \lim_{h\to 0} \frac{\pi_i(\mathbf{A} + h\mathbf{Y}) - \pi_i(\mathbf{A})}{h}$$

$$= \lim_{h\to 0} \frac{a_i + hy_i - a_i}{h} = y_i.$$

Therefore

$$D_{\mathbf{Y}}\pi_i(\mathbf{A}) = [0\ 0\ \ldots\ 1\ \ldots\ 0]\mathbf{Y} = \mathbf{e}_i^t\mathbf{Y}$$

or

$$[d\pi_i(\mathbf{A})] = \mathbf{e}_i^t = [\pi_i].$$

That is, the total differential of x_i is $dx_i = d\pi_i(\mathbf{A}) = \pi_i$, independent of **A**.

It is interesting to observe that the resulting relations allow us to compute the matrix of df, where $f\colon R^n \to R$, from the expression written in the total differential

$$df(\mathbf{X}_0) = f_{'1}(\mathbf{X}_0)\,dx_1 + f_{'2}(\mathbf{X}_0)\,dx_2 + \cdots + f_{'n}(\mathbf{X}_0)\,dx_n.$$

The matrix will then be given by

$$\begin{aligned}[df(\mathbf{X}_0)] &= f_{'1}(\mathbf{X}_0)\mathbf{e}_1^t + f_{'2}(\mathbf{X}_0)\mathbf{e}_2^t + \cdots + f_{'n}(\mathbf{X}_0)\mathbf{e}_n^t \\ &= [f_{'1}(\mathbf{X}_0)\;\; f_{'1}(\mathbf{X}_0)\;\; \ldots\;\; f_{'n}(\mathbf{X}_0)].\end{aligned}$$

This is exactly the $1 \times n$ matrix which we know to be the gradient of f.

PROBLEMS

1. Prove (6–5).
2. Show that the matrices of (6–6) and (6–7) are the same.
3. Suppose that $f(x, y, z)$ is a scalar-valued function which is C^1 in a neighborhood of the point $[x, y, z]$. Let $g(\mathbf{R}) = f[\mathbf{X}(\mathbf{R})]$. Find dg in terms of the new variables if $\mathbf{X}(\mathbf{R})$ is defined by:

   a) $$\mathbf{X} = \begin{bmatrix} x \\ y \\ z \end{bmatrix} = \begin{bmatrix} r\cos\theta \\ r\sin\theta \\ z \end{bmatrix}, \quad \mathbf{R} = [r, \theta, z], \text{ called polar coordinates;}$$

   b) $$\mathbf{X} = \begin{bmatrix} x \\ y \\ z \end{bmatrix} = \begin{bmatrix} \rho\cos\theta\sin\phi \\ \rho\sin\theta\sin\phi \\ \rho\cos\phi \end{bmatrix}, \quad \mathbf{R} = [\rho, \phi, \theta], \text{ called spherical coordinates.}$$

4. Find $\partial f/\partial x$, $\partial f/\partial y$, and $\partial f/\partial z$ for each of the following:

   a) $f = u^2 + \log(u^2 + uv + v^2)$, $u = x + y + z$, $v = x^2 + y^2 + z^2$

   b) $f = \cos uv + \sin vw + \tan u$, $u = xy$, $v = xy^2 + zy$, $w = z^2y + y^2$

   c) $f = \arctan(u^2 - uv)$, $u = r\sin\theta$, $v = r\cos\theta$, $r = (x^2 + y^2)^{1/2}$, $\theta = \arctan(y/x)$

5. Prove that $\operatorname{grad} f[g(\mathbf{X})] = f'[g(\mathbf{X})] \operatorname{grad} g(\mathbf{X})$, assuming that both functions are C^1.
6. Let $f\colon B \to R$, where $B \subset R^n$. Let $\mathbf{A} \in B$ and let $\mathbf{u} = [u_1, u_2, \ldots, u_n]$ be a vector of unit length in R^n. Define

   $$D_{\mathbf{u}}^1 f(\mathbf{A}) = D_{\mathbf{u}} f(\mathbf{A}) = \sum_{i=1}^{n} f_{'i}(\mathbf{A}) u_i, \qquad D_{\mathbf{u}}^2 f(\mathbf{A}) = D_{\mathbf{u}}[D_{\mathbf{u}}^1 f(\mathbf{A})],$$

   and in general,

   $$D_{\mathbf{u}}^{k+1} f(\mathbf{A}) = D_{\mathbf{u}}[D_{\mathbf{u}}^k f(\mathbf{A})],$$

   assuming that the required derivatives exist and are continuous. Prove that

   $$D_{\mathbf{u}}^k f(\mathbf{A}) = \sum_{i_1=1}^{n} \sum_{i_2=1}^{n} \cdots \sum_{i_k=1}^{n} f_{'i_1 i_2 \cdots i_k}(\mathbf{A}) u_{i_1} u_{i_2} \cdots u_{i_k}.$$

7. Using Taylor's Theorem with the Lagrange form of the remainder for functions of a single variable, show that if f has continuous kth partial derivatives in a neighborhood

of A, then for any $t > 0$ which is sufficiently small so that $\mathbf{A} + t\mathbf{u}$ is in this neighborhood,

$$f(\mathbf{A} + t\mathbf{u}) = f(\mathbf{A}) + \frac{t}{1!} D_{\mathbf{u}}f(\mathbf{A}) + \frac{t^2}{2!} D^2_{\mathbf{u}}f(\mathbf{A}) + \cdots + \frac{t^{k-1}}{(k-1)!} D^{k-1}_{\mathbf{u}}f(\mathbf{A}) + R_k,$$

where

$$|R_k| \le \frac{t^k}{k!} \max \{|D^k_{\mathbf{u}}f(\mathbf{A} + \tau\mathbf{u})| \mid 0 < \tau < t\}.$$

8. Write out the terms of the expansion given in Problem 7 through t^3 in terms of the partial derivatives of f and the components of $(\mathbf{X} - \mathbf{A})$ if $\mathbf{X} = [x, y]$, $\mathbf{A} = [a_1, a_2]$, and $\mathbf{A} + t\mathbf{u} = \mathbf{X}$. [*Hint:* $tu_1 = t\mathbf{u} \cdot \mathbf{e}_1 = x - a_1$, etc.]
9. Given that $|\mathbf{u}| = 1$ and $\mathbf{B} = [b_1, b_2, \ldots, b_n]$ is such that $|b_i| \le m$ for each i, prove that
$$\left|\sum_{i=1}^{n} b_i u_i\right| \le m\sqrt{n}.$$
10. Given that f is such that all of its kth partial derivatives at $\mathbf{X}$ are less than m in absolute value, prove that
$$|D^k_{\mathbf{u}}f(\mathbf{X})| \le m(\sqrt{n})^k.$$
11. Suppose that all of the kth partial derivatives of $f(\mathbf{X})$ are bounded by m for all $\mathbf{X}$ with $|\mathbf{X} - \mathbf{A}| < r$. Prove that if $|\mathbf{Z}| < r$, then
$$f(\mathbf{A} + \mathbf{Z}) = f(\mathbf{A}) + \sum_{i=1}^{k-1} \frac{|\mathbf{Z}|^i}{i!} D^i_{\mathbf{u}/|\mathbf{u}|} f(\mathbf{A}) + R,$$
where $\mathbf{u} = \mathbf{Z}/|\mathbf{Z}|$ and
$$|R| \le \frac{m}{k!} (|\mathbf{Z}|/\sqrt{n})^k.$$

6–3. THE IMPLICIT-FUNCTION THEOREM

In this section we turn to one of the main problems in the study of functions of vectors. When can a functional equation be solved for an implicitly defined variable?

Let us start by explaining exactly what we mean by this question. Suppose that we are given a functional relationship, such as

$$f(x, y, z) = 0$$

for example, which we know is satisfied at some point $[x_0, y_0, z_0]$. What we wish to do is solve for z, say, in terms of x and y. That is, we wish to find a function $z = g(x, y)$ such that

$$z_0 = g(x_0, y_0)$$

and

$$f[x, y, g(x, y)] = 0 \qquad \text{for all } x \text{ and } y \text{ in some neighborhood of } [x_0, y_0].$$

It is important to note that the new function $g(x, y)$, if it exists, is defined in an entirely separate space. The point $[x, y]$ is in a two-dimensional space, while $[x, y, z]$

is in a three-dimensional space. In some ways, it might be clearer to define the function g in another space altogether. Thus we might find $g(u, v)$ and then define the transformation

$$\mathbf{X} = \mathbf{X}(u, v) = \begin{bmatrix} x \\ y \\ z \end{bmatrix} = \begin{bmatrix} u \\ v \\ g(u, v) \end{bmatrix}.$$

Thus the requirement is that $f(\mathbf{X}(u, v)) = 0$ identically in some neighborhood of $[x_0, y_0]$. We do not usually find it necessary to write out the complete transformation in this detail. It suffices to realize that this is actually what is taking place when we speak about "solving for z in terms of x and y."

Now let us state the basic implicit-function theorem. It gives us the condition under which we can be assured of being able to solve for one of the variables in terms of the others. By changing the order of the components if necessary, we can always arrange that the variable we wish to solve for is x_n, the final component of $\mathbf{X}$. This change makes the statement of the theorem less confusing.

▶ **Theorem 6–7.** Let $\mathbf{A} = [a_1, a_2, \ldots, a_n]$ be an interior point of the set B in R^n and suppose that $f: B \to R$ is C^1 in B. Suppose that $f(\mathbf{A}) = 0$ and that $f_{\prime n}(\mathbf{A}) \neq 0$. Let $\mathbf{A}' = [a_1, a_2, \ldots, a_{n-1}] \in R^{n-1}$ and let $\mathbf{Y}$ represent an arbitrary vector in R^{n-1}. Then there exists a neighborhood S of $\mathbf{A}'$ in R^{n-1} and a unique function $g: S \to R$ such that g is C^1 in S,

$$a_n = g(\mathbf{A}'), \tag{6–12}$$

and if we set

$$\mathbf{G}(\mathbf{Y}) = \mathbf{X} = \begin{bmatrix} x_1 \\ x_2 \\ \vdots \\ x_{n-1} \\ x_n \end{bmatrix} = \begin{bmatrix} y_1 \\ y_2 \\ \vdots \\ y_{n-1} \\ g(\mathbf{Y}) \end{bmatrix}, \tag{6–13}$$

then $f[\mathbf{G}(\mathbf{Y})] = 0$ for all $\mathbf{Y}$ in S. Furthermore,

$$g_{\prime i}(\mathbf{A}') = -f_{\prime i}(\mathbf{A})/f_{\prime n}(\mathbf{A}). \tag{6–14}$$

Remarks. This theorem says that

$$f(x_1, x_2, \ldots, x_{n-1}, g(x_1, x_2, \ldots, x_{n-1})) = 0$$

in this $(n - 1)$-dimensional neighborhood of $\mathbf{A}'$. Since we wish to think of the function g as defining x_n, we would write

$$x_n = g(x_1, x_2, \ldots, x_{n-1}).$$

Then (6–12) can be interpreted as saying that

$$\frac{\partial x_n}{\partial x_i} = -\frac{\partial f/\partial x_i}{\partial f/\partial x_n}.$$

This relation is easier to remember if we write out the differential of f:

$$df = f_{,1}\, dx_1 + \cdots + f_{,n-1}\, dx_{n-1} + f_{,n}\, dx_n.$$

Since the constraint under which we found g was that $f = 0$, we must have $df = 0$ also. Setting $df = 0$ and solving the equation for dx_n in terms of the other dx_i gives us the differential relation which is equivalent to (6–12).

Proof. For the proof of this theorem we will assume that $n = 3$. The proof for the general case is exactly the same, but by making this simplification we can illustrate the proof with three-dimensional figures and so follow the arguments more easily. We proceed in three main steps. First, we find a neighborhood S in which we define the function g. This neighborhood is so chosen that g exists and is unique. Next, we prove that the function g so defined is continuous, and finally we prove that it is differentiable and that (6–12) holds.

To avoid getting tangled up in subscripts, we will use $[x, y, z]$ as the coordinates of the points of our space. We will let the point $\mathbf{A}$ be $[a, b, c]$ and hence $\mathbf{A}' = [a, b]$. We are given the function $f(x, y, z)$ with $f(a, b, c) = 0$ and $f_{,3}(a, b, c) \neq 0$. Let us assume that $f_{,3}(a, b, c) > 0$ in order to be definite. What we wish to do is show that the level surface of f $(x, y, z) = 0$ which passes through $[a, b, c]$ has a unique representation in the form $z = g(x, y)$ for all $[x, y]$ in some neighborhood of $[a, b]$. This situation is illustrated in Fig. 6–1. The base of the cylinder shown is supposed to be in the xy-plane. Hence the disk at the base of this cylinder is the neighborhood S.

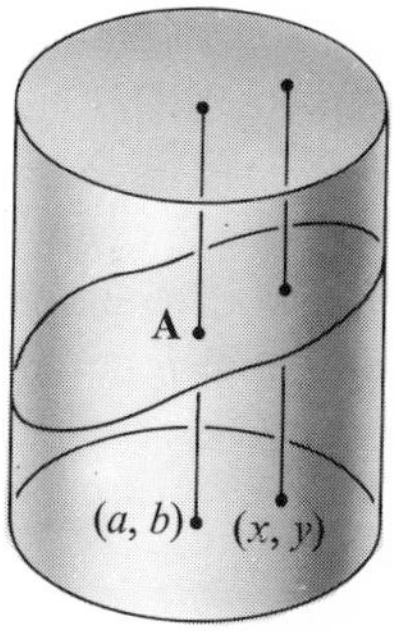

Fig. 6–1

We are assuming that $f_{,3}(a, b, c) > 0$. Furthermore, the assumption is that this derivative exists and is continuous in some neighborhood of $\mathbf{A}$. Therefore there must be some neighborhood of $\mathbf{A}$ such that for all $[x, y, z]$ in this neighborhood

$$|f_{,3}(x, y, z) - f_{,3}(a, b, c)| < \frac{f_{,3}(a, b, c)}{2}.$$

Then $f_{,3}(x, y, z) > 0$ for all points of this neighborhood. Call this neighborhood N.

Let $L(a, b)$ be the vertical line $x = a$, $y = b$ which passes through the point $\mathbf{A}$. Let $\mathbf{A}_1$ and $\mathbf{A}_2$ be two points of this line, one on each side of $\mathbf{A}$, but inside N. In particular, we might choose these two to be the points halfway between $\mathbf{A}$ and the "bottom" and the "top" of the sphere N, respectively. Along the line $L(a, b)$ the function f is a function of the single variable z alone. This function has a derivative, $f_{,3}(a, b, z)$, which is positive for all z between $\mathbf{A}_1$ and $\mathbf{A}_2$. Therefore the function $f(a, b, z)$ is a monotone strictly increasing function of z, which means that $f(\mathbf{A}_1) < 0$ and $f(\mathbf{A}_2) > 0$.

Now, the function f is continuous throughout N. Since $f(\mathbf{A}_1)$ is negative, there must exist some neighborhood of $\mathbf{A}_1$ in which f remains negative. Similarly, there exists a neighborhood of $\mathbf{A}_2$ at every point of which f is positive. By taking the smaller of the two radii we can assume that both these neighborhoods are of the same radius δ. Furthermore, we can assume that both these neighborhoods are contained in the neighborhood N. Note that neither of these two neighborhoods can contain the point $\mathbf{A}$ since $f = 0$ at $\mathbf{A}$. (See Fig. 6–2.)

We can now define the desired neighborhood S. We set

$$S = \{[x, y] \mid (x - a)^2 + (y - b)^2 < \delta^2\}.$$

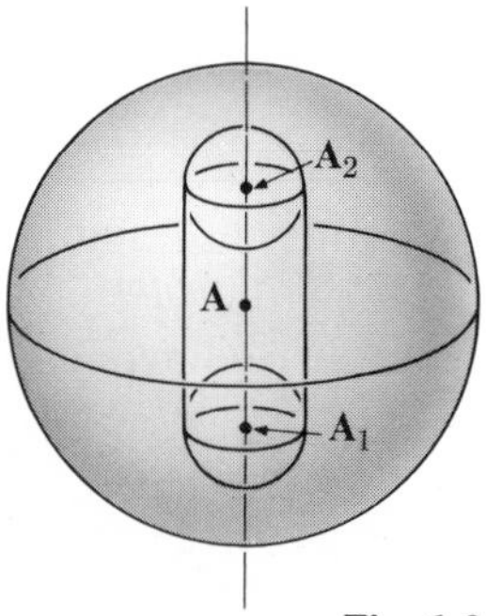

Fig. 6–2

Consider the closed cylinder

$$\overline{C} = \{[x, y, z] \mid (x - a)^2 + (y - b)^2 \leq \delta^2, c_1 \leq z \leq c_2\},$$

where c_1 and c_2 are the z-coordinates of the points $\mathbf{A}_1$ and $\mathbf{A}_2$, respectively. This entire cylinder is contained in N, and hence $f_{,3} > 0$ at every point of it. The point $\mathbf{A}$ is an interior point of the cylinder. The function f is positive at every point of the top face of the cylinder and is negative at every point of the bottom face.

At each point $[x, y]$ of S consider the vertical line $L(x, y)$. On this line f is a function of z alone. It is negative when $z = c_1$ and positive when $z = c_2$, and it is continuous. Therefore by the intermediate-value theorem there must exist at least one z between c_1 and c_2 for which $f = 0$. However, there is at most one such z. For if $f(x, y, z) = f(x, y, z') = 0$ and $z \neq z'$, then by Rolle's Theorem there must exist some z'' at which $f_{,3}(x, y, z'') = 0$. This z'' would also have to be between c_1 and c_2, which would violate the condition that $f_{,3} > 0$ in N. Therefore this value of z for which $f(x, y, z) = 0$ is unique.

For each $[x, y]$ in S let $g(x, y) = z$, the unique value which makes $f = 0$. We have therefore obtained a neighborhood S and a function g which is the required implicit function to make $f[x, y, g(x, y)] = 0$. We must next show that g is continuous. It suffices to prove this at $\mathbf{A}' = (a, b)$. Any other point of the neighborhood S leads to a point $[x, y, g(x, y)]$ which also satisfies all of the hypotheses of the theorem. Hence if we can prove the continuity of g at $\mathbf{A}'$, we could prove its continuity at any other point of S in exactly the same way.

Let $\epsilon > 0$ be given. Let N_ϵ be the neighborhood of radius ϵ and center $\mathbf{A}$. Then we repeat the above argument leading to the production of g, but starting with the sphere $N \cap N_\epsilon$. The values of g which are produced are defined for all $[x, y]$ in a disk S_ϵ and are all contained inside the sphere N_ϵ. In particular, then, $|g(x, y) - c| < \epsilon$ for all $[x, y]$ in the disk S_ϵ. This shows that g is continuous.

Finally, we prove that g is C^1 and that (6–12) holds. We do this with the help of the mean-value theorem. Let $\mathbf{Y} = [y_1, y_2]$ be any nonzero vector in R^2 and let $h \neq 0$ be sufficiently close to zero so that $\mathbf{A}' + h\mathbf{Y}$ is in S. Set

$$\mathbf{Z} = [hy_1, hy_2, g(\mathbf{A}' + h\mathbf{Y}) - g(\mathbf{A}')].$$

Then the continuity of g tells us that $\mathbf{Z} \to 0$ as $h \to 0$.

From the mean-value theorem we have the existence of some θ between 0 and 1 such that

$$f(\mathbf{A} + \mathbf{Z}) - f(\mathbf{A}) = \mathbf{Z} \cdot \operatorname{grad} f(\mathbf{A} + \theta\mathbf{Z}).$$

However, $f(\mathbf{A}) = 0$, and $\mathbf{Z}$ has been so chosen that $f(\mathbf{A} + \mathbf{Z}) = 0$ also. Therefore

$$hy_1 f_{'1}(\mathbf{X}) + hy_2 f_{'2}(\mathbf{X}) + [g(\mathbf{A}' + h\mathbf{Y}) - g(\mathbf{A}')]f_{'3}(\mathbf{X}) = 0,$$

where we have set $\mathbf{X} = \mathbf{A} + \theta\mathbf{Z}$. From this equation we find that

$$\frac{1}{h}[g(\mathbf{A}' + h\mathbf{Y}) - g(\mathbf{A}')] = -y_1 \frac{f_{'1}(\mathbf{X})}{f_{'3}(\mathbf{X})} - y_2 \frac{f_{'2}(\mathbf{X})}{f_{'3}(\mathbf{X})}.$$

Letting $h \to 0$, we see that $\mathbf{X} = \mathbf{A} + \theta\mathbf{Z} \to \mathbf{A}$. Hence we find

$$D_{\mathbf{Y}}g(\mathbf{A}') = -y_1 \frac{f_{'1}(\mathbf{A})}{f_{'3}(\mathbf{A})} - y_2 \frac{f_{'2}(\mathbf{A})}{f_{'3}(\mathbf{A})}, \tag{6–15}$$

which is exactly the desired result. Finally, we observe that the expression on the right of the last equation is a continuous function of $\mathbf{A}$ since f was given to be C^1. Therefore we can conclude that g is C^1. ▌

Now we turn to the problem of attempting to solve a simultaneous set of equations.

▶ **Theorem 6–8.** Let $\mathbf{F}: B \to R^k$, where B is a subset of R^n. Suppose that $k < n$, that $\mathbf{F}$ is C^1 in a neighborhood of a point $\mathbf{A}$ in B, and that the matrix

$$J = \begin{bmatrix} f_{1'1} & f_{1'2} & \cdots & f_{1'k} \\ f_{2'1} & f_{2'2} & \cdots & f_{2'k} \\ \vdots & & & \vdots \\ f_{k'1} & f_{k'2} & \cdots & f_{k'k} \end{bmatrix}, \tag{6–16}$$

where all of the partial derivatives are evaluated at $\mathbf{A}$, is nonsingular. Then there exists a neighborhood N of $[a_{k+1}, a_{k+2}, \ldots, a_n]$ in R^{n-k} and a unique function $\mathbf{G}: N \to R^k$ which is continuous and C^1 in N which is such that

$$[a_1, a_2, \ldots, a_k] = \mathbf{G}[a_{k+1}, \ldots, a_n];$$

and if $\mathbf{X}'' = [x_{k+1}, x_{k+2}, \ldots, x_n]$ is any point of N, then

$$\mathbf{X} = [g_1(\mathbf{X}''), g_2(\mathbf{X}''), \ldots, g_k(\mathbf{X}''), x_{k+1}, x_{k+2}, \ldots, x_n] \tag{6–17}$$

is in B and

$$\mathbf{F}(\mathbf{X}) = \mathbf{0}.$$

Remarks. All this theorem amounts to is a formal statement of the fact that if J is nonsingular, then we can solve the k equations $f_1(\mathbf{X}) = 0, f_2(\mathbf{X}) = 0, \ldots, f_k(\mathbf{X}) = 0$ for the k variables $x_1, x_2, \ldots, x_k$ in terms of the remaining $n - k$ variables.

Because of the importance of this theorem, we will give two proofs for it. The first is the classical "matrix theory" proof, which makes use of the previous theorem.

The second is the "linear algebra" proof, which is a generalization of the proof for Theorem 6–7; it actually includes Theorem 6–7.

Proof. Let J be the matrix given in (6–14). The assumption that J is nonsingular can be stated as $\det J \neq 0$. In particular, then, not all the terms in the top row of J can be zero. By interchanging the variables, if necessary, we can assume that $f_{1'1} \neq 0$. By the previous theorem we can then assume that there exists a neighborhood S_1 of $[a_2, a_3, \ldots, a_n]$ and a function $h_1(x_2, \ldots, x_n)$ which is C^1 in S_1 and such that

$$f_1(h_1, x_2, \ldots, x_n) = 0$$

for all points in S_1.

Letting $\mathbf{X} = [x_1, x_2, \ldots, x_n]$, we define $\mathbf{X}^{(1)} = [x_2, x_3, \ldots, x_n]$. We also define the change of variables:

$$\mathbf{X} = \mathbf{H}^{(1)}(\mathbf{X}^{(1)}) = [h_1(\mathbf{X}^{(1)}), x_2, x_3, \ldots, x_n].$$

Then we have

$$[d\mathbf{H}^{(1)}] = \begin{bmatrix} h_{1'2} & h_{1'3} & \cdots & h_{1'n} \\ 1 & 0 & \cdots & 0 \\ 0 & 1 & \cdots & 0 \\ \vdots & & & \vdots \\ 0 & 0 & \cdots & 1 \end{bmatrix}.$$

For this formula we abandon our usual convention concerning subscripts. By $h_{1'i}$ we will mean $\partial h_1/\partial x_i$. This notation is useful in order that the subscript indicate the actual number of the variable rather than the position in the argument of the function.

Again from the previous theorem we have $h_{1'i} = -f_{1'i}/f_{1'1}$ for each i. We can now define the composite function

$$\mathbf{F}^{(1)}(\mathbf{X}^{(1)}) = \mathbf{F}[\mathbf{H}^{(1)}(\mathbf{X}^{(1)})].$$

Since the first component of this function is identically zero, we can ignore it and assume that the new function has only $k - 1$ components. Thus we can write $\mathbf{F}^{(1)} = [f_2^{(1)}, f_3^{(1)}, \ldots, f_k^{(1)}]$. Consider now the matrix

$$J^{(1)} = \begin{bmatrix} f_{2'2}^{(1)} & f_{2'3}^{(1)} & \cdots & f_{2'k}^{(1)} \\ f_{3'2}^{(1)} & f_{3'3}^{(1)} & \cdots & f_{3'k}^{(1)} \\ \vdots & & & \vdots \\ f_{k'2}^{(1)} & f_{k'3}^{(1)} & \cdots & f_{k'k}^{(1)} \end{bmatrix}.$$

This matrix must have a nonzero determinant because: J has a nonzero determinant, the determinant of the product of two matrices is the product of their determinants, and

$$J \begin{bmatrix} 1 & h_{1'2} & h_{1'3} & \cdots & h_{1'n} \\ 0 & 1 & 0 & \cdots & 0 \\ 0 & 0 & 1 & \cdots & 0 \\ \vdots & & & & \vdots \\ 0 & 0 & 0 & \cdots & 1 \end{bmatrix} = \begin{bmatrix} f_{1'1} & 0 \; 0 & \cdots & 0 \\ \cdot & & & \\ \cdot & & J^{(1)} & \\ \cdot & & & \end{bmatrix}.$$

We are thus back to exactly the same situation we started with, except that we now have one less function and one variable fewer. We can continue with the same process on the new function. Continuing in this way, we get a sequence of functions

$$\begin{aligned} x_1 &= h_1(x_2, x_3, \ldots, x_n), \\ x_2 &= h_2(x_3, x_4, \ldots, x_n), \\ &\vdots \\ x_k &= h_k(x_{k+1}, \ldots, x_n) \end{aligned}$$

such that each h_i is continuous and C^1 in some neighborhood S_i of $[a_{i+1}, a_{i+2}, \ldots, a_n]$, and when the x_i are substituted into the f_i we will obtain zero identically. That is, the function $\mathbf{G} = [g_1, g_2, \ldots, g_k]$ will satisfy the requirements of the theorem when we define

$$\begin{aligned} g_k(x_{k+1}, \ldots, x_n) &= h_k(x_{k+1}, \ldots, x_n), \\ g_{k-1}(x_{k+1}, \ldots, x_n) &= h_{k-1}[g_k, x_{k+1}, \ldots, x_n], \\ &\vdots \\ g_2(x_{k+1}, \ldots, x_n) &= h_2[g_3, g_4, \ldots, g_k, x_{k+1}, \ldots, x_n], \\ g_1(x_{k+1}, \ldots, x_n) &= h_1[g_2, g_3, \ldots, g_k, x_{k+1}, \ldots, x_n]. \quad \blacksquare \end{aligned}$$

*Second proof.** This proof follows rather closely the basic ideas of the proof of Theorem 6–7, but is more complicated because of the higher number of dimensions involved. Because of the complexity of the proof, we will break it up into a number of simple steps. We will list a number of special definitions used for this proof alone, and we will then divide the argument up into six intermediate steps, or lemmas. We will first outline the proof by listing these definitions and lemmas.

Definition A. Let $J(\mathbf{X})$ be the matrix:

$$J(\mathbf{X}) = \begin{bmatrix} f_{1'1}(\mathbf{X}) & f_{1'2}(\mathbf{X}) & \cdots & f_{1'k}(\mathbf{X}) \\ f_{2'1}(\mathbf{X}) & f_{2'2}(\mathbf{X}) & \cdots & f_{2'k}(\mathbf{X}) \\ \vdots & & & \vdots \\ f_{k'1}(\mathbf{X}) & f_{k'2}(\mathbf{X}) & \cdots & f_{k'k}(\mathbf{X}) \end{bmatrix}.$$

Thus the matrix J of (6–16) is actually $J(\mathbf{A})$ according to this definition.

Definition B. For any $\mathbf{X}$ in $B \subset R^n$ and $\mathbf{Z}$ in R^k, define $h(\mathbf{X}, \mathbf{Z}) = |[J(\mathbf{X})]\mathbf{Z}|$.

Note that $[J(\mathbf{X})]\mathbf{Z}$ is a vector; $h(\mathbf{X}, \mathbf{Z})$ is the magnitude of this vector.

Definition C. For any positive integer j, any vector $\mathbf{A}$ in R^j, and any positive real number ρ, define

$$\begin{aligned} S(j, \rho, \mathbf{A}) &= \{\mathbf{X} \mid \mathbf{X} \in R^j, |\mathbf{X} - \mathbf{A}| < \rho\}, \\ C(j, \rho, \mathbf{A}) &= \{\mathbf{X} \mid \mathbf{X} \in R^j, |\mathbf{X} - \mathbf{A}| \le \rho\}, \\ K(j, \rho, \mathbf{A}) &= \{\mathbf{X} \mid \mathbf{X} \in R^j, |\mathbf{X} - \mathbf{A}| = \rho\}. \end{aligned}$$

---

* This second proof is rather long, but it is quite instructive. It will be well worth the reader's while to look it over rather carefully.

These three sets are respectively the open ball, the closed ball, and the boundary of the closed ball with center $\mathbf{A}$ and radius ρ.

Definition D. $h_0 = \min \{h(\mathbf{A}, \mathbf{Z}) \mid \mathbf{Z} \in K(k, 1, \mathbf{0})\}$.

The set $K(k, 1, \mathbf{0})$ is merely the set of those vectors in R^k with magnitude 1. This set is compact. The existence of the h_0 of this definition thus depends on the obvious fact that $h(\mathbf{A}, \mathbf{Z})$ is a continuous function of $\mathbf{Z}$.

Lemma 1. If $\mathbf{Z} \in K(k, 1, \mathbf{0})$, then

$$h(\mathbf{A}, \mathbf{Z}) \geq h_0 > 0.$$

Lemma 2. There exists a $\rho_1 > 0$ such that $S(n, \rho_1, \mathbf{A}) \subset B$ and if

$$[\mathbf{X}, \mathbf{Z}] \in S(n, \rho_1, \mathbf{A}) \times K(k, 1, \mathbf{0}),$$

then

$$h(\mathbf{X}, \mathbf{Z}) > h_0/2. \tag{6–18}$$

Definition E. For any $[\mathbf{X}, \mathbf{Y}] \in B \times B$, define $\boldsymbol{\epsilon}(\mathbf{X}, \mathbf{Y})$ to be the vector satisfying

$$\mathbf{F}(\mathbf{X}) - \mathbf{F}(\mathbf{Y}) = [d\mathbf{F}(\mathbf{Y})][\mathbf{X} - \mathbf{Y}] + \boldsymbol{\epsilon}(\mathbf{X}, \mathbf{Y})|\mathbf{X} - \mathbf{Y}|$$

if $\mathbf{X} \neq \mathbf{Y}$ and $\boldsymbol{\epsilon}(\mathbf{X}, \mathbf{Y}) = \mathbf{0}$ if $\mathbf{X} = \mathbf{Y}$.

Lemma 3. There exists a ρ_2 with $0 < \rho_2 < \rho_1$ such that if

$$[\mathbf{X}, \mathbf{Y}] \in C(n, \rho_2, \mathbf{A}) \times C(n, \rho_2, \mathbf{A}),$$

then

$$|\boldsymbol{\epsilon}(\mathbf{X}, \mathbf{Y})| \leq h_0/2. \tag{6–19}$$

Definition F. If $\mathbf{X} = [x_1, x_2, \ldots, x_n] \in R^n$, set

$$\mathbf{X}' = [x_1, x_2, \ldots, x_k],$$
$$\mathbf{X}'' = [x_{k+1}, x_{k+2}, \ldots, x_n].$$

Thus, when $\mathbf{X}$ is in R^n, we have $\mathbf{X}'$ in R^k and $\mathbf{X}''$ in R^{n-k}. We can write $\mathbf{X} = [\mathbf{X}', \mathbf{X}'']$. In particular, the vector $\mathbf{A}$ of the theorem can be decomposed as $\mathbf{A} = [\mathbf{A}', \mathbf{A}'']$.

Lemma 4. Let $\rho_3 = \rho_2/2$. If $\mathbf{X}'' \in S(n - k, \rho_3, \mathbf{A}'')$, $\mathbf{X}_1'$ and $\mathbf{X}_2' \in C(k, \rho_3, \mathbf{A}')$, and if $\mathbf{F}(\mathbf{X}_1', \mathbf{X}'') = \mathbf{F}(\mathbf{X}_2', \mathbf{X}'')$, then $\mathbf{X}_1' = \mathbf{X}_2'$.

Definition G. For any $\mathbf{X} = [\mathbf{X}', \mathbf{X}''] \in B$, set

$$\Psi(\mathbf{X}', \mathbf{X}'') = |\mathbf{F}(\mathbf{X}', \mathbf{X}'')|^2.$$

Definition H. $m = \min \{\Psi(\mathbf{X}', \mathbf{A}'') \mid \mathbf{X}' \in K(k, \rho_3, \mathbf{A}')\}$.

Lemma 5. The quantity m of the last definition is positive. Further, there exists a ρ_4 with $0 < \rho_4 < \rho_3$ such that

a) if $\mathbf{X}'' \in S(n - k, \rho_4, \mathbf{A}'')$, then $\Psi(\mathbf{A}', \mathbf{X}'') < m/2$, and

b) if $[\mathbf{X}', \mathbf{X}''] \in K(k, \rho_3, \mathbf{A}') \times S(n - k, \rho_4, \mathbf{A}'')$, then $\Psi(\mathbf{X}', \mathbf{X}'') > m/2$.

Lemma 6. If $\mathbf{X}_1'' \in S(n-k, \rho_4, \mathbf{A}'')$, then there exists an $\mathbf{X}_1'$ in $S(k, \rho_3, \mathbf{A}')$ such that $\mathbf{F}(\mathbf{X}_1', \mathbf{X}_1'') = \mathbf{0}$.

Lemma 6 shows the existence of the desired function $\mathbf{X}' = \mathbf{G}(\mathbf{X}'')$. Lemma 4 shows that this function is unique. The remainder of the lemmas supply the results needed to prove these two main results. Let us show this by giving the proofs of the two main lemmas first. Let us assume that Lemmas 1 to 5 have been proved and proceed with the proof of Lemma 6.

Proof of Lemma 6. Let $\mathbf{X}_1'' \in S(n-k, \rho_4, \mathbf{A}'')$ be fixed. Then the function $\Psi(\mathbf{X}', \mathbf{X}_1'')$ is continuously differentiable for every $\mathbf{X}'$ in $C(k, \rho_3, \mathbf{A}')$. In particular, it is continuous on this compact set and must therefore take on its minimum value at some point of the set. From Lemma 5, we see that $\Psi(\mathbf{X}', \mathbf{X}_1'') > m/2$ for every $\mathbf{X}'$ on $K(k, \rho_3, \mathbf{A}')$ which is the boundary of $C(k, \rho_3, \mathbf{A}')$. But at $\mathbf{A}'$, $\Psi(\mathbf{A}', \mathbf{X}_1'') < m/2$. Hence the minimum must occur at an interior point $\mathbf{X}_1' \in S(k, \rho_3, \mathbf{A}')$.

If the minimum occurs at an interior point, then grad $\Psi = \mathbf{0}$ at this point, where the gradient is taken with respect to $\mathbf{X}'$. Since $\Psi = \sum_{i=1}^k f_i^2$, we therefore have at $\mathbf{X}_1'$.

$$2\sum_{i=1}^{k}\sum_{j=1}^{k} f_i f_{i'j}\mathbf{e}_j = [\mathbf{F}(\mathbf{X}_1', \mathbf{X}_1'')]^t J(\mathbf{X}_1) = \mathbf{0}.$$

However, $\mathbf{X}_1 = [\mathbf{X}_1', \mathbf{X}_1''] \in S(n, \rho_1, \mathbf{A})$, and hence (6–18) shows that $J(\mathbf{X}_1)$ is nonsingular. Therefore we must have $\mathbf{F}(\mathbf{X}_1', \mathbf{X}_1'') = \mathbf{0}$. This proves the lemma.

Proof of *Lemma 4.* Let the hypotheses of the lemma be satisfied. Set $\mathbf{X}_1 = [\mathbf{X}_1', \mathbf{X}'']$ and $\mathbf{X}_2 = [\mathbf{X}_2', \mathbf{X}'']$. Then from Definition E,

$$\mathbf{0} = \mathbf{F}(\mathbf{X}_1) - \mathbf{F}(\mathbf{X}_2) = [d\mathbf{F}(\mathbf{X}_2)][\mathbf{X}_1 - \mathbf{X}_2] + \boldsymbol{\epsilon}(\mathbf{X}_1, \mathbf{X}_2)|\mathbf{X}_1 - \mathbf{X}_2|.$$

Suppose that $\mathbf{X}_1' \neq \mathbf{X}_2'$. Then $|\mathbf{X}_1 - \mathbf{X}_2| \neq 0$. Divide the above equation through by this quantity and set $(\mathbf{X}_1 - \mathbf{X}_2)/|\mathbf{X}_1 - \mathbf{X}_2| = [\mathbf{Z}, \mathbf{0}]$ where $\mathbf{Z} \in R^k$. Then the above equation is equivalent to

$$[d\mathbf{F}(\mathbf{X}_2)][\mathbf{Z}, \mathbf{0}] = -\boldsymbol{\epsilon}(\mathbf{X}_1, \mathbf{X}_2)$$

and hence

$$\begin{aligned}|[J(\mathbf{X}_2)]\mathbf{Z}| &= |[d\mathbf{F}(\mathbf{X}_2)][\mathbf{Z}, \mathbf{0}]| = h(\mathbf{X}_2, \mathbf{Z}) \\ &= |\boldsymbol{\epsilon}(\mathbf{X}_1, \mathbf{X}_2)|.\end{aligned}$$

This is a contradiction to (6–18) and (6–19). Therefore we must have $\mathbf{X}_1' = \mathbf{X}_2'$. This proves Lemma 4.

Now that we have seen the proofs of the two main lemmas, we turn to an examination of the proofs of the remaining lemmas in order.

Proof of Lemma 1. $h(\mathbf{A}, \mathbf{Z}) \geq h_0$ for every $\mathbf{Z} \in K(k, 1, \mathbf{0})$ since h_0 is defined as the minimum of these values. There must be a $\mathbf{Z}_0 \in K(k, 1, \mathbf{0})$ at which the minimum is taken on. That is,

$$h_0 = |J(\mathbf{A})\mathbf{Z}_0|.$$

However, $J(\mathbf{A})$ is nonsingular and $\mathbf{Z}_0 \neq \mathbf{0}$, hence $h_0 \neq 0$. Therefore $h_0 > 0$, which completes the proof of the lemma.

Proof of Lemma 2. Let $\rho_0 > 0$ be such that $S(n, \rho_0, \mathbf{A}) \subset B$. Then it is easily seen that $h(\mathbf{X}, \mathbf{Z})$ is continuous as a function of $[\mathbf{X}, \mathbf{Z}]$, at every point of the compact set $V = C(n, \rho_0/2, \mathbf{A}) \times K(k, 1, \mathbf{0})$ in R^{n+k}. It is therefore uniformly continuous on this set. That is, there must exist a $\rho_1 > 0$ with $\rho_1 < \rho_0/2$ such that if $|[\mathbf{X}, \mathbf{Z}] - [\mathbf{X}_0, \mathbf{Z}_0]| = [|\mathbf{X} - \mathbf{X}_0|^2 + |\mathbf{Z} - \mathbf{Z}_0|^2]^{1/2} < \rho_1$ and both $[\mathbf{X}, \mathbf{Z}]$ and $[\mathbf{X}_0, \mathbf{Z}_0]$ are in V, then

$$|h(\mathbf{X}, \mathbf{Z}) - h(\mathbf{X}_0, \mathbf{Z}_0)| < h_0/2.$$

If $\mathbf{X} \in S(n, \rho_1, \mathbf{A})$ and $\mathbf{Z} \in K(k, 1, \mathbf{0})$, then $|[\mathbf{X}, \mathbf{Z}] - [\mathbf{A}, \mathbf{Z}]| < \rho_1$, and hence

$$\begin{aligned} |h(\mathbf{X}, \mathbf{Z})| &\geq |h(\mathbf{A}, \mathbf{Z})| - |h(\mathbf{A}, \mathbf{Z}) - h(\mathbf{X}, \mathbf{Z})| \\ &> h_0 - h_0/2 \\ &= h_0/2. \end{aligned}$$

This proves the lemma.

Proof of Lemma 3. We must first show that $\boldsymbol{\epsilon}(\mathbf{X}, \mathbf{Y})$ is continuous in $B \times B$. Once this has been shown, the existence of the desired ρ_2 follows from the uniform continuity of $\boldsymbol{\epsilon}(\mathbf{X}, \mathbf{Y})$ in the compact set $C(n, \rho_1, \mathbf{A}) \times C(n, \rho_1, \mathbf{A})$ and the fact that $\boldsymbol{\epsilon}(\mathbf{X}, \mathbf{X}) = \mathbf{0}$ for each $\mathbf{X}$. The details can be left to the reader.

To prove that $\boldsymbol{\epsilon}(\mathbf{X}, \mathbf{Y})$ is continuous in $B \times B$, we observe first that if $\mathbf{X} \neq \mathbf{Y}$ and if $|\mathbf{X} - \mathbf{Y}| = b$, then there is some neighborhood of $[\mathbf{X}, \mathbf{Y}]$ contained in $B \times B$ in which $|\mathbf{X} - \mathbf{Y}| > b/2$. In this neighborhood, it is clear that $\boldsymbol{\epsilon}(\mathbf{X}, \mathbf{Y})$ is continuous, since

$$\boldsymbol{\epsilon}(\mathbf{X}, \mathbf{Y}) = \frac{1}{|\mathbf{X} - \mathbf{Y}|}\mathbf{F}(\mathbf{X}) - \frac{1}{|\mathbf{X} - \mathbf{Y}|}\mathbf{F}(\mathbf{Y}) - [d\mathbf{F}(\mathbf{Y})]\frac{(\mathbf{X} - \mathbf{Y})}{|\mathbf{X} - \mathbf{Y}|}\cdot$$

To show that this function is continuous when $\mathbf{X} = \mathbf{Y}$ is more difficult. We wish to show $\boldsymbol{\epsilon}(\mathbf{X}, \mathbf{Y})$ is continuous at $[\mathbf{X}, \mathbf{Y}] = [\mathbf{X}_1, \mathbf{X}_1]$, where $\mathbf{X}_1$ is some point of B. Let S be some neighborhood of $\mathbf{X}_1$ which is contained in B, and suppose that $\mathbf{X} \neq \mathbf{Y}$ are both in the neighborhood. Set $\mathbf{W} = \mathbf{X} - \mathbf{Y}$. Then

$$\begin{aligned} |\mathbf{W}|[\boldsymbol{\epsilon}(\mathbf{X}, \mathbf{Y}) - \boldsymbol{\epsilon}(\mathbf{X}_1, \mathbf{X}_1)] &= |\mathbf{W}|\boldsymbol{\epsilon}(\mathbf{X}, \mathbf{Y}) \\ &= \mathbf{F}(\mathbf{X}) - \mathbf{F}(\mathbf{Y}) - [d\mathbf{F}(\mathbf{Y})]\mathbf{W} \\ &= \sum_{i=1}^{n} [f_i(\mathbf{X}) - f_i(\mathbf{Y})]\mathbf{e}_i - \sum_{i=1}^{n} [\nabla f_i(\mathbf{Y}) \cdot \mathbf{W}]\mathbf{e}_i \\ &= \sum_{i=1}^{n} [\nabla f_i(\mathbf{U}_i) \cdot \mathbf{W}]\mathbf{e}_i - \sum_{i=1}^{n} [\nabla f_i(\mathbf{Y}) \cdot \mathbf{W}]\mathbf{e}_i \\ &= \sum_{i=1}^{n} ([\nabla f_i(\mathbf{U}_i) - \nabla f_i(\mathbf{Y})] \cdot \mathbf{W})\mathbf{e}_i. \end{aligned}$$

Here, we have used the mean-value theorem on each of the component functions of $\mathbf{F}$ separately. That is, for each i, $\mathbf{U}_i = \mathbf{Y} + \theta_i\mathbf{W}$ where θ_i is some real number between

0 and 1. Next, we use the triangle inequality and Schwarz's inequality to find

$$\begin{aligned}|\epsilon(\mathbf{X}, \mathbf{Y}) - \epsilon(\mathbf{X}_1, \mathbf{X}_1)| &\leq \frac{1}{|\mathbf{W}|}\sum_{i=1}^{n} |[\nabla f_i(\mathbf{U}_i) - \nabla f_i(\mathbf{Y})] \cdot \mathbf{W}| \\ &\leq \frac{1}{|\mathbf{W}|}\sum_{i=1}^{n} |\nabla f_i(\mathbf{U}_i) - \nabla f_i(\mathbf{Y})|\,|\mathbf{W}| \\ &= \sum_{i=1}^{n} |\nabla f_i(\mathbf{U}_i) - \nabla f_i(\mathbf{Y})|.\end{aligned}$$

This inequality holds whenever $\mathbf{X} \neq \mathbf{Y}$ in the neighborhood S. On the other hand, if $\mathbf{X} = \mathbf{Y}$, then the left-hand member is zero. The reader can now easily complete the proof of the continuity of $\epsilon(\mathbf{X}, \mathbf{Y})$ at $[\mathbf{X}_1, \mathbf{X}_1]$ using the uniform continuity of the gradients of the component functions at the point $\mathbf{X}_1$.

Finally, we have to prove Lemma 5.

Proof of Lemma 5. The first assertion of the lemma is that $m > 0$. This follows from Lemma 4, since there must exist an $\mathbf{X}_1' \in K(k, \rho_3, \mathbf{A}')$ such that $\Psi(\mathbf{X}_1', \mathbf{A}'') = m$. If $m = 0$, then $\mathbf{F}(\mathbf{X}_1', \mathbf{A}'') = \mathbf{0}$ which would contradict Lemma 4 since $\mathbf{F}(\mathbf{A}', \mathbf{A}'') = \mathbf{0}$.

Requirement (a) can be satisfied by some sufficiently small ρ_4' since $\Psi(\mathbf{A}', \mathbf{X}'') = 0$ when $\mathbf{X}'' = \mathbf{A}''$ and this is a continuous function of $\mathbf{X}''$. The function $\Psi(\mathbf{X}', \mathbf{X}'')$ is uniformly continuous in $K(k, \rho_3, \mathbf{A}') \times C(n - k, \rho_4', \mathbf{A}'')$. We can thus choose a $\rho_4 < \rho_4'$ such that if $|[\mathbf{X}_2', \mathbf{X}_2''] - [\mathbf{X}', \mathbf{X}'']| < \rho_4$ and both points are in the set $K(k, \rho_3, \mathbf{A}') \times C(n - k, \rho_4', \mathbf{A}'')$, then $|\Psi(\mathbf{X}_2', \mathbf{X}_2'') - \Psi(\mathbf{X}', \mathbf{X}'')| < m/2$. But then, since m is the minimum of $\Psi(\mathbf{X}', \mathbf{A}'')$ for $\mathbf{X}'$ in $K(k, \rho_3, \mathbf{A}')$, if $[\mathbf{X}', \mathbf{X}''] \in K(k, \rho_3, \mathbf{A}') \times S(n - k, \rho_4, \mathbf{A}'')$ we must have

$$\begin{aligned}\Psi(\mathbf{X}', \mathbf{X}'') &> \Psi(\mathbf{X}', \mathbf{A}'') - |\Psi(\mathbf{X}', \mathbf{A}'') - \Psi(\mathbf{X}', \mathbf{X}'')| \\ &> m - m/2 \\ &= m/2.\end{aligned}$$

This completes the proof of the lemma.

Taken together, these lemmas prove the existence and the uniqueness of the function $\mathbf{G}$. The continuity and differentiability of the resulting function can be proved in exactly the same way as the continuity and differentiability of the function $g(\mathbf{Y})$ was proved in Theorem 6–7. There is no need to repeat the details here. The reader may find it instructive to write down these details for himself. ▌

We did not state any formulas for the differential of the g_i in the above theorem. However, now that we know that the function $\mathbf{G}$ exists and is differentiable we can easily find its derivative.

Theorem 6–9. Let $\mathbf{F}$ satisfy the hypotheses of the previous theorem. Let $\mathbf{G}$ be the inverse function of the conclusion of that theorem. Let J be the matrix defined by (6–16) and let K be the matrix

$$K = \begin{bmatrix} f_{1'k+1} & f_{1'k+2} & \cdots & f_{1'n} \\ \vdots & & & \vdots \\ f_{k'k+1} & f_{k'k+2} & \cdots & f_{k'n} \end{bmatrix},$$

where the partial derivatives are evaluated at $\mathbf{A}$. Then the differential of $\mathbf{G}$ at $\mathbf{A}$ is given by

$$d\mathbf{G} = -J^{-1}K. \tag{6–20}$$

Proof. Let $\mathbf{H}: R^{n-k} \to R^n$ be the change of variables defined by (6–17). That is, $\mathbf{H}(\mathbf{X}') = \mathbf{X} = [\mathbf{G}(\mathbf{X}'), \mathbf{X}']$. Let $\mathbf{F}_1(\mathbf{X}') = \mathbf{F}[\mathbf{H}(\mathbf{X}')]$. Then, by the way in which $\mathbf{G}$ was obtained, we have $\mathbf{F}_1$ identically zero. Therefore, $d\mathbf{F}_1 = 0$. However, $d\mathbf{F}_1 = [d\mathbf{F}][d\mathbf{H}]$. From the definitions of this theorem and (6–16) we see that $d\mathbf{F} = [J, K]$, while from the definition of $\mathbf{H}$ we have

$$d\mathbf{H} = \begin{bmatrix} d\mathbf{G} \\ I \end{bmatrix},$$

where the I in the lower part of this matrix is the $(n - k) \times (n - k)$ identity matrix. Therefore

$$0 = d\mathbf{F}_1 = [J, K]\begin{bmatrix} d\mathbf{G} \\ I \end{bmatrix} = J[d\mathbf{G}] + K.$$

Hence we have

$$J[d\mathbf{G}] = -K;$$

and since J is given as nonsingular, multiplication on the left by J^{-1} gives us the result of the theorem. ▌

It might be of some interest to see how the results of the last theorem look in terms of the total differentials of the variables involved. Using the same notation as is in the theorem, we have $d\mathbf{F} = [J, K]$. Therefore the total differential of $\mathbf{F}$ is

$$d\mathbf{F} = [d\mathbf{F}]\, d\mathbf{X} = [J, K]\, d\mathbf{X} = J\begin{bmatrix} dx_1 \\ dx_2 \\ \vdots \\ dx_k \end{bmatrix} + K\begin{bmatrix} dx_{k+1} \\ dx_{k+2} \\ \vdots \\ dx_n \end{bmatrix}.$$

When we set $\mathbf{F} = \mathbf{0}$, we must also have $d\mathbf{F} = 0$. We can thus solve for the differential of $\mathbf{G}$, where $[x_1, x_2, \ldots, x_k] = \mathbf{G}[x_{k+1}, x_{k+2}, \ldots, x_n]$. We find that

$$d\mathbf{G} = \begin{bmatrix} dx_1 \\ dx_2 \\ \vdots \\ dx_k \end{bmatrix} = -J^{-1}K\begin{bmatrix} dx_{k+1} \\ dx_{k+2} \\ \vdots \\ dx_n \end{bmatrix}. \tag{6–21}$$

Any desired derivatives of the implicitly defined function can be read from this relationship.

Let us seen how such a calculation looks in a simple case. Suppose that we are given the functions

$$f(x, y, u, v) = 0, \qquad g(x, y, u, v) = 0,$$

and we wish to solve for x and y in terms of u and v. Although it might be difficult to find the functions themselves, it is easy to find their derivatives. We merely write

$$df = f'_1\,dx + f'_2\,dy + f'_3\,du + f'_4\,dv = 0,$$
$$dg = g'_1\,dx + g'_2\,dy + g'_3\,du + g'_4\,dv = 0.$$

Based on the assumption that $\det J \neq 0$, where J is defined by

$$J = \begin{bmatrix} f'_1 & f'_2 \\ g'_1 & g'_2 \end{bmatrix},$$

the last theorem tells us that we can solve for x and y in terms of u and v and find the derivatives of the resulting functions from formula (6–21). However, the condition that $\det J \neq 0$ is exactly the one required for us to be able to solve the above pair of equations for dx and dy in terms of du and dv. Indeed, doing so gives us

$$dx = -\frac{f'_3 g'_2 - f'_2 g'_3}{f'_1 g'_2 - f'_2 g'_1}\,du - \frac{f'_4 g'_2 - f'_2 g'_4}{f'_1 g'_2 - f'_2 g'_1}\,dv$$

and a similar expression for dy. Since the solution of a system of linear equations is the same whether or not expressed in matrix form, the above expressions give us the form of the total differentials of the "inverse" functions.

Definition 6–7. Let $f_1, f_2, \ldots, f_k$ be k continuously differentiable functions of the vector $\mathbf{X} = [x_1, x_2, \ldots, x_n]$, where $n \geq k$. Then by the *Jacobian* of $f_1, f_2, \ldots, f_k$ with respect to $x_1, x_2, \ldots, x_k$ we mean the quantity

$$\frac{\partial(f_1, f_2, \ldots, f_k)}{\partial(x_1, x_2, \ldots, x_k)} = \det \begin{bmatrix} f_{1'1} & f_{1'2} & \cdots & f_{2'k} \\ f_{2'1} & f_{2'2} & \cdots & f_{2'k} \\ \vdots & & & \vdots \\ f_{k'1} & f_{k'2} & \cdots & f_{k'k} \end{bmatrix}. \tag{6–22}$$

Theorem 6–10. With the same hypotheses as in Theorems 6–8 and 6–9, we have

$$g_{i'j} = \frac{\partial g_i}{\partial x_j} = -\frac{\partial(f_1, \ldots, f_{i-1}, f_i, f_{i+1}, \ldots, f_k)}{\partial(x_1, \ldots, x_{i-1}, x_j, x_{i+1}, \ldots, x_k)} \Big/ \frac{\partial(f_1, f_2, \ldots, f_k)}{\partial(x_1, x_2, \ldots, x_k)}.$$

Proof. The proof of this theorem is obtained by an application of Cramer's rule to (6–21) and is left as an exercise. Observe that $\partial g_i/\partial x_j$ can be thought of as $\partial x_i/\partial x_j$, where $x_i = g_i(x_{k+1}, \ldots, x_n)$. This way, it is easier to remember the form of the right-hand member of the result of this theorem (but don't forget the negative sign).

The formulas obtained by using Jacobians have a nice exact appearance. The only difficulty is that when the number of variables becomes large, the formulas become rather difficult to write down and work with. The evaluation of high-order determinants is difficult. It is usually easier to use matrix methods directly.

There is a special case of the theorems of this section which is important enough to deserve individual attention. This is the *inverse-function theorem.*

▶ **Theorem 6–11.** Let B be a subset of R^n. Let $\mathbf{F}:B \to R^n$ be C^1 in a neighborhood of a point $\mathbf{A}$ of B, and suppose that $[d\mathbf{F}]$ is a nonsingular matrix at $\mathbf{A}$. Then there exists a neighborhood S of $\mathbf{F}(\mathbf{A})$ and a function $\mathbf{G}:S \to B$ which is C^1 in S and such that $\mathbf{F}[\mathbf{G}(\mathbf{W})] = \mathbf{W}$ for all $\mathbf{W} \in S$.

Proof. Note that the function $\mathbf{G}$ is the inverse of $\mathbf{F}$ in some neighborhood of $\mathbf{A}$. That is, if we write $\mathbf{W} = \mathbf{F}(\mathbf{X})$, then $\mathbf{X} = \mathbf{G}(\mathbf{W})$. We prove this theorem by applying Theorems 6–8 and 6–9 to a new function.

Let

$$\mathbf{X} = [x_1, x_2, \ldots, x_n], \qquad \mathbf{W} = [w_1, w_2, \ldots, w_n],$$

and set

$$\mathbf{Z} = [x_1, x_2, \ldots, x_n, w_1, w_2, \ldots, w_n].$$

Define the function $\mathbf{R}(\mathbf{Z})$ by

$$\mathbf{R}(\mathbf{Z}) = \mathbf{F}(\mathbf{X}) - \mathbf{W};$$

that is, for each $i = 1, 2, \ldots, n$

$$r_i(\mathbf{Z}) = f_i(\mathbf{X}) - w_i.$$

We may then apply Theorem 6–8 to this function. Setting $\mathbf{R}(\mathbf{Z}) = \mathbf{0}$ and solving for the x_i in terms of the w_i gives the desired result. ▮

When, as in this theorem, we have a mapping $\mathbf{W} = \mathbf{F}(\mathbf{X})$ from R^n to R^n, we can look upon it as defining a change of variables. In this case, the Jacobian

$$\det[d\mathbf{F}] = \frac{\partial(w_1, w_2, \ldots, w_n)}{\partial(x_1, x_2, \ldots, x_n)}$$

is called the *Jacobian of the transformation,* or the Jacobian of the change of variables. Note that the determinant of the inverse matrix is exactly the Jacobian of the inverse transformation as found in the above theorem.

Before leaving this section, let us make a few remarks about the use of the term "variable." This is a commonly used term with a somewhat vague meaning. In this text we have used the term to mean a component of an arbitrary vector in the domain or range of a function. The phrase "independent variable" is often used to mean a component of a vector in the domain, while "dependent variable" indicates a component of the range. The reason that these terms become so ambiguous is that they are without proper meaning until the specific function under consideration is known. All too often the terms are used without reference to a particular function. Then, it becomes difficult to know what is meant.

The theorems of this section reveal some of the difficulty. For example, in the hypotheses of Theorem 6–11, the x_i are the independent variables and the w_i are the dependent variables. In the conclusion of the theorem, however, these roles have been interchanged. The situation is even worse in Theorem 6–8, where some of the variables become dependent while others are independent in the conclusion of the theorem. The question is, are all of the n variables independent at the start? We can answer this either way. If we look at the function $\mathbf{F}(\mathbf{X})$ by itself, then all of the variables are independent; but if we write $\mathbf{F}(\mathbf{X}) = \mathbf{0}$, then k of the variables must be dependent. The trouble is that we do not know which k until we make further specifications.

On the whole, it would be wise not to use the phrases "dependent variables" or "independent variables" unless the specific function under consideration is given.

PROBLEMS

1. a) Explain why the right-hand side of (6–15) is a continuous function of $\mathbf{A}$.
   b) Explain how we can conclude that $D_{\mathbf{Y}}g(\mathbf{A}')$ in (6–15) is a continuous function of A'.
2. Prove Theorem 6–10.
3. Suppose that $\mathbf{W} = \mathbf{F}(\mathbf{X})$ is a transformation of a subset of R^n into R^n which has a nonzero Jacobian in a neighborhood of some point. Prove that in this neighborhood
$$\frac{\partial(w_1, w_2, \ldots, w_n)}{\partial(x_1, x_2, \ldots, x_n)} \frac{\partial(x_1, x_2, \ldots, x_n)}{\partial(w_1, w_2, \ldots, w_n)} = 1.$$
4. For each of the following transformations, find the derivative, the Jacobian of the transformation, and the derivative of the inverse:
   a) $x = r\cos\theta$, $y = r\sin\theta$
   b) $x = r\cos\theta$, $y = r\sin\theta$, $z = z$
   c) $x = \rho\cos\theta\sin\phi$, $y = \rho\sin\theta\sin\phi$, $z = \rho\cos\phi$
   d) $u = x^2 + y^2 + z^2$, $v = x + y + z$, $w = xyz$
5. Suppose that the transformation $u = f(x, y)$, $v = g(x, y)$ has the Jacobian
$$J = \partial(u, v)/\partial(x, y) \neq 0.$$
   Prove that the partial derivatives of the inverse function are given by
$$\frac{\partial x}{\partial u} = \frac{1}{J}\frac{\partial v}{\partial y}, \quad \frac{\partial x}{\partial v} = -\frac{1}{J}\frac{\partial u}{\partial y}, \quad \frac{\partial y}{\partial u} = -\frac{1}{J}\frac{\partial v}{\partial x}, \quad \frac{\partial y}{\partial v} = \frac{1}{J}\frac{\partial u}{\partial x}.$$
6. Give the appropriate definitions and prove
$$\frac{\partial(u, v)}{\partial(x, y)}\frac{\partial(x, y)}{\partial(s, t)} = \frac{\partial(u, v)}{\partial(s, t)}.$$
7. Each of the following sets of equations determines u, v, and w implicitly as functions of x, y, and z (as appropriate). Find the differentials of u, v, and w and the partial derivatives of u, v, and w with respect to x, y, and z.
   a) $ux^2 + \log(xy + u) = 1$

b) $x^2uv = 1$
$ue^{xv} - 1 = 0$

c) $x^2 + 2uv = 1$
$x^3 - u^3 + v^3 = 1$

d) $u + v + w = x$
$uv + uw + vw = x^2$
$uvw = 1$

e) $x + y + z + u + v = 1$
$x^2 + y^2 + z^2 + u^2 + v^2 = 1$

6-4. EXAMPLES

In most simple situations the number of functions and the number of variables that occur are quite small. The difficulties which arise in the application of the results of the last section will be due to interlocking relations between the variables. Let us start by considering a simple example first. Suppose that we are given the functions

$$\begin{aligned} x &= f(u, v), \\ y &= g(u, v, w), \\ w &= h(v, x). \end{aligned} \tag{6-23}$$

We can think of them as a set of three functions in five variables. We could then hope to be able to solve for three of the variables in terms of the other two. Upon closer inspection, we find that this operation is trivial. The variables x, y, and w are (essentially) already given as functions of u and v. A diagram showing the dependence of the variables upon each other will make this clear. In this case, we get the following diagram:

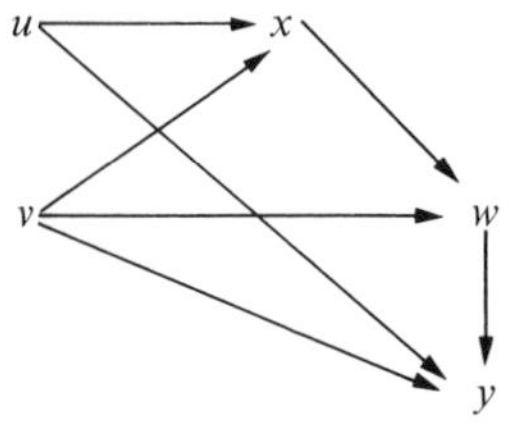

(6-24)

The arrows which end at a letter lead from the variables which explicitly define it. From this diagram it is clear that u and v determine x and hence w, and finally y. Thus all the variables are functions of u and v alone. For example,

$$\begin{aligned} w &= h[v, f(u, v)] = w(u, v), \\ y &= g\big(u, v, h[v, f(u, v)]\big) = y(u, v). \end{aligned}$$

We can also set $x = f(u, v) = x(u, v)$ in order to complete the notation.

What will the partial derivatives of x, y, and w be in terms of these independent variables u and v? We can find them by tracing through the composition of the functions, or we can use the equivalent differential relations. This second method is probably easier in this rather simple case. From (6-23) we have

$$\begin{aligned} dx &= f_{,1}\, du + f_{,2}\, dv, \\ dy &= g_{,1}\, du + g_{,2}\, dv + g_{,3}\, dw, \\ dw &= h_{,1}\, dv + h_{,2}\, dx. \end{aligned}$$

We merely have to eliminate dw and dx from the right-hand sides of these equations:

$$\begin{aligned} dx &= f_{,1}\,du + f_{,2}\,dv, \\ dw &= h_{,1}\,dv + h_{,2}(f_{,1}\,du + f_{,2}\,dv) \\ &= h_{,2}f_{,1}\,du + (h_{,1} + h_{,2}f_{,2})\,dv, \\ dy &= g_{,1}\,du + g_{,2}\,dv + g_{,3}[h_{,2}f_{,1}\,du + (h_{,1} + h_{,2}f_{,2})\,dv] \\ &= (g_{,1} + g_{,3}h_{,2}f_{,1})\,du + (g_{,2} + g_{,3}h_{,1} + g_{,3}h_{,2}f_{,2})\,dv. \end{aligned}$$

From the above equations we can immediately read the desired results. For example,

$$\frac{\partial w}{\partial v} = w_{,2} = h_{,1} + h_{,2}f_{,2}. \tag{6–25}$$

The same result can be rather confusing when written entirely in the "curly d" notation. It would appear as

$$\frac{\partial w}{\partial v} = \frac{\partial w}{\partial v} + \frac{\partial w}{\partial x}\frac{\partial x}{\partial v}.$$

The w on the left-hand side of this equation stands for the function $w = w(u, v)$, while the w's on the right stand for the function $w = h(v, x)$. Such ambiguity could be a source of serious confusion. It is for this reason that we encourage using the subscript notation as in (6–25).

When we have explicit dependences as in this case, we can use the diagram (6–24) to read off the partial derivatives. Rewriting (6–24) and adding a label to the arrow to indicate the partial derivative of the particular dependence indicated by that arrow, we have

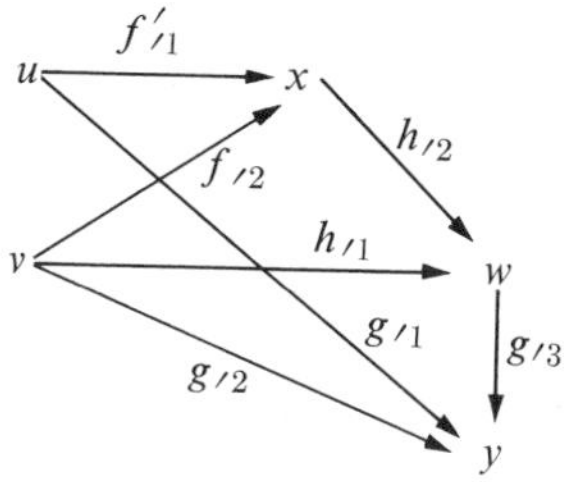

The expressions going into the partial derivatives can be read from this diagram by looking for all possible paths leading from the desired independent variable to the desired dependent variable. Each path leads to one term of the sum. The factors of that term are the partial derivatives along the entire path. Observe how the two paths from v to w in this diagram lead to the two terms of (6–24). The reason that this works is simply the chain rule.

Unfortunately this simple method cannot be used to solve all problems. Suppose we consider another set of relations:

$$\begin{aligned} x &= f(u, w), \\ y &= g(u, v, w), \\ w &= h(v, x). \end{aligned} \tag{6–26}$$

This system is only slightly different from the system considered above. This slight difference is crucial, however. The diagram of dependence now looks like

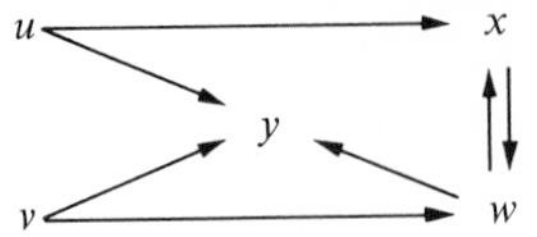

(6–27)

and the situation is not as clear as it was. It is by no means obvious that any two variables can be used as independent variables in this case. The situation on the right-hand edge of the diagram is what is disturbing. We find w depending on x and x depending on w. We must go back to the basic results of the last section. Again, since there are only a small number of variables, it is easier to use total differentials to analyze the situation. In this case,

$$\begin{aligned} dx &= f'_1\, du + f'_2\, dw, \\ dy &= g'_1\, du + g'_2\, dv + g'_3\, dw, \\ dw &= h'_1\, dv + h'_2\, dx. \end{aligned}$$

Suppose we wish to use u and v as independent variables, that is, we wish to solve the set of equations (6–26) for x, y, and w in terms of u and v. By the results of the last section, this can be done if and only if we can solve the last set of equations for dx, dy, and dw in terms of du and dv. Rewriting the above set of equations in the form

$$\begin{aligned} dx \qquad\quad - f'_2\, dw &= f'_1\, du, \\ dy - g'_3\, dw &= g'_1\, du + g'_2\, dv, \\ h'_2\, dx \qquad\quad - dw &= \qquad\qquad - h'_1\, dv, \end{aligned}$$

we see that this can be done if and only if the determinant of the coefficients on the left-hand side is nonzero, that is, if and only if $f'_2 h'_2 - 1 \neq 0$. If this is true, then we can solve the equations and find

$$dx = -\frac{f'_1}{f'_2 h'_2 - 1}\, du - \frac{f'_2 h'_1}{f'_2 h'_2 - 1}\, dv,$$

and so on. While these results are related to diagram (6–27), they do not follow immediately from it, and we certainly cannot use the simple method described earlier to write down the partial derivatives.

A common type of difficulty is the application of the implicit-function theorem to the problem of finding second- or higher-order derivatives. Let us see how this problem can be handled.

Suppose that we are given the function

$$f(x, y, z) = x^3 + y^3 - 2xz$$

and we wish to solve the functional relationship $f(x, y, z) = 0$ for x in terms of y and z in a neighborhood of the point $[1, 1, 1]$. This cannot be done explicitly (at least not very practically), but it can be done implicitly. We have

$$df = 0 = (3x^2 - 2z)\,dz + 3y^2\,dy - 2x\,dz,$$

and hence

$$dx = \frac{-3y^2}{3x^2 - 2z}\,dy + \frac{2x}{3x^2 - 2z}\,dz. \tag{6–28}$$

Suppose that we wish to find $\partial^2 x/\partial z^2$ and $\partial^2 x/\partial y\,\partial z$ (x being the dependent variable, y and z being independent). Let

$$u = \frac{\partial x}{\partial z} = \frac{2x}{3x^2 - 2z}\cdot$$

We can then compute

$$du = -\frac{(9x^2 + 2z)}{(3x^2 - 2z)^2}\,dx + 0\,dy + \frac{4x}{(3x^2 - 2z)^2}\,dz.$$

However, since x is taken as a dependent variable, we must substitute (6–28) into the above expression. We find

$$du = \frac{3y^2(9x^2 + 2z)}{(3x^2 - 2z)^3}\,dy - \frac{6x(x^2 + 2z)}{(3x^2 - 2z)^3}\,dz.$$

The desired expressions for $\partial^2 x/\partial z^2$ and $\partial^2 x/\partial y\,\partial z$ can be read directly from this equation. For example,

$$\frac{\partial^2 x}{\partial z^2} = \frac{\partial u}{\partial z} = -\frac{6x(x^2 + 2z)}{(3x^2 - 2z)^3}\cdot$$

It should be observed that the value of $\partial^2 x/\partial z^2$ is given by this expression only when the proper value for x is substituted into it. That is, x must be such that

$$f(x, y, z) = 0.$$

Now let us look at a slightly more general version of the same type of problem.

Suppose that we have a function $f(\mathbf{Y})$, where $\mathbf{Y} = [y_1, y_2, \ldots, y_k]$, and k functional relationships $g_i[\mathbf{X}, \mathbf{Y}] = 0$, $i = 1, 2, \ldots, k$, where $\mathbf{X} = [x_1, x_2, \ldots, x_n]$. Assume that the requirements of Theorem 6–8 hold and we can solve for the y_i in terms of the x_j. Thus there exists (in theory) a set of functions $y_i = h_i(\mathbf{X})$. Although we may not be able to actually find these functions, we can find their differentials in terms of the differentials of the g_i by the methods already described. These differentials will usually depend on both $\mathbf{X}$ and $\mathbf{Y}$. That is, we can define a new set of functions

$$p_{ij}(\mathbf{X}, \mathbf{Y}) = h_{i'j}(\mathbf{X}).$$

These are the functions which will actually be obtained in this case.

Set $w = w(\mathbf{X}) = f\big(\mathbf{H}(\mathbf{X})\big)$. Then $dw = [df][d\mathbf{H}]$. Hence

$$\frac{\partial w}{\partial x_l} = \sum_{i=1}^{k} f_{'i} h_{'l} = \sum_{i=1}^{k} f_{'i}(\mathbf{Y}) p_{il}(\mathbf{X}, \mathbf{Y}).$$

This is, of course, nothing but the chain rule. Here we have an expression for the partial derivative of w, but the expression will involve (explicitly) up to $n + k$ variables. To find the partial derivative of this expression with respect to x_r, say, we must look at the sum of terms of the following type:

$$d[f'_i(\mathbf{H}(\mathbf{X}))p_{il}(\mathbf{X}, \mathbf{H}(\mathbf{X}))] = p_{il}[df'_i][d\mathbf{H}] + f'_i[dp_{il}(\mathbf{X}, \mathbf{H}(\mathbf{X}))].$$

Consideration of the various terms appearing here gives us

$$\frac{\partial^2 w}{\partial x_r\, \partial x_l} = \sum_{i=1}^{k}\left(\sum_{j=1}^{k} f'_{ij}p_{il}p_{jr} + f'_i p_{il'r} + \sum_{j=1}^{k} f'_i p_{il'n+j}p_{jr}\right).$$

In this computation we need to observe that the f'_i depend only on the y_i, while the p_{ij} depend on both $\mathbf{X}$ and $\mathbf{Y}$. When we apply the chain rule to a function such as p_{il}, the partial derivatives $p_{il'j}$ assume all these variables to be "independent"; the relations between them are taken care of by the other parts of the chain rule.

The application of the above formula is usually easier than the formula might make it seem. We can best illustrate such an application by an example.

Suppose that we are given a function

$$w = f(r, \theta, z)$$

in terms of the cylindrical coordinates r, θ, and z. The relation between the cartesian coordinates and the cylindrical coordinates is given by

$$x = r\cos\theta, \qquad y = r\sin\theta, \qquad z = z.$$

The Jacobian of this last transformation is equal to r, and is zero only when $r = 0$.

A simple computation gives

$$dr = \cos\theta\, dx + \sin\theta\, dy,$$

$$d\theta = -\frac{\sin\theta}{r}\,dx + \frac{\cos\theta}{r}\,dy.$$

The chain rule then gives us

$$\frac{\partial w}{\partial x} = f'_1\frac{\partial r}{\partial x} + f'_2\frac{\partial \theta}{\partial x} = f'_1\cos\theta - f'_2\frac{\sin\theta}{r}.$$

This result could have been obtained by taking df and substituting in for each of the differentials to obtain df in terms of dx, dy, and dz, or, more simply, just by using the chain rule (6–9).

The above result is a function of r, θ, and z only. The variables x and y do not appear explicitly here. We may now apply the chain rule again to find $\partial^2 w/\partial x^2$:

$$\frac{\partial^2 w}{\partial x^2} = f'_{11}\cos^2\theta - f'_{12}\frac{\sin\theta\cos\theta}{r} + f'_1\frac{\sin^2\theta}{r}$$
$$- f'_{21}\frac{\sin\theta\cos\theta}{r} + f'_{22}\frac{\sin^2\theta}{r} + 2f'_2\frac{\sin\theta\cos\theta}{r^2}.$$

The final term came from differentiating $(\sin \theta)/r$ with respect to θ and with respect to r. Then, multiplying by the appropriate partial derivatives with respect to x results in the two equal terms which are combined to produce the one shown. The second and fourth terms are also equal, since we assume as much continuity as necessary and thus $f'_{12} = f'_{21}$.

In a similar way, we can calculate

$$\frac{\partial w}{\partial y} = f'_1 \sin \theta + f'_2 \frac{\cos \theta}{r},$$

and then

$$\begin{aligned}\frac{\partial^2 w}{\partial y^2} &= f'_{11} \sin \theta \frac{\partial r}{\partial y} + f'_{12} \sin \theta \frac{\partial \theta}{\partial y} + f'_1 \cos \theta \frac{\partial \theta}{\partial y} \\ &\quad + f'_{21} \frac{\cos \theta}{r} \frac{\partial r}{dy} + f'_{22} \frac{\cos \theta}{r} \frac{\partial \theta}{\partial y} - f'_2 \frac{\sin \theta}{r} \frac{\partial \theta}{\partial y} - f'_2 \frac{\cos \theta}{r^2} \frac{\partial r}{\partial y} \\ &= f'_{11} \sin^2 \theta + 2 f'_{12} \frac{\sin \theta \cos \theta}{r} + f'_{22} \frac{\cos^2 \theta}{r^2} \\ &\quad + f'_1 \frac{\cos^2 \theta}{r} - 2 f'_2 \frac{\sin \theta \cos \theta}{r^2}.\end{aligned}$$

We have $\partial^2 w/\partial z^2 = f'_{33}$; and if we add these partial derivatives, we find

$$\begin{aligned}\frac{\partial^2 w}{\partial x^2} + \frac{\partial^2 w}{\partial y^2} + \frac{\partial^2 w}{\partial z^2} &= f'_{11} + \frac{1}{r^2} f'_{22} + f'_{33} + \frac{1}{r} f'_1 \\ &= \frac{\partial^2 w}{\partial r^2} + \frac{1}{r^2} \frac{\partial^2 w}{\partial \theta^2} + \frac{\partial^2 w}{\partial z^2} + \frac{1}{r} \frac{\partial w}{\partial r}.\end{aligned}$$

In the last line we indicated the result in partial derivative form. The partial derivatives on the right all assume that w is a function of r, θ, and z, while the partial derivatives on the left assume that w is a function of x, y, and z. The particular combination of second partials that has been computed here appears very often in practice, especially in practical problems; it is called the *Laplacian* of the function w (or f). Several different notations are in common use for the Laplacian. Two of the most common are Δf and $\nabla^2 f$. Here we shall use only

$$\nabla^2 f = \sum_{i=1}^{n} \frac{\partial^2 f}{\partial x_i^2}.$$

As a final example for this section, let us consider the problem of the invariance of the gradient under coordinate transformations. Let $f: B \to R$ be a real-valued function which is C^1 in a region B contained in R^n, and suppose that $\mathbf{X}_0$ is an interior point of B.

The differential of f at $\mathbf{X}_0$ is $df(\mathbf{X}_0)$. The gradient (vector) is $\nabla f(\mathbf{X}_0)$, and the two are related by

$$\nabla f(\mathbf{X}_0) = [df(\mathbf{X}_0)]^t,$$

where $[df(\mathbf{X}_0)]$ is treated as a row matrix. Now, if we have a coordinate change which is one-to-one in some neighborhood of $\mathbf{X}_0$, it has an inverse, and we can write

$$\mathbf{X} = \mathbf{X}(\mathbf{W}) \qquad \text{or} \qquad \mathbf{W} = \mathbf{W}(\mathbf{X}).$$

Let $\mathbf{W}_0 = \mathbf{W}(\mathbf{X}_0)$ and suppose that this function is C^1 in a neighborhood of $\mathbf{X}_0$. Set

$$g(\mathbf{W}) = f(\mathbf{X}(\mathbf{W})).$$

Then

$$dg(\mathbf{W}_0) = [df(\mathbf{X}_0)][d\mathbf{X}(\mathbf{W}_0)],$$

and hence the formula for the gradient of f in terms of the new coordinate system is

$$\nabla g(\mathbf{W}_0) = [d\mathbf{X}(\mathbf{W}_0)]^t \, \nabla f(\mathbf{X}_0).$$

What happens to this formula when the coordinate change is one of euclidean motions? First, let us consider the case of translation. We have a constant vector $\mathbf{A}$ such that

$$\mathbf{W} = \mathbf{X} + \mathbf{A}, \qquad \mathbf{X} = \mathbf{W} - \mathbf{A}.$$

Then $[d\mathbf{X}] = I$, and we have $\nabla g(\mathbf{W}_0) = \nabla f(\mathbf{X}_0)$. The gradient is unchanged under this coordinate transformation.

Next, suppose that we have a coordinate change representing a "change of basis." That is,

$$\mathbf{X} = P\mathbf{W}, \qquad \mathbf{W} = P^{-1}\mathbf{X}, \tag{6–29}$$

where P is a nonsingular (constant) $n \times n$ matrix. In particular, this change is one of the euclidean motions if P is orthogonal. Equation (6–29) may be compared with (4–16) on page 124.

For a transformation defined by (6–29) we have $[d\mathbf{X}] = P$. The new gradient is therefore given by

$$\nabla g(\mathbf{W}_0) = P^t \ \nabla f(\mathbf{X}_0).$$

Comparing this equation with (6–29) and (4–18), we see that the gradient does not change like a vector, but like a *covector*. However, if P is an orthogonal matrix, then $P^{-1} = P^t$, and the two are the same. Hence we may say that the gradient transforms like a vector under rotations and reflections.

We often find the statement that the gradient is invariant under the euclidean motions of translation, rotation, and reflection. This is a loose statement since it means two entirely different things.

When we say that the gradient is invariant under translation, we mean that the "new" gradient, $\nabla g(\mathbf{W}_0)$, is exactly the same vector (i.e., ordered n-tuple) as the original gradient. It is *not* the translate of the original gradient.

On the other hand, when we perform a rotation or reflection, the "new" gradient is a different vector from the original gradient. However, it is the transform of the original gradient by exactly the same law by which the vectors (points) of the coordinate system were transformed. It can therefore be thought of as being the expression of the same vector in terms of the new coordinate system. The gradient is therefore invariant under rotations and reflections, but this invariance is expressed in a different way from the invariance under translation.

PROBLEMS

1. Find dy and dw as functions of du and dv for the system (6–26).
2. Under what conditions can the system (6–26) be solved for u, v, and y as functions of x and w? Assuming that the solution is possible, what will all of the partial derivatives be?
3. Suppose that $z = f(x, y)$ and $y = g(x, z)$, both functions being in C^1.
   a) Under what conditions can z and y be considered as functions of x? Under these conditions, solve for dz and dy.
   b) Answer the same question for x and y as functions of z.
4. Given $w = f(\mathbf{Y})$, where $\mathbf{Y} \in R^n$, suppose that $\mathbf{Y} = A\mathbf{X}$, where A is a nonsingular constant $n \times n$ matrix.
   a) What is $\partial w/\partial x_i$? b) What is $\partial^2 w/\partial x_i^2$? c) What is $\nabla^2 f$?
   d) What is $\nabla^2 f$ when the matrix A is orthogonal?
5. Find $\nabla^2 f$ when $f = f(\rho, \phi, \theta)$ and
$$x = \rho \cos\theta \sin\phi, \qquad y = \rho \sin\theta \sin\phi, \qquad z = \rho \cos\phi.$$
6. Let $\mathbf{X} \in R^n$ and let A be an $n \times n$ matrix of constants. Let
$$f(\mathbf{X}) = \mathbf{X}^t A\mathbf{X}.$$
   a) What is df? b) What is $d^2 f(=[f'_{ij}])$? c) What is $\nabla^2 f$?
7. Suppose that $f(x_1, x_2, \ldots, x_{n-1}, x_n) = 0$ defines
$$x_n = g(x_1, x_2, \ldots, x_{n-1})$$
implicitly. Determine all g'_{ij}, $1 \le i, j \le n - 1$, in terms of the partial derivatives of f.
8. Prove that the Laplacian of a function is invariant under euclidean motions.

CHAPTER 7

Curves and Surfaces

7–1. CURVES IN R^n

The reader is probably familiar with the concept of a curve in the plane. He may recall that this concept turned out to be deeper than it seemed at first, in particular when the concept of arc length was introduced. The basic difficulty is that a curve is more than just a set of points in the plane. The mapping which produces that set of points is important also. For example, consider the curves in the plane defined in the following ways:

$$C_1:\quad [x, y] = [t, t], \quad 0 \le t \le 1;$$

$$C_2:\quad [x, y] = [\sin t, \sin t], \quad 0 \le t \le \pi.$$

The point sets in the plane are the same, but the two curves are different. C_1 is the line segment from the point [0, 0] to [1, 1], while C_2 is the same line segment, traced out from the origin to [1, 1] and then back to the origin.

On the other hand, what about the curve

$$C_3:\quad [x, y] = [\sin t, \sin t], \quad 0 \le t \le \pi/2?$$

Isn't this in some sense "the same" curve as C_1? Both go over the point set in the same direction and for the same "distance." The only difference is the "rate" at which the lines are traced out. We must frame our definitions in such a way that these observations are taken into account.

There are several different ways in which we can give the definitions of curves. Each method has its advantages and disadvantages. We choose the following definitions because of their relative simplicity and the fact that they can be generalized to take care of much more complex situations at a later time. The following definition is divided into several parts. This procedure seems better than giving a large number of separate definitions.

Definition 7–1

1. A *curve* C in R^n is a function $\mathbf{F}{:}R[a, b] \to R^n$ which is continuous on the closed interval $R[a, b]$ of the reals. The terms *path* or *arc* are often used to denote a curve.

2. Given a curve C in R^n, the set of points $\{\mathbf{F}(x) \mid a \le x \le b\}$ is called the *carrier* of the curve. The point $\mathbf{F}(a)$ is called the *initial point* of the curve, and $\mathbf{F}(b)$ is called the *terminal point* of the curve.

3. If $C = [\mathbf{F}:R[a, b] \to R^n]$ is a curve, then the *negative* of the curve is the new curve $-C = [\mathbf{F}_1:R[-b, -a] \to R^n]$, where the function $\mathbf{F}_1$ is defined by
$$\mathbf{F}_1(x) = \mathbf{F}(-x).$$

4. If $C_1 = [\mathbf{F}_1:R[a, b] \to R^n]$ and $C_2 = [\mathbf{F}_2:R[c, d] \to R^n]$ are two curves such that the terminal point of C_1 is the same as the initial point of C_2 [i.e., $\mathbf{F}_1(b) = \mathbf{F}_2(a)$], then the *sum* or *union* of the two curves is the curve $C_1 + C_2 = [\mathbf{F}:R[a, b + d - c] \to R^n]$, where
$$\mathbf{F}(x) = \begin{cases} \mathbf{F}_1(x) & \text{for } a \le x \le b \\ \mathbf{F}_2(x + c - b) & \text{for } b \le x \le b + d - c. \end{cases}$$

5. A curve $C = [\mathbf{F}:R[a, b] \to R^n]$ is called a *smooth curve* if and only if $\mathbf{F}$ is continuously differentiable on $R[a, b]$ and $D\mathbf{F}(x) \ne \mathbf{0}$* for any $x \in R[a, b]$. Only right- and left-hand derivatives need exist at the endpoints, but these derivatives must be nonzero also.

6. Two smooth curves $C_1 = [\mathbf{F}_1:R[a, b] \to R^n]$ and $C_2 = [\mathbf{F}_2:R[c, d] \to R^n]$ are called *equivalent* or *smoothly equivalent* if and only if there exists a function $w:R[a, b] \to R[c, d]$ which is one-to-one, onto, order-preserving, and C^1 at every point of $R[a, b]$ with a nonzero derivative, and such that $\mathbf{F}_1(x) = \mathbf{F}_2[w(x)]$. In this case we write $C_1 \sim C_2$.

7. A curve C in R^n is a *piecewise smooth curve* if and only if
$$C = C_1 + C_2 + \cdots + C_N$$
for some finite number of smooth curves C_i. The terminal points of C_1, $C_2, \ldots, C_{N-1}$ are called the *corners* of the curve.

8. Two piecewise smooth curves C and C' are *equivalent* if and only if $C = C_1 + C_2 + \cdots + C_N$ and $C' = C'_1 + C'_2 + \cdots + C'_N$, where each C_i or C'_i is a smooth curve and for each i, $C_i \sim C'_i$. We then write $C \sim C'$.

9. A curve C in R^n is called *closed* if and only if its initial and terminal points coincide. A smooth closed curve must also be "smooth" at the "joint". That is, if we define
$$\mathbf{G}(x) = \begin{cases} \mathbf{F}(x), & a \le x \le b, \\ \mathbf{F}(x - b + a), & b \le x \le 2b - a, \end{cases}$$
then $\mathbf{G}(x)$ must have a continuous nonzero derivative at $x = b$.

10. A curve $C = [\mathbf{F}:R[a, b] \to R^n]$ is called *simple* if and only if $\mathbf{F}(t_1) \ne \mathbf{F}(t_2)$ for any $t_1 \ne t_2$, except possibly for $\mathbf{F}(a) = \mathbf{F}(b)$ in the case of a closed curve.

* By $D\mathbf{F}(x)$ we mean the directional (partial) derivative of $\mathbf{F}$ in the only available direction. Note that this derivative is actually a vector, $D\mathbf{F}(x) = [f_1(x), \ldots, f_n(x)]$. This vector can also be identified with the $n \times 1$ matrix $[d\mathbf{F}(x)]$. In fact, $D\mathbf{F}(x) = [d\mathbf{F}(x)]\mathbf{e}_1$, where $\mathbf{e}_1$ is a one-dimensional vector and hence can be identified with the 1×1 matrix [1].

Let us make a few comments about all of these definitions. Observe that the curve is defined to be the function. The function includes the domain and image (which in this case is the carrier). Speaking loosely, we will sometimes use the word *curve* when we really mean the *carrier* of the curve. The context will usually prevent any confusion on this point.

Actually this loose terminology is used almost universally. The set defined by $x^2 + y^2 = 1, z = 0$ (the unit circle in the xy-plane of R^3) is called a curve as soon as we assign a sense of direction to it. Giving it the counterclockwise direction in the xy-plane, we can make it fit the above definition by supplying a function mapping some segment of the real axis onto this set, which is easy to do. For example, we could set, for $0 \leq \theta \leq 2\pi$,

$$x = \cos\theta, \qquad y = \sin\theta, \qquad z = 0.$$

Note that the negative of a curve is nothing but the same curve traced out in the opposite direction. The sum of two curves is the result of "joining" the two "end to end." A *closed* curve is an "endless" curve, although, since it must be defined by a function, there will be some distinct point which will be the common initial and terminal point. A *simple* curve is one which never crosses itself.

The curves we shall consider in this book will be piecewise smooth unless otherwise specified. In fact, the only reason we do not stick to smooth curves entirely is that we will want to speak of curves, such as a square, which cannot be made smooth at the corners. As we shall see, smooth curves are curves with "continuously turning tangents."

It is the concept of equivalence of curves that is most important. In some sense, we would prefer to think of two equivalent curves as representing the "same" curve. This could be done. We could think of the curve as having some independent existence and of the various functions as merely defining different representations of the curve. The curve itself could be defined as the "equivalence class" of all equivalent functions. While this approach would be more correct, it leads to complications that we would prefer not to get into at this time. The definitions as given above will suffice for our purposes.

We find it convenient to use $\mathbf{X}(t)$ to represent the function defining the curve. The components of $\mathbf{X}$ are then the coordinates of the point $\mathbf{X}(t)$ on the curve.

Now we wish to discuss the idea of a tangent to a curve. Suppose that we fix a point $\mathbf{X}(t_0)$ on the curve. If t_1 is any other number in the interval, then $\mathbf{X}(t_1) - \mathbf{X}(t_0)$ is a secant vector of the curve. If we let $t_1 \to t_0$, then the *direction* of this secant vector should approach the direction of the tangent to the curve. Of course, $\mathbf{X}(t_1) - \mathbf{X}(t_0)$ tends to $\mathbf{0}$ as $t_1 \to t_0$. We can enlarge this vector without changing its direction by dividing by $t_1 - t_0$, thus obtaining a "longer" vector as t_1 approaches t_0. The limit of this vector

$$\frac{\mathbf{X}(t_1) - \mathbf{X}(t_0)}{t_1 - t_0}$$

as $t_1 \to t_0$ is exactly the vector $D\mathbf{X}(t_0)$, the derivative of $\mathbf{X}$ at t_0. Note that $D\mathbf{X}$ is actually a vector in this case. It is the column vector of the derivatives of the component functions of $\mathbf{X}(t)$.

We will find it useful to introduce a simple extension of the "prime" notation for the derivative. When we have a vector-valued function of a single real variable such as $\mathbf{F}(t)$ or $\mathbf{X}(t)$, we may write $\mathbf{F}'(t)$ or $\mathbf{X}'(t)$ to denote the vector whose components are the derivatives of the component functions of $\mathbf{F}$ or $\mathbf{X}$, respectively. That is, $\mathbf{X}'(t) = D\mathbf{X}(t)$.

Definition 7–2. Let $\mathbf{X}: R[a, b] \to R^n$ be a smooth curve in R^n. Let t_0 be a real number with $a < t_0 < b$. Then $\mathbf{X}'(t_0)$ is called a *tangent vector* to the curve at $\mathbf{X}(t_0)$.

For example, the curve C defined by

$$[x, y, z] = [a \cos t, a \sin t, bt]$$

represents a helix (for t in any closed interval). For any point t in the reals, the vector

$$\mathbf{T} = [-a \sin t, a \cos t, b]$$

is tangent to the curve. This particular vector is of length $[a^2 + b^2]^{1/2}$. What about the tangent to the equivalent curve C' given by

$$[x, y, z] = [a \cos t^2, a \sin t^2, bt^2]?$$

The curves C and C' are equivalent over corresponding intervals not containing $t = 0$. We could have, for example, $1 \leq t \leq 4$ in the first representation and $1 \leq t \leq 2$ in the second. Note that the second representation fails to be a smooth curve at $t = 0$ according to our definition since $\mathbf{X}' = \mathbf{0}$ there. A tangent vector to C' at any other t is given by

$$\mathbf{T}' = [-2at \sin t^2, 2at \cos t^2, 2bt].$$

How do $\mathbf{T}$ and $\mathbf{T}'$ compare at the same point of the curve? The point on C given by t_0 is the same as the point on C' given by $t_0^{1/2}$. Comparing, we see that

$$\mathbf{T}'(t_0^{1/2}) = 2t_0^{1/2}\mathbf{T}(t_0);$$

that is, the tangents are scalar multiples of each other at the same point.

This result holds true in general. The direction of the tangent vector to a curve are the same (at the same point) for all equivalent curves. (See the problems at the end of this section.) As the parametrization is changed, the length of the tangent vector changes. We can get the same tangent vector for all equivalent curves if we divide each through by its magnitude so as to obtain a vector of unit length in each case.

Definition 7–3. Let $\mathbf{X}(t)$ define a curve C in R^n. Let $\mathbf{T}$ be a tangent vector to C at some point $\mathbf{P}$. Then by the *unit tangent vector* to C at $\mathbf{P}$ we mean the vector

$$\mathbf{e}_t = \mathbf{T}/|\mathbf{T}|.$$

Several remarks about this definition should be made. First, we really should say "smooth curve" rather than "curve" in this definition. However, we shall assume in this text that all the curves we discuss are smooth, or at least piecewise smooth, unless otherwise specified. The next point is that we should also assume that $\mathbf{T} \neq \mathbf{0}$ in this definition. This we will do where it seems necessary. The curves we will speak about will all have this property. The final point that the reader should note is that the t used as a subscript to $\mathbf{e}_\mathrm{t}$ refers to "tangent" and not to the parameter t used to define the curve.

Before we continue, we need to prove a few simple theorems about the behavior of the derivatives of vector-valued functions.

Theorem 7–1. Let **F** and **G** be differentiable vector-valued functions of the real variable t. Then

$$\frac{d}{dt}(\mathbf{F} \cdot \mathbf{G}) = \mathbf{F} \cdot (\mathbf{G}') + (\mathbf{F}') \cdot \mathbf{G}.$$

Proof. This theorem follows from the standard formula for the product of real-valued functions. Breaking **F** and **G** up into components gives

$$\frac{d}{dt}\sum_{i=1}^{n} f_i g_i = \sum_{i=1}^{n} f_i g_i' + \sum_{i=1}^{n} f_i' g_i. \blacksquare$$

From this theorem we obtain the following useful result.

Theorem 7–2. Let $\mathbf{F}: R[a, b] \to R$ be differentiable and of constant magnitude on $R[a, b]$. Then $\mathbf{F}'$ is orthogonal to **F**.

Proof. Since **F** is of constant magnitude, $|\mathbf{F}|^2 = \mathbf{F} \cdot \mathbf{F}$ has a derivative which is identically zero. Therefore, by the previous theorem,

$$0 = \frac{d}{dt}(\mathbf{F} \cdot \mathbf{F}) = 2\mathbf{F} \cdot (\mathbf{F}').$$

Hence the conclusion of the theorem follows. ▮

In most cases of interest, the unit tangent vector of a curve is a differentiable function of the parameter. If it is, then its derivative will be vector orthogonal to the tangent vector, and hence can be thought of as a normal to the curve.

Definition 7–4. Let the curve C in R^n be given by the function $\mathbf{F}(t)$. Suppose that for all t the unit tangent vector $\mathbf{e}_\mathrm{t}(t)$ is a differentiable function of t. Then $\mathbf{N} = \mathbf{e}_\mathrm{t}'(t)$ is called a *principal normal* to the curve C at $\mathbf{F}(t)$. The *unit principal normal* there is $\mathbf{e}_\mathrm{n} = \mathbf{N}/|\mathbf{N}|$.

In the example of the helix given above,

$$\mathbf{e}_\mathrm{t} = [-(a/c)\sin t, (a/c)\cos t, b/c],$$

where $c = [a^2 + b^2]^{1/2}$. Hence a normal to this curve is

$$\mathbf{N} = [-(a/c)\cos t, -(a/c)\sin t, 0],$$

and a unit principal normal to the curve is

$$\mathbf{e}_n = [-\cos t, -\sin t, 0].$$

Note that this vector is parallel to the xy-plane and points directly toward the z-axis. It is actually a normal to the cylinder along whose surface the helix winds.

The plane through a given point of a curve determined by the tangent and principal normals is in some sense the "best fitting" plane to the curve at that point.

Definition 7–5. Let $\mathbf{e}_t$ and $\mathbf{e}_n$ be the unit tangent and principal normal vectors to a curve C at a point $\mathbf{P}$. Then the affine plane

$$\mathbf{P} + L\{\mathbf{e}_t, \mathbf{e}_n\}$$

is called the *osculating plane* of the curve at this point.

For example, the osculating plane of the helix described above at the point $[a, 0, 0]$ (corresponding to $t = 0$) is determined by the vectors $\mathbf{e}_t = [0, a, b]$ and $\mathbf{e}_n = [-1, 0, 0]$. In three dimensions, it is easiest to use the cross product of the two vectors to find a vector normal to the plane. In this case, we have $[0, -b, a]$. The equation of the osculating plane is thus

$$0(x - a) - b(y - 0) + a(z - 0) = 0$$

or

$$by - az = 0.$$

Now let us turn to the problem of finding the length of a curve. The question of arc length is no different for a curve in R^n than for a curve in the plane. For this reason we can make our discussion quite brief. The reader will have already seen these concepts discussed in the plane.

We approach the problem of finding the arc length of a given curve by approximating the curve by a *polygonal curve*, that is, a curve which is made up of a finite number of straight line segments. Given the curve $C = [\mathbf{X}: R[a, b] \to R^n]$, let $\mathcal{P}$ be any partition of the interval $R[a, b]$; That is,

$$\mathcal{P} = \langle t_0, t_1, \ldots, t_N \rangle,$$

where

$$a = t_0 < t_1 < t_2 < \cdots < t_N = b.$$

Fig. 7–1

This partition of $R[a, b]$ induces a partition of the curve. That is, we have the sequence of points $\mathbf{X}(t_0), \mathbf{X}(t_1), \ldots, \mathbf{X}(t_N)$ on the curve. These points can be used as the vertices of the approximating polygon as in Fig. 7–1.

The total length of this polygonal curve is

$$L(\mathcal{P}) = \sum_{i=1}^{N} |\mathbf{X}(t_i) - \mathbf{X}(t_{i-1})|. \tag{7-1}$$

Each segment of this polygon is a secant of the curve and hence should be shorter than the length of the segment of the curve it spans. On the other hand, as we increase the number of subdivisions, making the lengths of the straight line segments tend toward zero, we obviously have a better and better approximation to the curve.

Definition 7-6. Let $C = [\mathbf{X}:R[a, b] \to R^n]$. If the set of all $L(\mathcal{P})$ for all partitions $\mathcal{P}$ of $R[a, b]$ is bounded above, then the curve C is called *rectifiable*. Then the *length* of the curve C is defined to be the supremum (least upper bound) of $L(\mathcal{P})$ for all partitions $\mathcal{P}$.

Theorem 7-3. If C is a smooth curve in R^n, then it is rectifiable. Indeed, there exist $\tau_1, \tau_2, \ldots, \tau_n$ in $R[a, b]$ such that L, the length of C, satisfies the inequality

$$L \leq (b - a)\left(\sum_{i=1}^{n} [x_i'(\tau_i)]^2\right)^{1/2}.$$

Proof. If C is a smooth curve, then each of the component functions, $x_i(t)$, has a continuous derivative in the interval $R[a, b]$. For each i, let τ_i be the point in this interval at which $|x_i'(t)|$ assumes its maximum value. Then for every t,

$$|x_i'(t)| \leq m_i = |x_i'(\tau_i)|.$$

Now let $\mathcal{P}$ be any partition of the interval $R[a, b]$. Then

$$\begin{aligned} L(\mathcal{P}) &= \sum_{j=1}^{N} |\mathbf{X}(t_j) - \mathbf{X}(t_{j-1})| \\ &= \sum_{j=1}^{N}\left(\sum_{i=1}^{n} [x_i(t_j) - x_i(t_{j-1})]^2\right)^{1/2} \\ &= \sum_{j=1}^{N}\left(\sum_{i=1}^{n} (t_j - t_{j-1})^2[x_i'(t_{ij}')]^2\right)^{1/2} \\ &\leq \sum_{j=1}^{N} (t_j - t_{j-1})\left(\sum_{i=1}^{n} m_i^2\right)^{1/2} \\ &= (b - a)\left(\sum_{i=1}^{n} m_i^2\right)^{1/2}. \end{aligned}$$

Here the third step is merely the mean-value theorem applied to each of the functions separately. (Note that the t_{ij}', which are points between t_{j-1} and t_j, depend on i also. However, in the next step we replace each of them by its maximum possible value anyhow.) The last line implies the conclusion of the theorem. If each $L(\mathcal{P})$ is less than this, so is the least upper bound. ▌

Definition 7–7. Let $C = [\mathbf{X}:R[a, b] \to R^n]$ be a smooth curve. For each t in the interval $R[a, b]$ let C_t be the smooth curve defined by $C_t = [\mathbf{X}:R[a, t] \to R^n]$. Then the *arc length function* of C is the function $s(t)$ which, for each t, is the length of C_t.

The arc length function defined here will exist for any rectifiable curve. Note that it is an increasing function of t and that if c and d are any two values in the interval, then the length of the curve from $\mathbf{X}(c)$ to $\mathbf{X}(d)$ is given by $s(d) - s(c)$. These facts are evident and can be proved without much difficulty, but since the proofs are somewhat tedious, they will not be given here.

Theorem 7–4. Let $C = [\mathbf{X}:R[a, b] \to R^n]$ be a smooth curve. Then the arc length function $s(t)$ is differentiable in $R[a, b]$, and for any t

$$\frac{ds}{dt} = |\mathbf{X}'(t)|.$$

Proof. Let c be any point of the interval $a < c < b$. Suppose that d is any other point of the interval with $c < d$. Then from Theorem 7–3 we have

$$s(d) - s(c) \leq (d - c)\left(\sum_{i=1}^{n} [x_i'(\tau_i)]^2\right)^{1/2}. \tag{7–2}$$

where each τ_i is some number in the interval between c and d. On the other hand, $s(d) - s(c)$ is the length of the curve between $\mathbf{X}(c)$ and $\mathbf{X}(d)$, and hence is certainly greater than or equal to $|\mathbf{X}(d) - \mathbf{X}(c)|$ since this is the length of the "one-interval" polygonal approximation. But then

$$\begin{aligned} s(d) - s(c) \geq |\mathbf{X}(d) - \mathbf{X}(c)| &= \left(\sum_{i=1}^{n} [x_i(d) - x_i(c)]^2\right)^{1/2} \\ &= (d - c)\left(\sum_{i=1}^{n} [x_i'(\tau_i')]^2\right)^{1/2}. \end{aligned}$$

Here we used the mean-value theorem for each separate component again. The $\tau_{i'}$ are points in the interval from c to d.

Combining this result with (7–2), we find that

$$\left(\sum_{i=1}^{n} [x_i'(\tau_i')]^2\right)^{1/2} \leq \frac{s(d) - s(c)}{d - c} \leq \left(\sum_{i=1}^{n} [x_i'(\tau_i)]^2\right)^{1/2}.$$

Hold c fixed and let $d \to c$. Then each τ_i and τ_i' will tend toward c also. Thus the limit exists and is equal to $|\mathbf{X}'(c)|$; in a similar way, we see that the limit must exist as we approach c from below. The theorem is therefore proved. ▌

By integrating this result, we obtain the familiar formula for the length of the curve $C = [\mathbf{X}:R[a, b] \to R^n]$,

$$L = \int_a^b |\mathbf{X}'(t)|\, dt.$$

An important consequence of this formula is that the lengths of two smoothly equivalent curves are the same.

Theorem 7–5. If $C = [\mathbf{F}:R[a, b] \to R^n]$ is smoothly equivalent to $C' = [\mathbf{G}:R[c, d] \to R^n]$, then C and C' have the same length.

Proof. Let L be the length of C and let L' be the length of C'. Let $u:R[a, b] \to R[c, d]$ be the function which exhibits the equivalence; that is, $\mathbf{G}[u(t)] = \mathbf{F}(t)$ for every t. But then $\mathbf{F}'(t) = \mathbf{G}'(u)u'(t)$. Hence

$$L = \int_a^b |\mathbf{F}'(t)|\, dt = \int_a^b |\mathbf{G}'(u)|u'(t)\, dt = \int_c^d |\mathbf{G}'(u)|\, du = L'. \blacksquare$$

Note that we have the fact that $u'(t) > 0$ in this computation, because $u(t)$ was given as order-preserving and hence is an increasing function.

These results can be extended to any piecewise smooth curve by merely adding the lengths of the individual smooth sections of the curve. Therefore any piecewise smooth curve is rectifiable. Its length will also remain unchanged under piecewise smooth equivalence.

Note that if $\mathbf{F}:R[a, b] \to R^n$ defines a curve, then

$$\frac{ds}{dt} = |\mathbf{F}'|$$

and hence

$$\mathbf{F}' = \frac{ds}{dt}\mathbf{e}_t.$$

A smooth curve is such that $\mathbf{F}' \neq \mathbf{0}$ at any point; hence the arc length function $s(t)$ is a monotone increasing, differentiable function $s:R[a, b] \to R[0, L]$, where L is the length of the curve. The derivative $ds/dt \neq 0$, and hence there exists an inverse function $t = t(s):R[0, L] \to R[a, b]$. This inverse function is differentiable, and $t'(s) = 1/s'(t)$. If we define

$$\mathbf{X}(s) = \mathbf{F}[t(s)],$$

then we obtain an equivalent curve which has its own arc length function as the parameter because

$$\mathbf{X}' = (\mathbf{F}')t'(s) = [s'(t)\mathbf{e}_t]t'(s) = \mathbf{e}_t.$$

Thus any curve can be converted to an equivalent curve whose tangent vector is always of unit length. This conversion is often useful in theory. In practical problems, however, it usually complicates matters and is seldom done.

It is useful to note that the tangent vector, the principal normal vector, and the osculating plane can be determined without differentiating the arc length function.

Suppose $\mathbf{X}(t)$ gives the curve. Set $v(t) = |\mathbf{X}'(t)|$. Then

$$\mathbf{X}'(t) = v(t)\mathbf{e}_t.$$

Now, we know that

$$\frac{d\mathbf{e}_t}{dt} = c\mathbf{e}_n,$$

where c is some positive scalar function. But then

$$\mathbf{X}''(t) = D[\mathbf{X}'(t)] = v'(t)\mathbf{e}_t + v(t)c\mathbf{e}_n.$$

We see that $\mathbf{X}'' - (v'/v)\mathbf{X}' = v(t)c\mathbf{e}_n$ is a vector in the direction of $\mathbf{e}_n$. Indeed, this vector is a positive scalar multiple of $\mathbf{e}_n$. However, it happens we can determine the coefficient of $\mathbf{X}'$ without differentiating $v(t)$. We see that $\mathbf{X}'(t) \cdot \mathbf{X}''(t) = v(t)v'(t)$. Therefore we find that

$$cv(t)\mathbf{e}_n = \mathbf{X}''(t) - \frac{[\mathbf{X}'(t) \cdot \mathbf{X}''(t)]}{|\mathbf{X}'(t)|^2}\mathbf{X}'(t). \tag{7-3}$$

As an example of the use of this formula, let us find the tangent and normal vectors at $t = 1$ for the twisted cubic $\mathbf{X}(t) = [t, t^2, t^3]$. We have

$$\mathbf{X}'(t) = [1, 2t, 3t^2], \qquad \mathbf{X}''(t) = [0, 2, 6t],$$

so

$$\mathbf{e}_t = \mathbf{X}'(t)/|\mathbf{X}'(t)| = \frac{[1, 2t, 3t^2]}{(1 + 4t^2 + 9t^4)^{1/2}}$$

and

$$cv(t)\mathbf{e}_n = [0, 2, 6t] - \frac{(4t + 18t^3)}{(1 + 4t^2 + 9t^4)^{1/2}}[1, 2t, 3t^2].$$

In particular, at $t = 1$, $\mathbf{X}' = [1, 2, 3]$ and $\mathbf{X}'' = [0, 2, 6]$. We find $\mathbf{e}_t$ by dividing $\mathbf{X}'$ by its own magnitude, thus obtaining $\mathbf{e}_t = [1/\sqrt{14}, 2/\sqrt{14}, 3/\sqrt{14}]$. Using (7-3), we next calculate

$$cv\mathbf{e}_n = [0, 2, 6] - \tfrac{22}{14}[1, 2, 3] = [-\tfrac{11}{7}, -\tfrac{8}{7}, \tfrac{9}{7}].$$

Dividing this vector by its own magnitude (note that we can multiply it through by 7 before dividing) we find that

$$\mathbf{e}_n = \left[-11/\sqrt{266}, -8/\sqrt{266}, 9/\sqrt{266}\right].$$

If we only needed vectors in the correct directions, we could use $\mathbf{T} = [1, 2, 3]$ and $\mathbf{N} = [-11, -8, 9]$. These two vectors generate the osculating plane. Since we are in three-dimensional space, we can use the cross product of these two, $\mathbf{T} \times \mathbf{N} = [42, -42, 14]$ as the normal vector to the plane. The equation of the osculating plane at $t = 1$ is therefore

$$42(x - 1) - 42(y - 1) + 14(z - 1) = 0$$

or

$$3x - 3y + z = 1. \tag{7-4}$$

The point is that the vectors $\mathbf{X}'$ and $\mathbf{X}''$ generate the same plane as $\mathbf{e}_{\text{t}}$ and $\mathbf{e}_{\text{n}}$. Formula (7–3) is nothing but the Gram-Schmidt orthogonalization process being applied to obtain $\mathbf{e}_{\text{n}}$. Since the vectors $\mathbf{X}'$ and $\mathbf{X}''$ generate the osculating plane, in R^3 we can use the cross product of these two just as well as the cross product of $\mathbf{e}_{\text{t}}$ and $\mathbf{e}_{\text{n}}$ for the normal vector to the plane.

In the above example we find $\mathbf{X}' \times \mathbf{X}'' = [6, -6, 2]$, and the equation of the osculating plane, $6(x - 1) - 6(y - 1) + 2(z - 1) = 0$, is equivalent to (7–4).

What happens to the properties of curves under euclidean motions? Here we are talking about functions $\mathbf{X}: R[a, b] \to R^n$, so we are interested in transformations in the image space.

The translation of a curve given by $\mathbf{X}(t)$ will give a curve given by $\mathbf{X}(t) + \mathbf{A}$. It is trivial to see that the new curve has exactly the same arc length function, unit tangent, and normal vectors.

A rotation or reflection gives the new curve $\mathbf{X}^*(t) = P^t\mathbf{X}(t)$, where P is an orthogonal matrix. Then $\mathbf{X}^{*\prime}(t) = P^t\mathbf{X}'(t)$, and hence the arc length function is the same. The unit tangent and normal vectors are transformed in the same way as the vector $\mathbf{X}$. Thus they are invariant under euclidean motions in the same sense as discussed on page 250.

PROBLEMS

1. Let $[x_1, x_2, \ldots, x_n] = \mathbf{X}(t)$ define a curve in R^n. Prove that the formula
$$ds^2 = dx_1^2 + dx_2^2 + \cdots + dx_n^2$$
is correct.

2. Suppose that two smooth curves are smoothly equivalent. Prove that their tangent vectors are scalar multiples of each other.

3. Using the fact that $|\mathbf{F}(t)| = [\mathbf{F}(t) \cdot \mathbf{F}(t)]^{1/2}$, prove that
$$\frac{d}{dt}|\mathbf{F}(t)| = \frac{(\mathbf{F}') \cdot \mathbf{F}}{|\mathbf{F}|}.$$

4. Suppose that $\mathbf{F}(t)$ and $\mathbf{G}(t)$ are differentiable functions in R^3. Prove that
$$(\mathbf{F} \times \mathbf{G})' = (\mathbf{F}') \times \mathbf{G} + \mathbf{F} \times (\mathbf{G}').$$

5. Describe the following curves, find the unit tangent vector, and the unit principal normal vector at the point indicated. Find the length of the curve. Find the osculating plane at the point indicated
   a) $x = t \cos t,\ y = t \sin t,\ z = t/2,\ 0 \le t \le 2\pi$ at $t = \pi$
   b) $x = 3t,\ y = 2t^3,\ z = 3t,\ 0 \le t \le 2$ at $t = 1$
   c) $x = t^4,\ y = t - 1,\ z = t^2 + t,\ 0 \le t \le 4$ at $t = 1$
   d) $x = \cos t,\ y = \sin t,\ z = \log \sec t,\ 0 \le t \le \pi/4$ at $t = \pi/4$
   e) $x = 2t,\ y = t^2,\ z = \log t,\ 1 \le t \le 4$, at $t = 1$

6. Find the length of the following curve in R^4. Find the unit tangent and principal normal at $t = 0$: $x = 6 \sin t,\ y = t^3,\ z = 6 \cos t,\ w = 3t^2,\ 0 \le t \le 2$.

7–2. SOME OF THE GEOMETRY OF CURVES

In this section we will investigate some of the elementary properties of curves in space. Throughout, we will assume the existence and continuity of as many derivatives as necessary. In the last section we introduced the unit tangent and principal normal vectors. These two vectors generate a plane, the osculating plane of the curve. It should seem clear that the osculating plane is in some sense the "best fitting" plane to the curve. We will begin this section by seeing in exactly what way this is true.

The reader should recall the difference between the behavior of the curves $y = x, y = x^2, y = x^3, \ldots$ near $x = 0$ in the xy-plane. As $x \to 0, y \to 0$ in each case. However, with each higher power of x, y goes to zero "more rapidly." Thus, since $x^3 = x \cdot x^2$, if x is close to zero, then x^3 is much closer to zero than x^2. The commonly used expression is that the curve $y = x^n$ has *order of contact n* with the x-axis at $x = 0$. We will use a similar terminology in describing how closely the osculating plane fits the curve.

The osculating plane contains the tangent vector; hence the curve is tangent to this plane. But because the plane also contains the principal normal, there is even a higher order of contact. Suppose that the curve is given by the function $\mathbf{X}(s)$, where s is the arc length parameter. Then $\mathbf{X}' = \mathbf{e}_t$ and $\mathbf{X}'' = \kappa\mathbf{e}_n$, where κ is some (positive) scalar function of s. We shall assume that $\kappa \neq 0$ unless specifically stated. The curves we are interested in will have

$$\frac{d}{dt}\mathbf{e}_t \neq \mathbf{0}$$

everywhere. At some particular point on the curve, say the point given by $s = s_0$, let $\mathbf{X}_0 = \mathbf{X}(s_0)$, $\mathbf{u}_1 = \mathbf{e}_t(s_0)$, and $\mathbf{u}_2 = \mathbf{e}_n(s_0)$. The mutually orthogonal unit vectors $\mathbf{u}_1$ and $\mathbf{u}_2$ can be completed to become an orthonormal basis $\mathbf{u}_1, \mathbf{u}_2, \mathbf{u}_3, \ldots, \mathbf{u}_n$, which we treat as a fixed orthonormal basis, and we refer the components of $\mathbf{X}$ to this coordinate system. That is, for any point $\mathbf{X}(s)$ on the curve, we have

$$\mathbf{X}(s) - \mathbf{X}_0 = \sum_{i=1}^{n} [(\mathbf{X}(s) - \mathbf{X}_0) \cdot \mathbf{u}_i]\mathbf{u}_i.$$

The first two terms of this expansion give the orthogonal projection $\mathbf{P}$ of $\mathbf{X} - \mathbf{X}_0$ onto the osculating plane. The remaining terms give the vector $\mathbf{N}$ which measures the distance from $\mathbf{X}$ to the osculating plane; that is,

$$\mathbf{N} = \sum_{i=3}^{n} [(\mathbf{X} - \mathbf{X}_0) \cdot \mathbf{u}_i]\mathbf{u}_i.$$

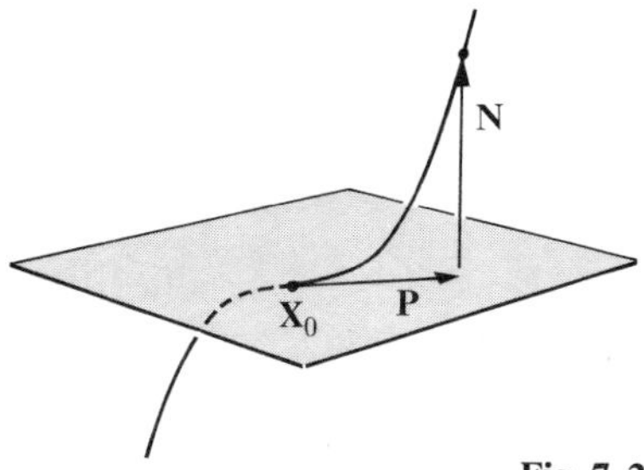

Fig. 7–2

Figure 7–2 gives an illustration (in three dimensions) of this situation.

The vectors $\mathbf{u}_i$ are constants. Therefore

$$\mathbf{N}'(s) = \frac{d}{ds}\mathbf{N}(s) = \sum_{i=3}^{n} (\mathbf{X}' \cdot \mathbf{u}_i)\mathbf{u}_i = \sum_{i=3}^{n} [\mathbf{e}_t(s) \cdot \mathbf{u}_i]\mathbf{u}_i.$$

At $s = s_0$, we have $\mathbf{e}_t = \mathbf{u}_1$, which is orthogonal to all of the other $\mathbf{u}_i$. Therefore $\mathbf{N}'(s_0) = \mathbf{0}$.

In a similar way

$$\mathbf{N}''(s) = \sum_{i=3}^{n} (\mathbf{X}'' \cdot \mathbf{u}_i)u_i = \sum_{i=3}^{n} [\kappa \mathbf{e}_n(s) \cdot \mathbf{u}_i]u_i.$$

Since at $s = s_0$, $\mathbf{e}_n = \mathbf{u}_2$, we also find that

$$\mathbf{N}''(s_0) = \mathbf{0}.$$

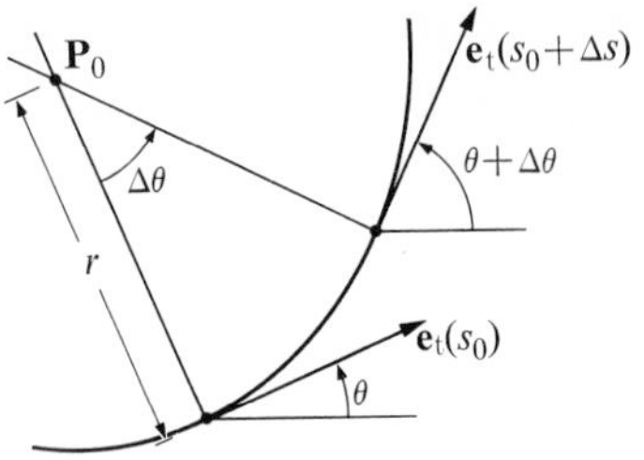

Fig. 7–3

This shows that the curve has a "second-order" tangency to the osculating plane. If the components of $\mathbf{N}$ are given a Taylor's series expansion in powers of $(s - s_0)$, the above result shows that the first nonvanishing terms will be of the order $(s - s_0)^3$ or higher.

Next, let us discuss the curvature of a curve. We begin with a heuristic discussion of the curvature of a curve in the plane. Suppose $\mathbf{e}_t(s_0)$ is the tangent vector to a plane curve at the point $\mathbf{X}(s_0)$. The tangent vector at $\mathbf{X}(s_0 + \Delta s)$ is $\mathbf{e}_t(s_0 + \Delta s)$. Let $\mathbf{e}_t(s_0)$ make the angle θ with the positive x-axis and let $\mathbf{e}_t(s_0 + \Delta s)$ make the angle $\theta + \Delta\theta$ with the same axis. At the points $\mathbf{X}(s_0)$ and $\mathbf{X}(s_0 + \Delta s)$ draw lines in the directions of the principal normals, as in Fig. 7–3. Let these two lines intersect at the point $\mathbf{P}_0$. Set

$$r = |\mathbf{P}_0 - \mathbf{X}(s_0)|.$$

The angle between the two normals at $\mathbf{P}_0$ is $\Delta\theta$, and the arc length of the curve between $\mathbf{X}(s_0)$ and $\mathbf{X}(s_0 + \Delta S)$, which we will call Δs, is thus approximately $r|\Delta\theta|$; that is,

$$|\Delta\theta|/|\Delta s| \doteq 1/r.$$

As $\Delta s \to 0$, the left-hand side of this relation approaches $|d\theta/ds|$. We can therefore set

$$|d\theta|/|ds| = 1/\rho$$

and call ρ the radius of curvature of the curve at the point $\mathbf{X}(s_0)$.

It happens that this derivative can be identified in another way. We have $\mathbf{e}_t = [\cos\theta, \sin\theta]$ and hence

$$\frac{d}{ds}\mathbf{e}_t = \left(\frac{d\theta}{ds}\right)[-\sin\theta, \cos\theta].$$

The vector $[-\sin\theta, \cos\theta]$ is orthogonal to $\mathbf{e}_t$ and of unit length. Therefore

$$|\mathbf{e}_t'| = |d\theta/ds| = 1/\rho.$$

This then is the heuristic background for the following definition.

Definition 7–8. Let a curve be defined by the function $\mathbf{X}(s)$, where s is the arc length parameter. Then

$$|d\mathbf{e}_t/ds| = |\mathbf{X}''(s)| = \kappa(s) \tag{7–5}$$

is called the *curvature* of the curve. The quantity $\rho(s) = 1/\kappa(s)$ is called the *radius of curvature* of the curve.

The *center of curvature* of the curve is the point $\mathbf{X}(s) + \rho(s)\mathbf{e}_n$. A circle of radius ρ with this center, in the osculating plane, gives the best circular approximation to the curve at the point $\mathbf{X}(s)$, just as the line through $\mathbf{X}(s)$ in the direction of $\mathbf{e}_t$ gives the best linear approximation. We shall not prove this assertion, or even define what we mean by "best approximation." This is just an intuitive discussion to help the reader visualize the meaning of these concepts.

From (7–5) and the definition of $\mathbf{e}_n$ we have

$$\frac{d}{ds}\mathbf{e}_t = \kappa(s)\mathbf{e}_n. \tag{7–6}$$

How can we determine the curvature of the curve if it is not given in terms of the arc length parameter? Suppose that the curve is given by $\mathbf{X}(t)$. Let $\mathbf{X}' = D\mathbf{X}$, $\mathbf{X}'' = D^2\mathbf{X}$, and set $v(t) = |\mathbf{X}'| = ds/dt$. The last function can be thought of as the speed of a particle moving along the curve if the parameter t is the time. We then have

$$\mathbf{X}' = v\mathbf{e}_t. \tag{7–7}$$

Now

$$\frac{d}{dt}\mathbf{e}_t = \left(\frac{d}{ds}\mathbf{e}_t\right)\left(\frac{ds}{dt}\right) = v\kappa\mathbf{e}_n.$$

Hence

$$\mathbf{X}'' = v'\mathbf{e}_t + v^2\kappa\mathbf{e}_n, \tag{7–8}$$

where we put $v' = dv/dt$. If we think of $\mathbf{X}'$ as representing the velocity of a moving particle, then $\mathbf{X}''$ represents the acceleration, and v' is the tangential component of the acceleration, while $v^2\kappa$ is the normal component of the acceleration.

We have $v = |\mathbf{X}'| = [\mathbf{X}' \cdot \mathbf{X}']^{1/2}$. Therefore

$$v' = \mathbf{X}' \cdot \mathbf{X}''/[\mathbf{X}' \cdot \mathbf{X}']^{1/2}.$$

Putting this expression into (7–8), we find that

$$\kappa = \frac{|(\mathbf{X}' \cdot \mathbf{X}')\mathbf{X}'' - (\mathbf{X}' \cdot \mathbf{X}'')\mathbf{X}'|}{(\mathbf{X}' \cdot \mathbf{X}')^2}. \tag{7–9}$$

If we restrict our attention to three-dimensional space, an even simpler formula can be obtained. In R^3 we can make use of the cross product of two vectors. Let us set $\mathbf{e}_b = \mathbf{e}_t \times \mathbf{e}_n$. Since $\mathbf{e}_t$ and $\mathbf{e}_n$ are orthogonal unit vectors, $\mathbf{e}_b$ is also a unit vector orthogonal to both $\mathbf{e}_t$ and $\mathbf{e}_n$. Indeed, $\mathbf{e}_t$, $\mathbf{e}_n$, and $\mathbf{e}_b$ form a right-handed triple of mutually orthogonal unit vectors.

Definition 7-9. Let $\mathbf{X}(t)$ define a smooth curve in R^3. If $\mathbf{e}_t$ and $\mathbf{e}_n$ are the unit tangent and principal normal vectors at some point of the curve, then the vector

$$\mathbf{e}_b = \mathbf{e}_t \times \mathbf{e}_n \tag{7-10}$$

is called the *unit binormal vector* to the curve at this point.

From (7-7) and (7-8), and with the help of this definition, we find that

$$\mathbf{X}' \times \mathbf{X}'' = v^3 \kappa \mathbf{e}_b \tag{7-11}$$

and hence

$$\kappa = \frac{|\mathbf{X}' \times \mathbf{X}''|}{(\mathbf{X}' \cdot \mathbf{X}')^{3/2}}\,. \tag{7-12}$$

This formula can be used to find the curvature in many practical cases.

It should be observed that the curvature as we have defined it is always positive (or zero). In the plane it is sometimes convenient to define a curvature which may be positive or negative, but such a definition is not as convenient in R^3 or any higher-dimensional space.

Continuing to restrict our attention to three-dimensional space, let us see what can be discovered about the derivative of $\mathbf{e}_b$ as defined in (7-10). From Theorem 7-2 we know that $(d/ds)\mathbf{e}_b$ is orthogonal to $\mathbf{e}_b$. However, using the result given in Problem 4 of the last section and from (7-10) we find that

$$\begin{aligned}\frac{d}{ds}\mathbf{e}_b &= \left(\frac{d}{ds}\mathbf{e}_t\right) \times \mathbf{e}_n + \mathbf{e}_t \times \left(\frac{d}{ds}\mathbf{e}_n\right)\\ &= \kappa\mathbf{e}_n \times \mathbf{e}_n + \mathbf{e}_t \times \left(\frac{d}{ds}\mathbf{e}_n\right)\\ &= \mathbf{e}_t \times \left(\frac{d}{ds}\mathbf{e}_n\right)\end{aligned}$$

since $\mathbf{e}_n \times \mathbf{e}_n = \mathbf{0}$. From this formula we see that $(d/ds)\mathbf{e}_b$ must be orthogonal to $\mathbf{e}_t$ as well as to $\mathbf{e}_b$. Since $\mathbf{e}_t$, $\mathbf{e}_n$, and $\mathbf{e}_b$ form an orthonormal set of generators for R^3, this means that $(d/ds)\mathbf{e}_b$ must be a scalar multiple of $\mathbf{e}_n$.

Definition 7-10. Let $\mathbf{e}_b$ be the unit binormal to a curve in R^3. Then the function $\tau(s)$ defined by

$$\frac{d}{ds}\mathbf{e}_b = -\tau(s)\mathbf{e}_n \tag{7-13}$$

is called the *torsion* of the curve.

The torsion measures the rate at which the curve is "twisting" out of the osculating plane. The sign in (7-13) is so chosen that a right-hand screw has a positive torsion (see the problems at the end of this section).

In Eq. (7-6) and (7-13) we have formulas for the derivatives of two of the three vectors $\mathbf{e}_t$, $\mathbf{e}_n$, and $\mathbf{e}_b$. To find the derivative of the third, we observe that since these vectors form a right-handed orthonormal set, we have $\mathbf{e}_n = -\mathbf{e}_t \times \mathbf{e}_b$. Hence

$$\begin{aligned}\frac{d}{ds}\mathbf{e}_n &= -\left(\frac{d}{ds}\mathbf{e}_t\right) \times \mathbf{e}_b - \mathbf{e}_t \times \left(\frac{d}{ds}\mathbf{e}_b\right)\\ &= -\kappa(s)\mathbf{e}_n \times \mathbf{e}_b + \tau(s)\mathbf{e}_t \times \mathbf{e}_n,\end{aligned}$$

or finally

$$\frac{d}{ds}\mathbf{e}_n = -\kappa(s)\mathbf{e}_t + \tau(s)\mathbf{e}_b. \tag{7–14}$$

We have therefore proved

▶ **Theorem 7–6.** Let $\mathbf{X}(s)$ define a curve in R^3 in terms of the arc length parameter s. Suppose that $\mathbf{X}(s)$ has a nonvanishing second derivative and a continuous third derivative. Let $\mathbf{e}_t$, $\mathbf{e}_n$, and $\mathbf{e}_b$ be the unit tangent, principal normal, and binormal vectors to the curve and let κ and τ be the curvature and torsion. Then

$$\begin{aligned}\frac{d}{ds}\mathbf{e}_t &= \kappa\mathbf{e}_n,\\ \frac{d}{ds}\mathbf{e}_n &= -\kappa\mathbf{e}_t + \tau\mathbf{e}_b,\\ \frac{d}{ds}\mathbf{e}_b &= -\tau\mathbf{e}_n.\end{aligned}$$

These three formulas are often called the Frenet formulas. They are more correctly known as the Serret-Frenet formulas since they were first published by Serret in 1851. Frenet published them a year later. These formulas are the basis for much of the classical differential geometry of curves. Here we will use them to obtain a formula for the torsion of a curve and also to prove an important uniqueness theorem.

From (7–8) and using the fact that

$$\frac{d}{dt}\mathbf{e} = \left(\frac{d}{ds}\mathbf{e}\right)\left(\frac{ds}{dt}\right) = v\frac{d}{ds}\mathbf{e},$$

we find that

$$\mathbf{X}''' = (v'' - v^3\kappa^2)\mathbf{e}_t + (3vv'\kappa + v^3\kappa')\mathbf{e}_n + v^3\kappa\tau\mathbf{e}_b, \tag{7–15}$$

where the primes indicate differentiation with respect to t. From (7–7), (7–8), and (7–15) we see that the matrix of the components of $\mathbf{X}'$, $\mathbf{X}''$, and $\mathbf{X}'''$ is a lower diagonal matrix. Hence the scalar triple product of these three vectors is given by

$$\mathbf{X}' \cdot \mathbf{X}'' \times \mathbf{X}''' = v^6\kappa^2\tau.$$

From (7–11) we then obtain the following formula for the torsion of a curve given in terms of an arbitrary parameter

$$\tau = \frac{\mathbf{X}' \cdot \mathbf{X}'' \times \mathbf{X}'''}{|\mathbf{X}' \times \mathbf{X}''|^2}. \tag{7–16}$$

Before going on to the next theorem, let us observe that if $\mathbf{F}: R[a, b] \to R^n$ is a differentiable function with $\mathbf{F}'(t) = \mathbf{0}$ for all $t \in R[a, b]$, then $\mathbf{F}(t)$ must be a constant. This follows from the fact that the derivative of each of the component functions must be zero, and hence must be a constant. The entire vector function is therefore itself a constant.

Now we will prove the following theorem. Note that the last sentence is the heart of the theorem. The rest of the statement consists of the necessary qualifications.

Theorem 7-7. Let $C = [\mathbf{F}(s): R[0, \mathrm{L}] \to R^3]$ and $C^* = [\mathbf{F}^*(s): R[0, L] \to R^3]$ be two smooth curves in R^3 defined in terms of their arc length parameters s, having nonvanishing second derivatives and continuous third derivatives. Suppose that the initial points of the curves coincide and that the two curves have the same unit tangent and principal normal vectors at $s = 0$. Then, if the curvature and torsion functions of the two curves are identical, the two curves coincide.

Proof. Let $\mathbf{e}_t(s)$, $\mathbf{e}_n(s)$, $\mathbf{e}_b(s)$, $\kappa(s)$, and $\tau(s)$ be the unit tangent, principal normal and binormal vectors, and the curvature and torsion functions for the curve C. The corresponding vectors and functions for the curve C^* will be indicated by asterisks. The hypotheses of the theorem tell us that $\mathbf{F}(0) = \mathbf{F}^*(0)$, $\mathbf{e}_t(0) = \mathbf{e}_t^*(0)$, $\mathbf{e}_n(0) = \mathbf{e}_n^*(0)$, and that $\kappa(s) = \kappa^*(s)$, $\tau(s) = \tau^*(s)$ for all s.

We start by computing, with the help of the Frenet formulas,

$$
\begin{aligned}
\frac{d}{ds}&(\mathbf{e}_t \cdot \mathbf{e}_t^* + \mathbf{e}_n \cdot \mathbf{e}_n^* + \mathbf{e}_b \cdot \mathbf{e}_b^*) \\
&= \kappa \mathbf{e}_n \cdot \mathbf{e}_t^* + \kappa^* \mathbf{e}_t \cdot \mathbf{e}_n^* - \kappa \mathbf{e}_t \cdot \mathbf{e}_n^* + \tau \mathbf{e}_b \cdot \mathbf{e}_n^* - \kappa^* \mathbf{e}_n \cdot \mathbf{e}_t^* \\
&\quad + \tau^* \mathbf{e}_n \cdot \mathbf{e}_b^* - \tau \mathbf{e}_n \cdot \mathbf{e}_b^* - \tau^* \mathbf{e}_b \cdot \mathbf{e}_n^* \\
&= (\kappa - \kappa^*)\mathbf{e}_n \cdot \mathbf{e}_t^* + (\kappa^* - \kappa)\mathbf{e}_t \cdot \mathbf{e}_n^* + (\tau - \tau^*)\mathbf{e}_b \cdot \mathbf{e}_n^* + (\tau^* - \tau)\mathbf{e}_n \cdot \mathbf{e}_b^* \\
&= 0.
\end{aligned}
$$

The function which was differentiated here is therefore a constant, independent of s. At $s = 0$ we have $\mathbf{e}_t = \mathbf{e}_t^*$ and $\mathbf{e}_n = \mathbf{e}_n^*$. Therefore we must also have $\mathbf{e}_b = \mathbf{e}_b^*$ at this point. These vectors are all of unit length, and hence we conclude that for all s

$$\mathbf{e}_t \cdot \mathbf{e}_t^* + \mathbf{e}_n \cdot \mathbf{e}_n^* + \mathbf{e}_b \cdot \mathbf{e}_b^* = 3. \tag{7-17}$$

Since these vectors are all of magnitude one, the only way that (7-17) can hold is for $\mathbf{e}_t = \mathbf{e}_t^*$, $\mathbf{e}_n = \mathbf{e}_n^*$, and $\mathbf{e}_b = \mathbf{e}_b^*$ for all s. But then

$$\frac{d}{ds}[\mathbf{F}(s) - \mathbf{F}^*(s)] = \mathbf{e}_t(s) - \mathbf{e}_t^*(s) = \mathbf{0},$$

and hence $\mathbf{F}(s) - \mathbf{F}^*(s)$ is a constant. Since $\mathbf{F}(0) = \mathbf{F}^*(0)$, we must have

$$\mathbf{F}(s) = \mathbf{F}^*(s),$$

thus proving the theorem. ▮

An interesting corollary to this theorem is that if two curves have identical torsion and (nonvanishing) curvature functions, then there must exist a euclidean motion which maps one into the other. The reader is invited to prove this corollary in the problem set below.

PROBLEMS

1. Let a curve be defined by $\mathbf{X}(t) = [x_1(t), x_2(t), \ldots, x_n(t)]$. Set

$$v^2 = \sum_{i=1}^{n} x_i'^2, \qquad w^2 = \sum_{i=1}^{n} x_i''^2, \qquad \text{and} \qquad u = \sum_{i=1}^{n} x_i' x_i''.$$

Prove that the curvature is given by

$$\kappa = \frac{1}{v^3}[v^2 w^2 - u^2]^{1/2}.$$

2. Let a curve in the xy-plane be defined by $y = f(x)$ [i.e., $x = t, y = f(t)$]. Prove that

$$\kappa = \frac{|f''|}{[1 + f'^2]^{3/2}}.$$

3. Let a curve in three-dimensional space be defined by $x = f(z), y = g(z)$. Derive a formula for the torsion in terms of the derivatives of f and g.
4. What is the role of the hypothesis in Theorems 7–6 and 7–7 that the second derivative is nonvanishing? Give an example showing that Theorem 7–7 need not remain true if this hypothesis is not included.
5. In the xy-plane, for any given θ, set $\mathbf{e}_r = [\cos\theta, \sin\theta]$ and $\mathbf{e}_\theta = [-\sin\theta, \cos\theta]$. A curve in the plane can be defined in terms of its polar coordinates by specifying r and θ as functions of t. Then $\mathbf{e}_r$ is also a function of t, and the curve is defined by

$$\mathbf{X}(t) = r(t)\mathbf{e}_r(t).$$

Prove that

$$\frac{d}{dt}\mathbf{X} = \frac{dr}{dt}\mathbf{e}_r + r\left(\frac{d\theta}{dt}\right)\mathbf{e}_\theta$$

and

$$\frac{d^2}{dt^2}\mathbf{X} = \left(\frac{d^2r}{dt^2} - r\frac{d^2\theta}{dt^2}\right)\mathbf{e}_r + \left(2\frac{dr}{dt}\frac{d\theta}{dt} + r\frac{d^2\theta}{dt^2}\right)\mathbf{e}_\theta.$$

Obtain formulas for $|\mathbf{X}'|$, $|\mathbf{X}''|$, and κ for this case. Give the formulas for the same quantities if r is a function of θ (the standard polar coordinate case).
6. Calculate the torsion and curvature for the right-handed helix $(a, b > 0)$.

$$x = a\cos\theta, \qquad y = a\sin\theta, \qquad z = b\theta.$$

7. Calculate the curvature and torsion for each of the curves of Problem 5 of the last section at the point given in that problem.

8. Suppose that $\mathbf{F}(t)$ is a continuously differentiable vector-valued function defined for all t and mapping R into R^n. Suppose that for all t, $\mathbf{F}'(t) = \mathbf{A}$ is a constant. Prove that $\mathbf{F}(t) = \mathbf{C} + t\mathbf{A}$, where $\mathbf{C}$ is another constant.
9. Let $\mathbf{X}(t)$, $a \leq t \leq b$, define a smooth curve in R^n whose curvature vanishes identically. Prove that the curve is a line segment.
10. Let $\mathbf{X}(t)$, $a \leq t \leq b$, and define a smooth curve in R^3 with nonvanishing curvature whose torsion is identically zero. Prove that the curve must lie in a plane. [*Hint:* $\mathbf{e}_b$ is a constant. Show that

$$\frac{d}{dt}[\mathbf{X}(t) \cdot \mathbf{e}_b] = 0$$

and then that $[\mathbf{X}(t) - \mathbf{X}(a)] \cdot \mathbf{e}_b = 0$.]
11. Let C and C^* be two smooth curves in R^3 defined in terms of their arc length parameters s, having nonvanishing second derivatives and continuous third derivatives. Suppose also that their curvature and torsion functions are identical. Prove that there must be a euclidean motion $\mathbf{T}:R^3 \to R^3$ such that $\mathbf{F}(s)$ and $\mathbf{T}[\mathbf{F}^*(s)]$ are identical (i.e., the two curves are identical under euclidean motions).

7-3. LINE INTEGRALS

To introduce the idea of the integral of a vector-valued function of a scalar, we could start by looking at the Riemann sums of the function and developing the entire theory from the beginning. However, we may assume that the reader is already familiar with the integral of a real-valued function. We can then obtain the properties of the integral of a vector-valued function with the help of the following definition of such an integral.

Definition 7-11. Let the function $\mathbf{G}:R[a, b] \to R^n$ be continuous. Then we define

$$\int_a^b \mathbf{G}(t)\, dt = \sum_{i=1}^{n} \mathbf{e}_i \int_a^b g_i(t)\, dt. \tag{7-18}$$

Recall that a function is continuous if and only if all of its components are continuous. Hence, if $\mathbf{G}$ is continuous, then all of the integrals on the right-hand side of (7-18) exist.

The first thing we must do is obtain some of the basic properties of this integral.

Theorem 7-8. Let $\mathbf{F}$ and $\mathbf{G}$ be continuous functions from $R[a, b]$ to R^n. Then,

$$\int_a^b [\mathbf{F}(t) + \mathbf{G}(t)]\, dt = \int_a^b \mathbf{F}(t)\, dt + \int_a^b \mathbf{G}(t)\, dt.$$

If c is any number such that $a < c < b$, then

$$\int_a^b \mathbf{F}(t)\, dt = \int_a^c \mathbf{F}(t)\, dt + \int_c^b \mathbf{F}(t)\, dt.$$

Finally, for $a < x < b$, the integral of $\mathbf{F}$ from a to x is a differentiable function of x and

$$\frac{d}{dx}\int_a^x \mathbf{F}(t)\,dt = \mathbf{F}(x).$$

These properties all follow from the similar properties for real-valued functions and can be proved by breaking $\mathbf{F}$ up into its components. The proofs are left to the reader.

An important fact about the integrals of real-valued functions is that they can be approximated by Riemann sums. A similar result holds for the integrals of vector-valued functions.

▶ **Theorem 7–9.** Let $\mathbf{F}: R[a, b] \to R$ be continuous for all points of $R[a, b]$. Then, given any $\epsilon > 0$, there exists a $\delta > 0$ such that if $\mathcal{P} = \langle t_0, t_1, \ldots, t_N \rangle$ is any partition of the interval $R[a, b]$ whose largest subdivision is smaller than δ, and if $x_1, x_2, \ldots, x_n$ is any sequence of real numbers such that $t_{i-1} \leq x_i \leq t_i$ for each i, then

$$\left| \int_a^b \mathbf{F}(t)\,dt - \sum_{i=1}^{N} \mathbf{F}(x_i)(t_i - t_{i-1}) \right| < \epsilon.$$

Proof. Each component of $\mathbf{F}$ is itself continuous on this interval and hence is uniformly continuous. Given $\epsilon > 0$ and one of the components, f_j, let $\delta_j > 0$ be such that $|x - \tau| < \delta_j$ implies $|f_j(x) - f_j(\tau)| < \epsilon/A$, where $A = (b - a)\sqrt{n}$. Now let $\mathcal{P}$ be any partition whose largest subinterval is smaller than δ_j, and let $R[t_{i-1}, t_i]$ be one of the intervals of this partition. Then by the mean-value theorem for integrals, there exists a τ_i, $t_{i-1} \leq \tau_i \leq t_i$, such that

$$\int_{t_{i=1}}^{t_i} f_j(t)\,dt = f_j(\tau_i)(t_i - t_{i-1}).$$

If each x_i is such that $t_{i-1} \leq x_i \leq t_i$, then $|x_i - \tau_i| \leq t_i - t_{i-1} < \delta_j$. Therefore

$$\left| \int_a^b f_j(t)\,dt - \sum_{i=1}^{N} f_j(x_i)(t_i - t_{i-1}) \right|$$

$$\leq \left| \int_a^b f_j(t)\,dt - \sum_{i=1}^{N} f_j(\tau_i)(t_i - t_{i-1}) \right| + \left| \sum_{i=1}^{N} [f_j(\tau_i) - f_j(x_i)](t_i - t_{i-1}) \right|$$

$$\leq 0 + \sum_{i=0}^{N} |f_j(\tau_i) - f_j(x_i)|(t_i - t_{i-1})$$

$$< \sum_{i=0}^{N} \frac{\epsilon}{A}(t_i - t_{i-1}) = \frac{\epsilon}{\sqrt{n}}.$$

Now we merely need to let δ be the minimum of the n δ_j's. If each component of a vector is less than $\epsilon/\sqrt{n}$, then the magnitude of the entire vector must be less than ϵ. ▮

The last result can be used to prove the following very important theorem.

▶ **Theorem 7-10.** Let $\mathbf{F}:R[a, b] \to R^n$ be continuous. Then

$$\left|\int_a^b \mathbf{F}(t)\, dt\right| \le \int_a^b |\mathbf{F}(t)|\, dt.$$

Proof. Using Theorem 7-9, given any $\epsilon > 0$, there exists a $\delta > 0$ such that if $\mathcal{P}$ is any partition whose largest subdivision is smaller than δ, and if $t_{i-1} \le x_i \le t_i$ for each i, then

$$\left|\int_a^b \mathbf{F}(t)\, dt - \sum_{i=1}^{N} \mathbf{F}(x_i)(t_i - t_{i-1})\right| < \epsilon. \tag{7-19}$$

In each interval, choose the x_i to satisfy the mean-value theorem for integrals for the real-valued continuous function $|\mathbf{F}(t)|$, that is, choose x_i such that

$$\int_{t_{i-1}}^{t_i} |\mathbf{F}(t)|\, dt = |\mathbf{F}(x_i)|(t_i - t_{i-1})$$

and hence

$$\int_a^b |\mathbf{F}(t)|\, dt = \sum_{i=1}^{N} |\mathbf{F}(x_i)|(t_i - t_{i-1}).$$

But, then, from (7-19) we have

$$\left|\int_a^b \mathbf{F}(t)\, dt\right| < \left|\sum_{i=1}^{N} \mathbf{F}(x_i)(t_i - t_{i-1})\right| + \epsilon$$

$$\le \sum_{i=1}^{N} |\mathbf{F}(x_i)|(t_i - t_{i-1}) + \epsilon = \int_a^b |\mathbf{F}(t)|\, dt + \epsilon.$$

Since ϵ is arbitrary, this can be true only if the conclusion of the theorem is true. Thus the theorem is proved. ▮

When we are given a curve in R^n and a function which is defined at every point of the curve, there are several different ways in which we can obtain an "integral along the curve." Let us give the definitions of two of these integrals at this point.

Definition 7-12. Let $C = [\mathbf{X}(t):R[a, b] \to R^n]$ be a smooth curve in R^n. Let G be a subset of R^n containing all of the points of C. Let the following functions be defined and continuous in G, with ranges as indicated: $f:G \to R$ and $\mathbf{F}:G \to R^n$. Then we define

$$\int_C f(\mathbf{X})\, ds = \int_a^b f[\mathbf{X}(t)]\, |\mathbf{X}'(t)|\, dt, \tag{7-20}$$

$$\int_C \mathbf{F}(\mathbf{X}) \cdot d\mathbf{X} = \int_a^b \mathbf{F}[\mathbf{X}(t)] \cdot [\mathbf{X}'(t)]\, dt. \tag{7-21}$$

While both these integrals have other representations, the two given above are the easiest to remember. The definition can be summarized by the conventions

$$ds = |\mathbf{X}'(t)|\,dt = |D\mathbf{X}(t)|\,dt,$$
$$d\mathbf{X} = \mathbf{X}'(t)\,dt = [D\mathbf{X}(t)]\,dt.$$

Note that $\mathbf{X}'(t)$ is a vector (or an $n \times 1$ matrix). Note also how much the first integral is simplified if the curve is given in terms of the parameter of arc length. Then $|\mathbf{X}'| = 1$. We have $\mathbf{X} = \mathbf{X}(s)$, and hence

$$\int_C f(\mathbf{X})\,ds = \int_a^b f[\mathbf{X}(s)]\,ds.$$

The second type of integral is sometimes written in terms of the differential of arc length also, with the help of the following convention:

$$d\mathbf{X} = \mathbf{X}'(t)\,dt = \mathbf{e}_t|\mathbf{X}'(t)|\,dt = \mathbf{e}_t\frac{ds}{dt}\,dt = \mathbf{e}_t\,ds. \tag{7–22}$$

Here $\mathbf{e}_t$ is the unit tangent vector to the curve. Any of these expressions can be substituted for $d\mathbf{X}$ in (7–21). Since different writers often prefer different notations, the reader should be aware of all of these equivalent notations.

There is still one more representation which is often found. The function $\mathbf{X} = \mathbf{X}(t)$ can be written in terms of its components

$$\mathbf{X}(t) = [x_1(t), x_2(t), \ldots, x_n(t)].$$

Then, following the above convention, we can also write

$$\begin{aligned} d\mathbf{X} &= [x_1'(t), \ldots, x_n'(t)]\,dt \\ &= [x_1'(t)\,dt, x_2'(t)\,dt, \ldots, x_n'(t)\,dt], \end{aligned}$$

or, since we also write

$$x_i'(t)\,dt = dx_i,$$

we have

$$d\mathbf{X} = [dx_1, dx_2, \ldots, dx_n].$$

The last notation is very often introduced into integrals of the form (7–21). When we do this we give the integral a special name.

Definition 7–13. Let the curve C and the function $\mathbf{F}$ be as in the previous definition. Then the *line integral* of $\mathbf{F}$ along C is the integral defined in (7–21). Any of the following notations may be used to represent it:

$$\begin{aligned} \int_C \mathbf{F}(\mathbf{X}) \cdot d\mathbf{X} &= \int_C \mathbf{F}(\mathbf{X}) \cdot \mathbf{e}_t\,ds \\ &= \int_C f_1(\mathbf{X})\,dx_1 + f_2(\mathbf{X})\,dx_2 + \cdots + f_n(\mathbf{X})\,dx_n. \end{aligned}$$

The last form of the line integral is often found in texts which do not make use of the vector notation. It is important to note that given an integral in this form, we can reconstruct the function **F**; it is merely the function whose components are the f_i. When we know the curve C, we can replace each dx_i by $x_i'(t)\,dt$ to obtain an integral which we can evaluate.

One of the reasons the line integral is so important is that it occurs in so many physical applications. For example, if **F**(**X**) is the force exerted on a particle at the point **X** (force is a vector quantity), then the work required to move the particle along the path C is given by

$$\int_C \mathbf{F}(\mathbf{X}) \cdot d\mathbf{X}.$$

Let us give an example which shows how an actual line integral can be evaluated. Let C be the helix defined by

$$\mathbf{X}(t) = [a \cos t, a \sin t, bt], \qquad 0 \le t \le 2\pi.$$

We wish to evaluate the line integral

$$\int_C y\,dx + x\,dy + z\,dz = \int_C [y, x, z] \cdot d\mathbf{X}, \tag{7-23}$$

which becomes

$$\int_0^{2\pi} -a^2 \sin^2 t\,dt + a^2 \cos^2 t\,dt + b^2 t\,dt = \int_0^{2\pi} [a^2 \cos 2t + b^2 t]\,dt = 2b^2\pi^2.$$

The fundamental theorem of calculus has an analogue for line integrals. We will now prove this result.

▶ **Theorem 7-11.** Let G be an open subset of R^n. Let $\phi: G \to R$ be a scalar-valued function which is C^1 at every point of G. Let $C = [\mathbf{X}(t): R[a, b] \to G]$ be a smooth curve in R^n, every point of which is contained in G. Let $\mathbf{A} = \mathbf{X}(a)$ and $\mathbf{B} = \mathbf{X}(b)$ be the initial and terminal points of the curve. Then

$$\int_C [\operatorname{grad} \phi(\mathbf{X})] \cdot d\mathbf{X} = \phi(\mathbf{B}) - \phi(\mathbf{A}). \tag{7-24}$$

Proof. Let $g(t) = \phi[\mathbf{X}(t)]$. Then

$$[g'(t)] = [d\phi(\mathbf{X})][d\mathbf{X}(t)] = [\operatorname{grad} \phi(\mathbf{X})] \cdot [\mathbf{X}'(t)].$$

Note that $[d\phi(\mathbf{X})]$ is a row matrix while $[d\mathbf{X}(t)]$ is a column vector (or matrix). We therefore find that

$$\begin{aligned}\int_C [\operatorname{grad} \phi] \cdot d\mathbf{X} &= \int_a^b [\operatorname{grad} \phi] \cdot [\mathbf{X}'(t)]\,dt \\ &= \int_a^b g'(t)\,dt = g(b) - g(a) = \phi(\mathbf{B}) - \phi(\mathbf{A}). \ \blacksquare\end{aligned}$$

This theorem makes it easy to evaluate a line integral when the function **F** can be identified as being the gradient of some function ϕ. For example, if **F** is the function which is defined in (7–23), then we see that $\mathbf{F} = [y, x, z] = \text{grad}\,(xy + \frac{1}{2}z^2)$. Hence

$$\int_C \mathbf{F} \cdot d\mathbf{X} = (xy + \tfrac{1}{2}z^2)\Big]_{(a,0,0)}^{(a,0,2b\pi)} = 2b^2\pi^2.$$

The problem is, under what conditions will a given vector-valued function be the gradient of some scalar-valued function? The rest of this section will be devoted to investigating some aspects of this problem.

The first thing that we observe is that if $\mathbf{F} = \text{grad}\,\phi$, then by Eq. (7–24) the value of the line integral over a given path C depends only on the endpoints of the path. No matter how the curve may wind about in joining these two points, only the initial and terminal points of the curve are needed to determine the value of the integral. Of course, the curve cannot leave the region in which $\mathbf{F} = \text{grad}\,\phi$.

Definition 7–14. Let $\mathbf{F}: G \to R^n$ be continuous at every point of G, a subset of R^n. Then we say that the line integral

$$\int_C \mathbf{F} \cdot d\mathbf{X}$$

(with the curve C unspecified*) is *independent of path* in G if and only if, given any two points $\mathbf{A}$ and $\mathbf{B}$ in G and two curves C_1 and C_2 which are contained in G and such that both have initial point $\mathbf{A}$ and terminal point $\mathbf{B}$, then

$$\int_{C_1} \mathbf{F} \cdot d\mathbf{X} = \int_{C_2} \mathbf{F} \cdot d\mathbf{X}.$$

A line integral is thus independent of path if and only if its value depends only on the initial and terminal points of the curve.

Before we continue we need to obtain a few properties of line integrals.

Theorem 7–12. Let $\mathbf{F}$ be continuous at every point of the curve C. Then

$$\int_{-C} \mathbf{F} \cdot d\mathbf{X} = -\int_C \mathbf{F} \cdot d\mathbf{X}.$$

Proof. Let $C = [\mathbf{X}(t): R[a, b] \to R^n]$. Then $-C = [\mathbf{X}_1(u): R[-b, -a] \to R^n]$, where $\mathbf{X}_1(u) = \mathbf{X}(-u)$ for every u, and

$$\int_{-C} \mathbf{F} \cdot d\mathbf{X} = \int_{-b}^{-a} \mathbf{F}[X_1(u)] \cdot [D\mathbf{X}_1(u)]\, du = -\int_b^a \mathbf{F}[\mathbf{X}(t)] \cdot [-D\mathbf{X}(t)]\, dt$$

$$= -\int_a^b \mathbf{F} \cdot d\mathbf{X}.$$

Here we have put $u = -t$ and made use of the facts that $D\mathbf{X}_1(u) = [d\mathbf{X}_1(u)] = [d\mathbf{X}(-u)][du(t)] = -[d\mathbf{X}(t)] = -D\mathbf{X}(t)$, $du = -dt$, and finally that the value of the integral changes in sign when the limits of integration are interchanged. This last statement is really the whole content of the theorem. ▌

---

* Henceforth, however, we always assume that the curve along which we integrate is a piecewise smooth curve, i.e. is given by a C^1 function except at a finite number of points.

Theorem 7–13. Let $\mathbf{F}:G \to R^n$ be continuous in a region G of R^n and let C_1 and C_2 be two curves contained in G which are such that the initial point of C_2 is the same as the terminal point of C_1. Then

$$\int_{C_1+C_2} \mathbf{F} \cdot d\mathbf{X} = \int_{C_1} \mathbf{F} \cdot d\mathbf{X} + \int_{C_2} \mathbf{F} \cdot d\mathbf{X}.$$

Proof. This theorem follows from the similar property of integrals of a real-valued function on the real line. The formal proof is left for the reader.

We now return to the problem of independence of path.

▶ **Theorem 7–14.** The line integral

$$\int_C \mathbf{F} \cdot d\mathbf{X}$$

is independent of path in a region G of R^n if and only if

$$\int_C \mathbf{F} \cdot d\mathbf{X} = 0$$

for every closed curve in G.

Proof. Suppose that the integral is independent of path in G. Let C be a closed curve in G, that is, $C = [\mathbf{X}:R[a, b] \to R^n]$ with $\mathbf{X}(a) = \mathbf{X}(b)$. Let C_1 and C_2 be the curves defined by the same function $\mathbf{X}(t)$, but with $C_1 = [\mathbf{X}:R[a, \frac{1}{2}(a + b)] \to R^n]$ and $C_2 = [\mathbf{X}:R[\frac{1}{2}(a + b), b] \to R^n]$. Then $C = C_1 + C_2$. On the other hand, the curves C_1 and $-C_2$ have the same initial and terminal points. Hence by our assumption of the independence of path,

$$\int_{C_1} \mathbf{F} \cdot d\mathbf{X} = \int_{-C_2} \mathbf{F} \cdot d\mathbf{X}.$$

Therefore

$$\int_C \mathbf{F} \cdot d\mathbf{X} = \int_{C_1} \mathbf{F} \cdot d\mathbf{X} + \int_{C_2} \mathbf{F} \cdot d\mathbf{X} = \int_{C_1} \mathbf{F} \cdot d\mathbf{X} - \int_{-C_2} \mathbf{F} \cdot d\mathbf{X} = 0.$$

The proof of the other half of the theorem is similar. The reader is asked to complete it as one of the problems at the end of this section. ▌

We can now return to the connection between independence of path and the existence of a scalar function ϕ such that $\mathbf{F} = \operatorname{grad} \phi$.

▶ **Theorem 7–15.** If $\mathbf{F}:G \to R^n$ is continuous in the open region G of R^n and if the line integral $\int_C \mathbf{F} \cdot d\mathbf{X}$ is independent of path in G, then there exists a function $\phi:G \to R$ such that $\mathbf{F}(\mathbf{X}) = \operatorname{grad} \phi(\mathbf{X})$.

Proof. Let $\mathbf{A}$ be some fixed point in G. For any point $\mathbf{X}$ in G define the function $\phi(\mathbf{X})$ by

$$\phi(\mathbf{X}) = \int_{\mathbf{A}}^{\mathbf{X}} \mathbf{F} \cdot d\mathbf{X}.$$

Here we can indicate the path of integration by merely showing the initial and terminal points of the curve. Since the integral is independent of path in G, any curve joining $\mathbf{A}$

and $\mathbf{X}$ will give the same value. We will now show that the function $\phi(\mathbf{X})$ defined in this way is the desired function. To do this, we must prove that $\partial\phi/\partial x_i = f_i(\mathbf{X})$ for each i. (The f_i are the components of $\mathbf{F}$.)

Let $\mathbf{X}$ be an arbitrary point of G. There is some neighborhood of $\mathbf{X}$ which is contained in G. Let $\mathbf{B}$ be some point of this neighborhood such that for every $j \neq i$, $b_j = x_j$, while $b_i < x_i$; that is, all the coordinates of B are identical with the coordinates of $\mathbf{X}$ except for the ith coordinate, which is smaller than the ith coordinate of $\mathbf{X}$. Let C_1 be any curve in G from $\mathbf{A}$ to $\mathbf{B}$. Let C_x be the curve from $\mathbf{B}$ to $\mathbf{X}$ defined by the function $\mathbf{P}: R[b_i, x_i] \to R^n$, where

$$\mathbf{P}(t) = [b_1, b_2, \ldots, b_{i-1}, t, b_{i+1}, \ldots, b_n].$$

Then $d\mathbf{P} = \mathbf{e}_i$, and hence along C_x, $d\mathbf{X} = \mathbf{e}_i\, dt$. Therefore

$$\phi(\mathbf{X}) = \int_{C_1+C_x} \mathbf{F}\cdot d\mathbf{X} = \phi(\mathbf{B}) + \int_{C_x} \mathbf{F}\cdot d\mathbf{X} = \phi(\mathbf{B}) + \int_{b_i}^{x_i} f_i[\mathbf{P}(t)]\, dt.$$

But, then, $\partial\phi/\partial x_i = f_i(\mathbf{X})$, which is what we wished to show.* ▮

Given a function $\mathbf{F}$, if we wish to find the function ϕ to satisfy the equation $\mathbf{F} = \text{grad}\,\phi$ we could actually compute the values of the integral in the above proof, or, as is usually simpler, we could perform "indefinite" integration, one component at a time. That is, we would hold all except one of the components of $\mathbf{X}$ fixed and integrate with respect to that one. Suppose, for example, that we have

$$\mathbf{F} = [2xy + z^2 \cos x, x^2 - 2yz^3, 2z \sin x - 3y^2z^3 + 4z].$$

Then $\mathbf{F}$ can be grad ϕ only if $\partial\phi/\partial x = 2xy + z^2 \cos x$. When we integrate this equation with respect to x, we find that $\phi = x^2y + z^2 \sin x + c$. Here c is a constant with respect to x only. We should really write $c = c(y, z)$, which, when differentiated with respect to y, must yield the second component of $\mathbf{F}$. That is, $x^2 + \partial c/\partial y = x^2 - 2yz^3$. Hence $\partial c/\partial y = -2yz^3$, and therefore $c(y, z) = -y^2z^3 + c_1(z)$.

Up to this point we have shown that the desired ϕ must be of the form $\phi = x^2y + z^2 \sin x - y^2z^3 + c_1(z)$. Differentiating this expression with respect to z and comparing with the third component of $\mathbf{F}$ shows that $dc_1/dz = 4z$. Therefore the only possible ϕ is

$$\phi = x^2y + z^2 \sin x - y^2z^3 + 2z^2 + k,$$

where k is any constant. Indeed, the process we have gone through suffices to show that grad $\phi = \mathbf{F}$. If we had started with a function which was not the gradient of some scalar function, we would have arrived at a contradiction at some point in the process.

For example, $\mathbf{F} = [y, x^2]$ cannot be the gradient of some function ϕ. If it were, then $\partial\phi/\partial x = y$ and hence $\phi = xy + c(y)$. But then, $\partial\phi/\partial y = x^2 = y + dc/dy$,

---

* Strictly speaking, the theorem has been proved only for regions G which are connected, that is, regions such that every pair of points can be connected by some smooth curve which remains in the region. It would hold separately in each connected component of a more general region.

which is impossible because we must then have $dc/dy = x^2 - y$, and a function of y alone cannot have a derivative which is a function of x.

Let us close this section by proving the following interesting result.

Theorem 7–16. Let $\mathbf{F}:G \to R^n$ be C^1 at every point of the open set G in R^n. Suppose further that the line integral $\int_C \mathbf{F} \cdot d\mathbf{X}$ is independent of path in G. Then for every $\mathbf{X}$ in G the matrix $[d\mathbf{F}(\mathbf{X})]$ is symmetric.

Proof. The matrix $[d\mathbf{F}]$ has the value of $f_{i'j}$ as its ij-th entry. The hypothesis that the line integral is independent of path means that there exists a function ϕ such that grad $\phi = \mathbf{F}$. But then $f_i = \phi_{'i}$ and hence $f_{i'j} = \phi_{'ij}$. We have seen that $\phi_{'ij} = \phi_{'ji}$ when these derivatives are continuous. Since our assumption of the differentiability of $\mathbf{F}$ includes the assumption of the continuity of these derivatives, we have

$$f_{i'j} = \phi_{'ij} = \phi_{'ji} = f_{j'i},$$

which proves the theorem. ▌

In the special case when $n = 2$, the line integral is often written in the form

$$\int_C P\,dx + Q\,dy, \tag{7–25}$$

where P and Q are functions of x and y. Here $\mathbf{F} = [P, Q]$ and hence

$$d\mathbf{F} = \begin{bmatrix} \dfrac{\partial P}{\partial x} & \dfrac{\partial P}{\partial y} \\ \dfrac{\partial Q}{\partial x} & \dfrac{\partial Q}{\partial y} \end{bmatrix}.$$

Therefore, if the line integral (7–25) is independent of path, the above matrix must be symmetric. But this is equivalent to the single condition

$$\frac{\partial P}{\partial y} = \frac{\partial Q}{\partial x}. \tag{7–26}$$

PROBLEMS

1. Prove Theorem 7–13.
2. Prove the remaining part of Theorem 7–14.
3. Evaluate directly from the definition each of the following line integrals:

a) $\int_C x\,dx + xy\,dy + xyz\,dz$, C given by $[x, y, z] = [t, 2t, t^2 - 1]$, $0 \le t \le 1$

b) $\int_C \dfrac{x\,dx + y\,dy}{[x^2 + y^2]^{1/2}}$, C given by $[x, y] = [\cos t, \sin t]$, $0 \le t \le 2\pi$

c) $\int_C y\,dx - x\,dy$, C the same as part (b)

4. Each of the following functions is the gradient of some ϕ. Find the function ϕ for which $\mathbf{F} = \text{grad}\,\phi$ in each case.
   a) $\mathbf{F} = [\cos(x+y), \cos(x+y)]$
   b) $\mathbf{F} = [1/y, -x/y^2]$
   c) $\mathbf{F} = \mathbf{X}/|\mathbf{X}| = \dfrac{1}{|\mathbf{X}|}[x_1, \ldots, x_n]$
   d) $\mathbf{F} = \mathbf{X}$
   e) $\mathbf{F} = |\mathbf{X}|\mathbf{X}$
   f) $\mathbf{F} = |\mathbf{X}|^\alpha \mathbf{X}, \alpha \neq -2$
   g) $\mathbf{F} = \mathbf{X}/|\mathbf{X}|^2$
   h) $\mathbf{F} = (x^2 + y^2)^{-1/2}[y, -x]$
   i) $\mathbf{F} = [y^2 + 2x\cos y, 2xy - x^2 \sin y]$
   j) $\mathbf{F} = [2xy^2 + z, 2yx^2 + 2yz^3, x + 3y^2z^2]$
5. Verify (7–26) for (a), (b), and (h) of Problem 4.
6. Evaluate $\int_C \mathbf{F} \cdot d\mathbf{X}$ directly from the definition for each of the given functions and curves.
   a) $\mathbf{F} = \mathbf{X}$, C given by $\mathbf{X} = [2t, t^2, \log t]$, $1 \leq t \leq 2$
   b) $\mathbf{F} = [x^2, xyz, z^2]$, C given by $\mathbf{X} = [t, t^2, t^3]$, $0 \leq t \leq 1$
   c) $\mathbf{F} = [2xz, -2yz, x^2 - y^2]$, C given by $\mathbf{X} = [2\cos t, 2\sin t, (1/\pi)t]$, $0 \leq t \leq 4\pi$
   d) $\mathbf{F} = [x^2y, -xy^2]$, C the boundary of the square $0 \leq x \leq 1, 0 \leq y \leq 1$, taken in the counterclockwise direction

7–4. MULTIPLE INTEGRALS

The concept of the Riemann integral as developed on the real line can be generalized in many different ways. In this section we wish to discuss the Riemann integral of real-valued functions in domains in R^n. We choose to define this integral as a direct generalization of the one-dimensional case.

It is assumed that the reader is familiar with iterated integrals as they are discussed in earlier courses. The multiple integral, as we define it here, is not the same as the iterated integral. The two are often confused since they usually have the same value. The main theorem we will prove is that under suitable conditions the multiple integral can be evaluated as an iterated integral.

The integral that we will be defining here is far from being the most general type of integral. The reason that we do not need to consider more complicated types of integrals is that we are going to restrict our attention to functions which are continuous and to regions which have sufficiently smooth boundaries. We start by defining the degree of smoothness.

Definition 7–15. A region B in R^n will be called *smoothly bounded* if and only if there exist a finite number of functions

$$g_1, g_2, \ldots, g_N : G \to R,$$

where G is an open set containing B, which are such that each g_i is C^1 throughout G, grad $g_i \neq 0$ at any point of B, and

$$B = \bigcap_{i=1}^{N} \{\mathbf{X} \mid g_i(\mathbf{X}) \leq 0\}. \tag{7–27}$$

Strictly speaking, this is the definition of *piecewise smoothly bounded*, but since all of the regions that we consider will satisfy this definition, we will ignore qualifications. Note that the boundary points of B are points on the level surfaces of one or more of the g_i (this follows from the continuity of these functions). We will usually assume that the regions we are discussing are closed and bounded (that is, compact).

It is easy to prove that a region of the type defined by (7–27) must be closed. If g is a continuous function and $g(\mathbf{X}_0) > 0$, then there is an entire neighborhood of $\mathbf{X}_0$ in which $g(\mathbf{X}) > 0$ [use $\epsilon = \frac{1}{2}g(\mathbf{X}_0)$ in the definition of continuity]. This will be true for each of the functions g_i in (7–27). Hence, by taking the smallest of the N neighborhoods, we see that the complement of the region B is open. Therefore B itself is closed.

It does not follow in the same way that a region of the type (7–27) must be bounded. This must be assumed separately.

The results we shall prove in this and the next chapters will be proved for very special types of regions. They hold true for more general regions, but any attempt to extend the proofs would make them more difficult to understand. We will therefore sometimes make some very strong assumptions.

Definition 7–16. A region B in R^n is called *convex* if and only if given any two points $\mathbf{P}_1$ and $\mathbf{P}_2$ in B, the entire line segment

$$L[\mathbf{P}_1, \mathbf{P}_2] = \{\mathbf{X} \mid \mathbf{X} = t\mathbf{P}_1 + (1 - t)\mathbf{P}_2, 0 \leq t \leq 1\}$$

is contained in B.

A convex region has a number of particularly valuable properties. We will now investigate a few of these.

Theorem 7–17. Let B be a convex region in R^n and let L be an affine subspace of R^n. Then the orthogonal projection of B onto L is itself convex.

Proof. Under euclidean motions, line segments are transformed into line segments, and hence convex regions are transformed into convex regions. Given an arbitrary affine subspace L, there exists a euclidean motion which transforms L into the subspace determined by $n - k$ coordinates being zero. In particular, it is enough to assume that, letting $\mathbf{X} = [x_1, x_2, \ldots, x_n]$,

$$L = \{\mathbf{X} \mid x_{k+1} = 0, x_{k+2} = 0, \ldots, x_n = 0\}.$$

Then G, the orthogonal projection of B onto L, is given by

$$G = \{[x_1, x_2, \ldots, x_k, 0, 0, \ldots, 0] \mid [x_1, \ldots, x_n] \in B \text{ for some } x_{k+1}, x_{k+2}, \ldots, x_n\}.$$

If $\mathbf{P} = [x_1, x_2, \ldots, x_k, 0, \ldots, 0]$ and $\mathbf{P}' = [x_1', x_2', \ldots, x_k', 0, \ldots, 0]$ are any two points of G, then there are two points $\mathbf{Q}$ and $\mathbf{Q}'$ in B such that

$$\mathbf{Q} = [x_1, \ldots, x_k, x_{k+1}, \ldots, x_n] \quad \text{and} \quad \mathbf{Q}' = [x_1', \ldots, x_k', x_{k+1}', \ldots, x_n'].$$

Since B is convex, $L[\mathbf{Q}, \mathbf{Q}'] \subset B$. However, every point on the line segment joining $\mathbf{P}$ and $\mathbf{P}'$ is the projection of a corresponding point of $L[\mathbf{Q}, \mathbf{Q}']$, and hence is a point of G. This proves the theorem. ▌

Suppose now that the region B in R^n is both convex and compact. Let B_n be projection of B onto the $(n - 1)$-dimensional subspace consisting of the first $n - 1$ components of $\mathbf{X}$ (i.e., set $x_n = 0$). We call B_n a projection "along the nth coordinate." In a similar way, we could obtain B_i, the projection of B along the ith coordinate, onto the $(n - 1)$-dimensional subspace obtained by setting $x_i = 0$. Since the nth coordinate is fixed as zero in any of these subspaces, we can identify the B_i with R^{n-1}. That is, we will assume that B_n is a subset of R^{n-1}. Given any $[x_1, \ldots, x_{n-1}] = \mathbf{X}'$ in B_n, let

$$P(\mathbf{X}') = \{x_n \mid [x_1, x_2, \ldots, x_{n-1}, x_n] \in B\}.$$

This set is nonempty (since B_n is the projection of B) and bounded (since B is bounded) Let

$$f_n(\mathbf{X}') = \inf P(\mathbf{X}')$$

and

$$g_n(\mathbf{X}') = \sup P(\mathbf{X}').$$

Since B is closed, both $[x_1, \ldots, x_{n-1}, f_n(\mathbf{X}')]$ and $[x_1, \ldots, x_{n-1}, g_n(\mathbf{X}')]$ must belong to B. The convexity of B shows that all the points between them belong to B. Because of the method of choice, no other point outside of the line segment joining these two points is in B. We can conclude that

$$B = \{[x_1, \ldots, x_n] \mid \mathbf{X}' = [x_1, \ldots, x_{n-1}] \in B_n \quad \text{and} \quad f_n(\mathbf{X}') \le x_n \le g_n(\mathbf{X}')\}. \tag{7–28}$$

The functions f_n and g_n obtained in this way are called the *surface functions* for B with respect to the nth coordinate. In an exactly similar way we could obtain the surface functions f_i and g_i corresponding to the ith coordinate. A representation of B over the projection B_i in the direction of the ith coordinate similar to (7–28) would then hold for each i.

Convexity is actually a more stringent requirement than we need. It is such a useful concept that it is important to introduce it, but we need something that is more frequently available.

Definition 7–17. A region B in R^n is called *semiconvex* if and only if the intersection of the region with any line parallel to one of the coordinate axes is always an interval.

We see that this requirement is exactly what is needed to obtain the surface functions for the region for each of the n possible projections in the direction of one of the coordinate axes. An equivalent definition would therefore be the requirement that the region (assuming that it is closed) be expressible in the form (7–28) for each of the n different coordinate variables.

We now define the type of region to which we will restrict our discussion:

Definition 7–18. Let a region B in R^n be compact, smoothly bounded, and such that it is the union of a finite number of compact, semiconvex, smoothly bounded regions which have only portions of their boundaries in common. Furthermore, suppose that each of these regions can be given in the form (7–28) for each of the n different coordinates and that the surface functions f_i and g_i are continuous over the projection in each case. Finally, suppose that every projection of each of the semiconvex subdomains is itself smoothly bounded (in R^{n-1}). Then the region B is called a *simple region.*

This definition greatly restricts the type of region we consider, but it happens that almost every region which might occur in a practical situation will satisfy these restrictions. Most of the exceptions would only require relaxing the demand that the regions be bounded.

Unfortunately, Definition 7–18 is dependent on the coordinate system. This dependence could be eliminated only with difficulty. Actually, it is not worth the effort to do so. Greater generality can be obtained by resorting to entirely different methods, but these methods tend to obscure matters in the early stages.

Next we wish to develop the concept of the volume of a simple region. We must first introduce the idea of a partition of an n-dimensional rectangle.

Definition 7–19. Let $\mathbf{A}$ and $\mathbf{B}$ be two points of R^n with $\mathbf{A} < \mathbf{B}$. Then by a *partition* $\mathcal{P}$ of $R[\mathbf{A}, \mathbf{B}]$ we mean the set of all points $\mathbf{P}_\sigma$ obtained in the following way. For each coordinate i let

$$a_i = x_i^{(0)} < x_i^{(1)} < \cdots < x_i^{(N_i)} = b_i$$

be a partition of the interval from a_i to b_i, Let $\sigma = \langle j_1, j_2, \ldots, j_n \rangle$ be any n-tuple of integers with

$$0 \leq j_i \leq N_i.$$

Then we define

$$\mathbf{P}_\sigma = [x_1^{(j_1)}, x_2^{(j_2)}, \ldots, x_n^{(j_n)}].$$

By a *rectangle of the partition* we mean a rectangle $R[\mathbf{A}_\sigma, \mathbf{B}_\sigma]$, where $\mathbf{A}_\sigma$ is one of the $\mathbf{P}_\sigma$ but with all of the $j_i < N_i$, and $\mathbf{B}_\sigma$ is another $\mathbf{P}_\sigma$ of which each j_i is one greater than that of A_σ, i.e.,

$$\mathbf{A}_\sigma = [x_1^{(j_1)}, \ldots, x_n^{(j_n)}], \qquad \mathbf{B}_\sigma = [x_1^{(j_1+1)}, \ldots, x_n^{(j_n+1)}].$$

Observe that what we are doing in this definition is partitioning each of the coordinate axes and erecting hyperplanes which divide the original rectangle into smaller rectangles. Each rectangle of the partition consists of those points which have each of their coordinates between two successive values of the partitions of the axes. Note that the original rectangle is the union of all of the rectangles of the partition. Points on the common "faces" are in two of the smaller rectangles, but every point is in at least one rectangle.

Definition 7–20. Let **A** and **B** be two points of R^n with $\mathbf{A} < \mathbf{B}$. Then the *volume* (or *n-dimensional volume*) of the rectangle $R[\mathbf{A}, \mathbf{B}]$ is defined to be

$$V(R[\mathbf{A}, \mathbf{B}]) = \prod_{i=1}^{n} (b_i - a_i). \tag{7–29}$$

If R_σ is one of the rectangles of a partition of $R[\mathbf{A}, \mathbf{B}]$, we will denote the volume of R_σ by ΔV_σ.

This definition is a natural generalization of the two- and three-dimensional cases we are more familiar with; it applies to spaces of any dimension, including $n = 1$. Of course the two-dimensional volume given by (7–29) is more familiarly known as *area*, and the one-dimensional volume is called *length.*

Definition 7–21. Let $\mathcal{P}$ be a partition of a rectangle $R[\mathbf{A}, \mathbf{B}]$ as given by Definition 7–19. Then the *mesh* of this partition is

$$\max \{x_i^{(j+1)} - x_i^{(j)} \mid 0 \le i \le n, 0 \le j < N_i\}.$$

In other words, the mesh of a partition is the length of the longest side of any rectangle of the partition.

Now we come to the theorem which is the main reason for restricting our discussion to simple regions. It is true for more general regions, but its proof for such cases is much more difficult.

Theorem 7–18. Let B be a simple region in R^n and let **A** and **B** be two points such that $B \subset R[\mathbf{A}, \mathbf{B}]$. Then, given any $\epsilon > 0$, there exists a $\delta > 0$ such that if $\mathcal{P}$ is any partition of $R[\mathbf{A}, \mathbf{B}]$ whose mesh is smaller than δ, then $\sum_b \Delta V_{\sigma_i} < \epsilon$, where b indicates that the sum extends over all σ_i such that the rectangle R_{σ_i} has a point in common with the boundary of B.

Proof. This theorem states that the boundary of a simple bounded region can be completely enclosed in a finite set of rectangles of arbitrarily small total volume. This will allow us to approximate as closely as we wish such a region by the union of a set of closed rectangles.

The notation tends to be rather cumbersome in the proof of this theorem, so let us sketch the proof for the case of three dimensions. There is no essential difference between the proof for this case and that for the general case.

The region B can be decomposed into a finite number of semiconvex regions as in Definition 7–18. It suffices to prove the theorem for one of these regions since we could use N ϵ_i's whose sum was the desired ϵ. Let us suppose therefore that B is itself semiconvex. Let B_3, B_2, and B_1 be the projections of B onto the xy-, xz-, and yz-planes, respectively. For each of the regions B_i there is a corresponding pair of continuous surface functions f_i and g_i from which the region can be obtained. For example,

$$B = \{[x, y, z] \mid [x, y] \in B_3, f_3(x, y) \le z \le g_3(x, y)\}.$$

Every point on the boundary of B can be obtained by specifying a point of one of the three regions and one of the two associated functions. Usually the resulting six sections of the boundary have considerable overlap, but there are cases (such as the cube) in which all six are required to obtain the entire boundary.

Let us look at one of these six sections. Let us take B_3 and the function $z = f(x, y) = f_3(x, y)$. Suppose that B_3 is contained in the rectangle $a_1 \leq x \leq b_1$, $a_2 \leq y \leq b_2$, and set $M = (b_1 - a_1)(b_2 - a_2)$, the area of this rectangle. Note that this is just the area of the projection of the three-dimensional rectangle containing B on the xy-plane.

The function f is continuous over the compact set B_3 and hence is uniformly continuous there. Given any $\epsilon > 0$, choose δ_1 small enough so that if the distance between $[x, y]$ and $[x', y']$ is less than δ_1, then

$$|f(x, y) - f(x', y')| < \epsilon/18M.$$

Now let

$$\delta = \min\{\epsilon/18M, \delta_1/\sqrt{2}\}$$

(in the general case, we would replace $\sqrt{2}$ by $\sqrt{n-1}$).

Suppose that we partition the rectangle enclosing B such that the mesh is less than δ. Then we ask, how many of the three-dimensional rectangles of the partition have points in common with the surface $z = f(x, y)$? We wish to find the total volume of all of these. Look at a particular subrectangle in the xy-plane. The maximum distance between any two points in this subrectangle is δ_1 (this was the reason for the $\sqrt{2}$), and hence the vertical distance between the maximum and minimum values of $f(x, y)$ is at most $\epsilon/18M$ over this rectangle. But then the total thickness of the rectangles of the partition which are over this subrectangle and which have a point in common with the surface $z = f(x, y)$ is at most $\epsilon/18M$ (the maximum distance between points of the surface) plus $2\epsilon/18M$ [the maximum thickness of a rectangle on top having a point in common with the maximum value of $z = f(x, y)$ and a similar one on the bottom]. This is a total thickness of $\epsilon/6M$. If ΔR is the area of the subrectangle in the xy-plane, then the total volume of these rectangles is $(\epsilon/6M)\Delta R$. Adding the volumes for all the subrectangles in B_3, we find that the sum of the ΔR is less than or equal to M, and hence the sum of the volumes of all the rectangles of the partition which have a point in common with $z = f(x, y)$ over B_3 is $\epsilon/6$.

The above procedure can be repeated for each of the other five cases. The final δ will be the minimum of the six different δ's which are determined in this way. With this δ, the entire boundary of B will be contained in a set of rectangles of the partition whose total volume is less than $6\epsilon/6 = \epsilon$. ▌

We can now define the n-dimensional volume of simple regions.

Definition 7–22. Let B be a simple region in R^n. Then by the *(n-dimensional) volume* of B we mean the infimum (greatest lower bound) of $\sum_{\#} \Delta V_\sigma$ for all partitions of a rectangle $R[\mathbf{A}, \mathbf{B}]$ containing B, where # indicates that the sum is taken over all the rectangles R_σ which have a point in common with B. The volume of a region B is indicated by $V(B)$.

The union of the set of all rectangles R_σ which have a point in common with B certainly contains B. Hence we would want $\sum_{\#} \Delta V_\sigma$ to be greater than or equal to the volume of B, no matter how we defined the latter. Since this must be true for every partition, the greatest lower bound of the sum must also be greater than or equal to the volume. On the other hand, if we looked at $\sum_i \Delta V_\sigma$, where the sum is taken over only those rectangles R_σ which are contained in B, we would obtain a quantity which was smaller than the volume we wished to define. The least upper bound of these sums could also be used as a definition.

The last theorem shows that no matter what ϵ we choose, there exists a partition such that $\sum_{\#} \Delta V_\sigma - \sum_i \Delta V_\sigma < \epsilon$. Thus the greatest lower bound of the $\sum_{\#} \Delta V_\sigma$ must be the same as the least upper bound of the $\sum_i \Delta V_\sigma$. Therefore, for the type of regions that we are discussing, Definition 7–22 is a reasonable definition for volume.

Having defined volume, we can now define the integral. We begin by defining the upper and lower Riemann sums for a function over a region.

Definition 7–23. Let B be a simple region in R^n. Let $f\colon B \to R$ be a real-valued function which is continuous on B. Define the function $\hat{f}\colon R^n \to R$ by

$$\hat{f}(\mathbf{X}) = \begin{cases} f(\mathbf{X}) & \text{if } \mathbf{X} \in B, \\ 0 & \text{if } \mathbf{X} \notin B. \end{cases}$$

Suppose that B is contained in the rectangle $R[\mathbf{A}, \mathbf{B}]$. Let $\mathcal{P}$ be any partition of of $R[\mathbf{A}, \mathbf{B}]$. For any rectangle R_σ of the partition $\mathcal{P}$, set

$$M_\sigma = \max \{\hat{f}(\mathbf{X}) \mid \mathbf{X} \in R_\sigma\}, \qquad m_\sigma = \min \{\hat{f}(\mathbf{X}) \mid \mathbf{X} \in R_\sigma\}.$$

Then the *upper* and *lower Riemann sums* for f over B with respect to $\mathcal{P}$ are

$$\overline{S}(f, \mathcal{P}) = \sum_{\#} M_\sigma \, \Delta V_\sigma, \qquad \underline{S}(f, \mathcal{P}) = \sum_{\#} m_\sigma \, \Delta V_\sigma,$$

respectively. The *upper* and *lower integrals* of f over B are

$$\overline{\int_B} f \, dV = \inf \{\overline{S}(f, \mathcal{P}) \mid \text{all partitions } \mathcal{P} \text{ of } R[\mathbf{A}, \mathbf{B}]\},$$

$$\underline{\int_B} f \, dV = \sup \{\underline{S}(f, \mathcal{P}) \mid \text{all partitions } \mathcal{P} \text{ of } R[\mathbf{A}, \mathbf{B}]\},$$

and the *integral* of f over B is

$$\int_B f \, dV = \overline{\int_B} f \, dV = \underline{\int_B} f \, dV,$$

provided that the upper and lower integrals are equal. If this happens, the function f is said to be *integrable* over B.

The function $\hat{f}$ is usually not continuous in one of the rectangles R_σ which include a boundary point of B. However, the numbers m_σ and M_σ exist regardless of the continuity of $\hat{f}$. The function $\hat{f}$ is continuous on the compact set $R_\sigma \cap B$, and hence it does have maximum and minimum values on this set. We merely have to compare these values with the only other value of $\hat{f}$, 0, in order to obtain m_σ and M_σ.

The upper and lower integrals can be defined equally well for functions which are not continuous. If the function were merely required to be bounded, then we could replace maximum and minimum by sup and inf in the definitions of m_σ and M_σ. In this case, there might be some question as to whether or not a given function is integrable. However, since we are restricting ourselves to continuous functions, this problem does not arise. A continuous function is always integrable over a simple region. We shall prove this.

▶ **Theorem 7–19.** Let B be a simple region in R^n. Let $f\colon B \to R$ be continuous on B. Then f is integrable over B.

Proof. Every upper sum is greater than the corresponding lower sum for the same partition. We shall begin by showing that for any two partitions $\mathcal{P}_1$ and $\mathcal{P}_2$, we must have

$$\underline{S}(f, \mathcal{P}_1) \leq \overline{S}(f, \mathcal{P}_2).$$

We do this by observing what happens to the upper and lower sums upon a refinement of the partition. Suppose that $\mathcal{P}'$ is a refinement of the partition $\mathcal{P}$; that is, the lattice of points making up $\mathcal{P}'$ contains the lattice points of $\mathcal{P}$ as a subset. Note that every rectangle of $\mathcal{P}$ is itself partitioned by this refinement.

Look at some rectangle R_σ in $\mathcal{P}$. Under the refinement $\mathcal{P}'$, R_σ is divided into a set of rectangles $R_{\sigma'_1}, R_{\sigma'_2}, \ldots, R_{\sigma'_k}$ in $\mathcal{P}'$. The sum of the volumes of these rectangles must be the same as the volume of R_σ. The maximum of f over any of the $R_{\sigma'_i}$ is less than or equal to the maximum of f over R_σ. Hence, summing over all of the rectangles of $\mathcal{P}'$ which are contained in R_σ, we find that

$$\sum M_{\sigma'_i}\, \Delta V_{\sigma'_i} \leq M_\sigma\, \Delta V_\sigma.$$

Taking the sum for both sides of this relation for all rectangles R_σ, we thus have

$$\overline{S}(f, \mathcal{P}') \leq \underline{S}(f, \mathcal{P}).$$

That is, *the upper sum decreases when we make a refinement.*

In exactly the same way, we can show that the *lower sum* increases upon refinement. Now suppose that we are given any two partitions, $\mathcal{P}_1$ and $\mathcal{P}_2$. By taking all of the points on each axis in both of the partitions, we can produce a new partition $\mathcal{P}$ which is the common refinement of both $\mathcal{P}_1$ and $\mathcal{P}_2$. But then

$$\underline{S}(f, \mathcal{P}_1) \leq \underline{S}(f, \mathcal{P}) \leq \overline{S}(f, \mathcal{P}) \leq \overline{S}(f, \mathcal{P}_2),$$

and hence every upper sum is greater than or equal to every lower sum. It thus follows that the upper integral will be greater than or equal to the lower integral. To show that the two are equal, all we have to do is show that given any $\epsilon > 0$, we can find some partition $\mathcal{P}$ such that

$$\overline{S}(f, \mathcal{P}) - \underline{S}(f, \mathcal{P}) < \epsilon.$$

If this can be done for every ϵ, then the least upper bound of the lower sums could not be properly less than the greatest lower bound of the upper sums.

Let V be the volume of the rectangle $R[\mathbf{A}, \mathbf{B}]$. Since f is continuous over the compact set B, it is uniformly continuous there. Hence there exists a δ_1 such that if $\mathbf{X}$ and $\mathbf{X}'$ are any two points of B with $|\mathbf{X} - \mathbf{X}'| < \delta_1\sqrt{n}$, then $|f(\mathbf{X}) - f(\mathbf{X}')| < \epsilon/2V$. Likewise, if $M = \max\{|f(\mathbf{X})| \mid \mathbf{X} \in B\}$, then by Theorem 7–18 there exists a δ_2 such that $\sum_b \Delta V_\sigma < \epsilon/4M$ for any partition $\mathcal{P}$ whose mesh is smaller than δ_2 and where the sum is taken over all of those rectangles which have a point in common with the boundary of B.

Let δ be the smaller of δ_1 and δ_2. Let $\mathcal{P}$ be any partition whose mesh is smaller than δ. Then

$$\overline{S}(f, \mathcal{P}) - \underline{S}(f, \mathcal{P}) = \sum_{\#} (M_\sigma - m_\sigma)\,\Delta V_\sigma$$
$$= \sum_{i^0} (M_\sigma - m_\sigma)\,\Delta V_\sigma + \sum_{b} (M_\sigma - m_\sigma)\,\Delta V_\sigma,$$

where the first sum extends over all the rectangles of the partition which are contained completely in the interior of B and the second sum extends over all the rectangles which have a point in common with the boundary of B.

Since f is continuous in B, $\hat{f}$ assumes the maximum and minimum values in one of the rectangles in the interior of B, and hence

$$\sum_{i^0} (M_\sigma - m_\sigma)\,\Delta V_\sigma \le \frac{\epsilon}{2V} \sum_{i^0} \Delta V \le \frac{\epsilon}{2}\,.$$

On the other hand, for any R_σ which has a point in common with the boundary, $M_\sigma \le M$ and $m_\sigma \ge -M$. Hence

$$\sum_{b} (M_\sigma - m_\sigma)\,\Delta V_\sigma \le 2M \sum_{b} \Delta V < \epsilon/2.$$

These two inequalities can be combined with the previous conclusion to prove the desired result. Since we can make the upper and lower sums arbitrarily close together, the integral must exist. ▌

The somewhat artificial treatment of the Riemann sums at the boundary (in particular, the introduction of the function $\hat{f}$) was done to simplify the proofs. It might seem more natural to let M_σ and m_σ be the maximum and minimum of f in $R_\sigma \cap B$. The above proofs would have been complicated, but the final result would have been the same, as shown by the following theorem:

▶ **Theorem 7–20.** Let B be a simple region in R^n and let $f\colon B \to R$ be continuous on B. Let $\mathcal{P}_i$, $i = 1, 2, \ldots$, be a sequence of partitions of the rectangle $R[\mathbf{A}, \mathbf{B}]$ which contains B. Suppose that the meshes of the $\mathcal{P}_i$ tend toward zero. For each rectangle $R_\sigma^{(i)}$ of the partition $\mathcal{P}_i$, let $\mathbf{X}_\sigma^{(i)}$ be some point in $R_\sigma^{(i)} \cap B$. Then

$$\lim_{i\to\infty} \sum_{\#} f(\mathbf{X}_\sigma^{(i)})\,\Delta V_\sigma^{(i)} = \int_B f\,dV.$$

Proof. Let $\mathbf{Y}_\sigma^{(i)}$ be the point in $R_\sigma^{(i)}$ at which $\hat{f}$ assumes its maximum value. Then

$$\begin{aligned}
\left|\overline{S}(f, \mathcal{P}_i) - \sum_{\#} f(\mathbf{X}_\sigma^{(i)})\,\Delta V_\sigma^{(i)}\right| \\
&= \left|\sum_{\#} [\hat{f}(\mathbf{Y}_\sigma^{(i)}) - f(\mathbf{X}_\sigma^{(i)})]\,\Delta V_\sigma^{(i)}\right| \\
&\le \sum_{\#} |\hat{f}(\mathbf{Y}_\sigma^{(i)}) - f(\mathbf{X}_\sigma^{(i)})|\,\Delta V_\sigma^{(i)} \\
&= \sum_{i^0} |\hat{f}(\mathbf{Y}_\sigma^{(i)}) - f(\mathbf{X}_\sigma^{(i)})|\,\Delta V_\sigma^{(i)} + \sum_{b} |\hat{f}(\mathbf{Y}_\sigma^{(i)}) - f(\mathbf{X}_\sigma^{(i)})|\,\Delta V_\sigma^{(i)}.
\end{aligned}$$

On the last line, the first sum extends over all of the $R^{(i)}$ which are interior to B, and the second sum extends over all of them which have a point in common with the boundary of B. Given $\epsilon > 0$, choose δ exactly as in the proof of the last theorem. Then we find that each of the last sums is less than $\epsilon/2$ whenever the mesh of $\mathcal{P}_i$ is less than δ. Since the meshes tend toward zero, the sums must tend toward the limit of the upper sums. In the last theorem we saw that these limits tend toward the integral. Hence the theorem follows. ▮

Theorem 7–20 tells us that we can approximate the integral as closely as we wish by a Riemann sum. This fact can be used to prove the following theorems, which are concerned with the basic properties of the integral. The formal proofs are left as exercises.

Theorem 7–21. Let B be a simple region and let f and g be continuous functions on B. Let c be any real number. Then

$$\int_B cf\,dV = c\int_B f\,dV,$$

$$\int_B (f + g)\,dV = \int_B f\,dV + \int_B g\,dV.$$

Theorem 7–22. Let B, B_1, and B_2 be three simple regions such that $B_1 \cup B_2 = B$ and $B_1 \cap B_2$ is a subset of the boundary of B_1. Let f be continuous in B. Then

$$\int_B f\,dV = \int_{B_1} f\,dV + \int_{B_2} f\,dV.$$

Theorem 7–23. Let B be a simple region in R^n and let $f\colon B \to R$ be continuous in B. Suppose that $f(\mathbf{X}) \ge 0$ for all $\mathbf{X} \in B$. Then

$$\int_B f\,dV \ge 0.$$

Further, if $f > 0$ at some interior point of B, then strict inequality holds in the above relation.

It is interesting to note that continuity of the surface functions need not be assumed in Definition 7–18 if the region is convex and compact. An outline of the proof follows.

Suppose that B' is one of the projections and g the corresponding upper surface function. Let $\mathbf{X}'_0$ be an interior point of B'. We will sketch the proof of the fact that g

is continuous at $\mathbf{X}'_0$. A similar proof would hold for the lower surface function and for the restricted continuity at the boundary of B'. Let δ be the radius of a neighborhood with center $\mathbf{X}'_0$ which is contained in B' together with its boundary. Let $a = g(\mathbf{X}'_0)$ and let b be a lower bound for the coordinate being defined throughout B. If $\mathbf{X}'_1$ is any point of B' at a distance δ from $\mathbf{X}'_0$, then the point $[\mathbf{X}'_1, b]$ (we will write it as if the coordinate in question is the last coordinate) lies below any point of B. Since $\mathbf{X}'_1$ is in B', there does exist some point $[\mathbf{X}'_1, c]$ in B, where $c > b$. The entire line segment from $[\mathbf{X}'_0, a]$ to $[\mathbf{X}'_1, c]$ must lie in B. By the way the upper surface function g is defined, for any $\mathbf{X}'$ in the projection of this line segment $g(\mathbf{X}')$ is greater than the corresponding coordinate on the line. That is, for any point $\mathbf{X}'$ in the neighborhood of radius δ about $\mathbf{X}'_0$,

$$g(\mathbf{X}') \geq a - \frac{(a - b)}{\delta} |\mathbf{X}' - \mathbf{X}'_0|.$$

Now, if g were not continuous at $\mathbf{X}'_0$, it would be possible to find a sequence of points $\mathbf{X}'_k$ whose limit is $\mathbf{X}'_0$ and such that the sequence $g(\mathbf{X}'_k)$ is bounded away from $a = g(\mathbf{X}'_0)$. By choosing a subsequence if necessary, we can assume that the sequence of $g(\mathbf{X}'_k)$ converges to $a' \neq a$. The condition displayed above shows that $a' \nless a$. Hence we must have $a' > a$. However, B is closed, each point $[\mathbf{X}'_k, g(\mathbf{X}'_k)]$ belongs to B, and these points converge to $[\mathbf{X}'_0, a']$. Therefore this last point must also belong to B. This contradicts the definition of $g(\mathbf{X}'_0) = a$. Therefore g must be continuous at $\mathbf{X}'_0$.

PROBLEMS

1. Prove that the volume of a region B is $\int_B 1\, dV$.
2. Prove Theorem 7–21.
3. Prove Theorem 7–22.
4. Prove Theorem 7–23.
5. Let B be a simple region. Let f and g be continuous on B such that $f(\mathbf{X}) \leq g(\mathbf{X})$ for every $\mathbf{X} \in B$. Prove that
$$\int_B f\, dV \leq \int_B g\, dV.$$
6. Under the conditions of Problem 5, prove that
$$\left|\int_B f\, dV\right| \leq \int_B |f|\, dV.$$
7. Let B be a simple region in R^n. Let $f\colon B \to R$ be continuous on B. Let V be the volume of B. Suppose also that B is such that any two points in B can be connected by a curve all of whose points are contained in B. Prove that there exists a point $\mathbf{X}_0$ in B such that
$$\int_B f\, dV = f(\mathbf{X}_0) \cdot V.$$
8. Prove that the intersection of two convex regions is convex.

9. Give an example of two convex regions which have a point in common and whose union is not convex.
10. A region B is *star shaped* with respect to a point $\mathbf{A}$ in B if and only if, given any $\mathbf{X} \in B$, the entire line segment $L[\mathbf{A}, \mathbf{X}]$ is contained in B. The *star center* of a region B is the set of all points in B with respect to which the region is star shaped. Prove that the star center of any region is convex.
11. Prove that an n-dimensional ball, $S_r(\mathbf{X}_0)$, is convex.
12. Prove that a closed rectangle, $R[\mathbf{A}, \mathbf{B}]$, in R^n is convex.

7–5. ITERATED INTEGRALS

The reader may wonder why we wrote dV in the integrals of the last section rather than $dx_1\, dx_2 \cdots dx_n$. The reason is that the later notation belongs to the concept of the iterated integral. To adapt it to multiple integrals requires more theory, and it is safer to use a notation such as dV. It happens that the distinction can usually be ignored since the values of the iterated integral and the multiple integral are always the same in any reasonable case. We will prove this assertion in this section.

Throughout this section we will restrict our attention to two dimensions. The properties that we prove for the two-dimensional case can be extended to any number of dimensions quite easily. The proofs would not be altered in any significant way.

First, let us make clear exactly what it is that we mean by an iterated integral. Suppose that we are given a function $f(x, y)$, depending on the two variables, x and y, which is continuous in some region in the plane. Then, for each fixed x, this function is a continuous function of y and hence can be integrated. The limits of integration may themselves depend on x. We would thus obtain a function of x,

$$g(x) = \int_{b_1(x)}^{b_2(x)} f(x, y)\, dy.$$

It could happen that the resulting function $g(x)$ is itself continuous. If so, then it could be integrated in turn. This second integration would yield the iterated integral.

Theorem 7–24. Let $B = \{[x, y] \mid a_1 \le x \le a_2,\ b_1(x) \le y \le b_2(x)\}$, where the functions $b_1(x)$ and $b_2(x)$ are continuous functions of x for $a_1 \le x \le a_2$. Let $f(x, y)$ be continuous in B. Then the function

$$g(x) = \int_{b_1(x)}^{b_2(x)} f(x, y)\, dy$$

is continuous in $a_1 \le x \le a_2$.

Proof. We will prove that $g(x)$ is continuous at $x = a$, where a is some number in the given interval. Let

$$L = \max \{b_2(x) - b_1(x) \mid a_1 \le x \le a_2\},$$
$$M = \max \{f(x, y) \mid (x, y) \in B\}.$$

Choose δ_1 such that $|x - a| < \delta_1$ implies that

$$|b_1(x) - b_1(a)| < \epsilon/3M,$$

where $\epsilon > 0$ is given beforehand. Choose δ_2 such that $|x - a| < \delta_2$ implies that

$$|b_2(x) - b_2(a)| < \epsilon/3M.$$

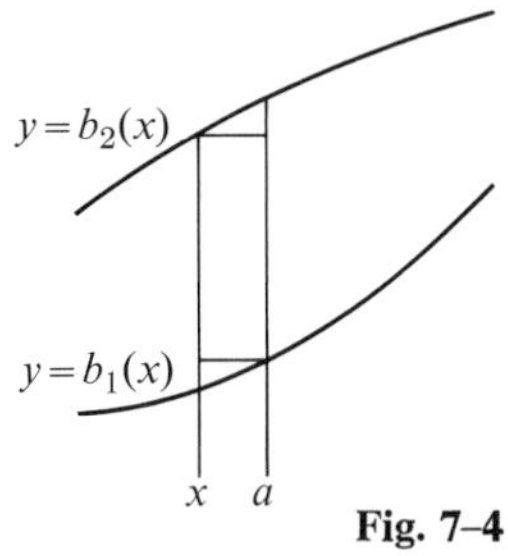

Fig. 7-4

To choose these δ's, we need only the continuity of b_1 and b_2 at the point a. Now we make use of the continuity (and hence the uniform continuity) of $f(x, y)$ in B. Choose δ_3 such that if $[x, y]$ and $[x', y']$ are any two points of B which are a distance δ_3 or less apart, then

$$|f(x, y) - f(x', y')| < \epsilon/3L.$$

Let δ be the minimum of these three δ_i and suppose that x is such that $|x - a| < \delta$. Let us suppose that $b_1(x) < b_1(a)$ and $b_2(x) < b_2(a)$. Any of the other possible cases could be handled in essentially the same way.

It may help to look at Figure 7–4 to follow the computations. We find that

$$\begin{aligned}
|g(x) - g(a)| &= \left|\int_{b_1(x)}^{b_2(x)} f(x, y)\,dy - \int_{b_1(a)}^{b_2(a)} f(a, y)\,dy\right| \\
&= \left|\int_{b_1(x)}^{b_1(a)} f(x, y)\,dy + \int_{b_1(a)}^{b_2(x)} [f(x, y) - f(a, y)]\,dy - \int_{b_2(x)}^{b_2(a)} f(a, y)\,dy\right| \\
&\le \int_{b_1(x)}^{b_1(a)} |f(x, y)|\,dy + \int_{b_1(a)}^{b_2(x)} |f(x, y) - f(a, y)|\,dy + \int_{b_2(x)}^{b_2(a)} |f(a, y)|\,dy \\
&\le M|b_1(a) - b_1(x)| + \frac{\epsilon}{3L} L + M|b_2(a) - b_2(x)| \\
&< \frac{\epsilon}{3} + \frac{\epsilon}{3} + \frac{\epsilon}{3}.
\end{aligned}$$

This proves the theorem. ▮

If the conditions of the above theorem are satisfied, then we can integrate the resulting function $g(x)$ and get an iterated integral. There are several different forms in which this iterated integral could be written. The following three are the most common.

$$\begin{aligned}
\int_{a_1}^{a_2} g(x)\,dx &= \int_{a_1}^{a_2} \left[\int_{b_1(x)}^{b_2(x)} f(x, y)\,dy\right] dx \\
&= \int_{a_1}^{a_2} \int_{b_1(x)}^{b_2(x)} f(x, y)\,dy\,dx \\
&= \int_{a_1}^{a_2} dx \int_{b_1(x)}^{b_2(x)} f(x, y)\,dy.
\end{aligned}$$

We will usually use the last notation. It has the advantage of indicating clearly which limits go with which variables of integration.

Now, let us prove the basic theorem.

Theorem 7–25. Let $b_1(x)$ and $b_2(x)$ be continuous functions in the interval $a_1 \leq x \leq a_2$. Let the region B be defined by

$$B = \{[x, y] \mid a_1 \leq x \leq a_2, b_1(x) \leq y \leq b_2(x)\}$$

and let $f(x, y)$ be continuous in B. Then the iterated integral of f over B is equal to the multiple integral; that is,

$$\int_{a_1}^{a_2} dx \int_{b_1(x)}^{b_2(x)} f(x, y)\, dy = \int_B f(x, y)\, dV.$$

Proof. The proof of this theorem is basically quite simple. The crux of the matter is that if we look at a small rectangle $R[[x_{j-1}, y_{i-1}], [x_j, y_i]]$, if

$$\Delta V_{ji} = (x_j - x_{j-1})(y_i - y_{i-1})$$

is the volume (area) of this rectangle and if $[x_j, y_i]$ is a point in the rectangle, then

$$\int_{x_{j-1}}^{x_j} dx \int_{y_{i-1}}^{y_i} f(x_j, y_i)\, dy = f(x_j, y_i)\, \Delta V_{ji},$$

and hence

$$\left| \int_{x_{j-1}}^{x_j} dx \int_{y_{i-1}}^{y_i} f(x, y)\, dy - f(x_j, y_i)\, \Delta V_{ji} \right| = \left| \int_{x_{j-1}}^{x_j} dx \int_{y_{i-1}}^{y_i} [f(x, y) - f(x_j, y_i)]\, dy \right| .$$

By uniform continuity, the last integral can be made as small as we want by making the mesh of the partition small enough. The integral is less than $\epsilon\, \Delta V_{ji}$ when the partition is such that f changes by less than ϵ in each rectangle. Adding all such integrals, we have approximations to the multiple integral and to the iterated integral. Difficulties at the boundary require us to complicate the proof slightly, but we have given the basic idea.

Let us now give the complete proof. We let $\epsilon > 0$ be arbitrarily given. Set $M = \max \{|f(x, y)| \mid [x, y] \in B\}$, $L = \max \{b_2(x) - b_1(x) \mid a_1 \leq x \leq a_2\}$, and $K = a_2 - a_1$.

Choose $\delta_1 > 0$ sufficiently small so that if the mesh of a partition $\mathcal{P}$ is less than δ_1, then

$$\left| \int_B f(x, y)\, dV - \sum_{\#} \hat{f}(\mathbf{X}_\sigma) \Delta V_\sigma \right| < \epsilon/4$$

for any choice of $\mathbf{X}_\sigma \in R_\sigma$ for each rectangle of the partition. The symbol # indicates that the summation extends over all of the rectangles which have a point in common with B, and $\hat{f}$ is the function that coincides with f in B and is zero everywhere else. Theorem 7–20 shows that such a δ_1 exists.

Choose $\delta_2 > 0$ sufficiently small so that if $|\mathbf{X} - \mathbf{X}'| < \delta_2\sqrt{2}$ for two points of B, then

$$|f(\mathbf{X}) - f(\mathbf{X}')| < \epsilon/4LK.$$

This can be done because f is uniformly continuous over the region B.

Choose $\delta_3 > 0$ such that if $|x - x'| < \delta_3$, then

$$|b_1(x) - b_1(x')| < \epsilon/4MK,$$

and choose $\delta_4 > 0$ such that if $|x - x'| < \delta_4$, then

$$|b_2(x) - b_2(x')| < \epsilon/4MK.$$

These last two choices are possible because of the uniform continuity of the functions $b_1(x)$ and $b_2(x)$ over the closed interval $a_1 \leq x \leq a_2$.

Let δ be the minimum of these four. Choose a partition $\mathcal{P}$ given by

$$a_1 = x_0 < x_1 < \cdots < x_{N'} = a_2,$$
$$b_1 = y_0 < y_1 < \cdots < y_N = b_2;$$

where b_1 and b_2 are the minimum and maximum values, respectively, of the functions $b_1(x)$ and $b_2(x)$ in the interval $R[a_1, a_2]$. Let the mesh of this partition be less than δ. Let $R_{ji} = \{[x, y] \mid x_{j-1} \leq x \leq x_j, y_{i-1} \leq y \leq y_i\}$. For each of these rectangles, define $\mathbf{X}_{ji} = [x_j, y_i]$ if R_{ji} is contained completely in B. If R_{ji} contains some point that is not in B, let $\mathbf{X}_{ji}$ be any such point. Set $\Delta y_i = y_i - y_{i-1}$ and $\Delta x_j = x_j - x_{j-1}$.

Now suppose that x is any number in the interval $x_{j-1} \leq x \leq x_j$ and suppose that the rectangle R_{ji} is contained completely in B. Then

$$\left|\int_{y_{i-1}}^{y_i} f(x, y)\,dy - f(x_j, y_i)\,\Delta y_i\right| = \left|\int_{y_{i-1}}^{y_i} [f(x, y) - f(x_j, y_i)]\,dy\right|$$
$$\leq \int_{y_{i-1}}^{y_i} \frac{\epsilon}{4LK}\,dy = \frac{\epsilon}{4LK}\,\Delta y_i.$$

Next, we find

$$\left|\int_{b_1(x)}^{b_2(x)} f(x, y)\,dy - \sum_{i=1}^{N} \hat{f}(\mathbf{X}_{ji})\,\Delta y_i\right|$$
$$= \left|\int_{b_1(x)}^{y_{i_1-1}} f(x, y)\,dy + \int_{y_{i_2}}^{b_2(x)} f(x, y)\,dy + \sum_{i=i_1}^{i_2}\left[\int_{y_{i-1}}^{y_i} f(x, y)\,dy - f(x_j, y_i)\,\Delta y_i\right]\right|$$
$$\leq M|y_{i_1-1} - b_1(x)| + M|b_2(x) - y_{i_2}| + \sum_{i=i_1}^{i_2} \frac{\epsilon}{4LK}\Delta y_i$$
$$< \frac{\epsilon}{4K} + \frac{\epsilon}{4K} + \frac{\epsilon}{4K} = \frac{3\epsilon}{4K}.$$

Here, in the first step, we divided the integral up, letting i_1 and i_2 be the indices such that R_{ji_1} is the lowest rectangle in the column so that it is contained entirely in B, while R_{ji_2} is the top rectangle with this property. Also $\hat{f}(\mathbf{X}_{ji}) = 0$ for all rectangles outside this range. By the choice of δ, the inequalities of the next line follow.

Now we use the above inequality to find

$$\left|\int_{a_1}^{a_2} dx \int_{b_1(x)}^{b_2(x)} f(x, y)\, dy - \sum_{j=1}^{N'} \sum_{i=1}^{N} \hat{f}(\mathbf{X}_{ji}) \Delta y_i \, \Delta x_j\right|$$

$$= \left|\sum_{j=1}^{N'} \int_{x_{j-1}}^{x_j} \left[\int_{b_1(x)}^{b_2(x)} f(x, y)\, dy - \sum_{i=1}^{N} \hat{f}(\mathbf{X}_{ji})\, \Delta y_i\right] dx\right|$$

$$< \sum_{j=1}^{N'} \int_{x_{j-1}}^{x_j} \frac{3\epsilon}{4K}\, dx = \frac{3\epsilon}{4K} \int_{a_1}^{a_2} dx = \frac{3\epsilon}{4}.$$

Finally,

$$\left|\int_{a_1}^{a_2} dx \int_{b_1(x)}^{b_2(x)} f(x, y)\, dy - \int_B f(x, y)\, dV\right|$$

$$\leq \left|\int_{a_1}^{a_2} dx \int_{b_1(x)}^{b_2(x)} f\, dy - \sum_{\#} \hat{f}(\mathbf{X}_\sigma)\, \Delta V_\sigma\right| + \left|\sum_{\#} \hat{f}(\mathbf{X}_\sigma)\, \Delta V_\sigma - \int_B f(x, y)\, dV\right|$$

$$< \frac{3\epsilon}{4} + \frac{\epsilon}{4} = \epsilon.$$

Since ϵ is arbitrary, the two integrals must actually be equal, and the theorem is proved. ▌

Theorems 7–24 and 7–25 can be generalized to any number of dimensions. Corresponding to Theorem 7–24, we could prove that

$$g(\mathbf{X}') = \int_{b_1(\mathbf{X}')}^{b_2(\mathbf{X}')} f(\mathbf{X}', x_n)\, dx_n$$

is continuous, where $b_1(\mathbf{X}')$ and $b_2(\mathbf{X}')$, defined and continuous over a region B', are the surface functions of a region B with respect to the coordinate x_n, f is continuous on B and $\mathbf{X}' = [x_1, x_2, \ldots, x_{n-1}]$.

Under the same conditions, Theorem 7–25 would correspond to

$$\int_{B'} dV_{n-1} \int_{b_1(\mathbf{X}')}^{b_2(\mathbf{X}')} f(\mathbf{X}', x_n)\, dx_n = \int_B f(\mathbf{X})\, dV_n.$$

By induction we could then use this result to break up multiple integrals into a complete sequence of one-dimensional integrals, i.e., into an iterated integral.

These above results have important consequences. For example:

▶ **Theorem 7–26.** Let $f(x, y)$ be continuous on the compact, smoothly bounded, semiconvex region B, which can be represented in either of the two ways

$$B = \{[x, y] \mid a_1 \leq x \leq a_2,\ b_1(x) \leq y \leq b_2(x)\}$$
$$= \{[x, y] \mid b_1 \leq y \leq b_2,\ a_1(y) \leq x \leq a_2(y)\}.$$

Then both of the iterated integrals exist and are equal, i.e.,

$$\int_{a_1}^{a_2} dx \int_{b_1(x)}^{b_2(x)} f(x, y)\, dy = \int_{b_1}^{b_2} dy \int_{a_1(y)}^{a_2(y)} f(x, y)\, dx.$$

Proof. Under the conditions of the theorem each of the iterated integrals exists and each is equal to the multiple integral. Hence the two must be equal. ▌

Note that a simple region can be decomposed into a finite number of semiconvex regions each of which satisfy the requirements of the theorem. These regions will have only portions of their boundary in common, but duplication over the boundary has has no effect on the integral. This follows from Theorem 7–18.

In higher dimensions there are more than two possible iterated integrals. Indeed, if B is a semiconvex region in R^n, there are $n!$ different iterated integrals (why?). All must still have the same value, however, if the function is continuous.

There seem to be no general rules which are of much value in converting a given multiple integral into an iterated integral. There are many different ways in which a region can be specified, and each requires its own method. A region which is not semiconvex can often be expressed as a single iterated integral by the proper choice of the order of integration. Otherwise, the region may have to be broken up into a number of semiconvex regions.

In order to convert a multiple integral into an iterated integral one must produce a sequence of regions, $B_1, B_2, \ldots, B_n$, together with an associated sequence of coordinates, say $x_1, x_2, \ldots, x_n$, such that each $B_i \in R^i = \{[x_1, x_2, \ldots, x_i]\}$ and $B_n = B$, the desired region of integration. Furthermore, each B_i must be representable by means of a pair of continuous surface functions over B_{i-1}. Thus, letting $\mathbf{X}_1 = [x_1]$, $\mathbf{X}_2 = [x_1, x_2]$, and so on, we have

$$\begin{aligned}
B_1 &= \{\mathbf{X}_1 \mid a_1 \le x_1 \le b_1\}, \\
B_2 &= \{\mathbf{X}_2 \mid \mathbf{X}_1 \in B_1,\ a_2(x_1) \le x_2 \le b_2(x_1)\}, \\
&\ \vdots \\
B_i &= \{\mathbf{X}_i \mid \mathbf{X}_{i-1} \in B_{i-1},\ a_i(\mathbf{X}_{i-1}) \le x_i \le b_i(\mathbf{X}_{i-1})\}, \qquad i = 3, \ldots, n.
\end{aligned}$$

The corresponding iterated integral would then be

$$\int_{a_1}^{b_1} dx_1 \int_{a_2(\mathbf{X}_1)}^{b_2(\mathbf{X}_1)} dx_2 \int \cdots \int_{a_n(\mathbf{X}_{n-1})}^{b_n(\mathbf{X}_{n-1})} f(\mathbf{X})\, dx_n.$$

Note that in each of the integrals the limits of integration depend only on the variables which are "further out" in the integration. This, of course, is the main point of the whole process.

As an example, let us write the iterated integral over the four-dimensional cone B defined by

$$x^2 + y^2 + z^2 \le w^2, \qquad 0 \le w \le 1. \tag{7–30}$$

For each fixed w, the cross section of this region in the three-dimensional xyz-space is the ball or solid sphere of radius w centered at the origin. Let S_3 be this ball

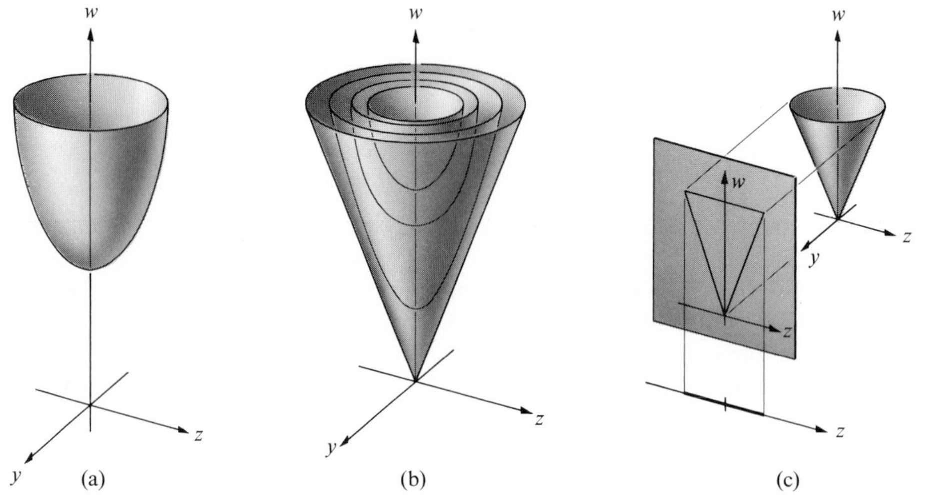

Fig. 7–5

of radius 1. This is the smallest region which contains all the cross sections. Therefore it is the projection of B into this space. For a fixed $[x, y, z]$ in this ball, by (7–30) we see that $(x^2 + y^2 + z^2)^{1/2} \le w \le 1$. Hence

$$\int_B f(x, y, z, w)\, dV_4 = \int_{S_3} dV_3 \int_{[x^2+y^2+z^2]^{1/2}}^{1} f\, dw.$$

Projecting S_3 along the x-axis, we obtain the disk of radius 1 in the xy-plane. Continuing in this way, we finally obtain

$$\int_B f\, dV = \int_{-1}^{1} dx \int_{-[1-x^2]^{1/2}}^{[1-x^2]^{1/2}} dy \int_{-[1-x^2-y^2]^{1/2}}^{[1-x^2-y^2]^{1/2}} dz \int_{[x^2+y^2+z^2]^{1/2}}^{1} f(x, y, z, w)\, dw.$$

It is interesting to see how the result would change if we made the first projection (the innermost integral) along the x-axis. For each fixed x, (7–30) defines the "cross section" in the yzw-space bounded by the paraboloid

$$y^2 + z^2 = w^2 - x^2, \qquad w \ge 0,$$

and the plane $w = 1$, as in Fig. 7–5(a). When $x = 0$, this paraboloid becomes a cone. Each of these paraboloids is contained inside the cone $y^2 + z^2 \le w^2, 0 \le w \le 1$; hence this cone is our first projection.

For a given $[y, z, w]$ in this cone, we can determine x by (7–30) to get the desired surface functions. We find that

$$-[w^2 - y^2 - z^2]^{1/2} \le x \le [w^2 - y^2 - z^2]^{1/2}.$$

Suppose we next project this cone along the y-axis. We obtain the triangular region bounded by $w = z$, $w = -z$, and $w = 1$. For a given (z, w) in this region, y varies between $-[w^2 - z^2]^{1/2}$ and $[w^2 - z^2]^{1/2}$.

Now projecting this region along the w-axis (onto the z-axis), we obtain the interval $-1 \leq z \leq 1$. For a fixed z in this interval, w lies in the range $|z| \leq w \leq 1$. Hence we finally have

$$\int_B f\,dV = \int_{-1}^{1} dz \int_{|z|}^{1} dw \int_{-[w^2-z^2]^{1/2}}^{[w^2-z^2]^{1/2}} dy \int_{-[w^2-y^2-z^2]^{1/2}}^{[w^2-y^2-z^2]^{1/2}} f\,dx.$$

It is often useful, and sometimes necessary, to break up an iterated integral into the sum of two or more integrals. For example, if B is the region in the xy-plane defined by $1 \leq x \leq 2$, $x \leq y \leq x^2$ (the upper triangular-shaped region in Fig. 7–6), then the iterated integral over B can be in either of the two forms

$$\int_1^2 dx \int_x^{x^2} f\,dy = \int_1^4 dy \int_{\sqrt{y}}^{\phi(y)} f\,dx,$$

where the function ϕ is defined by

$$\phi(y) = \begin{cases} y, & 1 \leq y \leq 2, \\ 2, & 2 \leq y \leq 4. \end{cases}$$

However, it is often more useful to have the last integral broken up into two parts:

$$\int_1^2 dy \int_{\sqrt{y}}^{y} f\,dx + \int_2^4 dy \int_{\sqrt{y}}^{2} f\,dx.$$

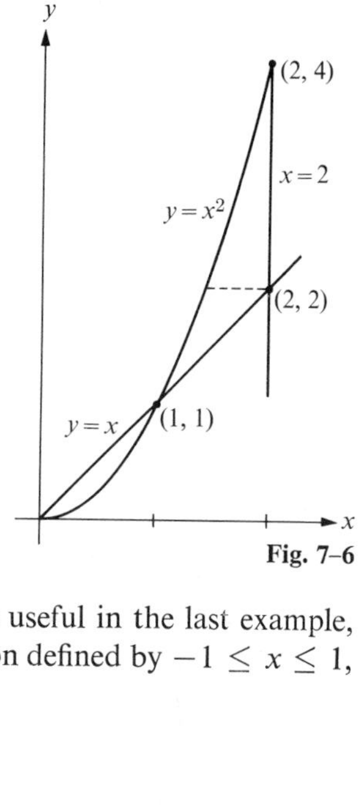

Fig. 7–6

While the decomposition into two integrals might be useful in the last example, it is necessary in the following example. Let B be the region defined by $-1 \leq x \leq 1$, $2x^2 - 1 \leq y \leq |x|$. Then

$$\begin{aligned}\int_B f\,dV &= \int_{-1}^{1} dx \int_{2x^2-1}^{|x|} f\,dy \\ &= \int_{-1}^{0} dy \int_{-[(1+y)/2]^{1/2}}^{[(1+y)/2]^{1/2}} f\,dx + \int_0^1 dy \int_{-[(1+y)/2]^{1/2}}^{-y} f\,dx \\ &\quad + \int_0^1 dy \int_y^{[(1+y)/2]^{1/2}} f\,dx.\end{aligned}$$

The reader should sketch the region and verify the necessity of this decomposition.

Finally, we should observe that an iterated may be perfectly valid and yet not represent a multiple integral over some region. But even then it may still be possible to change the order of integration. The iterated integral can be broken up into a finite number of iterated integrals in which the sign can be changed as necessary to reverse those limits of integration in which the lower limit is larger than the upper limit. The resulting integrals will then be equal to multiple integrals over some region, and the order of integration can then be changed. It is usually possible to recombine the resulting integrals. An example may help make this clearer.

Consider the integral

$$\int_0^2 dx \int_{x^2}^{x} f(x, y)\, dy = \int_0^1 dx \int_{x^2}^{x} f\, dy - \int_1^2 dx \int_x^{x^2} f\, dy$$

$$= \int_0^1 dy \int_y^{\sqrt{y}} f\, dx - \int_1^2 dy \int_{\sqrt{y}}^{y} f\, dx - \int_2^4 dy \int_{\sqrt{y}}^{2} f\, dx.$$

The signs of the last two integrals again can be changed by interchanging the innermost limits of integration. The three integrals can then be recombined to give

$$\int_0^2 dx \int_{x^2}^{x} f\, dy = \int_0^4 dy \int_{\phi(y)}^{\sqrt{y}} f\, dx,$$

where the function $\phi(y)$ is defined by

$$\phi(y) = \begin{cases} y & \text{if } 0 \le y \le 2, \\ 2 & \text{if } 2 \le y \le 4. \end{cases}$$

As mentioned earlier, it is exactly Theorem 7–26 which makes it possible for us to concentrate on iterated integrals instead of multiple integrals. However, we must be a little cautious. The reader is warned that very strong hypotheses have been used in this section. It is not always possible to change the order of integration in an iterated integral. *If* the function is continuous over the *simple region*, then the order of integration can be reversed. If these conditions are not satisfied, then the proof given here does not apply.

Actually, it is only in unusual cases that the conclusion of this last theorem fails. Almost every case which might occur in practice satisfies either the hypotheses of this theorem or other hypotheses which imply the same result. Thus it is most surprising when this result fails. However, the reader should still be suspicious whenever he must reverse the order of integration.

Let us exhibit more of the power of the last result by using it to prove the following theorem.

► **Theorem 7–27.** Let the function $f(x, y)$ be continuous in the closed rectangle $a_1 \le x \le a_2$, $b_1 \le y \le b_2$, and suppose that $\partial f/\partial y = f_{,2}(x, y)$ is also continuous in the same rectangle. Let y_0 be such that $b_1 < y_0 < b_2$. Then the function

$$g(y) = \int_{a_1}^{a_2} f(x, y)\, dx$$

is differentiable at y_0, and

$$g'(y_0) = \int_{a_1}^{a_2} f_{,2}(x, y_0)\, dx.$$

Proof. Note that this theorem tells us that we can differentiate under the integral sign *when the differentiated function is continuous.* The variable y in this theorem should be thought of as a parameter, which it usually is in the applications of this theorem.

To prove this theorem, we introduce the new function

$$h(y) = \int_{b_1}^{y} dt \int_{a_1}^{a_2} f_{,2}(x, t)\, dx.$$

Observe that we have introduced a new dummy variable t into the integral so as not to be confused by too many y's. Since $f_{,2}$ is continuous, its integral with respect to x is also continuous (why?). Therefore the function $h(y)$ exists. Furthermore, it is differentiable with respect to y. The derivative is

$$h'(y) = \int_{a_1}^{a_2} f_{,2}(x, y)\, dx.$$

On the other hand, by Theorem 7–26 we have

$$\begin{aligned} h(y) &= \int_{a_1}^{a_2} dx \int_{b_1}^{y} f_{,2}(x, t)\, dt = \int_{a_1}^{a_2} [f(x, y) - f(x, b_1)]\, dx \\ &= g(y) - g(b_1). \end{aligned}$$

Since the derivative of a constant is zero, the theorem follows. ▌

PROBLEMS

1. Reverse the order of the following integrals.

a) $\int_0^1 dx \int_0^{2x} f(x, y)\, dy$ b) $\int_0^1 dy \int_{-y^2/2}^{y^2/2} f(x, y)\, dx$

c) $\int_0^1 dx \int_{x^2}^{x} f(x, y)\, dy$ d) $\int_{-1}^1 dy \int_0^{\sqrt{1-y^2}} f(x, y)\, dx$

2. Write the following integrals in all possible orders. In some cases you may have to break the integral up into the sum of more than one integral.

a) $\int_0^2 dx \int_0^{(4-x^2)^{1/2}} dy \int_0^{4-x^2-y^2} f(x, y, z)\, dz$

b) $\int_0^2 dx \int_0^{(4-x^2)^{1/2}} dy \int_0^{4-x^2-y^2} f\, dz$

c) $\int_0^3 dx \int_0^{6-2x} dz \int_0^1 f\, dy$

d) $\int_0^3 dx \int_0^{6-2x} dz \int_0^{7-6z-2x} f\, dy$

3. Write the following integrals as iterated integrals (or as the sum of iterated integrals) in the order $dz\, dy\, f\, dx$.

a) $\int_0^1 dx \int_{-(1-x^2)^{1/2}}^{(x-x^2)^{1/2}} dy \int_0^{(1-x^2-y^2)^{1/2}} f\, dz$ b) $\int_{-1}^1 dx \int_{-(1-x^2)^{1/2}}^{(1-x^2)^{1/2}} dy \int_{-(1-x^2-y^2)^{1/2}}^{1-x} f\, dz$

4. Write as an iterated integral in the orders $dx\,dy\,f\,dz$ and $dz\,dx\,f\,dy$ the integral over the region G defined by

$$x^2 + y^2 \le e^{z^2}, \qquad z \ge (1 - x^2 - y^2)^{1/2}, \qquad 0 \le z \le 1.$$

5. Write an iterated integral over the region in R^4 which is common to both the sphere $x^2 + y^2 + z^2 + w^2 \le 4$ and the cylinder $x^2 + y^2 + z^2 \le 1$.

6. Let $f(x, y)$ and $f_{\prime 2}(x, y)$ be continuous for $a_1 \le x \le a_2, b_1 \le y \le b_2$. Further, let the functions $a_1(y)$ and $a_2(y)$ be continuous and differentiable for $b_1 \le y \le b_2$ and suppose that $a_1 < a_1(y) < a_2(y) < a_2$ for all y in this interval. Prove that

$$\frac{d}{dy}\int_{a_1(y)}^{a_2(y)} f(x, y)\,dx = f[a_2(y), y]a_2'(y) - f[a_1(y), y]a_1'(y) + \int_{a_1(y)}^{a_2(y)} f_{\prime 2}(x, y)\,dx.$$

This is known as *Leibnitz's rule.* [*Hint:* Set $h(y, z, w) = \int_z^w f(x, y)\,dx$.]

7–6. CHANGE OF VARIABLE IN MULTIPLE INTEGRALS

It is easy to change the variable in a one-dimensional integral. The reader may recall that he learned when he first studied the integral that if $f(t)$ is continuous in $R[a, b]$, if $h(w)$ is continuous and differentiable in $R[c, d]$, with $h(c) = a, h(d) = b$, and if $h(x) \in R[a, b]$ for all $x \in R[c, d]$, then

$$\int_a^b f(t)\,dt = \int_c^d f[h(w)]h'(w)\,dw.$$

This rule is most easily remembered with the help of the convention $dt = h'(w)\,dw$ when we make the change of variable $t = h(w)$.

For functions of several variables the situation becomes much more complex. Let us begin by stating one form of the theorem governing the change of variable in multiple integrals.

▶ **Theorem 7–28.** Let $f(\mathbf{X})$ be continuous in the simple region B in R^n. Let $\mathbf{X} = \mathbf{H}(\mathbf{W})$ be a continuous, continuously differentiable, one-to-one mapping of the simple region B' onto B. Let $J(\mathbf{W}) = \det[d\mathbf{H}(\mathbf{W})]$ and suppose that $J(\mathbf{W})$ is never zero at any interior point of B'. Then

$$\int_B f(\mathbf{X})\,dV_{\mathbf{X}} = \int_{B'} f[\mathbf{H}(\mathbf{W})]\,|J(\mathbf{W})|\,dV_{\mathbf{W}}. \tag{7–31}$$

Remarks. In the conclusion of this theorem we have introduced the notation $dV_{\mathbf{X}}$ and $dV_{\mathbf{W}}$. These symbols are part of the integration symbol. The subscript is merely to indicate the variable that is ranging over the region B or B'. Note that $J[\mathbf{W}]$ is exactly the Jacobian of the transformation $\mathbf{H}(\mathbf{W})$. This formula for change of variable is not difficult to remember in the formal form

$$\mathbf{X} = \mathbf{H}(\mathbf{W}), \qquad dV_{\mathbf{X}} = \det[d\mathbf{H}(\mathbf{W})]\,dV_{\mathbf{W}}.$$

Since $d\mathbf{H}$ is assumed to be continuous, so is $J(\mathbf{W})$. Since $J(\mathbf{W}) \ne 0$ in the interior of B', we can easily show that it is always either positive throughout the interior of B'

or negative there. Equation (7–31) is therefore equivalent to

$$\int_B f(\mathbf{X})\,dV_{\mathbf{X}} = \pm \int_{B'} f[\mathbf{H}(\mathbf{W})]J(\mathbf{W})\,dV_{\mathbf{W}},$$

where the sign is chosen as necessary.

At each interior point of B' the Jacobian $J(\mathbf{W}) \neq 0$, and hence by the inverse function theorem, the function $\mathbf{X} = \mathbf{H}(\mathbf{W})$ can be solved for $\mathbf{W} = \mathbf{G}(\mathbf{X})$ in some neighborhood. The nonvanishing of the Jacobian $J(\mathbf{W})$ therefore means that the mapping is locally one-to-one. The overall one-to-one character of the mapping must still be added as a hypothesis, however. Observe that there is no requirement that the mapping be one-to-one on the boundary. For example, the mapping

$$x = r\cos\theta, \qquad y = r\sin\theta$$

satisfies the requirements of the theorem if we let $B = \{[x, y] \mid x^2 + y^2 \leq 1, y \geq 0\}$ and $B' = \{[r, \theta] \mid 0 \leq r \leq 1, 0 \leq \theta \leq \pi\}$. The Jacobian here has the value r, which is zero only on part of the boundary of B'. One entire side of the rectangle B' corresponds to a single point on the boundary of B. Note that the same mapping defined on $B'' = \{[r, \theta] \mid 0 \leq r \leq 1, 0 \leq \theta \leq 3\pi\}$ is no longer one-to-one overall, but it is still locally one-to-one at all interior points of B''.

The proof of this theorem for the general case is quite complicated, and hence we will discuss it only for the two-dimensional case. The proof in the higher-dimensional case is essentially the same, merely needing more steps. The complications are mainly in the notation.

We begin by proving a much simpler theorem first.

Theorem 7–29. Let

$$B' = \{[x, v] \mid a \leq x \leq b, \phi_1(x) \leq v \leq \phi_2(x)\}$$

and

$$B = \{[x, y] \mid a \leq x \leq b, \psi_1(x) \leq y \leq \psi_2(x)\}$$

be regions in the xv- and xy-planes, respectively, where the functions ϕ_1, ϕ_2, ψ_1, and ψ_2 are continuous in the interval $a \leq x \leq b$. Let $g(x, v)$ be continuous and continuously differentiable throughout B' such that $g'_2 > 0$ at every interior point of B'. Let $[x, y] = \mathbf{G}(x, v) = [x, g(x, v)]$ map B' one-to-one onto B. Let $f(x, y)$ be continuous on B. Then

$$\int_B f(x, y)\,dV_{(x,y)} = \int_{B'} f[\mathbf{G}(x, v)] \det[d\mathbf{G}]\,dV_{(x,v)}.$$

Proof. Observe first that $\det[d\mathbf{G}] = g'_2$.

Let us assume that the region B is a rectangle, i.e., that $\psi_1(x) = c$ and $\psi_2(x) = d$ for all x. This assumption will make the picture slightly easier to see at the start.

Since $g'_2 > 0$, for each fixed x, the function $y = g(x, v)$ is a monotone strictly increasing function of v. That the mapping is one-to-one is a consequence of this fact and thus need not have been assumed in the theorem.

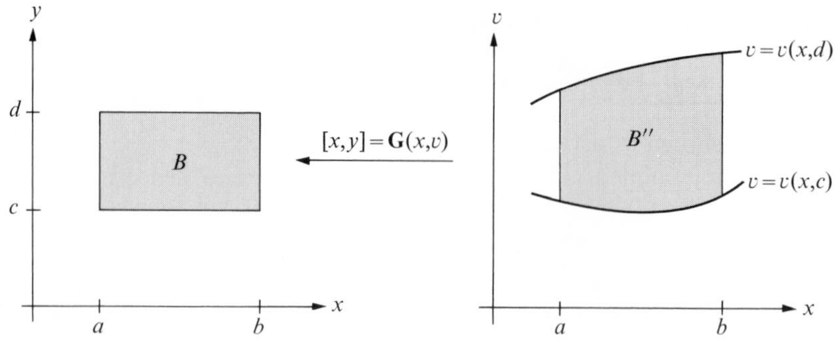

Fig. 7–7

We can solve $y = g(x, v)$ for the inverse function $v = v(x, y)$ since $g_{'2} > 0$. The functions ϕ_1 and ϕ_2 in the theorem are therefore the functions $v(x, c)$ and $v(x, d)$, respectively. Figure 7–7 illustrates the situation.

We see that for any fixed x

$$\int_c^d f(x, y)\, dy = \int_{v(x,c)}^{v(x,d)} f[x, g(x, v)]g_{'2}(x, v)\, dv,$$

and hence

$$\begin{aligned}\int_B f(x, y)\, dV_{\mathbf{X}} &= \int_a^b dx \int_c^d f(x, y)\, dy \\ &= \int_a^b dx \int_{v(x,c)}^{v(x,d)} f[\mathbf{G}(x, v)] \det [d\mathbf{G}]\, dv \\ &= \int_{B''} f[\mathbf{G}(x, v)] \det [d\mathbf{G}]\, dV_{(x,v)}.\end{aligned}$$

Note that we made use of the fact that $\det d\mathbf{G} = g_{'2}$ in this computation.

We may now proceed to the general situation. Even if the functions ψ_1 and ψ_2 are not constants, we can still solve for the function $v = v(x, y)$ as the inverse of $g(x, v)$ for each fixed x. The two sets of surface functions must also be related by the fact that $\psi_1(x) = g\big(x, \phi_1(x)\big)$ and $\psi_2(x) = g\big(x, \phi_2(x)\big)$ for each x. [The monotonicity of $g(x, v)$ is needed to show this.] These facts then show that

$$\int_{\psi_1(x)}^{\psi_2(x)} f(x, y)\, dy = \int_{\phi_1(x)}^{\phi_2(x)} f[x, g(x, v)]g_{'2}(x, v)\, dv$$

for each fixed x. The remainder of the proof follows exactly as above. ▌

We now extend the above result to a theorem which is much closer to the desired result.

Theorem 7–30. Let B and B' be simple regions in the xy-plane and uv-plane, respectively. Let $f(x, y)$ be continuous in B. Let $\mathbf{X} = \mathbf{H}(\mathbf{W}) = [h_1(u, v), h_2(u, v)]$ map B' one-to-one onto B. Furthermore, suppose that $\det [d\mathbf{H}(\mathbf{W})] > 0$ and $h_{1'1}(\mathbf{W}) > 0$ at every interior point of B'. Then

$$\int_B f(x, y)\, dV_{(x,y)} = \int_{B'} f\big(\mathbf{H}(\mathbf{W})\big) \det [d\mathbf{H}(\mathbf{W})]\, dV_{(u,v)}.$$

Proof. B' is the union of a finite number of semiconvex regions. It therefore suffices to assume that B' is already semiconvex. We do not simultaneously assume that B is also semiconvex, merely that it is simple. Since we are assuming that B' is semiconvex, for any fixed v the set $\{u \mid [u, v] \in B'\}$ must be a line segment. Since the function $x = h_1(u, v)$ has the derivative $h_{1'1} > 0$, we can solve for the inverse function $u = \phi(x, v)$, which is defined on an entire interval itself. For a fixed v, ϕ maps this interval in x onto the above interval $\{u \mid [u, v] \in B'\}$.

The inverse function theorem tells us that the inverse function $\phi(x, v)$ is continuously differentiable in a neighborhood of each point at which it is defined corresponding to an interior point of B'. Furthermore, $\phi_{'2} = -h_{1'2}/h_{1'1}$.

The transformation $\mathbf{H}$ can be written as $\mathbf{X} = [x, y] = \mathbf{H}(\mathbf{W}) = \mathbf{H}(u, v)$, where

$$x = h_1(u, v), \qquad y = h_2(u, v), \qquad d\mathbf{H} = \begin{bmatrix} h_{1'1} & h_{1'2} \\ h_{2'1} & h_{2'2} \end{bmatrix}.$$

Define a new transformation as follows:

$$[x, y] = \mathbf{G}[x, v], \qquad x = x, \qquad y = g(x, v),$$

where

$$g(x, v) = h_2[\phi(x, v), v].$$

A simple computation shows that if we set $J = \det [d\mathbf{H}]$ then

$$g_{'2} = J/h_{1'1}.$$

Now define the second transformation:

$$[x, v] = \mathbf{K}[u, v], \qquad x = h_1(u, v), \qquad v = v.$$

In this way, we have been able to break the transformation $\mathbf{H}$ up into a pair of transformations, each transforming a single variable at a time. Note that

$$\mathbf{H}(\mathbf{W}) = \mathbf{G}[\mathbf{K}(\mathbf{W})], \qquad [d\mathbf{H}] = [d\mathbf{G}][d\mathbf{K}] = \begin{bmatrix} 1 & 0 \\ g_{'1} & g_{'2} \end{bmatrix} \begin{bmatrix} h_{1'1} & h_{1'2} \\ 0 & 1 \end{bmatrix}.$$

Hence

$$J = \det [d\mathbf{H}] = \det [d\mathbf{G}] \det [d\mathbf{K}] = g_{'2} h_{1'1}.$$

Let $\mathbf{K}$ map the region B' onto a region B'' in the xv-plane. Since h_1 is monotone strictly increasing as a function of u, this mapping is one-to-one. We next note that a transformation of the type given here (or of the type given in Theorem 7–29) has an inverse which is of the same type. Therefore, if either of the two regions in Theorem 7–29 satisfy the hypotheses given there, so does the other. In particular, this means that the transformation $\mathbf{K}$, carrying B' onto B'' satisfies the hypotheses of Theorem 7–29. Hence, using $f[\mathbf{G}(x, v)] \det [d\mathbf{G}(x, v)]$ in place of f in this theorem, we have

$$\begin{aligned} \int_{B''} f[\mathbf{G}(x, v)] \det [d\mathbf{G}(x, v)]\, dV_{(x,v)} &= \int_{B'} f[\mathbf{H}(\mathbf{W})](\det [d\mathbf{G}])(\det [d\mathbf{K}])\, dV_{(u,v)} \\ &= \int_{B'} f[\mathbf{H}(\mathbf{W})](\det [d\mathbf{H}])\, dV_{(u,v)}. \qquad (7\text{–}32) \end{aligned}$$

The transformation $\mathbf{G}$ will carry the region B'' onto the region B. The region B can be broken up into a finite number of semiconvex regions. On each of these the hypotheses of Theorem 7–29 will be satisfied. The integrals of the conclusion of this theorem can be summed over all of these regions, giving

$$\int_B f(\mathbf{X})\, dV_{(x,y)} = \int_{B''} f[\mathbf{G}(x, v)](\det [d\mathbf{G}])\, dV_{(x,v)}$$

which, combined with (7–32), proves the theorem. ▌

We now proceed to the proof of Theorem 7–28. The last result we obtained differs from the desired result in two essentials. We assumed that $J > 0$ and that $h_{1'1} > 0$ at all of the interior points of B'. We must now consider the other possibilities.

We observe that if $g_{\prime 2} < 0$ in Theorem 7–29, then the limits of integration would be reversed in the one-dimensional integral. To obtain the proper result, we would have to multiply the right-hand side of the conclusion of the theorem by -1. Now $\det [d\mathbf{H}] = h_{1'1}g_{\prime 2}$ in the proof of Theorem 7–30). Hence, if we were to assume that $\det [d\mathbf{H}]$ were either everywhere positive or everywhere negative and at the same time that $h_{1'1}$ also never was zero or changed sign in the interior of B, we would find that

$$\int_B f(\mathbf{X})\, dV_{(x,y)} = \int_{B'} f[\mathbf{H}(\mathbf{W})]\, |\det [d\mathbf{H}]|\, dV_{(u,v)}. \tag{7–33}$$

Next, we observe that if $\det [d\mathbf{H}]$ is never zero but $h_{1'1} = 0$, then we must have $h_{2'1} \neq 0$. The proof of Theorem 7–30 would proceed just as well if we interchanged the roles of u and v throughout. Thus Eq. (7–33) holds if we assume that $\det [d\mathbf{H}]$ is never zero and $h_{2'1}$ is either everywhere positive or negative throughout B'.

Finally, for the general case in which we assume only that $\det [d\mathbf{H}]$ is never zero at an interior point of B', we divide B' up into four sets. Let

$$\begin{aligned}
D_1 &= \{\mathbf{X} \mid h_{1'1}(\mathbf{X}) > 0, \mathbf{X} \quad \text{an interior point of } B'\},\\
D_2 &= \{\mathbf{X} \mid h_{1'1}(\mathbf{X}) < 0, \mathbf{X} \quad \text{an interior point of } B'\},\\
D_3 &= \{\mathbf{X} \mid h_{1'1}(\mathbf{Y}) = 0, h_{2'1}(\mathbf{Y}) > 0 \quad \text{for all } \mathbf{Y} \text{ in some neighborhood of } \mathbf{X}\},\\
D_4 &= \{\mathbf{X} \mid h_{1'1}(\mathbf{Y}) = 0, h_{2'1}(\mathbf{Y}) < 0 \quad \text{for all } \mathbf{Y} \text{ in some neighborhood of } \mathbf{X}\}.
\end{aligned}$$

These four sets are mutually disjoint. Together with their boundary points, they make up all of B'. Usually the sets D_3 and D_4 are void, but this is not essential. Equation (7–33) must hold over every region formed here and hence must also be true over their union. ▌

As we commented earlier, the nonvanishing of the Jacobian of a mapping means that the mapping is locally one-to-one. The sign of the Jacobian determines the orientation of a region in R^n. While we do not wish to go into this problem here, we should at least mention a few specific facts about this concept.

Suppose we have a one-to-one mapping of a plane region onto another plane region. Let C be a small circle, traversed in the counterclockwise direction. The image of this circle will be a simple closed curve, C'. There are only two possible directions in which C' can be traversed. The mapping may lift the direction of traversal of C to a clockwise or counterclockwise traversal of C'. (Counterclockwise here means that the interior of the region bounded by C' will always be to the left.) A positive Jacobian means that the sense of traversal will remain the same, while a negative Jacobian will mean a reversal.

These comments are not in themselves satisfactory. What is meant by "clockwise" or "to the right"? A better way to think of the orientation is as follows. Let $\mathbf{H}(\mathbf{W}) = \mathbf{X}$ map a region of the uv-plane onto a region of the xy-plane. The image of a straight line will be some curve. In particular we can look at the image of lines parallel to the u and v axes through a point. These will be two curves meeting at the image point. Tangents to these curves will be $\mathbf{u}_1 = [h_{1'1}, h_{2'1}]$ and $\mathbf{u}_2 = [h_{1'2}, h_{2'2}]$. The first can be thought of as the "image" of $\mathbf{e}_1$, the second as the image of $\mathbf{e}_2$. Let U be an orthogonal matrix with positive determinant which makes a rotation of R^2 so that $U\mathbf{u}_1$ is in the direction of $\mathbf{e}_1$; that is, $U\mathbf{u}_1 = [a, 0]$, where $a > 0$. Let $U\mathbf{u}_2 = [b_1, b_2]$. Then

$$U[d\mathbf{H}] = \begin{bmatrix} a & b_1 \\ 0 & b_2 \end{bmatrix}.$$

Now $\mathbf{u}_2$ is less than 180° "counterclockwise" of $\mathbf{u}_1$ if and only if $\mathbf{e}_2 \cdot U\mathbf{u}_2 = b_2$ is greater than 0. But b_2 has the same sign as $\det(U[d\mathbf{H}]) = \det[d\mathbf{H}]$.

The above discussion can be generalized to any number of dimensions, but it will be enough to accept the fact that in each dimension there are two orientations. A mapping with $\det[d\mathbf{H}] > 0$ preserves the orientation, while one with $\det[d\mathbf{H}] < 0$ reverses it. In particular, the euclidean motion of reflection reverses the orientation, while the other euclidean motions preserve it.

Usually there is no difficulty if the Jacobian happens to vanish at isolated points, or even along surfaces, provided the Jacobian does not change sign. Such questions can always be handled with the help of the above theorem, deleting the points in question by enclosing them in small regions, and letting the volumes of these regions tend toward zero.

If the Jacobian is zero at some point and takes on both positive and negative values in every neighborhood of that point, then the mapping usually fails to be one-to-one. There are many possibilities here, and it is best to investigate each case on its own merits.

Finally, let us notice that the results of this section can be used to give a geometric meaning to the Jacobian.

Theorem 7–31. Let $\mathbf{W} = \mathbf{H}(\mathbf{X})$ define a one-to-one, continuous, and differentiable transformation of B into R^n, where B is a subset of R^n. Suppose that $\mathbf{X}_0$ is an interior point of B and that $J(\mathbf{X}) = \det[d\mathbf{H}(\mathbf{X})]$ is nonzero at $\mathbf{X}_0$. Then

$$J(\mathbf{X}_0) = \lim_{\delta \to 0} \frac{\text{vol } \mathbf{H}[S_\delta(\mathbf{X}_0)]}{\text{vol } S_\delta(\mathbf{X}_0)}.$$

The proof of this theorem is left as an exercise.

The transformation from polar coordinates to rectangular coordinates in the plane is defined by $x = r\cos\theta$, $y = r\sin\theta$. The Jacobian of this transformation is

$$J = \det\begin{bmatrix}\cos\theta & -r\sin\theta\\ \sin\theta & r\cos\theta\end{bmatrix} = r.$$

Hence the conversion of integrals from rectangular to polar coordinates is defined by

$$\int_{B_{x,y}} f\,dV_{x,y} = \int_{B_{r,\theta}} f\,r\,dV_{r,\theta}.$$

For example,

$$\int_0^a dy \int_0^{(a^2-y^2)^{1/2}} (x^2+y^2)\,dx = \int_B (x^2+y^2)\,dV_{x,y} = \int_{B'} (x^2+y^2)r\,dV_{r,\theta}$$

$$= \int_0^{\pi/2} d\theta \int_0^a r^3\,dr = a^4/8.$$

PROBLEMS

1. Prove Theorem 7-31.
2. Using Theorem 7-28, find the formulas for the change of a three-dimensional integral from cartesian coordinates to:

   a) cylindrical coordinates, b) spherical coordinates.
3. Convert each of the following integrals to polar coordinates, and integrate if possible.

   a) $\int_0^a dx \int_0^{(ax-x^2)^{1/2}} dy$ b) $\int_0^1 dx \int_0^x \dfrac{dy}{\sqrt{x^2+y^2}}$

   c) $\int_0^1 dx \int_{x^2}^x (x^2+y^2)^{-1/2}\,dy$ d) $\int_0^a dx \int_0^{(a^2-x^2)^{1/2}} e^{-(x^2+y^2)}dy$
4. Compute $\int_B (x^2+y^2)\,dV$, where B is the region bounded by the four hyperbolas $xy = 1$, $xy = 3$, $x^2 - y^2 = 1$, and $x^2 - y^2 = 2$ in the first quadrant, by performing the transformation $u = x^2 - y^2$, $v = 2xy$.
5. Compute $\int_0^1 dx \int_0^{1-x} y\log(1-x-y)\,dy$ with the help of the transformation $u = x + y$, $v = y/(x+y)$.
6. Prove that the volume of a region B in R^n is invariant under euclidean motions.

7-7. GREEN'S THEOREM

If we look again at Eq. (7-26), we will find that when the line integral $\int_C P\,dx + Q\,dy$ is independent of path in the plane, then $\partial P/\partial y = \partial Q/\partial x$. This observation is related to an important result in the theory of functions of several variables: Green's theorem.

▶ **Theorem 7–32.** Let B be a simple region in the xy-plane whose boundary C consists of a finite number of simple, closed, piecewise smooth curves. Suppose that C is so oriented that as it traversed in the positive direction (in the direction of increasing parameter), the region B is always to the left. Let $P(x, y)$ and $Q(x, y)$ be functions which have continuous derivatives in B. Then

$$\int_C P\,dx + Q\,dy = \int_B [Q_{\prime 1} - P_{\prime 2}]\,dV.$$

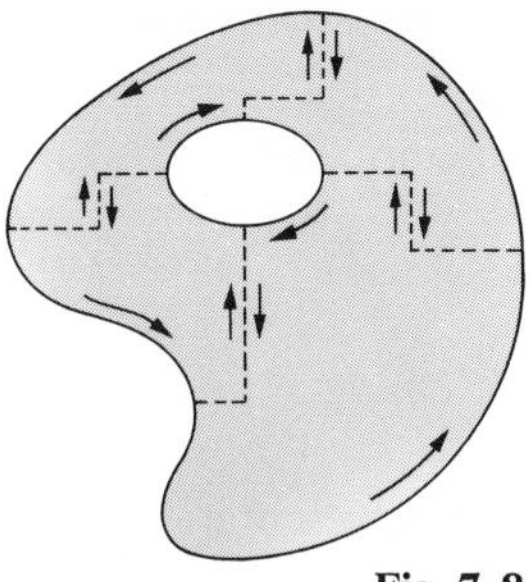

Fig. 7–8

Proof. Since B is a simple region, it can be decomposed into a finite number of semi-convex regions, $B_1, B_2, \ldots, B_N$, whose boundaries are the simple, closed, piecewise smooth curves $C_1, C_2, \ldots, C_N$. Each of these boundary curves is to be traversed in the direction which leaves the region bounded always to the left. This means that whenever two of these regions have a portion of their boundary in common, that part will be traversed in opposite directions in the two curves. See Fig. 7–8.

When we add the line integrals around each of these curves, the contributions of these common parts will cancel and we will be left with the integral around all of C. Hence it is sufficient to prove the theorem for a single region which is already semi-convex.

(There is an important property of the plane concealed in the above discussion. We must know that we can define a counterclockwise direction of rotation about every point of the plane in such a way that two adjacent regions will have opposite directions assigned to any common parts of their boundary.)

Let us assume that the region B has the two representations given by

$$\begin{aligned} B &= \{[x, y] \mid a_1(y) \le x \le a_2(y), b_1 \le y \le b_2\} \\ &= \{[x, y] \mid a_1 \le x \le a_2, b_1(x) \le y \le b_2(x)\} \end{aligned} \tag{7–34}$$

and proceed with the proof. Observe that the boundary C can be divided into four parts for each of the two representations. If we take the second representation of (7–34), for example, we can divide C into the following four curves:

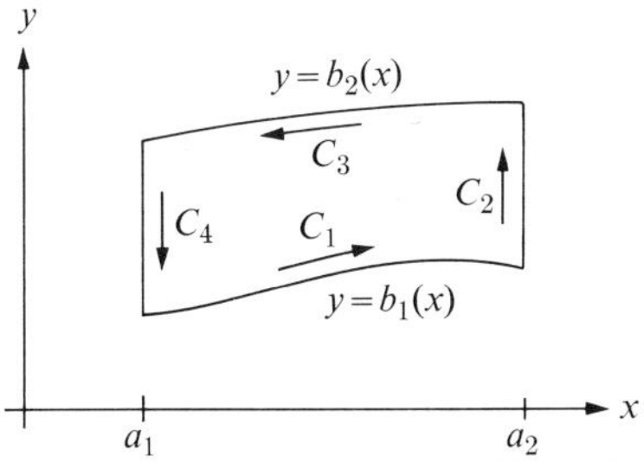

Fig. 7–9

$$C_1 = [x = t, y = b_1(t), a_1 \le t \le a_2],$$

$$C_2 = [x = a_2, y = t, b_1(a_2) \le t \le b_2(a_2)],$$

$$C_3 = [x = -t, y = b_2(-t), -a_2 \le t \le -a_1],$$

$$C_4 = [x = a_1, y = -t, -b_2(a_1) \le t \le -b_1(a_1)].$$

This decomposition is illustrated in Fig. 7–9. In some cases, one or more of the vertical segments may be eliminated since they reduce to a single point. Now we compute:

$$\int_B P'_2(x, y)\, dV = \int_{a_1}^{a_2} dx \int_{b_1(x)}^{b_2(x)} P'_2(x, y)\, dy$$
$$= \int_{a_1}^{a_2} (P[x, b_2(x)] - P[x, b_1(x)])\, dx = -\int_C P\, dx. \quad (7\text{–}35)$$

The representation of the last expression follows from the fact that $dx = 0$ along the two vertical parts of C (that is, along C_2 and C_3). Using x and $-x$ as the parameters along the bottom and top curves then gives the final result.

By using the other representation of B in a similar way we can obtain

$$\int_B Q'_1(x, y)\, dV = \int_C Q\, dy. \quad (7\text{–}36)$$

Adding (7–35) and (7–36) proves the theorem. ▌

Example. Suppose that we let $P = y$ and $Q = 0$. Then Green's theorem tells us that

$$\int_C y\, dx = -\int_B dV = -\text{ area of } B.$$

Can you explain the negative sign in this result? Isn't the integral of $y\, dx$ supposed to give the area of the region?

Although it might seem to be a severe restriction that Theorem 7–32 is valid only in a two-dimensional space, the theorem can actually be applied in a great many more situations than might be thought possible. Often a problem in a higher-dimensional space can be restricted to an affine plane in that space. A good example of this is the following:

Theorem 7–33. Let $G = S_r(\mathbf{A})$ be a ball in R^n. Let $\mathbf{F}: G \to R^n$ be differentiable in G. Then the line integral $\int_C \mathbf{F} \cdot d\mathbf{X}$ is independent of path in G if and only if the matrix $[d\mathbf{F}]$ is symmetric.

Proof. If the integral is independent of path, then $\mathbf{F} = \text{grad } g$ for some function g, and hence the equality of the mixed partial derivatives shows that the matrix $[d\mathbf{F}]$ is symmetric.

To prove the converse, let us suppose that $[d\mathbf{F}]$ is symmetric. The theorem will be proved if we can show that there exists a function g such that $\mathbf{F} = \text{grad } g$. We can define a function in the following way. For any point $\mathbf{B}$ of $S_r(\mathbf{A})$, set

$$g(\mathbf{B}) = \int_C \mathbf{F} \cdot d\mathbf{X},$$

where C is the curve made up of the finite number of straight line segments between the successive points: $\mathbf{A} = [a_1, a_2, \ldots, a_n]$, $\mathbf{B}_1 = [b_1, a_2, a_3, \ldots, a_n]$, $\mathbf{B}_2 = [b_1, b_2, a_3, \ldots, a_n], \ldots, B_{n-1} = [b_1, b_2, \ldots, b_{n-1}, a_n]$, and finally $\mathbf{B}_n = \mathbf{B} = [b_1, b_2, \ldots, b_n]$. Each is contained inside the ball, and hence the integral exists.

By choosing a fixed path of integration for each point of the sphere we obtain a uniquely defined function $g(\mathbf{X})$. We must now show that grad $g = \mathbf{F}$. By the construction of the curve C it is clear that $g_{'n} = f_n$. But what about the other components? We will now show that $\partial g/\partial x_{n-1}$ exists and is equal to f_{n-1}. We begin by showing that a different path can be substituted for C in the above definition. Consider the plane in R^n which contains the three points $\mathbf{B}$, $\mathbf{B}_{n-1}$, and $\mathbf{B}_{n-2}$. The last two segments of the curve C are contained in this plane. Let

$$\mathbf{B}'_{n-1} = [b_1, b_2, \ldots, b_{n-2}, a_{n-1}, b_n].$$

Then this point is also in the same plane. Let C' be the curve which is identical to C up to the point $\mathbf{B}_{n-2}$, and then follows the segments from $\mathbf{B}_{n-2}$ to $\mathbf{B}'_{n-1}$, and then to $\mathbf{B}$ (see Fig. 7–10).

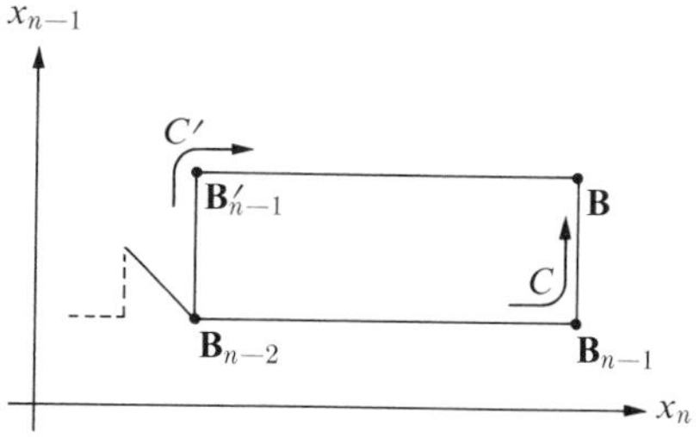

Fig. 7–10

Then we must have $\int_C \mathbf{F} \cdot d\mathbf{X} = \int_{C'} \mathbf{F} \cdot d\mathbf{X}$ since the difference of the two integrals is exactly the integral of $\mathbf{F} \cdot d\mathbf{X}$ around C_1, the boundary of the rectangle R_1 shown in Fig. 7–10, and by Green's theorem

$$\int_{C_1} \mathbf{F} \cdot d\mathbf{X} = \int_{C_1} f_n\, dx_n + f_{n-1}\, dx_{n-1} = \int_{R_1} [f_{n-1'n} - f_{n'n-1}]\, dV = 0,$$

where the last step follows by the symmetry of the matrix $[d\mathbf{F}]$. Now, exactly as in the proof of Theorem 7–15, we conclude that since, along the last segment of C', $\mathbf{F}$ depends only on its $(n-1)$th component, $\partial g/\partial x_{n-1} = f_{n-1}$.

The same type of proof shows that we can replace the path of integration by any other path in which two successive changes of coordinates are made in the opposite order. For example, instead of going from $\mathbf{B}_{k-1}$ to $\mathbf{B}_k$ to $\mathbf{B}_{k+1}$, we can pass through $\mathbf{B}'_k$ as indicated in this diagram:

$$\begin{array}{ccc} \mathbf{B}'_k = [\ldots, a_k, b_{k+1}, \ldots] & \dashrightarrow & \mathbf{B}_{k+1} = [\ldots, b_k, b_{k+1}, \ldots] \\ \uparrow & & \uparrow \\ \mathbf{B}_{k-1} = [\ldots, a_k, a_{k+1}, \ldots] & \longrightarrow & \mathbf{B}_k = [\ldots, b_k, a_{k+1}, \ldots] \end{array}$$

The same reasoning can be applied to the new paths. By changing the order one place at a time, we see that we can get the same result following any path which changes one of the a_i to b_i at each stage. By following the curve which ends by changing a_j to b_j as the final step, we find that $\partial g/\partial x_j = f_j$, and the theorem is proved. ▌

PROBLEMS

1. Prove (7–36).
2. Let $n = 3$ in Theorem 7–33. Using the argument given in the proof of this theorem, show how the path C can be replaced by a path in which the last stage goes from $[a_1, b_2, b_3]$ to $[b_1, b_2, b_3]$.
3. Prove that if G is a region of the type described in Green's theorem, then
$$\text{area } G = \tfrac{1}{2}\int_C (-y\,dx + x\,dy).$$
4. Let G be a region of the type given in Green's theorem. Let C be the boundary of G and suppose that $\mathbf{u}_n$ is the unit *outward* pointing normal vector to the curve C at each point. Prove that
$$\text{area } G = \tfrac{1}{2}\int_C \mathbf{X}\cdot\mathbf{u}_n\,ds.$$
5. Use Green's theorem to calculate the integral
$$\int_C \mathbf{F}\cdot d\mathbf{X}$$
for each of the following cases:
   a) C is the unit circle $x^2 + y^2 = 1$ traversed in the counterclockwise direction, and $\mathbf{F} = [xy, x^2]$.
   b) C is the boundary of the square $0 \le x \le 1, 0 \le y \le 1$, traversed in the clockwise direction, and $\mathbf{F} = [x^2 + y^2, 2xy]$.
6. Use Theorem 7–33 to determine which of the following functions has a line integral $\int \mathbf{F}\cdot d\mathbf{X}$ which is independent of path. Find a scalar function ϕ such that $\mathbf{F} = \text{grad}\,\phi$ for each such case.
   a) $\mathbf{F}(x, y, z) = [x^3y^8, x^4y^7 + z^2, 2yz]$
   b) $\mathbf{F}(x, y, z) = [y, z, x]$
   c) $\mathbf{F}(x, y, z, w) = [y + w, x + w, z + w, x + y + z]$
   d) $\mathbf{F}(x, y, z, w) = [xy + xz, \tfrac{1}{2}x^2 + yz + zw, \tfrac{1}{2}x^2 + \tfrac{1}{2}y^2 + yw, yw + yz]$

7–8. SURFACES

Working in three dimensions, we call the point set associated with the function $z = f(x, y)$ a *surface*. Similarly, we have discussed *level surfaces* of functions in three (or more) dimensions. In this section, we wish to begin a more formal discussion of surfaces. We treat the concept of a surface as a generalization of the concept of a curve. A curve is a one-dimensional entity in that it is a function of a variable in the one-dimensional space R^1. Similarly, we will define surfaces as being two dimensional.

Just as in the case of the definition of curves, we find that most of our difficulty in defining and working with surfaces comes from the fact that we wish to have different representations for the "same" (or equivalent) surfaces.

Definition 7–24. By a *smooth surface* S in R^n we mean a function $\mathbf{F}: B \to R^n$, where B is a compact subset of R^2 whose boundary consists of one or more piecewise smooth curves, $\mathbf{F}$ is continuous on B, and $\mathbf{F}$ is continuously differentiable on B except possibly at a finite number of isolated points. Another surface $S_1 = [\mathbf{F}_1 : B_1 \to R^n]$ is called *equivalent* to S if and only if there exists a mapping $\mathbf{H}: B \to B_1$ which is one-to-one, onto, continuously differentiable, and such that $\det [d\mathbf{H}] > 0$ for all points of B.

The two variables of R^2 in the region B are usually called the *parameters* of the surface.

The definition given here requires the function defining the surface to have a continuous derivative. This is a very restrictive condition which must be relaxed for a more general study of surfaces. Here, however, we find it convenient to treat only this special case. Most of the important results can be obtained without difficulty.

In this book, we will stick to the well-behaved cases as much as possible. As soon as we allow nondifferentiable functions to occur, the subject becomes very difficult. The resulting complexity would then interfere with the understanding of the basic ideas.

We must allow for isolated points at which the function fails to be differentiable however, because we want to be able to discuss such surfaces as the cone,

$$[x, y, z] = [u, v, (u^2 + v^2)^{1/2}], \qquad u^2 + v^2 \le 1.$$

Note that this surface is really defined in the form $z = f(x, y)$. Surfaces of this type fit naturally into Definition 7–24. The variables x and y can be used as the parameters of the mapping, just as they are in this case.

Note that the *point set* constituting the image of B is often spoken of as being the surface. This is loose terminology, but causes no confusion. Just remember that there must always be some function which maps the plane to the point set in question.

An important problem is how to produce a function which gives a desired surface. For example, suppose that we wish to have the functions which define a surface made up of straight-line segments joining points on the line segment $y = 0$, $z = 0$, $0 \le x \le 2$ to points on the circular arc $(x - 1)^2 + (z - 1)^2 = 1$, $y = 1$, $0 \le z \le 1$. Points with the same x-coordinate are to be joined. Thus for each x the points $[x, 0, 0]$ and $[x, 1, 1 - \sqrt{2x - x^2}]$ are to be joined. The line segment joining these will be one of our parameter curves. We can use y for the parameter here. The other parameter will then be most easily chosen to be the x-coordinate. However, for clarity we use new variables to represent these parameters. Thus a suitable set of functions defining the desired surface would be

$$x = u, \qquad y = v, \qquad z = v - v\sqrt{2u - u^2},$$
$$0 \le u \le 2, \qquad 0 \le v \le 1.$$

It is interesting to note that we would obtain an entirely different surface if we joined the points on the above line segment and circular arc which were uniformly spaced with respect to arc length. This could be done, for example, by using the parameter u to define the line segment in the form

$$x = u, \quad y = 0, \quad z = 0, \quad (0 \leq u \leq 2)$$

and the arc in the form $x = 1 - \cos[(\pi/2)u]$, $y = 1$, $z = 1 - \sin[(\pi/2)u]$. We could then let v measure the y-coordinate and obtain the following equations to define the surface:

$$x = (1 - v)u + v - v\cos\frac{\pi}{2}u, \quad y = v, \quad z = v - v\sin\frac{\pi}{2}u,$$
$$0 \leq u \leq 2, \quad 0 \leq v \leq 1.$$

A surface such as the paraboloid defined by $z = x^2 + y^2$ would most obviously be parametrized by its x- and y-coordinates

$$x = u, \quad y = v, \quad z = u^2 + v^2.$$

On the other hand, the same surface could also be parametrized with the help of polar coordinates:

$$x = r\cos\theta, \quad y = r\sin\theta, \quad z = r^2.$$

These are not the only possible choices. In many practical cases, there are often good reasons for choosing other parameters. It is frequently necessary to choose parameters which have physical significance, even though this might complicate the mathematical expressions.

What about the other side of the coin? Given a set of functions, how can we determine the nature of the surface which is defined? Although there is no single method that is always successful, it is usually useful to determine the form of the two sets of parameter curves. Often one of these will be fairly simple, and the surface can be visualized in terms of the family of these curves.

For example, suppose that we are given the parametric equations

$$x = 2(u^2 - 1)^{1/2}\cos v, \quad y = (u^2 - 1)^{1/2}\sin v, \quad z = u,$$
$$1 \leq u \leq 4, \quad 0 \leq v \leq 2\pi.$$

If we fix u and allow v to vary, we obtain a curve contained in the plane $z = u$. This curve is of the form $x = a\cos v$, $y = b\sin v$, where a and b are constants. This clearly is a closed curve. To discover its exact nature we merely have to observe that for all v

$$\frac{x^2}{a^2} + \frac{y^2}{b^2} = 1.$$

Hence these curves are all ellipses. Next, we observe that $a = 2b$ for every u. All of the ellipses are similar.

The other parameter curves are not so simple. We therefore use the v-curves to build up our picture of the surface. We see that the principal vertices of the ellipses are in the plane $y = 0$. It suffices to set $v = 0$. We then find the curve $x = 2(u^2 - 1)^{1/2}$, $y = 0$, $z = u$. While we may not recognize the curve in this form, we will when we eliminate the parameter u. We have $x^2 = 4u^2 - 4$ and $z^2 = u^2$. Therefore $x^2 = 4z^2 - 4$, and we see that the curve is a portion of a hyperbola.

Finally, we can see that the surface defined here is that part of one sheet of an elliptic hyperboloid of two sheets below $z = 4$.

We should remark that in our discussion of surfaces we will usually restrict our attention to *simple surfaces*, that is, to surfaces which have no multiple points (or self-intersections) except possibly at their boundaries. The requirement here is that there be no two distinct interior points $\mathbf{X}_1$ and $\mathbf{X}_2$ of the region B such that $\mathbf{F}(\mathbf{X}_1) = \mathbf{F}(\mathbf{X}_2)$.

When we are given a surface defined by the function $\mathbf{F}(u, v)$, $[u, v] \in B$, we find that we have two systems of curves on the surface. If we set $u = u_0$, then the curve $\mathbf{X} = \mathbf{F}(u_0, v)$, as v varies in an interval so that $[u_0, v]$ is in B, will be on the surface. There will be a whole family of such curves, one for each u_0. Similarly, the curves $\mathbf{X} = \mathbf{F}(u, v_0)$ for each fixed v_0 will form a second family of curves on the surface. These curves are called the *parameter curves* on the surface. A tangent to one of these curves at some point of the surface must be tangent to the surface itself. Since there are (in general) two distinct parameter curves (one from each family) passing through a given point of the surface, there will be two distinct tangents to the surface at that point. These two tangents will define an affine two-dimensional space, the *tangent plane*, to the surface at the given point.

Suppose, for example, that we are given a surface defined by $\mathbf{X} = \mathbf{F}(u, v)$. Then the two tangent vectors at $\mathbf{X}_0 = \mathbf{F}(u_0, v_0)$ are given by

$$\mathbf{U} = \mathbf{F}_{'1}(u_0, v_0), \qquad \mathbf{V} = \mathbf{F}_{'2}(u_0, v_0). \tag{7–37}$$

Note that $\mathbf{F} = [f_1, f_2, \ldots, f_n]$, and hence $\mathbf{F}_{'1} = [f_{1'1}, f_{2'1}, \ldots, f_{n'1}]$ and $\mathbf{F}_{'2} = [f_{1'2}, f_{2'2}, \ldots, f_{n'2}]$.

From the two vectors of (7–37) we can obtain another vector $\mathbf{W}$ which is in the same plane but which is orthogonal to $\mathbf{U}$ by setting

$$\mathbf{W} = \mathbf{V} - \frac{(\mathbf{U} \cdot \mathbf{V})}{(\mathbf{U} \cdot \mathbf{U})}\mathbf{U}.$$

(The reader should refer to the Gram-Schmidt process to see the reasons behind the choice of this combination.) Note that we have assumed that $\mathbf{U} \neq \mathbf{0}$ in this computation. We can now define a pair of orthogonal unit vectors in the tangent plane by setting

$$\mathbf{u}_1 = \mathbf{U}/|\mathbf{U}|, \qquad \mathbf{u}_2 = \mathbf{W}/|\mathbf{W}|.$$

For the purposes of this discussion, we will assume that $\mathbf{U}$ and $\mathbf{V}$ are nonzero and linearly independent; hence these two unit vectors can be defined. Note that they have been defined so that $\mathbf{u}_1$ is parallel to the tangent surface and points in the "u-direction." That is, it points along the parameter curve defined by $v = v_0$.

Now let us define a mapping from the uv-plane to the affine plane which is tangent to the surface at this point. The point with coordinates $[u, v]$ in the plane will be mapped first to the point $\mathbf{X} = \mathbf{F}(u, v)$ on the surface and then projected onto the tangent plane. To do this most easily, we introduce a new coordinate system.

We already have the two orthogonal unit vectors $\mathbf{u}_1$ and $\mathbf{u}_2$ which generate the tangent plane at $\mathbf{X}_0$. Let us complete these to an orthonormal basis for R^n. For any $\mathbf{X}$, we can express the vector $\mathbf{X} - \mathbf{X}_0$ in terms of this basis. We have

$$\mathbf{X} - \mathbf{X}_0 = \sum_{k=1}^{n} [\mathbf{u}_k \cdot (\mathbf{X} - \mathbf{X}_0)]\mathbf{u}_k.$$

The orthogonal projection of $\mathbf{X} - \mathbf{X}_0$ into the tangent plane is obtained by taking the first two terms of this expansion. That is, the mapping from the uv-plane to the tangent plane is given by

$$\mathbf{G}(u, v) = A[\mathbf{F}(u, v) - \mathbf{F}(u_0, v_0)],$$

where A is the $2 \times n$ matrix whose rows are the orthonormal vectors $\mathbf{u}_1$ and $\mathbf{u}_2$. Then $[d\mathbf{G}] = A[d\mathbf{F}]$. We can compute $[d\mathbf{G}]$ at the point $[u_0, v_0]$ and find

$$[d\mathbf{G}(u_0, v_0)] = \begin{bmatrix} \mathbf{u}_1^t \\ \mathbf{u}_2^t \end{bmatrix} [\mathbf{U}, \mathbf{V}] = \begin{bmatrix} \mathbf{u}_1 \cdot \mathbf{U} & \mathbf{u}_1 \cdot \mathbf{V} \\ \mathbf{u}_2 \cdot \mathbf{U} & \mathbf{u}_2 \cdot \mathbf{V} \end{bmatrix}$$

$$= \begin{bmatrix} |\mathbf{U}| & \dfrac{(\mathbf{U} \cdot \mathbf{V})}{|\mathbf{U}|} \\ 0 & \dfrac{1}{|\mathbf{W}|}\left[(\mathbf{V} \cdot \mathbf{V}) - \dfrac{(\mathbf{U} \cdot \mathbf{V})^2}{|\mathbf{U}|^2}\right] \end{bmatrix},$$

and therefore

$$\det [d\mathbf{G}(u_0, v_0)] = \frac{1}{|\mathbf{U}|\,|\mathbf{W}|} [|\mathbf{U}|^2|\mathbf{V}|^2 - (\mathbf{U} \cdot \mathbf{V})^2].$$

However, directly from the definition of $\mathbf{W}$, we compute

$$\mathbf{W} \cdot \mathbf{W} = \frac{1}{|\mathbf{U}|^2} [|\mathbf{U}|^2|\mathbf{V}|^2 - (\mathbf{U} \cdot \mathbf{V})^2],$$

and hence we find that

$$\det [d\mathbf{G}(u_0, v_0)] = [|\mathbf{U}|^2|\mathbf{V}|^2 - (\mathbf{U} \cdot \mathbf{V})^2]^{1/2}. \tag{7–38}$$

Let S be some small region of the uv-plane containing the point $[u_0, v_0]$. Then the function $\mathbf{G}$ maps this region onto the tangent plane. The area of the image is

$$\int_S \det [d\mathbf{G}(u, v)]\, dV_{uv}.$$

If S is small enough, $d\mathbf{G}(u, v)$ will remain close enough to $d\mathbf{G}(u_0, v_0)$ so that the area of the image of S on the tangent plane will be approximately

$$(\text{area } S) \cdot \det [d\mathbf{G}(u_0, v_0)].$$

At the same time, the tangent plane will be close enough to the surface so that we can consider the same quantity to be an approximation to the area of the image of S on the surface.

The concept of the area of a surface is not as simple as the concept of the length of a curve. Unless precautions are taken, an attempt to define the area of a surface by approximating the surface by plane pieces can lead to contradictions. Here we take the path of least resistance and merely define the area to be the value of a certain integral. The discussion we gave above is the motivation for this definition.

Definition 7–25. Let $S = [\mathbf{F}: B \to R^n]$ define a surface, B being a compact smoothly bounded region in the *uv*-plane. Let

$$s(u, v) = [|\mathbf{F}_{\prime 1}|^2 |\mathbf{F}_{\prime 2}|^2 - (\mathbf{F}_{\prime 1} \cdot \mathbf{F}_{\prime 2})^2]^{1/2}.$$

Then the *area* of the surface S is defined to be

$$\int_B s(u, v)\, dV_{uv}.$$

The last integral can be approximated by a Riemann sum. The region B can be divided up into small rectangles. Each is mapped onto the surface, and the resulting region projected onto a plane which is tangent to the surface at some point of the small region. The sum of the areas of the resulting projections will then approximate the Riemann sum derived from the last integral. It thus seems that this integral should coincide with our ideas of what surface area should be like.

Let us look at an actual example. If a is greater than zero, then the function

$$x = a \sin u \cos v, \qquad y = a \sin u \sin v, \qquad z = a \cos u,$$
$$0 \le u \le \pi, \qquad 0 \le v \le 2\pi$$

is the surface of a sphere of radius a. This is most easily seen by tracing out the parameter curves in space. Note that there is a "line" on the sphere which is covered twice by the mapping. The "north pole" and "south pole" correspond to what values of the parameters?

For this transformation, we can compute

$$\mathbf{F}_{\prime 1} = [a \cos u \cos v, a \cos u \sin v, -a \sin u],$$
$$\mathbf{F}_{\prime 2} = [-a \sin u \sin v, a \sin u \cos v, 0].$$

From these, we find

$$|\mathbf{F}_{\prime 1}|^2 = a^2, \qquad |\mathbf{F}_{\prime 2}|^2 = a^2 \sin^2 u, \qquad \mathbf{F}_{\prime 1} \cdot \mathbf{F}_{\prime 2} = 0.$$

The last result means that the parameter curves all cross at right angles on the sphere. From Def. 7–25 we find

$$s(u, v) = a^2 \sin u.$$

Then, according to the definition, the surface area of the sphere should be

$$\int_B a^2 \sin u\, dV_{uv} = \int_0^{2\pi} dv \int_0^{\pi} a^2 \sin u\, du = 2a^2 \int_0^{2\pi} dv = 4\pi a^2.$$

The entire discussion above is valid in any number of dimensions. If we are willing to restrict ourselves to three dimensions (where we usually do most of our problems), then we can make some simplifications. The two-dimensional tangent plane at a point of a surface can be specified by giving the *normal vector* to the surface at that point. In higher dimensions, there is an orthogonal subspace to the tangent plane. Only in three-dimensional space will this subspace be of dimension 1 so that it can be determined by a single vector.

For vectors in three-dimensional space, we can make use of the *cross product* to aid us in our computations. The cross product of two vectors **A** and **B** in R^3 is the vector $\mathbf{A} \times \mathbf{B}$, orthogonal to both **A** and **B**, which can be defined in the form

$$\mathbf{A} \times \mathbf{B} = \begin{vmatrix} a_2 & a_3 \\ b_2 & b_3 \end{vmatrix} \mathbf{e}_1 - \begin{vmatrix} a_1 & a_3 \\ b_1 & b_3 \end{vmatrix} \mathbf{e}_2 + \begin{vmatrix} a_1 & a_2 \\ b_1 & b_2 \end{vmatrix} \mathbf{e}_3.$$

This formula can be remembered by observing that the three terms on the right-hand side correspond to the formal expansion of the determinant

$$\begin{vmatrix} \mathbf{e}_1 & \mathbf{e}_2 & \mathbf{e}_3 \\ a_1 & a_2 & a_3 \\ b_1 & b_2 & b_3 \end{vmatrix}$$

according to the minors of the top row. It is assumed that the reader is familiar with the standard algebraic properties of the cross product. In particular, he should know the identities:

$$\begin{aligned} \mathbf{B} \times \mathbf{A} &= -\mathbf{A} \times \mathbf{B}, \\ \mathbf{A} \times (\mathbf{B} \times \mathbf{C}) &= (\mathbf{A} \cdot \mathbf{C})\mathbf{B} - (\mathbf{A} \cdot \mathbf{B})\mathbf{C}, \\ |\mathbf{A} \times \mathbf{B}|^2 &= |\mathbf{A}|^2|\mathbf{B}|^2 - (\mathbf{A} \cdot \mathbf{B})^2. \end{aligned} \tag{7-39}$$

The last one, known as Lagrange's identity, can be used to obtain a convenient formula. From the expression for $s(u, v)$ in Definition 7–25, we see that in three-dimensional space

$$s(u, v) = |\mathbf{F}'_1 \times \mathbf{F}'_2|. \tag{7-40}$$

Besides being a useful formula in its own right, Eq. (7–40) is interesting for another reason. The cross product on the right is a vector which is orthogonal to both $\mathbf{F}'_1$ and $\mathbf{F}'_2$; hence it must be orthogonal to the tangent plane to the surface.

Definition 7–26. Let $\mathbf{F}: B \to R^3$ define a surface in R^3. At any point $[u, v]$ of B define

$$\mathbf{N} = \mathbf{F}'_1(u, v) \times \mathbf{F}'_2(u, v). \tag{7-41}$$

This vector is called the *normal vector* to the surface at $\mathbf{F}(u, v)$. Define the *unit normal vector* to the surface to be

$$\mathbf{e}_n = \mathbf{N}/|\mathbf{N}|. \tag{7-42}$$

The formal differential elements of surface area are defined to be

$$dS = |\mathbf{N}|\, dV_{u,v} \tag{7-43}$$

and

$$d\mathbf{S} = \mathbf{N}\, dV_{u,v} = \mathbf{e}_n\, dS. \tag{7-44}$$

The calculations made above then show us that the area of a surface is given by

$$A = \int_B dS,$$

where dS is defined as in (7–43). The formal differential $d\mathbf{S}$ will be used to define surface integrals in a manner similar to the way in which we defined line integrals. The element $d\mathbf{S}$ for surfaces corresponds to the element $d\mathbf{X}$ for curves.

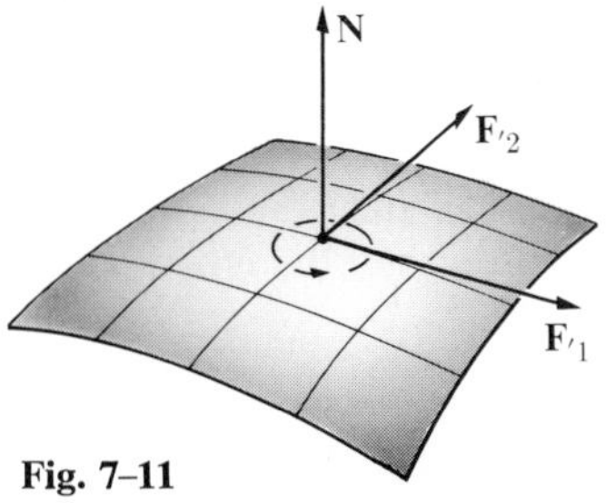

Fig. 7–11

There is one final topic that we should discuss in this section. That is the orientation of a surface. The orientation of a surface is specified by defining a sense of rotation in a neighborhood of each point of the surface. This can most conveniently be done with the help of an orthonormal pair of tangent vectors at each point of the surface. The vectors $\mathbf{u}_1$ and $\mathbf{u}_2$ as defined above will serve this purpose. Thus every surface which is specified as in Definition 7–24 has a natural orientation (the sense of rotation is always the counterclockwise one which carries $\mathbf{u}_1$ into $\mathbf{u}_2$ by a rotation through an angle of $\pi/2$).

In three-dimensional space, the orientation can be specified by means of the normal vector to the surface. The sense of rotation is the one defined by the "right-hand rule." If the right-hand thumb is pointed in the direction of the normal, then the fingers curl in the direction of the sense of rotation. The choice of the normal vector $\mathbf{N}$ in Definition 7–26 fits this definition. See Fig. 7–11.

There is a difference between orientation as defined here and the use of the term in the phrase "an oriented surface," which the reader may encounter from time to time. A surface is called oriented if there exists a "continuous" sense of orientation defined over the entire surface. In three-dimensional space, a continuous normal vector could be used for this purpose. A nonoriented surface, such as a Möbius strip, can be defined as in Definition 7–26, but it would have a "joint" at which the normal to the surface would have to "switch sides." We will not find it necessary to go into this question in this book.

PROBLEMS

1. Identify and sketch each of the following surfaces.

   a) $x = u\cos v,\ y = u\sin v,\ z = bu,\ 0 \le u \le c,\ 0 \le v \le 2\pi,\ b > 0,\ c > 0$

   b) $x = v\cos u,\ y = v\sin u,\ z = bu,\ 0 \le u \le 2\pi,\ a \le v \le c,\ b > 0,\ 0 < a < c$

   c) $x = a\cos v + b\cos u\cos v,\quad y = a\sin v + b\cos u\sin v,\quad z = b\sin u,\quad 0 \le u \le 2\pi,$ $0 \le v \le 2\pi,\ 0 < b < a$

   d) $x = a\cos v + u\sin\frac{v}{2}\cos v,\ y = a\sin v + u\sin\frac{v}{2}\sin v,\ z = u\cos\frac{v}{2},\quad -b \le u \le b,$ $0 \le v \le 2\pi,\ 0 < b < a$

   e) $x = \log u,\ y = au\sin v,\ z = au\cos v,\ 1 \le u \le b,\ 0 \le v \le 2\pi,\ a > 0,\ b > 1$

2. For each of the surfaces of Problem 1, find the normal vector $\mathbf{N}$ at each point of the surface. Find $s(u, v)$. Set up the integral for the area of the surface and evaluate if possible.
3. If a surface is defined by the equation $z = f(x, y)$ over some region B in the xy-plane, then x and y can be viewed as the parameters defining the surface. Prove that in this case, the area of the surface is given by

$$A = \int_B (1 + f_{,1}^2 + f_{,1}^2)^{1/2}\, dV_{xy}.$$

4. A surface of revolution can be defined by

$$x = f(z)\cos u, \qquad y = f(z)\sin u \qquad z = z,$$
$$0 \le u \le 2\pi, \qquad a \le z \le b,$$

where $f(z) > 0$ for $a < z < b$. Show that the area of such a surface is given by

$$A = 2\pi \int_a^b f(z)[1 + (f')^2]^{1/2}\, dz.$$

5. Prove that two equivalent surfaces have the same area.
6. Let a surface be defined by the functions $x = x(u, v)$, $y = y(u, v)$, $z = z(u, v)$. Prove that

$$\mathbf{N} = \frac{\partial(y, z)}{\partial(u, v)}\mathbf{e}_1 + \frac{\partial(z, x)}{\partial(u, v)}\mathbf{e}_2 + \frac{\partial(x, y)}{\partial(u, v)}\mathbf{e}_3.$$

7. Suppose that $\mathbf{F}: B \to R^3$ is such that $z = 0$ for all $[u, v] \in B$ (that is, the surface S is contained in the xy-plane). What does $s(u, v)$ become in this case? What does the formula for the area become?
8. Suppose that S is the level surface of $f(x, y, z) = 0$ with $[x, y] \in B$ and that $f_{,3} \neq 0$ for any point on the surface. Prove that the area is

$$A = \int_B \frac{1}{|f_{,3}|}(f_{,1}^2 + f_{,2}^2 + f_{,3}^2)^{1/2}\, dV_{xy}.$$

9. Find parametric equations to define the following surfaces:
   a) the "cylinder" whose cross sections in planes orthogonal to the z-axis are circles centered on the z-axis with radius $a + c\cos z$ $(0 < c < a)$;
   b) the spiral "cylinder" which has the spiral $x = a\cos\theta$, $y = a\sin\theta$, $z = b\theta$ as its "axis"; every plane through the z-axis intersects the surface in circles of radius c with centers on the given spiral $(0 < c < a < b)$.

7–9. SURFACE INTEGRALS

Surface integrals appear in many applications of calculus. There are two main types which occur. The first is the integral of a scalar-valued function over the surface, and the second is the integral of a vector-valued function dotted with the normal vector to the surface. The second is mathematically identical to the first, being the integral of the scalar-valued function which is the normal component of the vector function. However, these two types occur under different practical situations, so we should see them both.

Definition 7–27. Let B be a compact, smoothly bounded region in the uv-plane. Let $\mathbf{X} = \mathbf{X}(u, v): B \to R^3$ define a surface S in R^3. Let $g(\mathbf{X})$ be continuous at every point of S. We define the surface integral

$$\int_S g(\mathbf{X})\, dS = \int_B g[\mathbf{X}(u, v)]s(u, v)\, dV_{uv}.$$

where $s(u, v)$ is as defined in Definition 7–25. Let $\mathbf{F}$ be a vector-valued function which is continuous at every point of S. Then we define

$$\int_S \mathbf{F}(\mathbf{X}) \cdot d\mathbf{S} = \int_S \mathbf{F}(\mathbf{X}) \cdot \mathbf{e}_n\, dS = \int_B \mathbf{F}[\mathbf{X}(u, v)] \cdot \mathbf{N}(u, v)\, dV_{uv}.$$

where $\mathbf{N}$ and $\mathbf{e}_n$ are as given in Definition 7–26.

Note that the first integral could be defined in any number of dimensions. It is thus the basic type of surface integral. The second form occurs when the surface has a normal vector in three dimensions.

Let us give an example. Suppose we compute

$$\int_S \mathbf{X} \cdot d\mathbf{S},$$

where $\mathbf{X} = [x, y, z]$ and S is the surface of the sphere of radius a. The equations defining this surface were given in the last section (page 315), that is,

$$\mathbf{X} = a[\sin u \cos v, \sin u \sin v, \cos u],$$

where $0 \leq u \leq \pi$, $0 \leq v \leq 2\pi$. The normal vector is [see Eq. (7–41)]

$$\mathbf{N} = a^2 \sin u[\sin u \cos v, \sin u \sin v, \cos u],$$

and we easily compute $\mathbf{X} \cdot \mathbf{N} = a^3 \sin u$. Thus we find that

$$\int_S \mathbf{X} \cdot d\mathbf{S} = a^3 \int_B \sin u\, dV_{uv} = a^3 \int_0^{2\pi} dv \int_0^{\pi} \sin u\, du = 4\pi a^3.$$

Physically, this result should be no surprise. The normal vector at each point of the sphere should be parallel to $\mathbf{X}$. Thus $\mathbf{X} = a\mathbf{N}/|\mathbf{N}|$ at each point of the sphere, and the integral of $\mathbf{X} \cdot d\mathbf{S}$ should be a times the surface area of the sphere.

We can use Problem 6 of the last section to obtain a formula for the surface integral which is different in form. Suppose that we have a function $\mathbf{F} = [f_1, f_2, f_3]$ and a surface S defined by $\mathbf{X} = [x(u, v), y(u, v), z(u, v)]$ for $[u, v] \in B$. The result of Problem 6 of the last section then gives us

$$\int_S \mathbf{F} \cdot d\mathbf{S} = \int_B \left[f_1 \frac{\partial(y, z)}{\partial(u, v)} + f_2 \frac{\partial(z, x)}{\partial(u, v)} + f_3 \frac{\partial(x, y)}{\partial(u, v)}\right] dV_{uv}. \tag{7–45}$$

Recalling the theorem on change of variable in multiple integrals, we see that, in some sense, (7–45) could be interpreted as

$$\int_S f_1\, dV_{yz} + f_2\, dV_{zx} + f_3\, dV_{xy}.$$

The region of integration must be interpreted as being the projection of S onto the yz-, zx-, and xy-planes, respectively.

There exists another notation which is in common use to represent this point of view. Instead of writing dV_{yz}, most books use $dy\,dz$ in a formula of this type. Since this notation is found so often, it would be best for the reader to become familiar with it.

Definition 7-28. Let x and y be differentiable functions of u and v, i.e., $\mathbf{X} = [x, y] = \mathbf{X}(u, v)$, for $[u, v]$ in some region B of the uv-plane. Then, by the differential form $dx\,dy$, we mean

$$dx\,dy = \det[d\mathbf{X}]\,dV_{uv} = \frac{\partial(x, y)}{\partial(u, v)}\,dV_{uv}.$$

Note that the definition is not symmetric. The Jacobian changes sign if two of the variables are interchanged. Hence

$$dy\,dx = -\,dx\,dy. \tag{7-46}$$

Note also that the symbol $dx\,dy$ introduced here is not the same as the formal product of dx and dy that appears in the iterated integral. The product in the iterated integral is independent of the order. There is a close relation, of course. Indeed, it is exactly this relation which led to the use of the notation $dx\,dy$ in the first place.

The change of sign convention of (7-46) is not followed by all authors. In particular, texts which do not develop the change of variable formula for the multiple integral often treat the formal product $dx\,dy$ as representing the formal product in the iterated integrals. In this case, certain sign conventions would have to be introduced in some formulas.

By the convention of Definition 7-28, we find that we can rewrite the surface integral of (7-45) in the form

$$\int_S \mathbf{F} \cdot d\mathbf{S} = \int_S f_1\,dy\,dz + f_2\,dz\,dx + f_3\,dx\,dy. \tag{7-47}$$

This type of notation is often quite useful. In particular, it makes certain formulas which we will develop in later sections much easier to understand. Note that the surface integral representation of (7-47) is similar to the notation for line integrals used in Definition 7-13.

Using the convention of (7-47) is often the easiest method of evaluating a surface integral when the surface is defined by some means other than its parametric equations. Equation (7-47) breaks up the surface integral into three surface integrals, one for each component of $\mathbf{F}$. The $dy\,dz$ which appears in the first part, for example, can be interpreted as meaning that $\mathbf{e}_1 \cdot d\mathbf{S} = dy\,dz$ is the component of $\mathbf{e}_n\,dS$ in the x-direction. The first integral thus amounts to what would be obtained if the surface were expressed as one or more surfaces "over" the yz-plane, that is, using y and z as parameters. The differential element $dy\,dz$ is therefore the differential element of area in the yz-plane with a positive or negative sign indicating that the normal to the surface is in the same or opposite direction to $\mathbf{e}_1$.

An example may help make the discussion clearer. Let us again compute

$$\int_S \mathbf{X} \cdot d\mathbf{S}$$

over the surface S of the sphere of radius a. The orientation of the surface is to be that defined by the outward pointing normal. [Is this the same orientation as that defined by the parametric representation of Eq. (7–41)?] Using the conventions of (7–47), we have

$$\int_S \mathbf{X} \cdot d\mathbf{S} = \int_S x\, dy\, dz + y\, dz\, dx + z\, dx\, dy.$$

By the symmetry of the situation, the three surface integrals on the right-hand side of the expression are the same. It suffices to evaluate one of them. Let us choose the first.

Let B be the unit disk, $y^2 + z^2 \leq a^2$, in the yz-plane. The surface S can be defined in two parts over B. On the upper part, $x = (a^2 - y^2 - z^2)^{1/2}$, and the outward pointing normal is in the same direction as $\mathbf{e}_1$. Therefore $dy\, dz = dV$, where $dV = dV_{y,z}$ is the (positive) element of area in the yz-plane. The lower part of the surface is defined by $x = -(a^2 - y^2 - z^2)^{1/2}$. In this case, $dy\, dz = -dV$. Therefore

$$\begin{aligned}\int_S x\, dy\, dz &= \int_B (a^2 - y^2 - z^2)^{1/2}\, dV - \int_B -(a^2 - y^2 - z^2)^{1/2}\, dV \\ &= 2\int_B (a^2 - y^2 - z^2)^{1/2}\, dV = 2\int_0^{2\pi} d\theta \int_0^a (a^2 - r^2)^{1/2} r\, dr \\ &= 2 \cdot 2\pi[-\tfrac{1}{3}(a^2 - r^2)^{3/2}]\big|_0^a = \tfrac{4}{3}\pi a^3.\end{aligned}$$

Here the integral was evaluated by being converted to polar coordinates. This result must be multiplied by 3 to obtain the entire surface integral.

In this particular example, there is no gain in using (7–47). Indeed, the problem is probably more difficult in this way. However, if the surface were that of a cube, for example, then the computations would be about the same in difficulty. In some cases, it is quite difficult to express the entire surface in a single parametric formula. It might be easier to express it in parametric form over the various coordinate planes. This is exactly what we do in formula (7–47).

We should also note that the convention of (7–47) is of no aid in the evaluation of a surface integral of the type

$$\int_S g(\mathbf{X})\, dS.$$

The differential of surface area in this form must be evaluated by expressing the surface in parametric form (even when the parameters might be two of the coordinates).

In the remainder of this section, we will investigate some of the consequences of the notational conventions introduced here. To start with, we note that there are two distinct meanings which can be attached to the symbol dx. When we have x given as a function of other variables, say $x = x(u, v)$, then dx is the value of the linear transformation

$$dx = x'_1\,du + x'_2\,dv. \tag{7–48}$$

The second use of the symbol dx is in integrals. The symbol dx is used (just as dV is used in multiple integrals) to indicate that an integration is taking place, to indicate the variable with respect to which the integration is taking place, and to remind us of Δx.

In the second case, the symbol dx is just that—a *symbol.* It never has a "value." However, this symbol behaves in many respects as if it could be given a value. For example, if we have $x = x(t)$, then we can change the variable in the integral. We obtain a new integral which we write with a dt. This new integral is obtained by making the substitution

$$dx = x'(t)\,dt,$$

a relation which would make just as much sense if dx and dt were viewed as "variables" that could take on real values. Indeed, this is exactly the same relation that we find in the first case. Then dx is the value of the linear transformation dx at dt.

Suppose that we have a curve in the uv-plane defined by $u = u(t), v = v(t)$. Suppose also that we have a surface defined by $x = x(u, v)$, $y = y(u, v)$, $z = z(u, v)$. Then the curve in the uv-plane induces a curve C on the surface. This curve is the composition of the two functions. Now we might have a line integral

$$\int_C P\,dx + Q\,dy + R\,dz.$$

What is the meaning of the symbols dx, dy, and dz in this line integral? Referring to Definition 7–13, we see that we actually have

$$dx = x'_1\,du + x'_2\,dv, \qquad du = u'\,dt, \qquad dv = v'\,dt. \tag{7–49}$$

The intermediate step of (7–49) is exactly the same as (7–48).

All of this merely means that it is not necessary to distinguish between the different meanings of the symbol dx. We can treat the differential as a symbol with no intrinsic meaning itself but which behaves properly with respect to functional relationships. In this respect, differentials behave like the values of linear transformations.

So far we have discussed only single differentials. Now let us return to the form defined in Definition 7–28. Suppose that we let u and v themselves be defined as functions of u and v in the definition ($u = u, v = v$). Then this definition gives us

$$du\,dv = dV_{uv}.$$

Hence we can start using the form $du\,dv$ instead of dV_{uv}. Note, however, that $dv\,du = -du\,dv$ according to the conventions in use here. This *differential of order two* is still nothing but a symbol. That is all that dV is. We use dV only to indicate the integration process. Now we would like to discover some of the relations between these second-order differentials. In particular, how are they related to the first-order differentials, those of type dx?

Given the functions $x = x(u, v)$, $y = y(u, v)$, we have from Definition 7–28 the expansion

$$dx\,dy = (x'_1 y'_2 - x'_2 y'_1)\,du\,dv. \tag{7–50}$$

On the other hand, what happens if we multiply the expressions

$$dx = x'_1\,du + x'_2\,dv, \qquad dy = y'_1\,du + y'_2\,dv?$$

When we do so, we find that

$$(dx)(dy) = x'_1 y'_1\,du\,du + x'_1 y'_2\,du\,dv + x'_2 y'_1\,dv\,du + x'_2 y'_2\,dv\,dv. \tag{7–51}$$

Here we have written out the formal product, assuming that the multiplication is associative, the scalar functions commute with the differentials, the distributive law holds, and that addition of the forms is commutative. We have not assumed that the multiplication of differentials is commutative. Indeed, this we cannot assume. We have already seen that we must have $du\,dv = -\,dv\,du$. Substituting into (7–51) and comparing with (7–50), we see that the result will be the same provided we assume that $du\,du = dv\,dv = 0$.

It is possible to introduce an entire algebra for these differential forms. The standard computational rules of the real number system would hold with two exceptions. The product of two differentials must be anticommutative as in (7–46), and the product of two identical differentials must be zero. These two properties should be recognized as properties of the cross product of vectors in three dimensions. The algebra of vectors with the cross product is very similar to the algebra of these differential forms.

We should remark that it is customary these days to use a different notation (the "wedge product") for this product of differentials. We do not introduce this since we are not going to do more than comment on the algebra of differentials. We introduced this terminology so that we could write (7–47). There would be little purpose in identifying the classical notation for a surface integral for the reader if we then failed to use the classical notation.

The algebra of differentials can be extended to higher-order forms. For example, we could multiply $(x^2\,dx + xy\,dy)(x\,dy\,dz - yz\,dz\,dx + dx\,dy)$ to obtain

$$(x^2 - xy^2 z)\,dx\,dy\,dz.$$

The reader should verify that this is so. Note that $dy\,dz\,dx = -\,dy\,dx\,dz = dx\,dy\,dz$ since the sign changes with each interchange of two adjacent differentials. If any two factors in the third-order differential are the same, the differential is zero. The sign change convention is closely related to the definition of the sign of a determinant (as is the fact that the value must be zero when two factors are equal). Again, this should remind us of the way in which the cross product can be evaluated. Actually, the connection between the product of differentials and determinants is quite real. It comes directly out of Definition 7–28.

Finally, let us observe that we can define the differential of a differential form. If f is any function of x, y, and z, we will call f a differential of order zero. We can then define the differential of f to be

$$df = f_{,1}\,dx + f_{,2}\,dy + f_{,3}\,dz. \tag{7-52}$$

Suppose that we are given a differential form of order one, say

$$\omega = f_1\,dx + f_2\,dy + f_3\,dz. \tag{7-53}$$

Then we define the differential of ω to be

$$d\omega = (df_1)\,dx + (df_2)\,dy + (df_3)\,dz,$$

the indicated products being in the sense defined above.

Similarly, if we have the second-order differential

$$\omega^* = g_1\,dy\,dz + g_2\,dz\,dx + g_3\,dx\,dy,$$

then we can define its differential as

$$d\omega^* = (dg_1)\,dy\,dz + (dg_2)\,dz\,dx + (dg_3)\,dx\,dy.$$

In a later section we will show how these formal definitions can be used to simplify some formulas. At this stage, we must view these conventions as pure formalism.

PROBLEMS

1. Set $\mathbf{F}(\mathbf{X}) = \mathbf{X}$ and $\mathbf{G}(\mathbf{X}) = \mathbf{X}/|\mathbf{X}|$. For each of the surfaces of Problem 1 of the last section, set up the integrals

$$\int_S \mathbf{F}\cdot d\mathbf{S} \quad\text{and}\quad \int_S \mathbf{G}\cdot d\mathbf{S}$$

and evaluate if possible.

2. Let f be a scalar-valued function with continuous second derivatives. Prove that $d(df) = 0$.
3. Let ω be a differential form of the type (7-53), where the functions f_1, f_2, and f_3 have continuous second derivatives. Prove that $d(d\omega) = 0$.
4. Let $P(x, y)$ and $Q(x, y)$ be functions having continuous partial derivatives at every point of a compact region B in the xy-plane. Let C be a simple, closed, piecewise smooth curve which forms the boundary of B. Let

$$\omega = P\,dx + Q\,dy.$$

Show that Green's theorem is equivalent to

$$\int_C \omega = \int_B d\omega.$$

CHAPTER 8

Vector Analysis

8–1. THE DIVERGENCE AND CURL

In this chapter we restrict our attention to three-dimensional space. This allows for many simplifications. In particular, we find that many formulas are much simpler when we can make use of the cross product of two vectors (as we saw earlier in the discussion of surfaces). Most of the results that we will obtain can be generalized in some manner to higher-dimensional space, but only with difficulty in some cases. By restricting our attention to three-dimensional space we can obtain the main results and learn a few useful methods at the same time.

The techniques that are discussed in this chapter belong to a collection of results usually called "vector analysis." These techniques have proved to be very valuable tools in the physical sciences. The most extensive use of vector analysis at the undergraduate level seem to be in the fields of physics and electrical engineering, but these tools are useful in many other fields as well.

Here we concentrate on the mathematics and leave the applications for development in other courses. We will, however, offer a physical interpretation of some of our results at a few points. Many people find it easiest to understand these topics with the help of a physical model, such as fluid flow.

A real-valued function f defined over some region in R^3 is sometimes called a *scalar field.* We can think of this function as assigning a real number to each point of some region of space. Many examples are possible. For example, the air pressure at each point of the atmosphere is a scalar field. The temperature at each point in the metal of an engine block is another example.

In a similar way, a vector-valued function $\mathbf{F}$ defined in a region in R^3 is often called a *vector field.* At each point of the region there is assigned some vector. The velocity of a fluid is an example of a vector field. At each point of a region, there exists a vector representing the speed and direction of the flow at that point.

In most applications the functions defining scalar or vector fields will depend on time as well as on the point in space. In one sense, these functions should be considered as defined in R^4, but the time dependence always occupies a special position, different from the space variables. For our purpose it is best to treat the dependence on time separately, and to consider these functions to be defined in R^3 alone.

In an earlier chapter, we found a method of obtaining a vector field from a scalar field. If $f(\mathbf{X})$ is a scalar-valued function, then grad f is a vector field.* The vector grad f at some point has the direction of maximum increase of the function f. It is orthogonal to the level surface of f through that point, and its magnitude is equal to the value of the directional derivative in this direction of maximal increase.

While this particular vector field is naturally of considerable mathematical interest, it is also of interest in many physical problems. If f is the scalar field representing the electrical potential, then $-\text{grad } f$ is a vector field which gives the electric force field. Similarly, the gravitational force field is the gradient of a scalar (potential) field. In fact, most of the vector fields which are of interest in beginning physics courses are found to be the gradient of some scalar field.

In most applications the components of the vectors (points) in R^3 are denoted by x, y, and z rather than x_1, x_2, and x_3. We will follow that practice here also. Thus we will write $\mathbf{X} = [x, y, z]$ and $f(\mathbf{X}) = f(x, y, z)$. Unless otherwise specified, we will always assume that the variables x, y, and z occur in that order. Following this convention, we may use the notation for the partial derivatives $f_{,1} = \partial f/\partial x$ and so on.

For heuristic reasons, there are advantages in using the "del" notation in writing the gradient of a scalar function. In this chapter, we will usually use the del notation. In more general contexts, this symbol would give rise to some false impressions, but that difficulty will not arise here. Thus we will write

$$\text{grad } f = \nabla f.$$

The symbol "∇" can be thought of as representing a symbolic operator. This symbolism will turn out to be useful in remembering some formulas. We can write

$$\nabla = \mathbf{e}_1 \frac{\partial}{\partial x} + \mathbf{e}_2 \frac{\partial}{\partial y} + \mathbf{e}_3 \frac{\partial}{\partial z}, \tag{8–1}$$

and think of this operator as being applied in a formal manner to the function f to obtain the gradient

$$\nabla f = \mathbf{e}_1 \frac{\partial f}{\partial x} + \mathbf{e}_2 \frac{\partial f}{\partial y} + \mathbf{e}_3 \frac{\partial f}{\partial z}.$$

Thus, for example, we have $|\mathbf{X}| = (x^2 + y^2 + z^2)^{1/2}$ and hence

$$\begin{aligned} \nabla|\mathbf{X}| &= \mathbf{e}_1 \frac{x}{[x^2 + y^2 + z^2]^{1/2}} + \mathbf{e}_2 \frac{y}{[x^2 + y^2 + z^2]^{1/2}} + \mathbf{e}_3 \frac{z}{[x^2 + y^2 + z^2]^{1/2}} \\ &= \frac{1}{|\mathbf{X}|}[x\mathbf{e}_1 + y\mathbf{e}_2 + z\mathbf{e}_3] = \frac{\mathbf{X}}{|\mathbf{X}|}. \end{aligned}$$

We should also remark here that the symbols $\mathbf{i}, \mathbf{j}$, and $\mathbf{k}$ are often found in place of $\mathbf{e}_1, \mathbf{e}_2$, and $\mathbf{e}_3$ as we are using here. This is especially true in older books and in

---

* The gradient is actually a covector, but as we noted before, we are not considering this distinction here.

some newer books primarily concerned with applications. The reader should be aware of this alternative use since he will find it in many standard references.

Note that some of our earlier results can be used to simplify some computations. For example, we saw earlier that $\nabla f(g(\mathbf{X})) = [f'(g(\mathbf{X}))]\, \nabla g(\mathbf{X})$. Hence we have

$$\nabla \frac{1}{|\mathbf{X}|} = -\frac{1}{|\mathbf{X}|^2}[\nabla|\mathbf{X}|] = -\frac{|\mathbf{X}|}{|\mathbf{X}|^3}.$$

We can now define two operations on vector fields. They will result in a scalar and a vector field, respectively. The first is the divergence.

Definition 8–1. Let $\mathbf{F} = [f_1, f_2, f_3]$ be a continuously differentiable function in some open set in R^3. Then the *divergence* of $\mathbf{F}$ is the scalar function

$$\operatorname{div} \mathbf{F} = f_{1'1} + f_{2'2} + f_{3'3} = \frac{\partial f_1}{\partial x} + \frac{\partial f_2}{\partial y} + \frac{\partial f_3}{\partial z}.$$

We will denote the divergence of $\mathbf{F}$ by either of the forms

$$\operatorname{div} \mathbf{F} = \nabla \cdot \mathbf{F}.$$

Since $\mathbf{F} = f_1\mathbf{e}_1 + f_2\mathbf{e}_2 + f_3\mathbf{e}_3$, the symbolic notation in the last line of this definition can be thought of as representing the dot product of the del operator defined in (8–1) with $\mathbf{F}$. The partial derivative $\partial/\partial x$ then will operate only on the first component of $\mathbf{F}$, and so on.

For example, we compute

$$\nabla \cdot \mathbf{X} = \nabla \cdot [x, y, z] = \frac{\partial x}{\partial x} + \frac{\partial y}{\partial y} + \frac{\partial z}{\partial z} = 3.$$

Definition 8–2. Let $\mathbf{F} = [f_1, f_2, f_3]$ be a continuously differentiable function in some open set in R^3. Then the *curl* of $\mathbf{F}$ is the vector field

$$\operatorname{curl} \mathbf{F} = (f_{3'2} - f_{2'3})\mathbf{e}_1 + (f_{1'3} - f_{3'1})\mathbf{e}_2 + (f_{2'1} - f_{1'2})\mathbf{e}_3.$$

We will denote the curl of $\mathbf{F}$ by either of the forms

$$\operatorname{curl} \mathbf{F} = \nabla \times \mathbf{F}.$$

The representation $\nabla \times \mathbf{F}$ comes from viewing the del operator as the vector defined in (8–1). An easy way to remember the formula for the curl given in Definition 8–2 is by means of the mnemonic device:

$$\nabla \times \mathbf{F} = \begin{vmatrix} \mathbf{e}_1 & \mathbf{e}_2 & \mathbf{e}_3 \\ \dfrac{\partial}{\partial x} & \dfrac{\partial}{\partial y} & \dfrac{\partial}{\partial z} \\ f_1 & f_2 & f_3 \end{vmatrix}. \tag{8–2}$$

If this determinant is expanded by cofactors of the top row, and the derivative operators of the second row are allowed to operate on the functions in the bottom row in exactly the manner of multiplying out the determinant, we will obtain the same result as the formula of Definition 8–2.

As an example, let us find

$$\nabla \times \frac{\mathbf{X}}{|\mathbf{X}|} = \begin{vmatrix} \mathbf{e}_1 & \mathbf{e}_2 & \mathbf{e}_3 \\ \dfrac{\partial}{\partial x} & \dfrac{\partial}{\partial y} & \dfrac{\partial}{\partial z} \\ \dfrac{x}{|\mathbf{X}|} & \dfrac{y}{|\mathbf{X}|} & \dfrac{z}{|\mathbf{X}|} \end{vmatrix}$$

$$= \mathbf{e}_1 \left(\frac{\partial}{\partial y} \frac{z}{|\mathbf{X}|} - \frac{\partial}{\partial z} \frac{y}{|\mathbf{X}|} \right) - \mathbf{e}_2 \left(\frac{\partial}{\partial x} \frac{z}{|\mathbf{X}|} - \frac{\partial}{\partial z} \frac{x}{|\mathbf{X}|} \right)$$

$$+ \mathbf{e}_3 \left(\frac{\partial}{\partial x} \frac{y}{|\mathbf{X}|} - \frac{\partial}{\partial y} \frac{x}{|\mathbf{X}|} \right)$$

$$= \mathbf{e}_1 \left[-\frac{zy}{|\mathbf{X}|^3} + \frac{zy}{|\mathbf{X}|^3} \right] - \mathbf{e}_2 \left[-\frac{xz}{|\mathbf{X}|^3} + \frac{xz}{|\mathbf{X}|^3} \right] + \mathbf{e}_3 \left[-\frac{xy}{|\mathbf{X}|^3} + \frac{xz}{|\mathbf{X}|^3} \right]$$

$$= \mathbf{0}.$$

As another example, we calculate

$$\nabla \times [x^2, xy, xz] = \begin{vmatrix} \mathbf{e}_1 & \mathbf{e}_2 & \mathbf{e}_3 \\ \dfrac{\partial}{\partial x} & \dfrac{\partial}{\partial y} & \dfrac{\partial}{\partial z} \\ x^2 & xy & xz \end{vmatrix}$$

$$= \mathbf{e}_1[0 - 0] - \mathbf{e}_2[z - 0] + \mathbf{e}_3[y - 0]$$

$$= [0, -z, y].$$

The divergence could be generalized to any number of dimensions in an obvious manner. It would be the sum of the major diagonal elements of the matrix $[d\mathbf{F}]$. It is not so clear what the proper generalization of the curl would be. Other than saying that it is *not* a vector, we will not go into this.

Both the divergence and the curl seem to depend on the coordinate system. Actually, they are independent of the particular (orthogonal, right-handed) coordinate system. Thus, if $\mathbf{u}_1, \mathbf{u}_2, \mathbf{u}_3$ constitute a right-handed system of orthonormal vectors and if we set

$$\mathbf{X} = \sum_{i=1}^{3} y_i \mathbf{u}_i, \qquad \mathbf{F} = \sum_{i=1}^{3} g_i \mathbf{u}_i,$$

then we can prove that

$$\operatorname{div} \mathbf{F} = \sum_{i=1}^{3} \frac{\partial f_i}{\partial x_i} = \sum_{i=1}^{3} \frac{\partial g_i}{\partial y_i}.$$

The invariance of the divergence under translations is obvious. Therefore let us consider the change of coordinates in R^3 representing a rotation or reflection. Such a change of coordinates will be given by $\mathbf{W} = P\mathbf{X}$, where P is an orthogonal matrix. This is the same as $\mathbf{X} = P^t\mathbf{W}$. Now, given the function $\mathbf{F}(\mathbf{X})$, we change the variable $\mathbf{X}$ by the given transformation. We also wish to similarly transform the "value" of the function; that is, we set

$$\mathbf{G}(\mathbf{W}) = P\mathbf{F}[P^t\mathbf{W}].$$

Then

$$[d\mathbf{G}(\mathbf{W})] = P[d\mathbf{F}(\mathbf{X})]P^t.$$

The divergence of **F** is the trace of the matrix $[d\mathbf{F}(\mathbf{X})]$. The trace of a matrix is invariant under the similarity transformation (Theorem 4–31, page 143), and hence $\text{div}\,\mathbf{G}(\mathbf{W}) = \text{div}\,\mathbf{F}(\mathbf{X})$. The same proof holds in R^n for any n.

A similar result holds for the curl (in R^3). We will not prove this at present. Later we will prove some formulas which will make this result very easy to prove. Essentially we will show that the divergence and curl can be characterized by coordinate-free properties.

Note that we already know that the gradient is independent of the coordinate system. We already have a coordinate-free representation of the gradient. The gradient of a function f is the unique vector whose magnitude and direction give the maximum rate of change of f; this does not depend on the coordinate system.

A discussion of the physical meaning of the divergence and curl will be deferred until after we know some of their mathematical properties. As usual, the first properties that we investigate are the linearity properties. For the sake of completeness, we will include the properties of the gradient in the statement of the following theorem, even though these formulas were obtained earlier.

▶ **Theorem 8–1.** Let f, g, **F**, and **G** be scalar- and vector-valued functions which are continuously differentiable in some open set in R^3. Let k be a scalar constant. Then

$$\nabla kf = k\,\nabla f, \qquad \nabla(f+g) = \nabla f + \nabla g,$$
$$\nabla\cdot kf = k\,\nabla\cdot f, \qquad \nabla\cdot(f+g) = \nabla\cdot f + \nabla\cdot g,$$
$$\nabla\times kf = k\,\nabla\times f, \qquad \nabla\times(f+g) = \nabla\times f + \nabla\times g.$$

These formulas state that the gradient, divergence, and curl operators are linear (in the sense of being linear transformations on the vector space of functions). The proofs of these properties are trivial and can be left as an exercise.

A much more interesting problem is the behavior of these operators when applied to the product of two functions. We have already seen what happens when we take the gradient of the product of two scalar-valued functions. We are now interested in the corresponding formulas for the divergence and curl of the product of a scalar-valued function with a vector-valued function. Note that this is one way that we can obtain a vector-valued function as the product of two functions. The only other way is to take the cross product of two vector-valued functions. The second type of product will be discussed in the problems at the end of the section.

▶ **Theorem 8–2.** Let f and g be scalar-valued functions and let **G** be a vector-valued function. Assume that all of these functions are continuously differentiable in some open set in R^3. Then

$$\nabla(fg) = (\nabla f)g + f(\nabla g), \tag{8–3}$$
$$\nabla\cdot(f\mathbf{G}) = (\nabla f)\cdot\mathbf{G} + f(\nabla\cdot\mathbf{G}), \tag{8–4}$$
$$\nabla\times(f\mathbf{G}) = (\nabla f)\times\mathbf{G} + f(\nabla\times\mathbf{G}). \tag{8–5}$$

Proof. These formulas are easy to remember if we note that they all follow the basic pattern, which we know, of the derivative of the product of functions. The differentiation operator ∇ operates on each part of the product separately, but when it operates on a scalar function, it must be the gradient. Note, too, that when the cross product is involved, we must maintain the same order between the "factors"; otherwise the sign would change.

To prove these formulas, we merely have to compute the left-hand sides. For the proof of (8–3), we compute

$$\begin{aligned}\nabla(fg) &= \left[\frac{\partial fg}{\partial x}, \frac{\partial fg}{\partial y}, \frac{\partial fg}{\partial z}\right] \\ &= [gf'_1 + fg'_1, gf'_2 + fg'_2, gf'_3 + fg'_3] \\ &= g(\nabla f) + f(\nabla g),\end{aligned}$$

which, except for the order of the factors, is (8–3).

In a similar manner, to prove (8–4) we proceed as follows:

$$\begin{aligned}\nabla \cdot (f\mathbf{G}) &= \frac{\partial fg_1}{\partial x} + \frac{\partial fg_2}{\partial y} + \frac{\partial fg_3}{\partial z} \\ &= fg_{1'1} + g_1 f'_1 + fg_{2'2} + g_2 f'_2 + fg_{3'3} + g_3 f'_3 \\ &= f(\nabla \cdot \mathbf{G}) + \mathbf{G} \cdot (\nabla f),\end{aligned}$$

which, except for the order of the factors, is identical to the right-hand side of (8–4).

The proof of (8–5) is similar, except that greater care must be taken about the order of the factors. Its proof is left as an exercise. ▮

These formulas are often useful in finding the divergence or curl of a given vector field. For example, we found that $\nabla \cdot \mathbf{X} = 3$ and $\nabla|\mathbf{X}| = \mathbf{X}/|\mathbf{X}|$. Hence

$$\begin{aligned}\nabla \cdot (|\mathbf{X}|\mathbf{X}) &= |\mathbf{X}|(\nabla \cdot \mathbf{X}) + \mathbf{X} \cdot (\nabla|\mathbf{X}|) \\ &= 3|\mathbf{X}| + \mathbf{X} \cdot \mathbf{X}/|\mathbf{X}| = 4|\mathbf{X}|.\end{aligned}$$

Similarly,

$$\begin{aligned}\nabla \cdot (\mathbf{X}/|\mathbf{X}|) &= \frac{1}{|\mathbf{X}|}(\nabla \cdot \mathbf{X}) + \mathbf{X} \cdot \nabla \frac{1}{|\mathbf{X}|} = \frac{3}{|\mathbf{X}|} + \mathbf{X} \cdot \left(-\frac{1}{|\mathbf{X}|^2}\nabla|\mathbf{X}|\right) \\ &= \frac{3}{|\mathbf{X}|} - \frac{1}{|\mathbf{X}|^2}\frac{\mathbf{X} \cdot \mathbf{X}}{|\mathbf{X}|} = \frac{2}{|\mathbf{X}|}.\end{aligned}$$

Now let us consider what happens if we apply the del operator more than once. If f is a scalar-valued function, then ∇f is a vector-valued function. If f has continuous second partial derivatives, then ∇f will have continuous first partials. We can thus take the divergence or curl of ∇f. In the case of the divergence, we find that

$$\nabla \cdot \nabla f = \nabla \cdot [f'_1, f'_2, f'_3] = f'_{11} + f'_{22} + f'_{33}.$$

We recognize this as being the *Laplacian* of f, which we defined on page 249. This explains the reason for the use of the notation $\nabla^2 f$ for the Laplacian. We write

$$\nabla \cdot \nabla f = \nabla^2 f = \frac{\partial^2 f}{\partial x^2} + \frac{\partial^2 f}{\partial y^2} + \frac{\partial^2 f}{\partial z^2}. \tag{8-6}$$

Since the gradient of f is a vector-valued function, we could also take the curl of the gradient. We find that

$$\nabla \times \nabla f = \begin{bmatrix} \mathbf{e}_1 & \mathbf{e}_2 & \mathbf{e}_3 \\ \dfrac{\partial}{\partial x} & \dfrac{\partial}{\partial y} & \dfrac{\partial}{\partial z} \\ f'_1 & f'_2 & f'_3 \end{bmatrix} = [f'_{32} - f'_{23}, f'_{13} - f'_{31}, f'_{21} - f'_{12}].$$

However, assuming continuous second partial derivatives, all of the mixed partial derivatives are equal in the respective components of this vector, and hence we find that

$$\nabla \times \nabla f = \mathbf{0}. \tag{8-7}$$

These are the only two possibilities starting with a scalar-valued function. If we start with a vector-valued function, then there are three ways in which we can use the del operator twice. One of these ways gives a simple result. In one of the problems at the end of this section, the reader will be invited to prove that

$$\nabla \cdot \nabla \times \mathbf{F} = 0 \tag{8-8}$$

whenever $\mathbf{F}$ has continuous second partial derivatives. The proof of this fact is similar to the proof given above.

The remaining two combinations, $\nabla(\nabla \cdot \mathbf{F})$ and $\nabla \times (\nabla \times \mathbf{F})$, occur less frequently. They turn out to be related. Indeed, we can show that

$$\nabla \times (\nabla \times \mathbf{F}) = \nabla(\nabla \cdot \mathbf{F}) - \nabla^2 \mathbf{F}, \tag{8-9}$$

where we interpret

$$\nabla^2[f_1, f_2, f_3] = [\nabla^2 f_1, \nabla^2 f_2, \nabla^2 f_3].$$

The identity given in (7–39) is helpful in remembering (8–9).

Formulas (8–7) and (8–8) are easy to remember. Formula (8–7) can be remembered by recalling that the cross product of two identical vectors is zero. Formula (8–8) can be remembered by recalling that the scalar triple product is zero if two of the vectors are the same.

PROBLEMS

1. Prove Theorem 8–1. 2. Prove Eq. (8–5). 3. Prove Eq. (8–8). 4. Prove Eq. (8–9).

5. Prove

$$\nabla \cdot (\mathbf{F} \times \mathbf{G}) = \mathbf{G} \cdot \nabla \times \mathbf{F} - \mathbf{F} \cdot \nabla \times \mathbf{G}.$$

6. Find the divergence of each of the following functions:

   a) $\mathbf{F}(\mathbf{X}) = [x^2, y^2, z^2]$
   b) $\mathbf{F}(\mathbf{X}) = [x^2e^{-y}, y^2e^{-z}, z^2e^{-x}]$
   c) $\mathbf{F}(\mathbf{X}) = \mathbf{X}/|\mathbf{X}|^3$
   d) $\mathbf{F}(\mathbf{X}) = |\mathbf{X}|^2\mathbf{X}$
   e) $\mathbf{F}(\mathbf{X}) = |\mathbf{X}|^\alpha \mathbf{X}$, where α is any real number
   f) $\mathbf{F}(\mathbf{X}) = [yz, xz, xy]$

7. Find the curl of each of the functions of Problem 6.

8. Let $\mathbf{X} = [x, y, z]$ and $\mathbf{Y} = [y, z, x]$. Find the curls of each of the following functions:

   a) $\mathbf{F}(\mathbf{X}) = \mathbf{Y}$
   b) $\mathbf{F}(\mathbf{X}) = |\mathbf{Y}|^2\mathbf{X}$
   c) $\mathbf{F}(\mathbf{X}) = |\mathbf{X}|^2\mathbf{Y}$

9. Find the Laplacian of each of the following functions for $\mathbf{X} \neq \mathbf{0}$:

   a) $f(\mathbf{X}) = |\mathbf{X}|^2$
   b) $f(\mathbf{X}) = 1/|\mathbf{X}|$
   c) $f(\mathbf{X}) = |\mathbf{X}|^\alpha$
   d) $f(\mathbf{X}) = \log |\mathbf{X}|$
   e) $f(\mathbf{X}) = \log \dfrac{1}{\sqrt{x^2 + y^2}}$
   f) $f(\mathbf{X}) = u(x)v(y)w(z)$; where u, v, and w are functions having continuous derivatives

10. Let $\mathbf{A}$ be a constant vector. Assign a meaning to the operator $\mathbf{A} \cdot \nabla$ so that the following formula is true

$$\nabla \times (\mathbf{A} \times \mathbf{F}) = \mathbf{A}(\nabla \cdot \mathbf{F}) - (\mathbf{A} \cdot \nabla)\mathbf{F}.$$

11. Using the same convention you introduced in Problem 10, prove that

$$\nabla \times (\mathbf{F} \times \mathbf{G}) = \mathbf{F}(\nabla \cdot \mathbf{G}) - \mathbf{G}(\nabla \cdot \mathbf{F}) + (\mathbf{G} \cdot \nabla)\mathbf{F} - (\mathbf{F} \cdot \nabla)\mathbf{G}.$$

12. Prove that if $\mathbf{A}$ is a constant vector, then

$$\nabla \cdot (\mathbf{A} \times \mathbf{F}) = -(\mathbf{A} \times \nabla) \cdot \mathbf{F} = -\mathbf{A} \cdot (\nabla \times \mathbf{F}).$$

13. Prove the following theorem: If $\mathbf{F}$ is continuously differentiable in the ball $S_r(\mathbf{A})$ and if $\nabla \times \mathbf{F} = \mathbf{0}$ at every point of this ball, then there exists a scalar-valued function g in this ball such that

$$\operatorname{grad} g = \mathbf{F}.$$

   [*Hint:* Use Theorem 7–33.]

14. Prove that $(\mathbf{A} \cdot \nabla)f = \mathbf{A} \cdot (\nabla f)$.

15. Give an example showing that $\nabla \times \mathbf{F}$ is not necessarily orthogonal to $\mathbf{F}$.

8–2. GAUSS' THEOREM

Green's Theorem gave us a formula relating an integral over a two-dimensional region to another integral over the boundary of that region. This theorem can be generalized to three dimensions in two different ways. One of these ways can, in fact, generalize the theorem to any number of dimensions in a simple way, but we will restrict our attention to three dimensions here.

Definition 8–3. Let B be a smoothly bounded region in the plane. Then by ∂B we mean the set of curves which form the boundary of B, each with an orientation such that the region B is always to the left as one of these curves is traversed in the positive direction. If G is a smoothly bounded region in R^3, then by ∂G we mean the set of boundary surfaces of G, each with the orientation of the *outward* normal.

Note that we define the orientation of a surface by means of the normal. If a parametrization of a surface gives rise to a normal which points in the wrong direction, we can obtain the correct orientation by interchanging the roles of the parameter variables.

Now Green's theorem gave us

$$\int_{\partial B} P\,dx + Q\,dy = \int_B (Q_{'1} - P_{'2})\,dV_{xy}. \tag{8–10}$$

The expression inside the right-hand integral can be thought of as the divergence of the vector-valued function $\mathbf{F} = [Q, -P]$. What would the left-hand integral be in terms of the function $\mathbf{F}$?

Suppose that the boundary curve ∂B is given by $\mathbf{X} = [x(s), y(s)]$, where we use the arc length as the parameter. Then the tangent vector is

$$\mathbf{e}_t = \left[\frac{dx}{ds}, \frac{dy}{ds}\right] = [x', y'].$$

Since we can write $dx = x'\,ds$ and $dy = y'\,ds$, we have

$$P\,dx + Q\,dy = [Q, -P] \cdot [y', -x']\,ds.$$

Let us set

$$\mathbf{e}_n = [y', -x'] = \left[\frac{dy}{ds}, -\frac{dx}{ds}\right]. \tag{8–11}$$

Then Green's theorem can be restated as

$$\int_{\partial B} \mathbf{F} \cdot \mathbf{e}_n\,ds = \int_B \nabla \cdot \mathbf{F}\,dV. \tag{8–12}$$

But what is the vector $\mathbf{e}_n$? We see that it is orthogonal to the tangent vector $\mathbf{e}_t$ and hence is a vector normal to the curve.

The tangent vector $\mathbf{e}_t$ is of unit length. Hence, if θ is the angle from $\mathbf{e}_1$ (the direction of the positive x-axis) to $\mathbf{e}_t$, then $\mathbf{e}_t = [\cos\theta, \sin\theta]$. If the interior of the region is to the "left" of $\mathbf{e}_t$, as in Fig. 8–1, then the exterior normal must be to the "right." That is,

$$\begin{aligned}\mathbf{e}_n &= [\cos(\theta - \pi/2), \sin(\theta - \pi/2)]\\ &= [\sin\theta, -\cos\theta]\end{aligned}$$

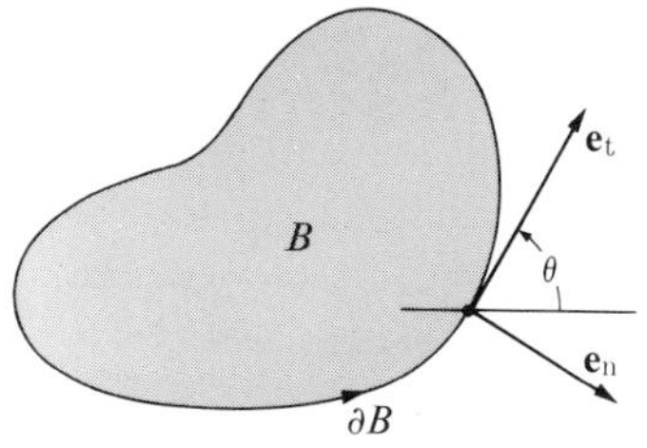

Fig. 8–1

must be the outward pointing normal vector. Since $\mathbf{e}_t = [dx/ds, dy/ds]$, we must have $\cos\theta = dx/ds$ and $\sin\theta = dy/ds$. Therefore the vector $\mathbf{e}_n$ defined in (8–11) must be the same unit outward pointing normal vector that we found here. (This is not a proof. The idea of the region B being "to the left" as we traverse ∂B is too vague a concept. We really should replace it by the statement that $\mathbf{e}_n$, as defined above, will be an outward pointing normal.)

It is formula (8–11) that can be generalized to three or more dimensions. This generalization is called *Gauss' theorem* or the *divergence theorem.*

▶ **Theorem 8–3** (*Gauss' theorem*). Let G be a simple region in R^3. Let $\mathbf{F}$ be a vector-valued function which is continuously differentiable at every point of G. Then

$$\int_{\partial G} \mathbf{F} \cdot \mathbf{e}_n \, dS = \int_G \nabla \cdot \mathbf{F} \, dV.$$

Proof. We prove this theorem by considering one component of $\mathbf{F}$ at a time. We begin by assuming that

$$\mathbf{F} = f_3 \mathbf{e}_3. \tag{8–13}$$

A similar proof will hold for the other two components. The results can then be added to give the conclusion of the theorem.

Since the region considered in the theorem can be broken up into a finite number of compact, smoothly bounded, semiconvex regions, we may as well assume that the region G is itself semiconvex. This region can then be represented in the form

$$G = \{[x, y, z] \mid [x, y] \in B, z_1(x, y) \leq z \leq z_2(x, y)\},$$

where B is some simple region in the xy-plane and z_1 and z_2 are functions which are continuous on B. (See Fig. 8–2.)

To prove the theorem for such a region and for a function of the type given by (8–13) we can ignore the surface integrals over the "sides" of the region G. The "sides" [portions of the surface for which $[x, y]$ is in the boundary of B] are such that the normal vector is orthogonal to $\mathbf{e}_3$. Hence $\mathbf{F} \cdot \mathbf{e}_n$ is zero over this part of the boundary of G.

On the upper and lower faces, we can use x and y as the parameters defining the surface. On the lower face, in order to get the outward pointing normal we must use the parameters in the order y, x. On the top face, we find that

$$f_3 \mathbf{e}_3 \cdot \mathbf{e}_n \, dS = f_3 \, dV_{xy} = f_3 \, dx \, dy,$$

using the conventions of Definitions 7–28. On the lower face, we find that

$$f_3 \mathbf{e}_3 \cdot \mathbf{e}_n \, dS = f_3 \, dy \, dx = -f_3 \, dx \, dy.$$

Therefore we have

$$\int_{\partial G} \mathbf{F} \cdot d\mathbf{S} = \int_B \big(f_3[x, y, z_2(x, y)] - f_3[x, y, z_1(x, y)]\big) \, dx \, dy,$$

where we write $\mathbf{F} \cdot d\mathbf{S}$ to represent $\mathbf{F} \cdot \mathbf{e}_n \, d\mathbf{S}$.

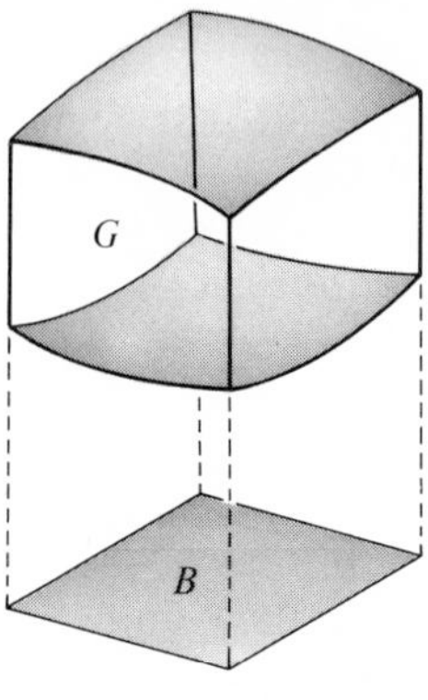

Fig. 8–2

On the other hand, we can use the fact that the multiple integral can be written as an iterated integral. Then we find that

$$\begin{aligned}\int_G \nabla \cdot \mathbf{F}\, dV &= \int_G f_{3'3}\, dV = \int_B dx\, dy \int_{z_1(x,y)}^{z_2(x,y)} f_{3'3}(x, y, z)\, dz \\ &= \int_B \big(f_3[x, y, z_2(x, y)] - f_3[x, y, z_1(x, y)]\big)\, dx\, dy \\ &= \int_{\partial G} \mathbf{F} \cdot d\mathbf{S}. \ \blacksquare\end{aligned}$$

Before turning to the more important theoretical applications of this theorem, let us give a computational example. Suppose we are asked to compute

$$\int_{\partial G} \mathbf{F} \cdot \mathbf{e}_{\mathrm{n}}\, dS,$$

where $\mathbf{F} = [x^2, xy, yz]$ and G is the cube

$$\{[x, y, z] \mid 0 \le x \le 1, 0 \le y \le 1, 0 \le z \le 1\}.$$

It is simple enough to compute this integral directly, but we must break it up into six parts, one for each face of the cube. Instead, we can use Gauss' theorem and compute

$$\begin{aligned}\int_{\partial G} \mathbf{F} \cdot \mathbf{e}_{\mathrm{n}}\, dS &= \int_G \nabla \cdot F\, dV = \int_G (3x + y)\, dx\, dy\, dz \\ &= \int_0^1 dx \int_0^1 dy \int_0^1 (3x + y)\, dz = \int_0^1 dx \int_0^1 (3x + y)\, dy \\ &= \int_0^1 (3x + \tfrac{1}{2})\, dx = 2.\end{aligned}$$

Now let us look at some other applications of this theorem. Recalling that $\nabla \cdot \mathbf{X} = 3$, we see that for any simple region $\mathbf{G}$

$$\int_{\partial G} \mathbf{X} \cdot d\mathbf{S} = 3 \int_G dV = 3V(G),$$

where $V(G)$ is the volume of the region G. In particular, if G is a sphere of radius r, centered at the origin, then at each point of the surface of the sphere $\mathbf{X}$ is in the direction of the normal vector and hence $\mathbf{X} \cdot d\mathbf{S} = r\, dS$. The above formula then tells us that the surface area of a sphere of radius r is $3r$ times the volume of that sphere. Is this true?

Imagine a fluid flowing in a region of space. If ΔS is the area of a small piece of (imaginary) surface with unit normal $\mathbf{e}_{\mathrm{n}}$, then the mass of fluid flowing through this piece of surface in the direction of $\mathbf{e}_{\mathrm{n}}$ (called the flux through this piece of surface) is approximately $\rho \mathbf{V} \cdot \mathbf{e}_{\mathrm{n}}\, \Delta S$, where ρ is the density and $\mathbf{V}$ the velocity of the fluid. The mass, flowing through a more extended surface S is thus

$$\int_S \rho \mathbf{V} \cdot \mathbf{e}_{\mathrm{n}}\, dS.$$

The divergence theorem therefore tells us that if G is a simple region with boundary ∂G, then the total mass of fluid escaping from G is

$$\int_{\partial G} \rho \mathbf{V} \cdot \mathbf{e}_n \, dS = \int_G \nabla \cdot (\rho \mathbf{V}) \, dV,$$

provided that $\mathbf{V}$ and ρ are continuously differentiable throughout G. If this is so and if no matter is being created or destroyed, the principle of conservation of mass tells us that the above integrals must have a value of zero. This must be true for every simple region G. The only way that the integral of a continuous function can be zero over every simple region is for the function itself to be zero. Therefore the principle of conservation of mass is equivalent to $\nabla \cdot (\rho \mathbf{V}) = 0$.

In particular, if the fluid is incompressible, then ρ is a constant and the velocity field of the flow must be "divergence free," that is, $\nabla \cdot \mathbf{V} = 0$.

The above ideas can be extended to lead to a characterization of the divergence of a vector field. Suppose that $\mathbf{F}$ is a vector-valued function which has a continuous derivative in a neighborhood of a point $\mathbf{A}$. Let $G = \overline{S}_\delta(\mathbf{A})$, that is, a closed ball of radius δ with center at $\mathbf{A}$. The radius δ should be small enough so that $\mathbf{F}$ has continuous derivatives in G. According to Gauss' theorem,

$$\int_G \nabla \cdot \mathbf{F} \, dV = \int_{\partial G} \mathbf{F} \cdot d\mathbf{S}.$$

The value of the integral on the left-hand side must lie between the maximum and minimum values of $\nabla \cdot \mathbf{F}$ in G times the volume of G. Now, if we divide through by the volume of G and let the radius of the sphere tend to zero, we find (recall that we are assuming that $\nabla \cdot \mathbf{F}$ is continuous)

$$\nabla \cdot \mathbf{F}(\mathbf{A}) = \lim_{\delta \to 0} \frac{1}{V(G)} \int_{\partial G} \mathbf{F} \cdot d\mathbf{S}.$$

The expression on the right can be viewed as the "average flux" out of the sphere. The integral measures the total normal component of $\mathbf{F}$ summed over the area of the sphere. Dividing by the volume of the sphere gives the average.

In the discussion above, there is nothing special about using a sphere. We would obtain the same result if G became smaller in such a way that both its volume and its maximum diameter tended toward zero.

Theorem 8–4. Let $\mathbf{F}$ have a continuous derivative in a neighborhood of a point $\mathbf{A}$. Then

$$\operatorname{div} \mathbf{F}(\mathbf{A}) = \lim \frac{1}{V(G)} \int_{\partial G} \mathbf{F} \cdot d\mathbf{S},$$

where $V(G)$ is the volume of simple region G which contains a point $\mathbf{A}$, and the limit is taken as the maximum diameter of G tends toward zero.

This theorem allows us to give another proof of the invariance of the divergence under euclidean motions. Since the surface integral and volume are independent of euclidean motions, this result shows us that the divergence must also be invariant.

PROBLEMS

1. Let G be a smoothly bounded compact region in R^3. Let ∂G be the boundary surface of G. Let $\mathbf{e}_n$ be the unit (outward pointing) normal vector to ∂G at each point. If g is a scalar-valued function, we often write $\partial g/\partial n$ to mean $D_{\mathbf{e}_n}g = (\nabla g) \cdot \mathbf{e}_n$. This is called the normal derivative of g.

   a) Prove that
$$\int_{\partial G} \frac{\partial g}{\partial n}\, dS = \int_G \nabla^2 g\, dV.$$
   b) Prove that
$$\int_{\partial G} f\frac{\partial g}{\partial n}\, dS = \int_G [f\nabla^2 g + (\nabla f) \cdot (\nabla g)]\, dV.$$
   c) Prove that
$$\int_{\partial G} \left[f\frac{\partial g}{\partial n} - g\frac{\partial f}{\partial n}\right] dS = \int_G [f\nabla^2 g - g\nabla^2 f]\, dV.$$

2. Let G be a smoothly bounded region in R^3. Prove that

   a) $V(G) = \frac{1}{3}\int_{\partial G} \mathbf{X} \cdot d\mathbf{S}$, b) $V(G) = \int_{\partial G} x\, dy\, dz.$

3. Let $\mathbf{A}$ be a constant vector and $\mathbf{F}$ a vector field. Express
$$\int_{\partial G} (\mathbf{A} \times \mathbf{F}) \cdot d\mathbf{S}$$
as an integral over the simple region G in R^3. Find the value of this integral when $\mathbf{F}(\mathbf{X}) = \mathbf{X}$.

4. Let G_1 and G_2 be two simple regions with $G_1 \subset G_2$ and $\mathbf{0} \notin G_2 - G_1$. Prove that if $\mathbf{F} = \mathbf{X}/|\mathbf{X}|^3$, then
$$\int_{\partial G_1} \mathbf{F} \cdot \mathbf{e}_n\, dS = \int_{\partial G_2} \mathbf{F} \cdot \mathbf{e}_n\, dS.$$

5. Let ρ be the density and $\mathbf{V}$ the velocity of a fluid. Suppose that these fields are both continuous and have continuous derivatives. Prove that
$$(\nabla \rho) \cdot \mathbf{V} = -\rho(\nabla \cdot \mathbf{V}).$$

6. Let G be the conical region determined by $3\sqrt{x^2 + y^2} \le z \le 6$. Compute both $\int_{\partial G} \mathbf{F} \cdot \mathbf{e}_n\, dS$ and $\int_G \nabla \cdot \mathbf{F}\, dV$ directly for each of the following functions $\mathbf{F}$, thus verifying Gauss' theorem for these cases.

   a) $\mathbf{F}(\mathbf{X}) = \mathbf{X}$ b) $\mathbf{F}(\mathbf{X}) = [x^2y, x^2z, z - 6]$ c) $\mathbf{F}(\mathbf{X}) = [0, 0, z^2]$

7. Prove that the x-coordinate of the centroid of a region G is given by
$$\bar{x} = \frac{1}{V(G)} \int_{\partial G} x^2\, dy\, dz.$$

8. Given that f and $\mathbf{F}$ are differentiable throughout a simple region G, prove that
$$\int_G (f\nabla \cdot \mathbf{F} + \mathbf{F} \cdot \nabla f)\, dV = \int_{\partial G} f\mathbf{F} \cdot \mathbf{e}_n\, dS.$$

8–3. STOKES' THEOREM

Green's Theorem was written in the form

$$\int_{\partial B} P\,dx + Q\,dy = \int_B (Q_{,1} - P_{,2})\,dV_{xy}. \tag{8–14}$$

This theorem can be generalized to give Gauss' theorem, as we did in the last section, or it can be generalized in another way. Instead of integrating over a volume with the surface forming the boundary of that volume, we might integrate over a surface with the curve forming the boundary of that surface in space. It is obvious what the left-hand side of (8–14) would become when it is generalized, but it is not so clear what the right-hand side would become. Recalling the definition of the curl, however, we see that if B is a smoothly bounded region in the plane, with ∂B as its boundary curve, then Green's theorem can be written in the form

$$\int_{\partial B} \mathbf{F} \cdot d\mathbf{X} = \int_B (\nabla \times \mathbf{F}) \cdot d\mathbf{S},$$

where we let $d\mathbf{S} = \mathbf{e}_3\,dx\,dy$ and set $\mathbf{F} = [P, Q, R]$. The function R can be anything in this case since it will not affect either of the integrals.

The generalization of this result to bounded surfaces in three-dimensional space is known as Stokes' Theorem.

Definition 8–4. Let B be a compact region in the uv-plane whose boundary is the piecewise smooth, simple, closed curve ∂B. Let $\mathbf{X}: B \to R^3$ be continuously differentiable at each point of B. Then the surface S defined by $\mathbf{X}$ over B is said to have the boundary ∂S, where ∂S is the curve defined by the function $\mathbf{X}: \partial B \to R^3$. The orientation of ∂S is the orientation induced under this mapping by the orientation of ∂B.

This definition can be viewed as saying that if we stand near the boundary of S so that the normal vector $\mathbf{X}_{,1} \times \mathbf{X}_{,2}$ is on the top of the surface and face the direction of the tangent vector to ∂S, then the surface is to our left. Another way of viewing the definition is in terms of the "right-hand rule." If we point the fingers of our right hand along the positive direction of the curve, and if the surface is on the palm side of the hand, then the thumb points in the direction of the normal vector to the surface.

▶ **Theorem 8–5** (*Stokes' theorem*). Let S be a piecewise smoothly bounded surface in R^3 and let ∂S be its boundary curve. Suppose that $\mathbf{F}$ is a vector-valued function which is continuously differentiable at every point of S. Then

$$\int_{\partial S} \mathbf{F} \cdot d\mathbf{X} = \int_S (\nabla \times \mathbf{F}) \cdot \mathbf{e}_n\,dS.$$

Proof. For the purpose of this proof we will assume that $\mathbf{X} = \mathbf{X}(u, v)$ has continuous second partial derivatives. This will allow us to give a simpler proof than we would otherwise have. Let

$$\mathbf{X} = [x_1, x_2, x_3] \qquad \text{and} \qquad \mathbf{W} = [u, v].$$

Then we find that

$$
\begin{aligned}
\int_{\partial S} \mathbf{F}(\mathbf{X}) \cdot d\mathbf{X} &= \int_{\partial S} \sum_{i=1}^{3} f_i(\mathbf{X})\, dx_i \\
&= \int_{\partial B} \sum_{i=1}^{3} f_i[\mathbf{X}(\mathbf{W})] x_{i'1}\, du + \sum_{i=1}^{3} f_i[\mathbf{X}(\mathbf{W})] x_{i'2}\, dv \\
&= \int_B \left(\frac{\partial}{\partial u} \sum_{i=1}^{3} f_i[\mathbf{X}(\mathbf{W})] x_{i'2} - \frac{\partial}{\partial v} \sum_{i=1}^{3} f_i[\mathbf{X}(\mathbf{W})] x_{i'1} \right) du\, dv \\
&= \int_B \left(\sum_{i=1}^{3} \sum_{j=1}^{3} f_{i'j} x_{j'1} x_{i'2} + \sum_{i=1}^{3} f_i x_{i'21} \right. \\
&\qquad \left. - \sum_{i=1}^{3} \sum_{j=1}^{3} f_{i'j} x_{j'2} x_{i'1} - \sum_{i=1}^{3} f_i x_{i'12} \right) du\, dv \\
&= \int_B \left[\sum_{i=1}^{3} \sum_{j=1}^{3} f_{i'j} (x_{j'1} x_{i'2} - x_{j'2} x_{i'1}) \right] du\, dv \\
&= \int_B \left[\sum_{i=1}^{3} \sum_{j=1}^{3} f_{i'j} \frac{\partial(x_j, x_i)}{\partial(u, v)} \right] du\, dv \\
&= \int_S \sum_{i=1}^{3} \sum_{j=1}^{3} f_{i'j}\, dx_j\, dx_i.
\end{aligned}
$$

In the third step of this proof we made use of Green's Theorem in the *uv*-plane. In the fifth line we made use of the fact that $x_{i'21} = x_{i'12}$. The last line of the theorem is easily recognized as the desired result, for, according to our conventions, $dx_i dx_i = 0$ for every i and

$$
\begin{aligned}
\mathbf{e}_n\, dS = d\mathbf{S} &= \mathbf{e}_1\, dy\, dz + \mathbf{e}_2\, dz\, dx + \mathbf{e}_3\, dx\, dy \\
&= \mathbf{e}_1\, dx_2\, dx_3 + \mathbf{e}_2\, dx_3\, dx_1 + \mathbf{e}_3\, dx_1\, dx_2. \quad \blacksquare
\end{aligned}
$$

This proof is highly computational. To a mathematician it is disappointing since it is not clear what the main point of the proof is. There appears to be some sort of reciprocity between the operation of differentiation of functions (or differential forms) and the boundary operation, but the nature of this reciprocity is not obvious.

The theorems of Green, Gauss, and Stokes are very useful in applications. It may therefore be surprising to discover that such well-known theorems are all really simple variations of one single result. There is one theorem that includes all three. This general result is also known as Stokes' theorem since, in a real sense, Stokes' theorem as we stated above is the most general of the three. Both Green's theorem and the divergence theorem apply to regions whose dimension is the same as the space they are embedded in. In Stokes' theorem, this is not necessary. Thus the curve forming the boundary of the piece of surface does not determine the surface; many different surfaces can have the same boundary curve.

Since it is a most interesting point, let us show that the theorems of Green, Gauss, and Stokes are essentially identical. For this purpose we make use of those conventions concerning differential forms that we introduced at the end of Section 7–9.

First, let us look at Gauss' theorem:

$$\int_{\partial G} \mathbf{F} \cdot d\mathbf{S} = \int_G \nabla \cdot \mathbf{F}\, dV.$$

Let us write

$$\omega = \mathbf{F} \cdot \mathrm{d}\mathbf{S} = f_1\, dy\, dz + f_2\, dz\, dx + f_3\, dx\, dy.$$

Then

$$\begin{aligned} d\omega &= (f_{1'1}\, dx + f_{1'2}\, dy + f_{1'3}\, dz)\, dy\, dz + \cdots \\ &= f_{1'1}\, dx\, dy\, dz + f_{2'2}\, dy\, dz\, dx + f_{3'3}\, dz\, dx\, dy \\ &= \nabla \cdot \mathbf{F}\, dx\, dy\, dz. \end{aligned}$$

In this computation we made use of the fact that the product of three differentials vanishes whenever two of them are the same. We also need to know that $dy\, dz\, dx = -\, dy\, dx\, dz = dx\, dy\, dz$ and $dz\, dx\, dy = -\, dx\, dz\, dy = dx\, dy\, dz$. The above computation shows that Gauss' theorem can be stated in the form

$$\int_{\partial G} \omega = \int_G d\omega.$$

We have already seen that Green's theorem could be written in exactly the same form. (See Problem 4 at the end of Section 7–9.) What about Stokes' theorem? Let us set

$$\omega = \mathbf{F} \cdot d\mathbf{X} = f_1\, dx + f_2\, dy + f_3\, dz = \sum_{i=1}^{3} f_i\, dx_i.$$

But then

$$d\omega = \sum_{i=1}^{3} (df_i)\, dx_i = \sum_{i=1}^{3} \left(\sum_{j=1}^{3} f_{i'j}\, dx_j \right) dx_i = \sum_{i=1}^{3} \sum_{j=1}^{3} f_{i'j}\, dx_j\, dx_i,$$

which we recognize as the expression we obtained in the course of the proof of Stokes' theorem. Therefore Stokes' theorem can also be written in the form

$$\int_{\partial S} \omega = \int_S d\omega. \tag{8–15}$$

Stated in this form, Stokes' theorem can be given a meaning in a space of any number of dimensions, S being a "surface" of the same or any lower dimension. In this sense, Stokes' theorem is an important theorem in many branches of mathematics. Much of its importance, however, is in the proper interpretation of differential forms and the boundary operations. The purely heuristic discussion we have given in this text does almost nothing toward explaining the real meaning of these operations. This must await more advanced courses.

Let us now return to the "classical form" of Stokes' theorem and discuss some of its applications. First, let us suppose that we have a vector field $\mathbf{G}(\mathbf{X})$ given throughout some region of space and that this field is such that there is some other field $\mathbf{F}$ with $\mathbf{G} = \nabla \times \mathbf{F}$. (Theorem 8–7, proved later in this section, tells us something about the possibility of this being true.)

The field $\mathbf{G}$ can be thought of as the vector field of the flow of an incompressible fluid. (Why is the field $\mathbf{G}$ necessarily divergence free?)

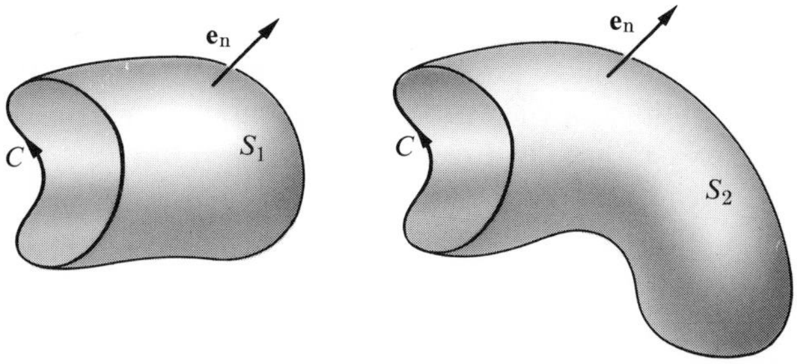

Fig. 8–3

Let C be some simple closed curve in space and suppose that there are two surfaces, S_1 and S_2, both of which have the same boundary C, as illustrated in Fig. 8–3. Then the total flux of the flow through S_1 and S_2 is given respectively by

$$\int_{S_1} \mathbf{G} \cdot \mathbf{e}_n \, dS, \qquad \int_{S_2} \mathbf{G} \cdot \mathbf{e}_n \, dS.$$

Since $\mathbf{G} = \nabla \times \mathbf{F}$, Stokes' theorem shows that either of these integrals is equal to

$$\int_C \mathbf{F} \cdot d\mathbf{X},$$

and hence the two integrals are equal.

In terms of a physical example, the above result is almost obvious. The total flux through either of these surfaces can be thought of as the amount of fluid escaping through the "sides" of a sack whose "mouth" is C. This amount must be the same for any sack with the same "mouth."

Let us verify Stokes' theorem for a specific case. Suppose $\mathbf{F} = [y, -x, z]$ and S is the hemisphere $x^2 + y^2 + z^2 = 1, z \geq 0$, with the orientation given by the "outward" pointing normal (i.e., $\mathbf{e}_n = \mathbf{X}/|\mathbf{X}|$). Then ∂S is the circle $x^2 + y^2 = 1$, $z = 0$ traversed in the "positive" or "counterclockwise" direction in the xy-plane; that is, ∂S is given by $\mathbf{X} = [\cos\theta, \sin\theta]$, $0 \leq \theta \leq 2\pi$. Hence

$$\begin{aligned}\int_{\partial S} \mathbf{F} \cdot d\mathbf{X} &= \int_0^{2\pi} [\sin\theta, -\cos\theta, 0] \cdot [-\sin\theta, \cos\theta, 0] \, d\theta \\ &= -\int_0^{2\pi} d\theta = -2\pi.\end{aligned}$$

On the other hand, $\nabla \times \mathbf{F} = [0, 0, -2]$, and hence

$$\int_S \nabla \times \mathbf{F} \cdot d\mathbf{S} = \int_S [0, 0, -2] \cdot [dy\,dz, dz\,dx, dx\,dy] = -2 \int_S dx\,dy = -2\pi,$$

where the last integral, being evaluated merely over the projection of S, is the area of the unit circle.

In the last section, we used Gauss' theorem to obtain a coordinate-free characterization of the divergence of a vector field. In a similar way, we can obtain a characterization of the curl of a vector field with the help of Stokes' theorem. Let $\mathbf{e}$ be any vector of magnitude one and let $\mathbf{A}$ be any point in space. Suppose that $\mathbf{F}$ has a continuous derivative in a neighborhood of the point $\mathbf{A}$. Let S be a disk of radius δ with center $\mathbf{A}$, lying in the plane through $\mathbf{A}$ and orthogonal to $\mathbf{e}$. We assume that $\mathbf{e}$ defines the direction of the normal vector at each point of S. The situation is as shown in Fig. 8-4. The curve ∂S has the direction as shown in this figure. Stokes' theorem then gives us

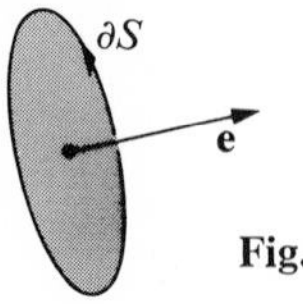

Fig. 8-4

$$\int_S (\nabla \times \mathbf{F}) \cdot d\mathbf{S} = \int_{\partial S} \mathbf{F} \cdot d\mathbf{X}.$$

If we let $A(S)$ be the area of the surface S, then the integral on the left will be approximately $A(S)$ times $\mathbf{e} \cdot [\nabla \times \mathbf{F}(\mathbf{A})]$. Dividing both sides by $A(S)$ and letting the radius of the disk tend toward zero, we find that

$$[\nabla \times \mathbf{F}(\mathbf{A})] \cdot \mathbf{e} = \lim_{\delta \to 0} \frac{1}{A(S)} \int_{\partial S} \mathbf{F} \cdot d\mathbf{X}.$$

The line integral on the right-hand side measures the total tangential component of $\mathbf{F}$ around the circle. Thus the curl of a vector field can be viewed as a vector whose component in any direction is the circulation per unit area around a small circle orthogonal to that direction. The curl measures the local "rotation" of the vector field.

The reasoning used to obtain the above formula remains valid when S is some surface other than a disk. All that is necessary is that S lies in the plane orthogonal to $\mathbf{e}$ and that its diameter tends toward zero.

Theorem 8-6. Let $\mathbf{F}$ have a continuous derivative in a neighborhood of the point $\mathbf{A}$. Let $\mathbf{e}$ be a fixed vector of magnitude one. Then

$$[\nabla \times \mathbf{F}(\mathbf{A})] \cdot \mathbf{e} = \lim \frac{1}{A(S)} \int_{\partial S} \mathbf{F} \cdot d\mathbf{X},$$

where $A(S)$ is the area of the smoothly bounded surface S which contains the point $\mathbf{A}$ and is in the plane through $\mathbf{A}$ orthogonal to $\mathbf{e}$, and the limit is taken as the maximum diameter and therefore the area of S tends toward zero.

In the next section we will see some applications of this theorem, but we can note here that this theorem serves to show that the curl of a vector field is independent of orthogonal transformations of coordinates which is orientation preserving. That is, a given vector field has the same curl in any right-handed coordinate system.

In the problems at the end of the last section, it was shown that if a vector field has a vanishing curl inside a sphere, then it is the gradient of some scalar field. A similar theorem holds for a vanishing divergence.

Theorem 8–7. Let $\mathbf{F}$ have a continuous derivative in the ball $S_r(\mathbf{A})$ and suppose that $\nabla \cdot \mathbf{F} = 0$ at every point of this ball. Then there exists a function $\mathbf{G}$ in this ball such that

$$\nabla \times \mathbf{G} = \mathbf{F}.$$

Proof. Let us assume that $\mathbf{A} = \mathbf{0}$ for simplicity. In the general case, we can make a translation and use a similar proof. For any point $\mathbf{X} = [x, y, z]$ in the sphere, define

$$\mathbf{G}(\mathbf{X}) = \int_0^1 [\mathbf{F}(t\mathbf{X}) \times (t\mathbf{X})]\, dt.$$

The point $t\mathbf{X}$ is in the ball for any t between 0 and 1 whenever $\mathbf{X}$ is in the ball. Thus this function is defined for every $\mathbf{X}$ in the ball. It now remains to be shown that this is the function which satisfies the requirements of the theorem.

To calculate the curl of $\mathbf{G}$, we can take the curl of the expression inside the integral sign (Theorem 7–27). With the help of the identity given in Problem 11 of Section 8–1, we compute

$$\nabla \times \mathbf{G}(\mathbf{X}) = \int_0^1 [\mathbf{F}(t\mathbf{X})(\nabla \cdot t\mathbf{X}) - t\mathbf{X}\big(\nabla \cdot \mathbf{F}(t\mathbf{X})\big) + (t\mathbf{X} \cdot \nabla)\mathbf{F}(t\mathbf{X}) - \big(\mathbf{F}(t\mathbf{X}) \cdot \nabla\big)t\mathbf{X}]\, dt.$$

In this expression the differential operator operates on x, y, and z, with t being treated as a constant. Hence we find that

$$\nabla \cdot t\mathbf{X} = 3t,$$
$$\nabla \cdot \mathbf{F}(t\mathbf{X}) = t[f_{1'1}(t\mathbf{X}) + f_{1'2}(t\mathbf{X}) + f_{1'3}(t\mathbf{X})] = 0.$$

The last step above follows from the hypothesis of the theorem, since the expression in brackets is the value of the divergence of $\mathbf{F}$ at $t\mathbf{X}$:

$$(t\mathbf{X} \cdot \nabla)\mathbf{F}(t\mathbf{X}) = [t^2 x f_{1'1} + t^2 y f_{1'2} + t^2 z f_{1'3}, t^2 x f_{2'1} + \cdots, \cdots] = t^2 \frac{d}{dt}\mathbf{F}(t\mathbf{X}).$$
$$\big(\mathbf{F}(t\mathbf{X}) \cdot \nabla\big)t\mathbf{X} = [tf_1(t\mathbf{X}), tf_2(t\mathbf{X}), tf_3(t\mathbf{X})] = t\mathbf{F}(t\mathbf{X}).$$

Substituting into the above integral, we find that

$$\nabla \times \mathbf{G}(\mathbf{X}) = \int_0^1 \left[2t\mathbf{F}(t\mathbf{X}) + t^2 \frac{d}{dt}\mathbf{F}(t\mathbf{X})\right] dt$$
$$= \int_0^1 \frac{d}{dt}[t^2\mathbf{F}(t\mathbf{X})]\, dt = \mathbf{F}(\mathbf{X}). \blacksquare$$

PROBLEMS

1. A vector field is normal to a surface at each point of the surface. Prove that the curl of this field is tangent to the surface at each point of the surface.
2. Let **A** be a constant vector. Express
$$\int_{\partial S} (\mathbf{A} \times \mathbf{X}) \cdot d\mathbf{X}$$
as an integral over the surface S.
3. Let G be the unit cube given by $0 \leq x \leq 1, 0 \leq y \leq 1, 0 \leq z \leq 1$. Let S be the surface consisting of the five faces of this cube for which $z > 0$. Let S have the outward pointing normal. For each of the following functions, evaluate both $\int_S \nabla \times \mathbf{F} \cdot d\mathbf{S}$ and $\int_{\partial S} \mathbf{F} \cdot d\mathbf{X}$, thus verifying Stokes' theorem for these particular cases.
a) $\mathbf{F} = [y, z, x]$ b) $\mathbf{F} = [x^2, xy, xz]$
4. Follow the directions of Problem 3, using the same two functions but with the surface S being the upper half of the unit sphere, defined by $x^2 + y^2 + z^2 = 1, z \geq 0$. Let S have the outward pointing normal.
5. The function **G** satisfying Theorem 8–7 is not uniquely determined. If $\mathbf{G}_1$ and $\mathbf{G}_2$ both satisfy Theorem 8–7, what conditions must $\mathbf{H}(\mathbf{X}) = \mathbf{G}_1 - \mathbf{G}_2$ satisfy? [*Hint:* See problem 13, Section 8–1.]
6. For each of the following functions, check as to whether or not the hypotheses of Theorem 8–7 are satisfied, and if they are, find a function **G** such that $\mathbf{F} = \nabla \times \mathbf{G}$.
a) $\mathbf{F} = [z, 0, y^2 - x^2]$ b) $\mathbf{F} = [x, y, -2z]$ c) $\mathbf{F} = [1/x, y/x, 0]$
7. Does $\mathbf{G} = [x^2y, xy^2, zy]$ satisfy Problem 6(a)? If so, verify the condition you obtained in Problem 5.
8. Prove that
$$\int_S (\nabla f) \times \mathbf{e}_\text{n}\, dS = -\int_{\partial S} f\, d\mathbf{X}.$$
9. The electric and magnetic fields **E** and **B** are functions of the three-space coordinates, x, y, and z, and the time t. In the absence of current (moving charges), these fields satisfy the two relations
$$\int_{\partial S} \mathbf{E} \cdot d\mathbf{X} = -\frac{\partial}{\partial t}\int_S \mathbf{B} \cdot \mathbf{e}_\text{n}\, dS, \qquad c^2 \int_{\partial S} \mathbf{B} \cdot d\mathbf{X} = \frac{\partial}{\partial t}\int_S \mathbf{E} \cdot \mathbf{e}_\text{n}\, dS,$$
where c is a constant and S is any smooth surface. From these two equations, prove that for any smooth surface S
$$\int_S \left(\nabla \times \mathbf{E} + \frac{\partial \mathbf{B}}{\partial t}\right) \cdot \mathbf{e}_\text{n}\, dS = 0 \quad \text{and} \quad \int_S \left(c^2\nabla \times \mathbf{B} - \frac{\partial \mathbf{E}}{\partial t}\right) \cdot \mathbf{e}_\text{n}\, dS = 0.$$
And from these results, prove that
$$\nabla \times \mathbf{E} = -\frac{\partial \mathbf{B}}{\partial t}, \qquad c^2\nabla \times \mathbf{B} = \frac{\partial \mathbf{E}}{\partial t}.$$
(These are two of Maxwell's equations for this special case.)

8–4. CURVILINEAR COORDINATES

A point **X** in three-dimensional space can often be defined more conveniently for a particular problem in terms of other coordinates. For example, a point can be specified by its cylindrical coordinates r, θ, and z, where the cartesian coordinates of the point are given by

$$\mathbf{X} = [r \cos \theta, r \sin \theta, z]. \tag{8–16}$$

Similarly, a point can be defined by its spherical coordinates, ρ, ϕ, and θ, where

$$\mathbf{X} = [\rho \cos \theta \sin \phi, \rho \sin \theta \sin \phi, \rho \cos \phi]. \tag{8–17}$$

Note that such a "coordinate system" is merely a transformation or "change of variables." There exists a "new" coordinate space with vectors **U** and a function $\mathbf{X} = \mathbf{X}(\mathbf{U})$ defining the transformation back to the cartesian coordinates in R^3.

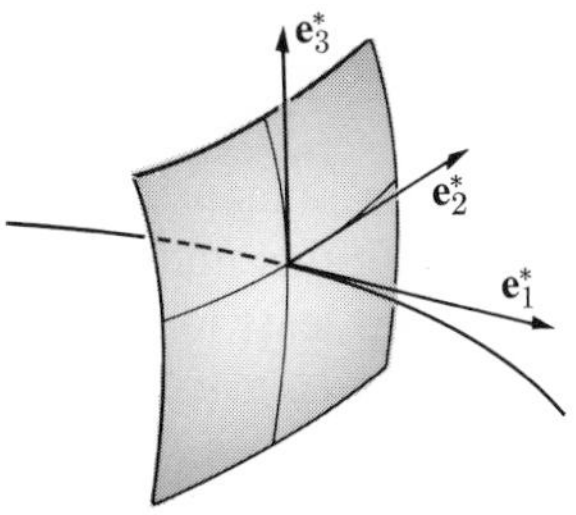

Fig. 8–5

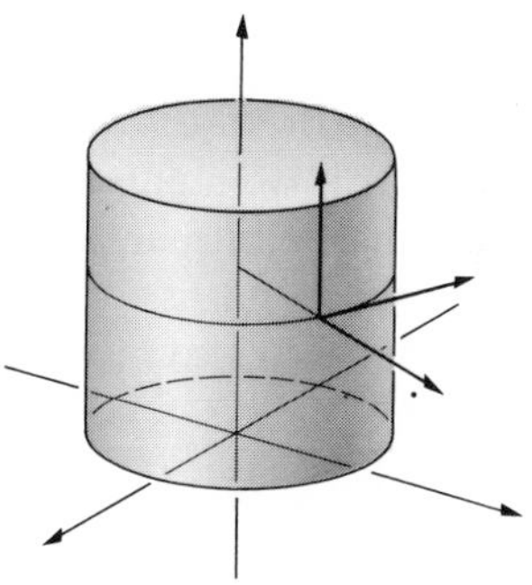

Fig. 8–6

With any such change of variables there is attached a natural set of unit vectors. Suppose, for example, that we are given the transformation $\mathbf{X} = \mathbf{X}(\mathbf{U}) = \mathbf{X}(u_1, u_2, u_3)$. Fixing two of the coordinates and allowing the third to vary, we obtain a curve through each point of R^3. At any point, there are three such curves, one for each of the u_i. The three vectors tangent to these curves are $\mathbf{X}_{,1}$, $\mathbf{X}_{,2}$, $\mathbf{X}_{,3}$. From these tangent vectors we can obtain the three corresponding unit vectors

$$\mathbf{e}_i^* = \mathbf{X}_{,i}/|\mathbf{X}_{,i}|, \quad i = 1, 2, 3 \tag{8–18}$$

(see Fig. 8–5).

These unit vectors are usually designated in a way that suggests their source. For example, in the case of cylindrical coordinates, we write

$$\begin{aligned} \mathbf{X}_{,1} &= [\cos \theta, \sin \theta, 0], & \mathbf{e}_r &= [\cos \theta, \sin \theta, 0], \\ \mathbf{X}_{,2} &= [-r \sin \theta, r \cos \theta, 0], & \mathbf{e}_\theta &= [-\sin \theta, \cos \theta, 0], \\ \mathbf{X}_{,3} &= [0, 0, 1], & \mathbf{e}_z &= [0, 0, 1]. \end{aligned} \tag{8–19}$$

The unit vectors here form an orthonormal set. See Fig. 8–6. It also happens that the unit vectors found for spherical coordinates constitute an orthonormal set. There are many transformations which give rise to systems of vectors which are not orthonormal sets, but these cases occur less often. In this chapter we will restrict our attention to coordinate systems which result in orthogonal systems of coordinate vectors. That is, we will assume throughout that the coordinate transformation is such that the three vectors defined in (8–18) are orthogonal.

Suppose that we have some vector field **G(X)**. If this vector field is defined in terms of the coordinates u_1, u_2, and u_3, i.e., $\mathbf{G(X)} = \mathbf{F(U)} = \mathbf{G[X(U)]}$, then we may be interested in having the expansion of **G** in terms of the unit vectors of the new coordinate system at each point in space. That is, we may wish to find

$$\mathbf{G(X)} = \mathbf{F(U)} = f_1\mathbf{e}_1^* + f_2\mathbf{e}_2^* + f_3\mathbf{e}_3^*.$$

The difficulty is that the vectors $\mathbf{e}_i^*$ are functions of the point in space.

For example, let us suppose that we are given a function $f(\mathbf{U})$, a scalar-valued function defined in terms of the coordinates **U**. What is the expansion of the gradient of f in terms of the coordinate vectors of the **U**-coordinates? We will now solve this problem.

We have $\mathbf{X} = \mathbf{X}(u_1, u_2, u_3)$. We have assumed that the vectors $\mathbf{X}_{'i}$ are orthogonal, meaning that if we multiply the rows of the matrix $[\partial x_i/\partial u_j]$ by constants, we can convert the matrix into an orthogonal matrix and hence a nonsingular matrix. Another way of seeing this is to observe that the row vectors of this matrix must be linearly independent. We can therefore solve for $\mathbf{U} = \mathbf{U(X)}$ (at least locally). Now suppose we have $f = f(\mathbf{U})$. Then

$$\nabla f = \sum_i \frac{\partial f}{\partial x_i}\mathbf{e}_i = \sum_{i,j} \frac{\partial f}{\partial u_j}\frac{\partial u_j}{\partial x_i}\mathbf{e}_i = \sum_{i,j,k} f_{'j}u_{j'i}(\mathbf{e}_i \cdot \mathbf{e}_k^*)\mathbf{e}_k^*.$$

Here all sums extend from 1 to 3. We indicate only those indices over which we are summing. The second step is the application of the chain rule. In the third step we make use of the fact that the $\mathbf{e}_k^*$ form an orthonormal set and expand the $\mathbf{e}_i$ in linear combinations of the $\mathbf{e}_k^*$.

Now, for each k

$$\mathbf{e}_k^* = \mathbf{X}_{'k}/|\mathbf{X}_{'k}|$$

and hence

$$\mathbf{e}_i \cdot \mathbf{e}_k^* = \frac{1}{|\mathbf{X}_{'k}|}\frac{\partial x_i}{\partial u_k} = \frac{1}{|\mathbf{X}_{'k}|}x_{i'k}.$$

Since $\mathbf{X} = \mathbf{X(U)}$ and $\mathbf{U} = \mathbf{U(X)}$ are inverse functions, the matrices $[x_{i'j}]$ and $[u_{j'k}]$ must be inverses of each other. That is,

$$\sum_i u_{j'i}x_{i'k} = \delta_{jk}.$$

Hence

$$\nabla f = \sum_{i,j,k} f_{'j}u_{j'i}\frac{1}{|\mathbf{X}_{'k}|}x_{i'k}\mathbf{e}_k^* = \sum_{j,k}\frac{1}{|\mathbf{X}_{'k}|}f_{'j}\,\delta_{jk}\mathbf{e}_k^* = \sum_k \frac{1}{|\mathbf{X}_{'k}|}f_{'j}\mathbf{e}_k^*.$$

This is the desired result. Let us state it as a theorem.

Theorem 8–8. Let $\mathbf{X} = \mathbf{X}(\mathbf{U})$ be a change of coordinates in R^3, such that the unit coordinate vectors given by (8–18) form an orthonormal system at each point in some open set. Let $f = f(\mathbf{U})$ be a scalar-valued function defined in terms of the coordinates $\mathbf{U}$. Then

$$\nabla f = \frac{1}{|\mathbf{X}_{'1}|} f_{'1}\mathbf{e}_1^* + \frac{1}{|\mathbf{X}_{'2}|} f_{'2}\mathbf{e}_2^* + \frac{1}{|\mathbf{X}_{'3}|} f_{'3}\mathbf{e}_3^*. \tag{8–20}$$

Let us apply this result to the case of a function given in terms of cylindrical coordinates. We then have $f = f(r, \theta, z)$. By (8–19) we have $|\mathbf{X}_{'1}| = 1$, $|\mathbf{X}_{'2}| = r$, and $|\mathbf{X}_{'3}| = 1$. Hence

$$\nabla f = \frac{\partial f}{\partial r}\mathbf{e}_r + \frac{1}{r}\frac{\partial f}{\partial \theta}\mathbf{e}_\theta + \frac{\partial f}{\partial z}\mathbf{e}_z. \tag{8–21}$$

Next, let us find a similar formula for the divergence of a vector field whose components are given in terms of the vectors $\mathbf{e}_i^*$. We could continue just as above, applying the chain rule several times, but we find it instructive to use Theorem 8–4 instead. This theorem tells us that

$$\nabla \cdot \mathbf{F} = \lim \frac{1}{V(G)} \int_{\partial G} \mathbf{F} \cdot d\mathbf{S},$$

where the limit is taken as the maximum diameter of G tends toward zero. Now, if we have

$$\mathbf{F} = \mathbf{F}(\mathbf{U}) = f_1\mathbf{e}_1^* + f_2\mathbf{e}_2^* + f_3\mathbf{e}_3^*,$$

then it is clear that the above integral will be greatly simplified if we let G be bounded by level surfaces of the u_i, that is, if we let $G = \mathbf{X}(R)$ where

$$R = \{\mathbf{U} \mid a_1 \le u_1 \le a_1 + \delta, a_2 \le u_2 \le a_2 + \delta, a_3 \le u_3 \le a_3 + \delta\}.$$

For the sake of convenience, we have made R a cube in the $u_1u_2u_3$-space. As δ tends toward zero, the maximum diameter of G also tends toward zero.

The surface of G is made up of six "faces," each of which is defined by fixing one of the variables and letting the other two vary over the cross section of the cube R. For example, if we set $u_1 = a_1$, then we find that the function

$$\mathbf{X} = \mathbf{X}(a_1, u_2, u_3)$$

defines one of these faces as u_2 and u_3 vary in the rectangle

$$R_{23} = \{[u_2, u_3] \mid a_2 \le u_2 \le a_2 + \delta, a_3 \le u_3 \le a_3 + \delta\}.$$

On this particular face the differential of the surface area is

$$d\mathbf{S} = \pm \mathbf{X}_{'2} \times \mathbf{X}_{'3}\, du_2\, du_3,$$

where the sign must be chosen so that $d\mathbf{S}$ points in the direction of the outward normal.

Let us set

$$h_1 = |\mathbf{X}_{'1}|, \qquad h_2 = |\mathbf{X}_{'2}|, \qquad h_3 = |\mathbf{X}_{'3}|. \tag{8–22}$$

Then, since we are assuming that the $\mathbf{e}_i^*$ form an orthonormal system, the above result can be written in the form

$$d\mathbf{S} = \pm h_2 h_3 \mathbf{e}_1^* \, du_2 \, du_3.$$

If we further assume that the vectors $\mathbf{e}_1^*$, $\mathbf{e}_2^*$, and $\mathbf{e}_3^*$ form a right-handed system, then we have

$$d\mathbf{S} = \begin{cases} h_2 h_3 \mathbf{e}_1^* \, du_2 \, du_3 & \text{when} \quad u_1 = a_1 + \delta \\ -h_2 h_3 \mathbf{e}_1^* \, du_2 \, du_3 & \text{when} \quad u_1 = a_1. \end{cases} \tag{8–23}$$

(In any case, the sign must be different on the two opposite faces.)

Next, we compute the value of the Jacobian of the transformation:

$$\begin{aligned} \frac{\partial(x_1, x_2, x_3)}{(\partial u_1, u_2, u_3)} &= \det[\mathbf{X}'_1, \mathbf{X}'_2, \mathbf{X}'_3] = \det[h_1\mathbf{e}_1^*, h_2\mathbf{e}_2^*, h_3\mathbf{e}_3^*] \\ &= h_1 h_2 h_3 \det[\mathbf{e}_1^*, \mathbf{e}_2^*, \mathbf{e}_3^*] = h_1 h_2 h_3. \end{aligned}$$

The vectors here are all column vectors of the given matrix. The last line follows from our assumption that the $\mathbf{e}_i^*$ form a right-handed orthonormal set. This makes the final matrix an orthogonal matrix with determinant $+1$.

We are assuming that the functions h_1, h_2, and h_3 are continuous. Hence

$$\lim_{\delta \to 0} \frac{V(G)}{\delta^3} = \lim_{\delta \to 0} \frac{1}{\delta^3} \int_R h_1 h_2 h_3 \, dV_{u_1 u_2 u_3} = h_1(\mathbf{A}) h_2(\mathbf{A}) h_3(\mathbf{A}), \tag{8–24}$$

where $\mathbf{A} = [a_1, a_2, a_3]$ is the fixed point in the $\mathbf{U}$-space at which we are finding the divergence.

By the way we have defined the region G, the surface integrals over the separate faces split off the components of $\mathbf{F}$. For example, the first component, $f_1\mathbf{e}_1^*$, has a zero contribution to the surface integral except on the two faces as in (8–23). Thus we find that

$$\int_{\partial G} f_1 \mathbf{e}_1^* \cdot d\mathbf{S} = \int_{\substack{\partial G \\ u_1 = a_1, \\ u_1 = a_1 + \delta}} \mathbf{F} \cdot dS = \int_{\substack{\partial G \\ u_1 = a_1 + \delta}} f_1 h_2 h_3 \, du_2 \, du_3 - \int_{\substack{\partial G \\ u_1 = a_1}} f_1 h_2 h_3 \, du_2 \, du_3.$$

Set

$$g(u_1, u_2, u_3) = h_2 h_3 f_1.$$

Then we have

$$\int_{\partial G} f_1 \mathbf{e}_1^* \cdot d\mathbf{S} = \int_{R_{23}} [g(a_1 + \delta, u_2, u_3) - g(a_1, u_2, u_3)] \, du_2 \, du_3.$$

Suppose that g has a continuous derivative. Then by the approximation theorem

$$\begin{aligned} g(u_1, u_2, u_3) = g(\mathbf{A}) &+ (u_1 - a_1) g'_1(\mathbf{A}) + (u_2 - a_2) g'_2(\mathbf{A}) \\ &+ (u_3 - a_3) g'_3(\mathbf{A}) + \epsilon(\mathbf{U}) |\mathbf{U} - \mathbf{A}|. \end{aligned}$$

The function $\epsilon(\mathbf{U}) \to 0$ as $\mathbf{U} \to \mathbf{A}$. Hence, if δ is small enough, $\epsilon(\mathbf{U})$ will remain small throughout R. Let $\epsilon > 0$ be given. Then we can find a δ_0 such that if $\delta < \delta_0$, then

$$\epsilon > \max \{|\epsilon(\mathbf{U})| \mid \mathbf{U} \text{ is in } R\}.$$

Note also that for any $\mathbf{U}$ in R,

$$w = |\mathbf{U} - \mathbf{A}| < \sqrt{3}\,\delta.$$

Hence we find [letting $w = |\mathbf{U} - \mathbf{A}|$, and letting ϵ_1 and ϵ_2 be values of $\epsilon(\mathbf{U})$] that

$$\int_{\partial G} f_1\mathbf{e}_1^* \cdot d\mathbf{S} = \int_{R_{23}} [g_{'1}(\mathbf{A})\,\delta + \epsilon_1(\mathbf{U})w + \epsilon_2(\mathbf{U})w]\,du_2\,du_3 = g_{'1}(\mathbf{A})\,\delta^3 + v,$$

where

$$|v| = \left|\int_{R_{23}} [\epsilon_1 w + \epsilon_2 w]\,du_2\,du_3\right| < (2\epsilon\sqrt{3}\,\delta)\int_{R_{23}} du_2\,du_3 = 2\sqrt{3}\,\epsilon\,\delta^3.$$

Therefore, the limit of v/δ^3 as $\delta \to 0$ is zero. Combining this result with (8–24), we thus have shown that

$$\lim_{\delta\to 0} \frac{1}{V(G)} \int_{\partial G} f_1\mathbf{e}_1^* \cdot d\mathbf{S} = \frac{1}{h_1h_2h_3}\,g_{'1} = \frac{1}{h_1h_2h_3}\frac{\partial}{\partial u_1}(h_2h_3f_1).$$

In an exactly similar way we can find expressions for the integrals of the other two components of $\mathbf{F}$. Putting these results together gives us the following result.

Theorem 8–9. Let $\mathbf{X} = \mathbf{X}(\mathbf{U})$ be a change of coordinates in R^3 such that the unit coordinate vectors given by (8–18) form an orthonormal system at each point of some open set. Let

$$\mathbf{F} = \mathbf{F}(\mathbf{U}) = f_1\mathbf{e}_1^* + f_2\mathbf{e}_2^* + f_3\mathbf{e}_3^*$$

be a vector field defined in terms of the coordinates $\mathbf{U}$. Let the functions h_i be defined by (8–22). Then

$$\nabla \cdot \mathbf{F} = \frac{1}{h_1h_2h_3}\left[\frac{\partial}{\partial u_1}(h_2h_3f_1) + \frac{\partial}{\partial u_2}(h_1h_3f_2) + \frac{\partial}{\partial u_3}(h_1h_2f_3)\right]. \tag{8–25}$$

Let us apply this theorem to the case of a function given in cylindrical coordinates, where we have a function

$$\mathbf{F} = f_r\mathbf{e}_r + f_\theta\mathbf{e}_\theta + f_z\mathbf{e}_z.$$

From (8–19) we find that

$$h_r = 1, \qquad h_\theta = r, \qquad h_z = 1. \tag{8–26}$$

Hence

$$\nabla \cdot \mathbf{F} = \frac{1}{r}\left[\frac{\partial}{\partial r}(rf_r) + \frac{\partial}{\partial \theta}(f_\theta) + \frac{\partial}{\partial z}(rf_z)\right]$$
$$= \frac{1}{r}[f_r + rf_{r'1} + f_{\theta'2} + rf_{z'3}].$$

That is,

$$\nabla \cdot \mathbf{F} = \frac{\partial f_r}{\partial r} + \frac{1}{r} f_r + \frac{1}{r}\frac{\partial f_\theta}{\partial \theta} + \frac{\partial f_z}{\partial z}. \tag{8–27}$$

The preceding theorems can be combined to give the Laplacian of a function given in terms of the new coordinate system, because the Laplacian of a scalar function f is the divergence of the gradient of f. In the case of a function defined in terms of cylindrical coordinates, for example,

$$\nabla^2 f = \nabla \cdot (\nabla f) = \nabla \cdot \left[f'_1 \mathbf{e}_r + \frac{1}{r} f'_2 \mathbf{e}_\theta + f'_3 \mathbf{e}_z \right]$$

$$= f'_{11} + \frac{1}{r} f'_1 + \frac{1}{r^2} f'_{22} + f'_{33}.$$

In the curly d notation, this would be written

$$\nabla^2 f = \frac{\partial^2 f}{\partial r^2} + \frac{1}{r}\frac{\partial f}{\partial r} + \frac{1}{r^2}\frac{\partial^2 f}{\partial \theta^2} + \frac{\partial^2 f}{\partial z^2}.$$

Under hypotheses similar to that of Theorems 8–8 and 8–9, we can prove that

$$\nabla^2 f = \frac{1}{h_1 h_2 h_3}\left(\frac{\partial}{\partial u_1}\frac{h_2 h_3}{h_1}\frac{\partial f}{\partial u_1} + \frac{\partial}{\partial u_2}\frac{h_1 h_3}{h_2}\frac{\partial f}{\partial u_2} + \frac{\partial}{\partial u_3}\frac{h_1 h_2}{h_3}\frac{\partial f}{\partial u_3}\right). \tag{8–28}$$

Methods similar to those used above, but starting from Theorem 8–6, can be used to obtain the following formula for the curl of a vector field:

$$\begin{aligned}\nabla \times \mathbf{F} = {} & \frac{1}{h_2 h_3}\left[\frac{\partial}{\partial u_2}(h_3 f_3) - \frac{\partial}{\partial u_3}(h_2 f_2)\right]\mathbf{e}_1^* \\ & + \frac{1}{h_3 h_1}\left[\frac{\partial}{\partial u_3}(h_1 f_1) - \frac{\partial}{\partial u_1}(h_3 f_3)\right]\mathbf{e}_2^* \\ & + \frac{1}{h_1 h_2}\left[\frac{\partial}{\partial u_1}(h_2 f_2) - \frac{\partial}{\partial u_2}(h_1 f_1)\right]\mathbf{e}_3^*.\end{aligned} \tag{8–29}$$

The proof is not difficult, but it is somewhat tedious. It will be left as an exercise. However, let us demonstrate the use of this formula by applying it to a vector field in cylindrical coordinates. Using (8–26), we find that

$$\begin{aligned}\nabla \times \mathbf{F} = {} & \frac{1}{r}\left[\frac{\partial}{\partial \theta}(f_z) - \frac{\partial}{\partial z}(r f_\theta)\right]\mathbf{e}_r + \left[\frac{\partial}{\partial z}(f_r) - \frac{\partial}{\partial r}(f_z)\right]\mathbf{e}_\theta \\ & + \frac{1}{r}\left[\frac{\partial}{\partial r}(r f_\theta) - \frac{\partial}{\partial \theta}(f_r)\right]\mathbf{e}_z \\ = {} & \left(\frac{1}{r}\frac{\partial f_z}{\partial \theta} - \frac{\partial f_\theta}{\partial z}\right)\mathbf{e}_r + \left(\frac{\partial f_r}{\partial z} - \frac{\partial f_z}{\partial r}\right)\mathbf{e}_\theta + \left(\frac{1}{r} f_\theta + \frac{\partial f_\theta}{\partial r} - \frac{1}{r}\frac{\partial f_r}{\partial \theta}\right)\mathbf{e}_z.\end{aligned}$$

PROBLEMS

1. Let the coordinates for spherical coordinates be given in the order ρ, ϕ, and θ. The transformation is defined by (8–17).
   a) Find $\mathbf{e}_\rho$, $\mathbf{e}_\phi$, and $\mathbf{e}_\theta$ for spherical coordinates.
   b) Find the formula for the gradient of f when f is given in spherical coordinates.
   c) Find the formula for the divergence of $\mathbf{F}$ when $\mathbf{F}$ is given in terms of spherical coordinates and is decomposed into components in terms of the unit vectors for these coordinates.
   d) Find the curl of $\mathbf{F}$ in spherical coordinates.
   e) Let f be given in terms of spherical coordinates. Find the Laplacian of f.
2. Prove (8–28).
3. Prove (8–29). It will suffice to prove that the first component is correct.

Answers to Problems

Answers to Problems

Section 1–2

4. $L\{\mathbf{0}\}$ consists of the single vector $\mathbf{0}$. It is a subspace.
5. Yes for (a), (b), (c), (f), (h)
6. $a_i = b_i$ for every i.
9. $n_1 n_2 \ldots n_k$

Section 1–3

1. [1, 0, 4, 0], [0, 1, −2, 0], [0, 0, 0, 1]
2. [1, 0, 1, 1], [0, 1, 2, −1]
3. [1, 1, 0, 0], [0, 0, 1, 0], [0, 0, 0, 1]
4. [0, 1, 1, 0], [0, 0, 0, 1]
5. [0, 1, 0, 0], [0, 0, 1, 0], [0, 0, 0, 1]
11. Yes

Section 1–4

2. n
5. a) dimension 2 b) independent c) independent d) dimension 3 e) dimension 4 f) dimension 1

Section 1–5

5. $L = L\{[1, 3, -2, 5, 7]\}$, $M = L\{\mathbf{e}_2, \mathbf{e}_3, \mathbf{e}_4, \mathbf{e}_5\}$
6. $L = L\{[1, 0, 2, 0, 1], [0, 1, 1, 0, 0], [0, 0, 0, 1, -4]\}$, $M = L\{\mathbf{e}_3, \mathbf{e}_5\}$
7. $L = L\{[1, 0, \frac{7}{3}, -\frac{4}{3}, -2], [0, 1, -\frac{5}{3}, \frac{5}{3}, -1]\}$, $M = L\{\mathbf{e}_3, \mathbf{e}_4, \mathbf{e}_5\}$
8. $L = R^5$, $M = \{\mathbf{0}\}$
9. $L = L\{[1, 0, 0, 0, -1], [0, 1, 0, 1, 0], [0, 0, 1, 0, 0]\}$, $M = L\{\mathbf{e}_4, \mathbf{e}_5\}$
10. $\mathrm{L} = L\{[1, 1, 0, 0, 0], [0, 0, 1, 1, 1]\}$, $M = L\{\mathbf{e}_2, \mathbf{e}_4, \mathbf{e}_5\}$
12. 5. $[1, 3, -2, 5, 7] + [0, -1, 5, -1, 2]$
    6. $[1, 2, 4, 4, -15] + [0, 0, -1, 0, 20]$
    7. $[1, 2, -1, 2, -4] + [0, 0, 4, 2, 9]$
    8. $[1, 2, 3, 4, 5] + \mathbf{0}$
    9. $[1, 2, 3, 2, -1] + [0, 0, 0, 2, 6]$
    10. $[1, 1, 3, 3, 3] + [0, 1, 0, 1, 2]$

Section 2–1

4. (c) is not a linear transformation.

a) $\begin{bmatrix} 3 & 0 & -1 \\ 1 & 2 & -1 \\ 1 & 1 & -5 \end{bmatrix}$
b) $\begin{bmatrix} 1 & 0 & 0 \\ -1 & 0 & 0 \\ 0 & 0 & 1 \end{bmatrix}$
d) $\begin{bmatrix} 0 & 0 & 0 \\ 0 & 1 & 0 \\ 1 & -1 & 1 \end{bmatrix}$

e) $\begin{bmatrix} 0 & 1 & 0 \\ 0 & 0 & 1 \\ 1 & 0 & 0 \end{bmatrix}$
f) $\begin{bmatrix} -1 & 0 & 0 \\ 0 & -1 & 0 \\ 0 & 0 & -1 \end{bmatrix}$

5. a) $[30, -11, 13], [39, 7]$ b) $[-27, 15, -8], [-68, -5]$ c) $[-3, 1, 1], [3, 1]$
d) $[-1, 0, -3], [-5, -2]$
e) $[x_1 - 3x_2 + 4x_3, 2x_2 - x_3, 3x_1 + 2x_3], [5x_1 - 8x_2 + 2x_3, 2x_1 + x_3]$
6. $[-\frac{4}{11}, \frac{3}{11}, \frac{6}{11}]$
7. P_{n-1}

Section 2–2

4. a) $\mathbf{e}_1, \mathbf{e}_2, \mathbf{e}_3$ b) $[1, -1, 0], [0, 0, 1]$ d) $\mathbf{e}_2, \mathbf{e}_3$
5. $A: \mathbf{e}_1, \mathbf{e}_2, \mathbf{e}_3$; $B: \mathbf{e}_1, \mathbf{e}_2$
6. a) $[1, 0, 0, \frac{1}{3}], [0, 1, 0, -\frac{1}{3}], [0, 0, 1, 0]$ b) $[1, 0, 0, 1], [0, 1, 0, 3], [0, 0, 1, 1]$
c) $[1, 0, -1, -2], [0, 1, -2, -5]$ d) $[1, 0, 0, 0], [0, 1, \frac{1}{2}, 0]$

Section 2–3

2. a) $L\{\mathbf{0}\}$ b) $L\{\mathbf{e}_2\}$ d) $L\{[1, 0, -1]\}$
3. a) $L\{\mathbf{0}\}$ b) $L\{[8, 1, -16]\}$
4. a) R^3 b) $L\{\mathbf{e}_2, \mathbf{e}_3\}$
5. a) $L\{\mathbf{0}\}$ b) $L\{\mathbf{0}\}$ c) $L\{[5, -2, 1]\}$ d) $L\{[1, -2, 1]\}$
6. a) $x_4[1, 0, 0, 1] + x_3[-1, 0, 1, 0] + x_2[4, 1, 0, 0] + (x_1 - 4x_2 + x_3 - x_4)\mathbf{e}_1$
b) $x_4[5, -3, 0, 1] + x_3[7, -3, 1, 0] + (x_1 - 7x_3 - 5x_4)\mathbf{e}_1 + (x_2 + 3x_3 + 3x_4)\mathbf{e}_2$
c) $x_1[1, -1, -2, -4] + (x_2 + x_1)\mathbf{e}_2 + (x_3 + 2x_1)\mathbf{e}_3 + (x_4 + 4x_1)\mathbf{e}_4$
d) $x_4[1, 1, -1, 1] + (x_1 - x_4)\mathbf{e}_1 + (x_2 - x_4)\mathbf{e}_2 + (x_3 + x_4)\mathbf{e}_3$

Section 2–4

8. $z_1 = 4x_1 + x_2$, $z_2 = 7x_1 + 3x_2$
9. $x_1 = y_1 - \frac{4}{3}y_2 + \frac{5}{3}y_3$, $x_2 = \frac{1}{3}y_2 - \frac{2}{3}y_3$, $x_3 = \frac{1}{3}y_2 + \frac{1}{3}y_3$

Section 2–5

8. a) $\begin{bmatrix} 10 & 26 \\ 10 & 6 \end{bmatrix}$ b) $\begin{bmatrix} 18 & -37 & 13 & 15 \\ 44 & 19 & 26 & 44 \\ 9 & 7 & -16 & 6 \end{bmatrix}$

c) $\begin{bmatrix} 2 & 1 & 5 \\ 5 & -4 & 7 \\ 3 & -2 & -4 \end{bmatrix}$ d) $\begin{bmatrix} 41 & -17 & 7 \\ 36 & -32 & 43 \\ 16 & 38 & 3 \end{bmatrix}$

9. (d) and (f) are singular.

Section 2–6

4. a) $\begin{bmatrix} 1 & 4 & 2 & 2 \\ 2 & 0 & 0 & 1 \end{bmatrix}\begin{bmatrix} \frac{3}{2} & -2 & -1 & 0 \\ \frac{1}{2} & 2 & 1 & 1 \end{bmatrix}$ b) $\begin{bmatrix} 0 & 2 & 0 \\ -4 & 0 & 0 \end{bmatrix}\begin{bmatrix} -2 & 1 & 0 \\ 2 & 0 & 0 \end{bmatrix}$

c) $\begin{bmatrix} 1 & 0 & 0 \\ 4 & 1 & 0 \\ 10 & 4 & 1 \end{bmatrix}\begin{bmatrix} 1 & 0 & 0 \\ 2 & 1 & 0 \\ 3 & -2 & 1 \end{bmatrix}$

5. There are many possibilities. The following are only a sample.
a) $\langle [0, 0, -1, 0], [0, 0, 0, 1], [1, 0, 1, -2], [0, 1, 3, 2] \rangle$
b) $\langle [\frac{1}{2}, -\frac{1}{2}, 0], [-1, 3, 0], [0, 0, 1] \rangle$ c) $\langle [1, -1, -1], [0, 1, -2], [0, 0, 1] \rangle$

Section 2–7

1. n^2

2. a) $n!$

Section 2–8

2. a) $\frac{1}{12}\begin{bmatrix} -2 & 3 & 4 \\ 2 & -3 & 8 \\ 6 & -3 & 0 \end{bmatrix}$ b) $\frac{1}{2}\begin{bmatrix} 3 & 1 & -1 \\ -4 & 0 & 2 \\ -1 & -1 & 1 \end{bmatrix}$ c) $\frac{1}{24}\begin{bmatrix} 8 & 0 & 0 \\ 2 & 6 & 0 \\ 27 & 21 & -12 \end{bmatrix}$

d) $\begin{bmatrix} 1 & -4 & -3 & 3 \\ -1 & 5 & 3 & -2 \\ 3 & -10 & -8 & 9 \\ 0 & 4 & 3 & -4 \end{bmatrix}$ e) $\begin{bmatrix} 25 & 18 & -2 & -4 \\ -39 & -27 & 4 & 5 \\ 40 & 28 & -4 & -5 \\ -9 & -6 & 1 & 1 \end{bmatrix}$

f) $\begin{bmatrix} 7 & 8 & -9 & 3 \\ -4 & 4 & -2 & 1 \\ 3 & -7 & 5 & -2 \\ -1 & 3 & -2 & 1 \end{bmatrix}$ g) $\begin{bmatrix} 31 & 8 & -12 & -6 \\ 5 & 2 & 1 & 0 \\ -18 & -4 & 11 & 5 \\ -4 & -1 & 2 & 1 \end{bmatrix}$

3. a) $\mathcal{B} = \langle [3, -1, 0, 0], [-2, 1, 0, 0], [5, -2, 1, 0], [1, -3, 0, 1] \rangle$,
$\mathcal{B}^* = \langle [1, 0, 2], [0, 1, -3], [0, 0, 1] \rangle$, rank $= 2$
b) $\mathcal{B} = \langle [-1, -2, 0], [1, 1, 0], [1, 3, 1] \rangle$,
$\mathcal{B}^* = \langle [1, 0, 2, -1], [0, 1, 0, 3], [0, 0, 1, 0], [0, 0, 0, 1] \rangle$, rank $= 2$
c) $\mathcal{B} = \langle [-1, -3, 4, -1], [2, 3, -6, 2], [0, -1, 3, -1], [0, 0, -2, 1] \rangle$,
$\mathcal{B}^* = \langle \mathbf{e}_1, \mathbf{e}_2, \mathbf{e}_3 \rangle$, rank $= 3$
d) $\mathcal{B} = \langle [1, -2, -2, -4], [1, -1, -1, -2], [0, 2, 3, 6], [-1, 2, 3, 7] \rangle$, $\mathcal{B}^* = \langle \mathbf{e}_1, \mathbf{e}_2 \rangle$
e) $\mathcal{B} = \langle [5, 0, 0, -1], [-3, -1, 2, 2], [1, 1, -1, -1], [1, -1, 2, 1] \rangle$, $\mathcal{B}^* = \langle \mathbf{e}_1, \mathbf{e}_2, \mathbf{e}_3, \mathbf{e}_4 \rangle$

Section 2–9

3. a) 4 b) 4 c) 3 d) 1 e) 2 f) 2

Section 2–10

3. a) $[3, 2, 0, -5] + t[-2, 2, 1, 0]$ b) $[5, 3, 0, 0] + t_1[-2, 1, 1, 0] + t_2[-1, 2, 0, 1]$
c) $[0, 0, 2, -1]$ d) $[-1, 3, -2, 0] + t[-1, 2, -2, 1]$
e) $[3, 0, 0, 0] + t_1[2, 1, 0, 0] + t_2[-5, 0, 1, 0] + t_3[-1, 0, 0, 1]$
f) $[12, -3, 0] + t[-3, 1, 1]$
4. a) $t[-2, 1, 1]$ b) $t_1[1, 2, 1, 0, 0] + t_2[-3, -1, 0, 1, 0] + t_3[-2, 1, 0, 0, 1]$
c) $t[0, 2, 0, -1]$

Section 3–2

8. a) $\tau(1, 3) \circ \tau(2, 5)$, $\sigma \circ \rho = \langle 5, 1, 4, 2, 6, 3 \rangle$, $\rho \circ \sigma = \langle 4, 4, 2, 5, 3, 1 \rangle$
b) $\tau(4, 5) \circ \tau(5, 6)$, $\sigma \circ \rho = \langle 2, 3, 5, 6, 4, 1 \rangle$, $\rho \circ \sigma = \langle 2, 3, 4, 6, 1, 5 \rangle$
c) $\tau(1, 3) \circ \tau(1, 2)$, $\sigma \circ \rho = \langle 3, 1, 4, 5, 6, 2 \rangle$, $\rho \circ \sigma = \langle 3, 4, 2, 5, 6, 1 \rangle$
d) $\tau(3, 4) \circ \tau(2, 5) \circ \tau(1, 6)$, $\sigma \circ \rho = \langle 5, 4, 3, 2, 1, 6 \rangle$, $\rho \circ \sigma = \langle 1, 6, 5, 4, 3, 2 \rangle$

Section 3–3

8. a) -948 b) 0 c) 0

Section 3–4

8. a) $\begin{bmatrix} -5 & -14 & 3 \\ -5 & 4 & -3 \\ 10 & -2 & -6 \end{bmatrix}$ b) $\begin{bmatrix} 2 & 8 & -2 \\ 0 & -6 & 3 \\ 2 & -4 & 1 \end{bmatrix}$ c) $\begin{bmatrix} 4 & 18 & 6 \\ 8 & -12 & 12 \\ 6 & -9 & -3 \end{bmatrix}$

d) $\begin{bmatrix} 8 & -3 & 1 \\ -7 & 3 & -1 \\ -2 & 1 & 0 \end{bmatrix}$ e) $\begin{bmatrix} 4 & 6 & -2 \\ 8 & 12 & -4 \\ 10 & 15 & -5 \end{bmatrix}$

9. b) $[c_{ij}]$, where $c_{ij} = (-1)^{i+j}$ for $j \geq i$ and is zero otherwise. c) c^n

Section 4–2

1. $u_1 = 1/\sqrt{2}$, $u_2 = \sqrt{\frac{3}{2}}\,x$, $u_3 = \sqrt{\frac{10}{29}}\,(x^2 - \frac{3}{2})$, $u_4 = \sqrt{\frac{35}{94}}\,(x^3 - \frac{2}{5}\sqrt{\frac{3}{2}})$
5. a) [1, 0, 0, 3], [3, 2, −4, −1], [6, 0, 5, −2]
   b) [1, 0, 1, 0], [2, 1, −2, 0], [1, −4, −1, 9], [2, −8, −2, −4]
   c) [1, 0, 5, 0], [5, 1, −1, 1], [5, 0, −1, −26], [10, −54, −2, 2]
   d) [1, 1, 0, 0, 0], [−1, 1, 2, 0, 0], [2, −2, 2, 1, 0], [1, −1, 1, −6, 13], [2, −2, 2, −12, −6]
6. a) $L\{[60, -5, 2, 1]\}$ b) $L\{[0, 1, 2, -2], [0, 0, 1, 1]\}$
   c) $L\{[0, 1, 2, 0], [0, 2, -1, 1], [4, 4, -2, -10]\}$

Section 4–3

7. $\begin{bmatrix} \cos\theta & -\sin\theta \\ \sin\theta & \cos\theta \end{bmatrix}$ 8. $\begin{bmatrix} 1 & 0 \\ 0 & -1 \end{bmatrix}$

Section 4–4

9. a) $x^2 - x$, 0, 1, [1, −1], [2, −1] b) $x^2 - 1$, 1, −1, [1, 1], [1, 3]
   c) $x^2 - 5x + 4$, 1, 4, [2, 5], [1, 1] d) $x^2 + x - 12$, 3, −4, [1, 1], [0, 1]
   e) $x^2 + x - 12$, 3, −4, [7, 1], [0, 1] f) x^2, 0, 0, [2, 1] is the only one.
10. a) $-x^3 + x^2 + 2x$, 0, 2, −1, [1, −1, 3], [3, −2, 7], [1, 1, 0]
    b) $-x^3 + 2x^2 + 3x$, 0, 3, −1, [−2, −2, 3], [1, −1, 3], [0, 1, −2]
    c) $-x^3 + 4x^2 - x - 6$, 2, 3, −1, [1, −3, 5], [−2, 2, −1], [0, 1, −2]
    d) $-x^3 + 3x^2 + x - 3$, 1, 3, −1, [3, 4, 2], [1, 2, 1], [7, 9, 4]
11. i, $[5, 2 - i]$, $[5, 2 + i]$

Section 4–5

12. $n = 2$, $\lambda_1 = 1$, $\lambda_2 = 3$, $\omega_1 = \sqrt{k/m}$, $\omega_2 = \sqrt{3k/m}$, $\mathbf{Y}_1 = [1, 1]$, $\mathbf{Y}_2 = [1, -1]$; $n = 3$, $\lambda_1 = 2$, $\lambda_2 = 2 - \sqrt{2}$, $\lambda_3 = 2 + \sqrt{2}$, $\mathbf{Y}_1 = [1, 0, -1]$, $\mathbf{Y}_2 = [1, \sqrt{2}, 1]$, $\mathbf{Y}_3 = [1, -\sqrt{2}, 1]$

Section 5–1

16. 2^n, $2n$

Section 5–4

1. a) [1, −2] b) $[2x, 4 - 2y]$, [0, 2] c) $\left(\dfrac{1}{x^2 + y^2}\right)[2x, 2y]$

d) $\cos(x+y)[1,1]$, $y = \frac{1}{2}(2n+1)\pi - x$
e) $[2x, 18y]$, $[0,0]$
f) $\frac{1}{2x^2}[x^2 - 4y^2, 8y]$
g) $e^{xy}[y, x]$, $[0,0]$
h) $-\frac{1}{x^2}[2x^2 + y, -x]$

2. a) $[2x, -4y, 2z]$, $[0,0,0]$
b) $[y^2 - z^2, 2xy, -2xz]$, $[0, y, \pm y]$, $[x, 0, 0]$
c) $[2x, 2y, 2z]$, $[0,0,0]$
d) $\frac{1}{2z^2}[2xz, 2yz, -x^2 - y^2 + z^2]$, $[0, 0, z]$

4. $(1/\sqrt{3})[1,1,1]$
5. No. There is some point at which grad f is orthogonal to $\mathbf{B} - \mathbf{A}$.

Section 5–5

2. a) $x - 2y = 12$
b) $2x + 7y = -31$
c) $2x - 5y = 29$
d) $x + y = -3$
e) $2x - 45y = 229$
f) $12x + 5y = -1$
g) $5x - 2y = 20$
h) $3x - 2y = 16$

3. a) $x - 2y + 4z = 15$
b) $15x + 2y + 8z = 45$
c) $x - y + 4z = 18$
d) $4x - 4y + 7z = 36$

4. Problem 1: a) $x - 2y + 4$
b) $2x + 4y - 1$
c) $2x - 2$
d) $x\cos 1 + y\cos 1 + \sin 1 - \cos 1$
e) $2x - 1$
f) $\frac{1}{2}x$
g) $y + 1$
h) $-2x + y + 1$

Problem 2: a) $2x + 2z - 2$ b) $-x - 2z + 2$ c) $2x + 2z - 2$ d) x

6. $x - y + 2z + u - v = 8$
7. $\frac{R_0}{V_0} e^{-W_0/kT_0}\left(v - \frac{v_0}{V_0}V - \frac{v_0}{kT_0}W + \frac{v_0 W_0}{kT_0^2}T + v_0\right)$

Section 5–6

1. a) $f_{,11} = 2 - 6xy^2$, $f_{,12} = -6x^2y$, $f_{,22} = -2x^3$
b) $f_{,11} = e^{x^2y}[(4x^2y^2 - 2x^2y + 2y - 1)\cos x - 2xy\sin x]$
$f_{,12} = e^{x^2y}[(2x^3y + 2x)\cos x - x^2 \sin x]$, $f_{,22} = e^{x^2y}x^4\cos x$

Section 5–7

3. a) $[0,0]$; min at $[2^{1/2}, \pm 2^{3/4}]$
b) $[0,0,z]$; no max or min
c) $[0,0,0]$; no max or min
d) none

4. a) max 19 at $[\pm 1, 0, 0, 3]$, min $-6\sqrt{10}$ at $[0,0,0,-\sqrt{10}]$
b) max $\frac{1}{3}\sqrt{3}$ at $[\pm 1/\sqrt{3}, \pm 1/\sqrt{3}, 1/\sqrt{3}]$, min $-\frac{1}{3}\sqrt{3}$ at $[\pm\frac{1}{3}\sqrt{3}, \mp\frac{1}{3}\sqrt{3}, 1/\sqrt{3}]$
c) max $\sqrt{2}/e$ at $[1/\sqrt{2}, 2]$, no min

5. $[0, \pm 1]$

Section 5–8

1. a) $[10/3, 10/3]$ max; $[0,0]$, $[0,10]$, $[0,-10]$ saddle points
b) $[1,1]$ min
c) max at $[\pi/2, 3\pi/2]$; min at $[3\pi/2, 3\pi/2]$ saddle points at $[\pi/2, \pi/2]$, $[7\pi/6, 7\pi/6]$, $[11\pi/6, 11\pi/6]$, $[3\pi/2, \pi/2]$, $[7\pi/6, 5\pi/6]$, $[11\pi/6, \pi/6]$
d) saddle point at $[1,1]$
e) min along lines $y = \pm x$
f) saddle points

2. a) minimum b) maximum c) minimum d) saddle e) maximum
f) saddle g) minimum h) saddle

9. $m = \frac{1}{\Delta}\left(\sum \frac{y_i}{x_i} \sum \frac{1}{x_j^2} - \sum \frac{y_i}{x_i^2} \sum \frac{1}{x_j}\right), b = \frac{1}{\Delta}\left[n \sum \frac{y_i}{x_i^2} - \sum \frac{1}{x_i} \sum \frac{y_j}{x_j}\right],$

where $\Delta = n \sum \frac{1}{x_i^2} - \left(\sum \frac{1}{x_i}\right)^2$

Section 6–1

8. a) $\begin{bmatrix} 2x & -2y \\ 2y & 2x \end{bmatrix}, d\mathbf{F} = \begin{bmatrix} du \\ dv \end{bmatrix} = \begin{bmatrix} 2x\,dx - 2y\,dy \\ 2y\,dx + 2x\,dy \end{bmatrix}$

b) $\begin{bmatrix} 2xy + z^2 & x^2 + 2yz & y^2 + 2zx \\ yzR^2 + 2x^2yz & xzR^2 + 2xy^2z & xyR^2 + 2xyz^2 \end{bmatrix}$, where $R^2 = 1 + x^2 + y^2 + z^2$

c) $\begin{bmatrix} ye^{xy}(z + \sin z) & x(z + \sin z)e^{xy} & (1 + \cos z)e^{xy} \\ (2x + x^2yz)e^{xyz} & x^3ze^{xyz} & x^3ye^{xyz} \\ 2xy \log(1 + z^2) & x^2 \log(1 + z^2) & 2x^2yz/(1 + z^2) \end{bmatrix}$

d) $\begin{bmatrix} 1 & 1 \\ y^2 + 2xy & 2xy + x^2 \\ 2xy^3 + 3x^2y^2 & 3x^2y^2 + 2x^3y \end{bmatrix}$

9. a) $[0, 0, 1] + s[0, 1, 0] + t[0, 0, 1]$,
b) $[0, 1, 1] + t[0, 1, -2]$,
c) $[1, 1, 1] + s[1, -1, 0] + t[1, 0, -1]$

Section 6–2

3. a) $[f_{,1} \cos\theta + f_{,2} \sin\theta, -f_{,1} r \sin\theta + f_{,2} r \cos\theta, f_{,3}]$
b) $[f_{,1} \cos\theta \sin\phi + f_{,2} \sin\theta \sin\phi + f_{,3} \cos\phi, \rho f_{,1} \cos\theta \cos\phi + \rho f_{,2} \sin\theta \cos\phi$
$- \rho f_{,3} \sin\phi, -\rho f_{,1} \sin\theta \sin\phi - \rho f_{,2} \sin\theta \sin\phi]$

4. a) $\partial f/\partial x = 2u + (2u + v + 2ux + 4vx)\Delta^{-1}$,
$\partial f/\partial y = 2u + (2u + v + 2uy + 4vy)\Delta^{-1}$,
$\partial f/\partial z = 2u + (2u + v + 2uz + 4vz)\Delta^{-1}$, where $\Delta = u^2 + uv + v^2$
b) $\partial f/\partial x = -yv \sin uv + y \sec^2 u - y^2u \sin uv + y^2w \sin vw$,
$\partial f/\partial y = -xv \sin uv + x \sec^2 u - (2xy + z)u \sin uv + (2xy + z)w \sin vw$
$+ (z^2 + 2y)v \sin vw$
$\partial f/\partial z = -yu \sin uv + yw \sin vw + 2zyv \sin vw$

8. $f(\mathbf{A}) + (x - a_1)f_{,1}(\mathbf{A}) + (y - a_2)f_{,2}(\mathbf{A}) + \frac{1}{2}(x - a_1)^2 f_{,11}(\mathbf{A}) + \frac{1}{2}(y - a_2)^2 f_{,22}(\mathbf{A})$
$+ (x - a_1)(y - a_2)f_{,12}(\mathbf{A}) + \frac{1}{6}(x - a_1)^3 f_{,111}(\mathbf{A}) + \frac{1}{6}(y - a_2)^3 f_{,222}(\mathbf{A})$
$+ \frac{1}{2}(x - a_1)^2(y - a_2)f_{,112}(\mathbf{A}) + \frac{1}{2}(x - a_1)(y - a_2)^2 f_{,122}(\mathbf{A})$

Section 6–3

a) $\begin{bmatrix} \cos\theta & -r\sin\theta \\ \sin\theta & r\cos\theta \end{bmatrix}, \quad J = r, \quad \begin{bmatrix} \cos\theta & \sin\theta \\ -\frac{1}{r}\sin\theta & \frac{1}{r}\cos\theta \end{bmatrix}$

b) $\begin{bmatrix} \cos\theta & -r\sin\theta & 0 \\ \sin\theta & r\cos\theta & 0 \\ 0 & 0 & 1 \end{bmatrix}, \quad J = r, \quad \begin{bmatrix} \cos\theta & \sin\theta & 0 \\ -\frac{1}{r}\sin\theta & \frac{1}{r}\cos\theta & 0 \\ 0 & 0 & 1 \end{bmatrix}$

c) $\begin{bmatrix} \cos\theta\sin\phi & \rho\cos\theta\cos\phi & -\rho\sin\theta\sin\phi \\ \sin\theta\sin\phi & \rho\sin\theta\cos\phi & \rho\cos\theta\sin\phi \\ \cos\phi & -\rho\sin\phi & 0 \end{bmatrix}$, $J = \rho^2 \sin\phi$

$$\begin{bmatrix} \cos\theta\sin\phi & \sin\theta\sin\phi & \cos\phi \\ \frac{1}{\rho}\cos\theta\cos\phi & \frac{1}{\rho}\sin\theta\cos\phi & -\frac{1}{\rho}\sin\phi \\ -\frac{1}{\rho}\frac{\sin\theta}{\sin\phi} & \frac{1}{\rho}\frac{\cos\theta}{\sin\phi} & 0 \end{bmatrix}$$

d) $\begin{bmatrix} 2x & 2y & 2z \\ 1 & 1 & 1 \\ yz & xz & xy \end{bmatrix}$, $J = 2[x^2(y - z) + y^2(z - x) + z^2(x - y)]$,

$$\frac{1}{J}\begin{bmatrix} x(y-z) & -2x(y^2 - z^2) & 2(y-z) \\ -y(x-z) & 2y(x^2 - z^2) & -2(x-z) \\ z(x-y) & -2z(x^2 - y^2) & 2(x-y) \end{bmatrix}$$

7. a) $du = -\dfrac{2xu(xy+u) + y}{x^2(xy+u)+1}\,dx - \dfrac{x}{x^2(xy+u)+1}\,dy$

b) $du = -\dfrac{uv}{vx - 1}\,dx, \qquad dv = \dfrac{2v - v^2x}{vx^2 - x}\,dx$

c) $du = \dfrac{x^2u - xv^2}{u^3 + v^3}\,dx, \qquad dv = -\dfrac{xu^2 + x^2v}{u^3 + v^3}\,dx$

d) $du = -\dfrac{1}{\Delta}u(u - 2x)(v - w)\,dx, \qquad dv = -\dfrac{1}{\Delta}v(v - 2x)(w - u)\,dx,$

$dw = -\dfrac{1}{\Delta}w(w - 2x)(u - v)\,dx, \qquad \Delta = (u - v)(v - w)(w - u)$

e) $du = \dfrac{x - v}{v - u}\,dx + \dfrac{y - v}{v - u}\,dy + \dfrac{z - v}{v - u}\,dz,\ dv = \dfrac{x - u}{u - v}\,dx + \dfrac{y - u}{u - v}\,dy + \dfrac{z - u}{u - v}\,dz$

Section 6–4

1. $dy = \Delta^{-1}(-g'_1 - f'_1 g'_3 h'_2 + f'_2 g'_1 h'_2)\,du + \Delta^{-1}(-g'_2 + f'_2 g'_2 h'_2 - g'_3 h'_1)\,dv,$
$dw = -\Delta^{-1} f'_1 h'_2\,du - \Delta^{-1} h'_1\,dv$

2. $f'_1 h'_1 \neq 0,\ du = \dfrac{1}{f'_1}[dx - f'_2\,dw],\ dv = \dfrac{1}{h'_1}[-h'_2\,dx + dw],$

$dy = \dfrac{1}{f'_1 h'_1}[(g'_1 h'_1 - f'_1 g'_2 h'_2)\,dx + (f'_1 g'_2 - f'_2 g'_1 h'_1 + f'_1 g'_3 h'_1)\,dw]$

3. a) $f'_2 g'_2 \neq +1,\ dz = \dfrac{f'_1 + f'_2 g'_1}{1 - f'_2 g'_2}\,dx,\ dy = \dfrac{g'_1 + f'_1 g'_2}{1 - f'_2 g'_2}\,dx$

b) $f'_1 + f'_2 g'_1 \neq 0,\ dx = \dfrac{1 - f'_2 g'_2}{f'_1 + f'_2 g'_1}\,dz,\ dy = \dfrac{g'_1 + f'_1 g'_2}{f'_1 + f'_2 g'_1}\,dz$

4. a) $\displaystyle\sum_{j=1}^{n} f'_j a_{ji}$ b) $\displaystyle\sum_{j=1}^{n}\sum_{k=1}^{n} f'_{jk} a_{ji} a_{ki}$

c) $\displaystyle\sum_{i=1}^{n}\sum_{j=1}^{n}\sum_{k=1}^{n} f'_{jk} a_{ji} a_{ki} = \sum_{j=1}^{n}\sum_{k=1}^{n} f'_{jk} b_{jk}$, where $[b_{jk}] = AA^t$ d) $\displaystyle\sum_{j=1}^{n} f'_{jj}$

5. $f_{,11} + \dfrac{1}{\rho^2} f_{,22} + \dfrac{1}{\rho^2 \sin^2 \phi} f_{,33} + \dfrac{2}{\rho} f_{,1} + \dfrac{\cos \phi}{\rho^2 \sin^2 \phi} f_{,2}$

6. a) $(A + A^t)\mathbf{X}$ b) $(A + A^t)$ c) $2(\text{trace } A)$

7. $-\dfrac{f_{,ii}}{f_{,n}} + \dfrac{f_{,i}f_{,nj} + f_{,j}f_{,ni}}{f_{,n}^2} - \dfrac{f_{,i}f_{,j}f_{,nn}}{f_{,n}^3}$

Section 7–1

5. a) $\mathbf{e}_t = (5 + 4\pi^2)^{-1/2}[-2, -2\pi, 1]$,
$\mathbf{e}_n = (4\pi^6 - 40\pi^4 + 5\pi^2 + 100)^{-1/2}[4\pi^3 - 7\pi, 10 - 4\pi^2, 6\pi]$,
$L = (\pi/4)\sqrt{5 + 4\pi^2} + \frac{5}{8} \log [(1/\sqrt{5})(4\pi + \sqrt{5 + 4\pi^2})]$, $2x - \pi y + (4 - 2\pi^2)z = -\pi^3$

b) $\mathbf{e}_t = (1/\sqrt{6})[1, 2, 1]$, $\mathbf{e}_n = (1/\sqrt{3})[-1, 1, -1]$,
$L = 3\sqrt{2} \int_0^2 (1 + 2t^4)^{1/2}\, dt$, $x - z = 0$

c) $\mathbf{e}_t = (1/\sqrt{26})[4, 1, 3]$, $\mathbf{e}_n = (1/\sqrt{6058})[48, -27, -55]$,
$L = \int_0^4 [2 + 4t + 4t^2 + 16t^6]^{1/2}\, dt$, $x + 14y - 6z = -11$

d) $\mathbf{e}_t = [-\frac{1}{2}, \frac{1}{2}, 1/\sqrt{2}]$, $\mathbf{e}_n = [0, \sqrt{\frac{2}{3}}, -1/\sqrt{3}]$,
$L = \log (1 + \sqrt{2})$, $3x + y + \sqrt{2}\, z = 2\sqrt{2} + \sqrt{2} \log \sqrt{2}$.

e) $\mathbf{e}_t = [\frac{2}{3}, \frac{2}{3}, \frac{1}{3}]$, $\mathbf{e}_n = [-\frac{1}{3}, \frac{2}{3}, -\frac{2}{3}]$, $L = 15 + \log 4$, $2x - y + 2z = 3$

6. $\mathbf{e}_t = [1, 0, 0, 0]$, $\mathbf{e}_n = [0, 0, -1/\sqrt{2}, 1/\sqrt{2}]$, $L = 20$

Section 7–2

3. $\tau = (f''g''' - f'''g'')/(f''^2 + g''^2 + f'^2g''^2 + f''^2g'^2 - 2f'f''g'g'')$

5. $[r'^2 + r^2\theta'^2]^{1/2}$, $[r''^2 + (4r'^2 - 2rr'')\theta'^2 + r^2\theta'^4 + r^2\theta''^2 + 4rr'\theta'\theta'']^{1/2}$,
$|2r'^2\theta' - rr''\theta' + rr'\theta''|/[r'^2 + r^2\theta'^2]^{3/2}$, $[r'^2 + r^2]^{1/2}$, $[r''^2 + 4r'^2 - 2rr'' + r^2]^{1/2}$,
$|2r'^2 - rr'' + rr'|/[r'^2 + r^2]^{3/2}$

6. $\kappa = a/(a^2 + b^2)$, $\tau = b/(a^2 + b^2)$

7. a) $(40 - 30\pi^2 + 8\pi^4)^{1/2}/2(5 + 4\pi^2)^{3/2}$, $2(\pi^2 - 6)/(10 - 15\pi^2 + 2\pi^4)$
b) $2/9\sqrt{3}$, 0 c) $\sqrt{932}/5\sqrt{5}$, $\frac{48}{932}$ d) $\sqrt{3}/2$, $\frac{5}{6}$ e) 2, $\frac{4}{9}$

Section 7–3

3. a) $\frac{3}{2}$ b) 0 c) 2π

4. a) $-\sin (x + y)$ b) x/y c) $|\mathbf{X}|$ d) $\frac{1}{2}|\mathbf{X}|^2$
e) $\frac{1}{3} |\mathbf{X}|^3$ f) $\dfrac{1}{\alpha + 2} |\mathbf{X}|^{\alpha+2}$ g) $\log |\mathbf{X}|$ h) $\arctan (x/y)$
i) $xy^2 - x^2 \sin y$ j) $x^2y^2 + xz + y^2z^3$

6. a) $11 + \frac{1}{2}(\log 2)^2$ b) $\frac{11}{2}$ c) 16 d) $-\frac{2}{3}$

Section 7–5

1. a) $\displaystyle\int_0^2 dy \int_{y/2}^1 f\, dx$ b) $\displaystyle\int_{-1/2}^{1/2} dx \int_{\sqrt{2|x|}}^1 f\, dy$
c) $\displaystyle\int_0^1 dy \int_y^{\sqrt{y}} f\, dx$ d) $\displaystyle\int_0^1 dx \int_{-(1-x^2)^{1/2}}^{(1-x^2)^{1/2}} f\, dy$

2. a) $\int_0^2 dy \int_0^{(4-y^2)^{1/2}} dx \int_0^{(4-x^2-y^2)^{1/2}} f\,dz = \int_0^2 dz \int_0^{(4-z^2)^{1/2}} dy \int_0^{(4-z^2-y^2)^{1/2}} f\,dx$, etc.

b) $\int_0^2 dy \int_0^{(4-y^2)^{1/2}} dx \int_0^{4-x^2-y^2} f\,dz = \int_0^4 dz \int_0^{(4-z^2)^{1/2}} dx \int_0^{(4-x^2-z)^{1/2}} f\,dz$, etc.

c) $\int_0^1 dy \int_0^6 dz \int_0^{(6-z)/2} f\,dx$, etc.

d) $\int_0^6 dz \int_0^{(6-z)/2} dx \int_0^{7-6z-2x} f\,dy$

$$= \int_0^3 dx \int_0^1 dy \int_0^{6-2x} f\,dz + \int_0^3 dx \int_1^{7-2x} dy \int_0^{(7-y-2x)/2} f\,dz$$

$$= \int_0^6 dz \int_0^1 dy \int_0^{(6-z)/2} f\,dx + \int_0^6 dz \int_1^{7-6z} dy \int_0^{(7-6z-y)/2} f\,dx, \text{ etc.}$$

3. a) $\int_0^1 dz \int_{-[1-z^2]^{1/2}}^0 dy \int_0^{(1-y^2-z^2)^{1/2}} f\,dx + \int_0^1 dz \int_0^{z(1-z^2)^{1/2}} dy \int_{1/2-(1/4-y^2)^{1/2}}^{(1-y^2-z^2)^{1/2}} f\,dx$

$$+ \int_0^{1/\sqrt{2}} dz \int_{z(1-z^2)^{1/2}}^{1/2} dy \int_{1/2-(1/4-y^2)^{1/2}}^{1/2+(1/4+y^2)^{1/2}} f\,dx$$

b) $\int_{-1}^0 dz \int_{-(1-z^2)^{1/2}}^{(1-z^2)^{1/2}} dy \int_{-(1-z^2-y^2)^{1/2}}^{(1-z^2-y^2)^{1/2}} f\,dx + \int_0^1 dz \int_{-1}^{-(2z-z^2)^{1/2}} dy \int_{-(1-y^2)^{1/2}}^{(1-y^2)^{1/2}} f\,dx$

$$+ \int_0^1 dz \int_{[2z-z^2]^{1/2}}^1 dy \int_{-(1-y^2)^{1/2}}^{(1-y^2)^{1/2}} f\,dx$$

$$+ \int_0^2 dz \int_{-(2z-z^2)^{1/2}}^{(2z-z^2)^{1/2}} dy \int_{-(1-y^2)}^{1-z} f\,dx$$

4. $\int_0^1 dz \int_{-e^{z^2/2}}^{e^{z^2/2}} dy \left[\int_{-(e^{z^2}-y^2)^{1/2}}^{-(1-z^2-y^2)^{1/2}} f\,dx + \int_{(i-z^2-y^2)^{1/2}}^{(e^{z^2}-y^2)^{1/2}} f\,dx\right]$

$$= \int_{-e}^e dx \int_{-(e^2-x^2)^{1/2}}^{(e^2-x^2)^{1/2}} dy \int_{\phi(x,y)}^1 f\,dz, \quad \text{where}$$

$$\phi(x, y) = \begin{cases} [1 - x^2 - y^2]^{1/2} & \text{if } x^2 + y^2 < 1, \\ [\log (x^2 + y^2)]^{1/2} & \text{if } x^2 + y^2 \geq 1. \end{cases}$$

5. $\int_{-1}^1 dx \int_{-(1-x^2)^{1/2}}^{(1-x^2)^{1/2}} dy \int_{-(1-x^2-y^2)^{1/2}}^{(1-x^2-y^2)^{1/2}} dz \int_{-(4-x^2-y^2-z^2)^{1/2}}^{(4-x^2-y^2-z^2)^{1/2}} f\,dw$

Section 7–6

3. a) $\pi^2/8$ b) $\log(1 + \sqrt{2}/2)$ c) $\sqrt{2}/2 - 1$ d) $\sqrt{2} - \frac{1}{2}\int_0^\pi e^{-a^2\cos^2\theta}\,d\theta$

4. $\frac{1}{4}$

5. $-\frac{11}{36}$

Section 7–7

5. a) 0 b) 0

6. a) $\phi = 4x^4y^8 + yz^2$ c) $xy + xw + yw + zw + \frac{1}{2}z^2$

Section 7–8

1. a) cone b) "spiral staircase" c) torus d) Möbius strip e) exponential horn
2. a) $\mathbf{N} = [-bu \cos v, -bu \sin v, u]$, $s = (b^2 + 1)^{1/2}u$, $A = \pi c^2(b^2 + 1)^{1/2}$
   b) $\mathbf{N} = [-b \sin u, b \cos u, -v]$,
   $s = (b^2 + v^2)^{1/2}$, $A = (\pi c/b)(b^2 + c^2)^{1/2} - (\pi a/b)(a^2 + b^2)^{1/2} + \pi b \log [c + (b^2 + c^2)^{1/2}]/[a + (a^2 + b^2)^{1/2}]$
   c) $\mathbf{N} = [-ab \cos u \cos v - b^2 \cos^2 u \cos v, ab \cos u \sin v + b^2 \cos^2 u \sin v, - ab \sin u - b^2 \sin u \cos u]$, $s = a + b \cos u$, $A = 4\pi^2 ab$
   e) $\mathbf{N} = [-a^2 u, a \sin v, a \cos v]$, $s = a[1 + a^2 u^2]^{1/2}$
9. a) $x = (a + c \cos u) \cos v$, $y = (a + c \cos u) \sin v$, $z = u$
   b) $x = (a + c \cos u) \cos v$, $y = (a + c \cos u) \sin v$, $z = bv + c \sin u$

Section 7–9

1. a) 0, 0 b) $-2\pi^2 b(c^2 - a^2)$, $\frac{1}{3}[(4\pi^2 + b^2c^2)^{3/2} - (4\pi^2 + b^2a^2)^{3/2} - b^3(c^2 - a^2)]$
   e) $\frac{3}{2}a^2(b^2 - 1) - \pi a^2 b^2 \log b$

Section 8–1

6. a) $2(x + y + z)$ b) $2xe^{-y} + 2ye^{-z} + 2ze^{-x}$ c) 0 d) $5|\mathbf{X}|^2$
   e) $(3 + \alpha)|\mathbf{X}|$ f) 0
7. a) $\mathbf{0}$ b) $[-y^2e^{-z}, -z^2e^{-x}, x^2e^{-y}]$ c) $\mathbf{0}$ d) $\mathbf{0}$ e) $\mathbf{0}$ f) $\mathbf{0}$
8. a) $[-1, -1, -1]$ b) $\mathbf{0}$
   c) $[-x^2 - y^2 - 3z^2 + 2xy, -3x^2 - y^2 - z^2 + 2yz, -x^2 - 3y^2 - z^2 + 2xz]$
9. a) 6 b) 0 c) $(\alpha + 1)|\mathbf{X}|^{-2}$
   d) $1/|\mathbf{X}|^2$ e) 0 f) $u''vw + uv''w + uvw''$
10. $\mathbf{A} \cdot \nabla = a_1 \dfrac{\partial}{\partial x} + a_2 \dfrac{\partial}{\partial y} + a_3 \dfrac{\partial}{\partial z}$

Section 8–2

3. $-\int_G \mathbf{A} \cdot (\nabla \times \mathbf{F})\, dV$, 0
6. a) 24π b) 0 c) 96π

Section 8–3

2. $2\int_S \mathbf{A} \cdot \mathbf{e}_n\, dS$
3. a) 1 b) $\frac{1}{2}$
4. a) $-\pi$ b) 0
5. $\mathbf{H} = \operatorname{grad} \phi$, where ϕ is harmonic in $S_r(\mathbf{A})$
6. a) $[\frac{1}{4}x^2y^2 - \frac{1}{4}y^3, \frac{1}{4}xy^2 - \frac{1}{4}x^3, -\frac{1}{3}z^2, \frac{1}{3}zy]$ b) $[yz, -zx, 0]$
   c) $[zy/2x, -z/x, (2y - zy)/2x]$
7. Yes

Section 8–4

1. a) $\mathbf{e}_\rho = [\cos\theta\sin\phi, \sin\theta\sin\phi, \cos\phi]$, $\mathbf{e}_\phi = [\cos\theta\cos\phi, \sin\theta\cos\phi, -\sin\phi]$,
$\mathbf{e}_\theta = [-\sin\theta, \cos\theta, 0]$

b) $$\frac{\partial f}{\partial\rho}\mathbf{e}_\rho + \frac{1}{\rho}\frac{\partial f}{\partial\phi}\mathbf{e}_\phi + \frac{1}{\rho\sin\phi}\frac{\partial f}{\partial\theta}\mathbf{e}_\theta$$

c) $$\frac{2}{\rho}f_\rho + \frac{\cos\phi}{\rho\sin\phi}f_\phi + \frac{\partial f_\rho}{\partial\rho} + \frac{1}{\rho}\frac{\partial f_\phi}{\partial\phi} + \frac{1}{\rho\sin\phi}\frac{\partial f_\theta}{\partial\theta}$$

d) $$\left(\frac{1}{\rho}\frac{\partial f_\theta}{\partial\phi} - \frac{1}{\rho\sin\phi}\frac{\partial f_\phi}{\partial\theta} + \frac{\cos\phi}{\rho\sin\phi}f_\theta\right)\mathbf{e}_\rho + \left[\frac{1}{\rho\sin\phi}\frac{\partial f_\rho}{\partial\theta} - \frac{\partial f_\theta}{\partial\rho} - \frac{1}{\rho}f_\theta\right]\mathbf{e}_\phi + \left[\frac{\partial f_\phi}{\partial\rho} - \frac{1}{\rho}\frac{\partial f_\rho}{\partial\phi} + \frac{1}{\rho}f_\phi\right]\mathbf{e}_\theta$$

e) $$\frac{\partial^2 f}{\partial\rho^2} + \frac{1}{\rho^2}\frac{\partial^2 f}{\partial\phi^2} + \frac{1}{\rho^2\sin^2\phi}\frac{\partial^2 f}{\partial\theta^2} + \frac{2}{\rho}\frac{\partial f}{\partial\rho} + \frac{\cos\phi}{\rho^2\sin\phi}\frac{\partial f}{\partial\phi}$$

Index

Index

ABCDE6987